A Charlton Standard Catalogue

Canadian Collector Coins

Royal Canadian Mint Issues
Volume Two

NINTH EDITION

2019

Mark Drake
Publisher

The Charlton Press

TORONTO, ONTARIO, CANADA

Library and Archives Canada Cataloguing in Publication

Canadian Coins (Charlton Press)
　　　　Canadian Collector Coins: a Charlton Standard Catalogue. Volume Two:
　　　　Royal Canadian Mint Issues

　　　Annual
　　　Canadian Collector Coins: a Charlton Standard Catalogue
　　　ISSN 1928-8816
　　　ISBN 978-0-88968-412-6

　　　　　1. Coins, Canadian--Catalogs. 2. Coins, Canadian--Prices--Periodicals.
and collecting. I. Title

CJ18610.S82 59- 2005-　　　　737.4971'029　　　C2005-902187-X

Printed in Canada
in the Province of Quebec

EDITORIAL

Editor	Mark Drake
Graphic Technician	Mary-Anne Luzba
Cover Photography	Royal Canadian Mint

SPECIAL MENTION

We would like to thank the Royal Canadian Mint for their help providing assistance with the 2017-2018 images and content. We ould also like to thank all past contributors for submitting prices, answering requests or supplying information which assisted in ilding the many past editions of this catalogue.

CONTRIBUTORS TO THE NINTH EDITION

We would like to thank the following for their contributions to the 9th Edition of *Canadian Coins, Volume Two*: **Jaime** amenbaum, Ontario; **Douglas Hawkes**, Ontario; **R.E. Landry**; **Christie Paquet**, Senior Engraver, Royal Canadian Mint, Ottawa; dd Sandham, Ontario

The Charlton Press

Editorial Office
P.O. Box 414, Station F
Toronto, Ontario M4Y 2L8
Tel.: **(416) 962-2665** • Toll Free: **1-866-663-8827**
www.charltonpress.com email: chpress@charltonpress.com

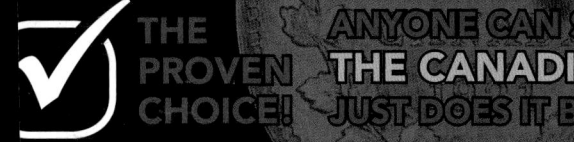

APPLICATION FOR RCNA MEMBERSHIP / DEMANDE D'ADHÉSION À L' ARNC

Application for membership in **The Royal Canadian Numismatic Association** may be made by any reputable party upon payment of the required dues.
Les demandes d'adhésion à **l'Association royale de numismatique du Canada** peuvent être faites par une partie de bonne réputation sur paiement des frais exigés.

Established · Fondée 1950

❏ Mr. / M.   ❏ Mrs. / Mme   ❏ Ms. / Mlle
❏ Renewal / Renouvèlement   ❏ Reinstatement / Réintégration *previous #_____*

Full Name / Nom   *for family membership include name of spouse / pour une adhésion familiale, inclure le nom du conjoint*

Mailing Address / Adresse postale complète

City / Ville   Province / State / État   Country / Pays   Postal Code/Zip

Phone / N° de téléphone   Email / Courriel

Signature of Applicant / Signature du demandeur   Sponsored By / Commandité par

Junior applicants (under age 18), state birth date / pour une adhésion junior (moins de 18 ans), inclure la date de naissance: _____

My numismatic speciality / spécialité numismatique (*optional/optionnel*): _____

❏ *I would like to be contacted by a mentor who also has my speciality. J'aimerais être mis en contact avec un mentor qui partage mes intérêt numismatiques.*

Membership Types: *Check only one* **Types d'adhésion:** *cochez une seule option*	Standard		Digital*	
	1 year	2 year	1 year	2 year
Regular: Canada and USA residents, age 18+ **Régulier:** adresses **Canadiennes et aux États-unis** (18 ans et plus)	❏ $45.00	❏ $88.00	❏ $34.00	❏ $66.00
Regular: Foreign (non-USA) **Régulier:** étranger (autre que les États-unis)	❏ $85.00	❏ $168.00	❏ $34.00	❏ $66.00
Junior: Applicants under age 18 *must be sponsored by a parent or guardian Les membres de moins de 18 ans doivent être commandités par un parent ou un gardien*	❏ $27.50	❏ $53.00	❏ $18.50	❏ $35.00
Family: Canada and USA residents. Member, spouse and children under age 18, (one printed and mailed *CN Journal* only) **Familial:** membre, époux (se) et enfants de moins de 18 ans. Un seul Journal	❏ $50.00	❏ $98.00	❏ $34.00	❏ $66.00
Corporate / Entreprises: Clubs, Societies / Sociétés, Libraries / Librairies and non-profit organizations / et autres organisations sans but lucratif	❏ $45.00	❏ $88.00	N.A.	N.A.
Life Membership / Adhésion à Vie:*	❏ $1,195.00		❏ $895.00	
Life Membership Senior: (65+) **Adhésion à Vie Aîné:*** (65 ans et plus)	❏ $895.00		❏ $695.00	
Life Membership Foreign: Adhésion à Vie Etranger:	❏ $2,195.00		❏ $895.00	

Dues shown are in Canadian$ to Canadian addresses and US$ to all international addresses and are exempt from Canadian sales taxes.

* (A Digital Membership includes all of the benefits of membership except a printed copy of *The CN Journal*.)

** (After one year of regular membership. Details of payment plan available on request.) Mail completed application with dues to:

Les cotisations sont indiquées en dollars canadiens à des adresses canadiennes, ou en dollars américains à toutes les autres adresses. Les cotisations sont exonérées de taxes sur les ventes domestiques.

* (Adhésions numériques comprennent tous les avantages de l'adhésion, sauf une copie imprimée de *Le Journal canadien de numismatique*.)

** (Après un an comme membre régulier. Détails du plan de paiement disponibles sur demande.) Envoyez la demande d'adhésion dûment complétée et le paiement à :

The Royal Canadian Numismatic Association
l'Association royale de numismatique du Canada

5694 Highway #7 East, Suite 432, Markham ON Canada L3P 1B4

Phone / Tel: 647-401-4014 Fax / Télécopie: 905-472-9645 Email / Courriel: *info@rcna.ca*

Apply online at: www.rcna.ca/paydues.php   01/01/2015

the Royal Canadian Mint(s)

Ottawa facility

The Royal Canadian Mint's headquarters occupy the historic building in central Ottawa where the Mint was founded in 1908. Today, the Ottawa facility produces hand-crafted collector and commemorative coins, gold bullion coins, medals and medallions. This is where the master tooling is done to create the dies that strike coin designs for both circulation and commemorative issues. The Mint's gold refining and advanced engineering operations are also located in Ottawa.

Winnipeg facility

The Winnipeg Mint is the high-tech, high-volume manufacturing facility. Every single Canadian circulation coin is produced in Winnipeg – literally billions each year. Established in 1976, the Winnipeg plant occupies a 14,864 m2 state-of-the-art facility.

TABLE OF CONTENTS

GOLD COINS

PALLADIUM COINS

PLATINUM COINS

COLLECTOR SETS

te: 1. For some sets the mintage was pre-announced as a maximum number of sets to be issued. In other cases the mintage was open-ended with the issue period a function of time. In the pricing tables for sets the mintage number denotes the number of sets sold. The final number is usually only available after a second year of RCM Reports.

    2. Within the set listings are sets with different finishes and compositions. Currently the four main finish categories are Uncirculated, Brilliant Uncirculated, Specimen and Proof. Usually, these sets contain exact design copies of the circulating business strike coins, but there are a few exceptions when commemorative coins are involved.

    3. For a complete explanation on finishes, see page xvii in the introduction.

MAPLE LEAF BULLION COINS

INTRODUCTION

The first non-circulating legal tender coin (NCLT) struck in Canada was a 1908 Edward VII gold sovereign. This coin was struck at the Ottawa Branch Mint in specimen quality along with specimen examples of the other five denominations (one cent, five cents, ten cents, twenty-five cents and fifty cents) that made up the circulating coins of the day. The difference between the five subsidiary coins and the gold sovereign was that the latter, being struck only in specimen quality, had no circulating counterpart. While the 1908 gold sovereign was not a commemorative issue, the current thinking is that it was struck to establish a series. There are still a few questions regarding this NCLT coin that have yet to be answered. One is "How was it distributed?"

Modern Canadian NCLT coinage began with the issue of the 1967 centennial anniversary specimen gold set. This set contained seven coins, the most important being a $20 gold coin. This coin was similar to the 1908 sovereign in that there was no circulating counterpart. This coin also set the stage for the next forty years. The Royal Canadian Mint sold 334,288 gold sets in 1967, creating a production bottleneck that was not cleared until well into 1968. The sales volume of 1967 collector coins was not lost on the organising officials of the Montreal 1976 Olympics games, for 1972 saw the beginning of the greatest issue of NCLT coins in Canadian history.

Canadian Coins, Volume Two: Collector Issues, 2017, seventh edition, records and lists over forty years of non-circulating legal tender coins issued by the Royal Canadian Mint in Canada.

COMMEMORATIVE COINS

Commemorative coins are issued to commemorate a particular personage, event, either historic or current, or a place. Such coins have a distinct design with reference to the occasion for which they are issued. Many coins of this category are collector items only, but a great number were issued for circulation to promote a major national event, such as the Vancouver 2010 Olympic Winter Games.

Vast numbers of thematic coins highlighting monuments, sites, historical personalities, endangered species, or just wild species common to a specific area, are now being inserted into this commemorative mix. The line between commemorative and thematic coins is blurred, and probably intentionally so.

Types of Commemoratives

We shall include thematic coins among the commemoratives. Commemorative/thematic coins can be divided into two categories:

1. **Commemorative/thematic legal tender circulating issues.**

These are the everyday coins used in commerce which bear a design commemorating an event. They are issued at face value, without a premium, within a certain time frame. Usually, the concept is centred on one denomination, but may encompass all denominations for an event of outstanding national significance such as the Centennial of Confederation. This category of commemorative is issued in "business strike" or circulation finish.

2. **Non circulating legal tender commemorative/themati[c] issues.**

NCLT coins are deemed legal tender by a mint, but there is n[o] expectation that they will be released into circulation. In theory, the[y] may be used in commerce to purchase goods and services, but the[ir] recognition as a medium of exchange, and their acceptance by th[e] modern day public, is questionable. In this category we will find sing[le] coins and sets, depending on how the issuing authorities develope[d] their marketing strategies. The selling price has no relationship eith[er] to the face value or the intrinsic value. The selling price, intrinsic valu[e] and face value diminish in that order. The issuing authorities genera[lly] have no intention ever to redeem commemorative or thematic issues.

The earlier issues may command a substantial market price increase ov[er] the original issue price because of the increased intrinsic value of preciou[s] metals. Modern commemorative coins usually need time and additio[nal] increases in intrinsic value to return a profit.

FINISHES

Sales of modern collector coins are basically driven by the fini[sh] on the coins. The Royal Canadian Mint currently uses nine differe[nt] finishes. See the next page for an outline of the different finishes use[d]. A collector should be well versed in the different finishes as they will, [at] times, greatly affect the value of the issue.

SETS VS. SERIES

Coins with themes issued in a single year have been designat[ed] as sets. Coins with themes issued over multiple years have be[en] designated as series.

FRATERNAL AFFILIATION

Over the years, coin clubs have sprung up in many Canad[ian] communities. In addition, both Canada and the United States have natio[nal] organisations which hold annual conventions. Coin clubs constitute one [of] the most attractive features of present-day collecting. They offer beginn[er] collectors the opportunity for good fellowship and the encouragement [of] knowledge of more experienced collectors. The larger groups maint[ain] lending libraries and publish a journal or newsletter on a regular basis.

Memberships and other information can be obtained from:

Royal Canadian Numismatic Association
5694 Highway # 7 East, Suite 432
Markham, Ontario
Canada L3P 1B4
Tel.: (647) 401-4014 Fax: (905) 472-9645
Email: info@rcna.ca

Ontario Numismatic Association
P.O. Box 40033, Waterloo Sq. P.O.
75 King Street South
Waterloo, Ontario
Canada N2J 4V1
www.ontario-numismatic.org/index.html

COLLECTOR COINS
Finishes 1953 to 2018

Introduction: A coin finish simply means the surface quality imparted to a blank during the striking process. At the striking stage the main factors influencing the quality of the finish are: (1) the quality of the blanks, (2) the finish of the dies, (3) the speed and pressure of the press, and (4) the number of times the blank is struck.

Circulation Finish: *Brilliant Relief Against a Satin Background.* This is the most common finish found on all business strikes, from the one cent to the two dollar coins. These are production coins struck at the rate of 700 to 800 per minute. They are allowed to tumble into waiting hoppers, then put through counting and wrapping machines before being sent to the banks.

Uncirculated Finish: *Brilliant Relief Against a Satin Background.* This process is very similar to the circulation finish above with common dies being used, but with slower striking speeds and definitely more care in the loading and unloading of the press. There are far fewer handling marks than the circulation variety, but still marks may be found.

The Uncirculated finish is used by the Numismatic Department of the Mint on singles and sets offered to collectors, or sold into the giftware market.

Proof-Like Finish: *Frosted to Semi-Mirror Relief Against a Semi-Mirror Background.* These coins are produced on a slow moving press with reasonably high pressure. The planchets and dies are polished with each coin being removed from the press individually. Large coins may be struck more than once.

The following die states are found on proof-like coins:

Ultra Heavy Cameo: Full frosting across the relief of the coin, both effigy and legend, when viewed from all directions under full lighting conditions.

Heavy Cameo: The frosting is neither full nor evenly applied across the relief of the coin. In fact, some areas may appear bright when viewed under full lighting conditions.

Cameo: Touches of frosting may appear on the relief of the coin. There will be bright areas when the coin is viewed under full lighting conditions.

No Cameo: No frosting, all relief areas will appear bright. There is no difference in contrast between the bright field and a bright relief. The majority of coins are from this die state.

Nickel has a hardness higher than silver making the striking of coins more difficult. In 1968 with the change from silver to nickel coinage came the need for a new finish on numismatic items. That finish is:

68 / PR-69 This price is based on the item still being in the original package as issued by the Mint.

69 / PR-70 This price is based on the item being graded by a reputable third-party grading company.

Brilliant Uncirculated Finish: *Brilliant Design, Legends and Dates Against a Brilliant Background.* Coins are struck by a slow moving press using high pressure, and polished dies. Blanks are inserted, and coins removed by hand. This finish was used on all packaged singles and sets offered by the Mint from 1968 to 2004. In 2004 production of sets was divided between Uncirculated and Brilliant Uncirculated.

Specimen Finish: From 1968 to 2018 there have been six different modifications used by the Mint on specimen coinage.

1858-1881:	A Brilliant Relief Against a Brilliant Background.
1902-1938:	A Frosted Relief against a Frosted Background.
1937-1967:	A Brilliant Relief against a Brilliant Background.
1968-1995:	A Brilliant Relief against a Brilliant Background
1996-2009:	A Brilliant Relief, Frosted Legends and Date against a Lined Background
2010-2018:	A Brilliant Relief, Frosted Legends and Date against a Laser Lined Background

Proof Finish: Frosted Relief Against a Mirror Field. This is the highest quality finish used by the Royal Canadian Mint on Canadian coinage. By definition, all coins with this finish are designated Ultra Heavy Cameo (UHC). They are identified in the pricing tables by PR.

Reverse Proof Finish: Mirror Relief Against a Frosted Background. This type of finish is at times called "satin matte" because of the background texture. All elements of the design that are in relief have a highly reflective finish.

Bullion Finish: Brilliant Relief Against a Parallel Lined Background. This finish was first used in 1979 on gold maple leafs for the bullion program. The finish is found on gold, platinum, palladium and silver maples. As this finish is the standard used on the maple leaf issues the grading designation is Mint State (MS). Starting in 2014, a new finish was introduced with brilliant relief against a radiating lined background. This was done to provide advanced visual security.

Bullion-Specimen (Reverse Proof): Brilliant Relief Against a Satin Background. A finish not often used, it can be found on special edition bullion singles and sets.

Bullion-Proof: Frosted Relief Against a Mirror Background. This finish is the same as that found on all numismatic proof issues.

ONE CENT

ONE CENT, ROUND, ELIZABETH II PROOF, 1997-2012.

From 1997 to 2012 the composition of the one cent coin included in the Standard Proof Set fluctuated between bronze and copper. The one ce
coin in the Premium Proof Set for 2012 was struck on a fine silver planchet.

The last bronze cent issued for circulation was struck in 1996. It was a 12-sided coin and is listed in *Canadian Coins, Numismatic Issues, Volume Or*

Obverse	Obverse	Obverse	Reverse
1997-2003	2004-2006	2007-2012	1997-2012
	Without Mint Logo	With Mint Logo	

Designers:
Obv.:	1997-2003:	Dora de Pédery-Hunt
	2004-2012:	Susanna Blunt
Rev.:	1997-2012:	G. E. Kruger-Gray

Engravers:
Obv.:	1997-2003:	Dora de Pédery-Hunt
	2004-2012:	Susan Taylor
Rev.:	1997-2012:	Thomas Shingles

	Bronze	**Copper**	**Silver**
Composition:	98.0% Cu, 0.5% Sn, 0.15% Zn	1.00% Cu	99.99% Ag, Selectively gold plated
Silver content:			3.0 g, 0.096 tr oz
Weight:	2.5 g	2.5 g	3.05 g
Diameter:	19.1 mm	19.1 mm	19.05 mm
Thickness:	1.45 mm	1.45 mm	1.3 mm
Edge:	Plain	Plain	Plain
Die Axis:	↑↑	↑↑	↑↑
Finish:	Proof	Proof	Proof
Case of Issue:	Included in Proof Sets, see page 553		

DATE	DESCRIPTION	COMP.	QUANTITY SOLD	ISSUE PRICE	FINISH	PR-69	PR-7
1997	Diademed Portrait / Maple Twig	Bronze	113,647	N.I.I.	Proof	10.	—
1998		Bronze	93,632	N.I.I.	Proof	10.	—
1999		Bronze	95,113	N.I.I.	Proof	10.	—
2000		Bronze	90,921	N.I.I.	Proof	10.	—
2001		Bronze	74,194	N.I.I.	Proof	10.	—
2002		Bronze	65,315	N.I.I.	Proof	15.	—
2003		Bronze	62,007	N.I.I.	Proof	15.	—
2004	Uncrowned Portrait / Maple Twig	Copper	57,614	N.I.I.	Proof	15.	—
2005		Copper	63,562	N.I.I.	Proof	15.	—
2006		Bronze	53,822	N.I.I.	Proof	15.	—
2007	Uncrowned Portrait, Mint Logo / Maple Twig	Copper	37,413	N.I.I.	Proof	15.	—
2008		Copper	38,630	N.I.I.	Proof	15.	—
2009		Bronze	27,549	N.I.I.	Proof	15.	—
2010		Copper	32,342	N.I.I.	Proof	15.	—
2011		Copper	32,910	N.I.I.	Proof	15.	—
2012		Copper	27,254	N.I.I.	Proof	15.	—
2012	Premium Proof Set, Selectively gold plated	Silver	19,789	N.I.I.	Proof	75.	—

NE CENT, 90TH ANNIVERSARY OF THE ROYAL CANADIAN MINT, 1908-1998.

To commemorate the opening of the Royal Canadian Mint in 1908 a five-coin set was issued featuring the original reverse designs that appeared the 1908 coins, except the coins now feature the double date 1908-1998. The set was issued in two finishes, matte and mirror proof. The matte set nt does not carry the country of origin "Canada". This error was corrected on the mirror proof issues.

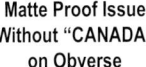

Matte Proof Issue
Without "CANADA"
on Obverse

Mirror Proof Issue
Reverse

Mirror Proof Issue
With "CANADA"
on Obverse

Designers and Engravers:
Obv.:	Dora de Pédery-Hunt
Rev.:	Ago Aarand, G. W. DeSaulles
Composition:	92.5% Ag, 7.5% Cu, Copper plate
Silver content:	5.24 g, 0.169 tr oz
Weight:	5.67 g
Diameter:	25.4 mm
Thickness:	1.5 mm **Die Axis:** ↑↑
Edge:	Plain **Finish:** See below
Case of Issue:	See Special Issue Proof Sets, page 553

DATE	DESCRIPTION	QUANTITY SOLD	ISSUE PRICE	FINISH	PR-68	PR-69
1998 (1908-)	Matte proof, Without "CANADA"	18,376	N.I.I.	Matte Proof	35.	—
1998 (1908-)	Mirror proof, With "CANADA"	24,893	N.I.I.	Mirror Proof	25.	—

IE CENT, 50TH ANNIVERSARY OF THE CORONATION OF QUEEN ELIZABETH II, 1953-2003.

This one cent coin which carries the double date 1953-2003 is from the Special Edition Proof Set issued in 2003 to commemorate the 50th iversary of the Coronation of Queen Elizabeth II.

Designers and Engravers:
Obv.:	Mary Gillick, Dora de Pédery-Hunt
Rev.:	G. E. Kruger-Gray Edge: Plain
Composition:	Copper
Weight:	2.5 g
Case of Issue:	See Special Issue Proof Sets, page 552

Diameter:	19.05 mm
Thickness:	1.25 mm
Die Axis:	↑↑
Finish:	Proof

DATE	DESCRIPTION	QUANTITY SOLD	ISSUE PRICE	FINISH	PR-69	PR-70
2003 (1953-)	50th Anniv. Coronation Queen Elizabeth II	21,537	N.I.I.	Proof	25.	—

E CENT, ROYAL CANADIAN MINT ANNUAL REPORT, SELECTIVELY GOLD PLATED, 2003.

his one cent coin is the first in a series of six coins, one of which was to be included each year with the Annual Mint Report, leading up to the al Canadian Mint's centennial in 2008. However, this series was discontinued with the issue of the 2006 Annual Mint Report. See the One Cent vatives listed on page 7.

Designers and Engravers:
Obv.:	Dora de Pédery-Hunt, Ago Aarand
Rev.:	G. E. Kruger-Gray
Composition:	Copper plated zinc, Selectively gold plated
Weight:	2.25 g **Edge:** Plain
Diameter:	19.05 mm **Die Axis:** ↑↑
Thickness:	1.45 mm **Finish:** Proof
Case of Issue:	See Derivatives, page 7

DATE	DESCRIPTION	QUANTITY SOLD	ISSUE PRICE	FINISH	PR-69	PR-70
003	Copper plated zinc, Selectively gold plated	7,746	N.I.I.	Proof	50.	—

ONE CENT, 75TH ANNIVERSARY OF THE VOYAGEUR DOLLAR PROOF SET, 1935-2010.

This one cent coin is from the Special Limited Edition Proof Set issued in 2010 to commemorate Emanuel Hahn's classic voyageur design whic first appeared on the 1935 silver dollar.

Designers and Engravers:
Obv.:   Sir. E. B. MacKennal
Rev.:   Fred Lewis
Composition: Copper
Weight: 2.5 g
Diameter: 19.05 mm
Thickness: 1.45 mm
Case of Issue: See Special Issue Proof Sets, page 557
Edge: Plain
Die Axis: ↑↑
Finish: Proof

DATE	DESCRIPTION	QUANTITY SOLD	ISSUE PRICE	FINISH	PR-69	PR-7
2010 (1935-)	75th Anniv. Voyageur Silver Dollar Proof Set	4,996	N.I.I.	Proof	25.	—

ONE CENT, 100TH ANNIVERSARY OF THE STRIKING OF CANADA'S 1911 SILVER DOLLAR, 1911-2011.

This one cent coin which carries the double date 1911-2011 is from the Special Edition Proof Set issued in 2011 to commemorate the 10 anniversary of the striking of Canada's 1911 silver dollar.

Designers and Engravers:
Obv.:   Sir E. B. MacKennal
Rev.:   Original design by L. C. Wyon, Modified by W. H. J. Blakemore
Composition: Copper
Weight: 5.67 g
Diameter: 25.4 mm
Thickness: 1.6 mm
Edge: Plain
Case of Issue: See Special Issue Proof Sets, page 553
Die Axis: ↑↑
Finish: Proof

DATE	DESCRIPTION	QUANTITY SOLD	ISSUE PRICE	FINISH	PR-69	PR-
2011 (1911-)	100th Anniv. Canada's 1911 Silver Dollar	5,952	N.I.I.	Proof	40.	—

ONE CENT, FAREWELL TO THE PENNY, SELECTIVELY GOLD PLATED, 2012.

The last one cent coin was struck at the Royal Canadian Mint on May 4th, 2012. This half-ounce silver one cent coin was issued to mark the of production of Canada's one-cent piece.

Designers and Engravers:
Obv.:   Susanna Blunt, Susan Taylor
Rev.:   G. E. Kruger-Gray, RCM Staff
Composition: 99.99% Ag, Selectively gold plated
Silver content: 15.87 g, 0.5 tr oz
Weight: 15.87 g
Diameter: 34.0 mm
Thickness: 2.2 mm
Finish: Proof
Edge: Reeded
Die Axis: ↑↑
Case of Issue: Maroon leatherette clam style case, black flocked insert, encapsulated coin, COA, custom box

DATE	DESCRIPTION	QUANTITY SOLD	ISSUE PRICE	FINISH	PR-69	PR
2012	Fine silver, (½ oz), Selectively gold plated	29,998	54.95	Proof	70.	—

NE CENT, FINE SILVER, 2012.

These coins are from the five-coin "Farewell to the Penny" special limited edition proof set issued in 2012. Also see page 554.

Edward VII / Small Leaves Design	George V / Small Leaves Design	George V / Two Maples Leaves Design

George W. DeSaulles	George W. DeSaulles	Sir E.B. MacKennal	W. H. J. Blakemore	Sir E. B. MacKennal	Fred Lewis

Elizabeth II / Centennial Design	Elizabeth II / Maple Twig Design

Arnold Machin	Alex Colville	Susanna Blunt	G. E. Kruger-Gray

signers:			Engravers:	
Obv.:	See obverse illustrations		Obv.:	Susan Taylor
Rev.:	See reverse illustrations		Rev.:	Samantha Strath
mposition:	99.99% Ag			
ver content:	14.7 g, 0.473 (per set)			
ight:	2.94 g (per coin); 14.7 (set)		Edge:	Plain
ameter:	19.1		Die Axis:	↑↑
ickness:	1.25 mm		Finish:	Proof
se of Issue:	See Special Issue Proof Sets, page 554			

DATE	DESCRIPTION	QUANTITY SOLD	ISSUE PRICE	FINISH	PR-69	PR-70
2012	Edward VII / Small Leaves Design	5,001	N.I.I.	Proof	90.	—
2012	George V / Small Leaves Design with CANADA	5,001	N.I.I.	Proof	90.	—
2012	George V / Two Maple Leaves Design	5,001	N.I.I.	Proof	90.	—
2012	Elizabeth II / Centennial Design	5,001	N.I.I.	Proof	90.	—
2012	Elizabeth II /Maple Twig Design	5,001	N.I.I.	Proof	90.	—

E CENT, THE PENNY, FIVE OUNCE SILVER COIN, 2012.

This five-ounce silver one cent coin was issued to mark the end of production of Canada's one cent piece.

Designers and Engravers:			
Obv.:	Susanna Blunt, Susan Taylor		
Rev.:	G. E. Kruger-Gray, RCM Staff		
Composition:	99.99% Ag		
Silver content:	157.6 g, 5.06 tr oz		
Weight:	157.6 g	Edge:	Reeded
Diameter:	65.0 mm	Die Axis:	↑↑
Thickness:	N/A	Finish:	Proof
Case of Issue:	Maroon leatherette clam style case, black flocked insert, encapsulated coin, COA, custom box		

DATE	DESCRIPTION	QUANTITY SOLD	ISSUE PRICE	FINISH	PR-69	PR-70
012	Fine silver, (5 oz), The Penny	1,499	495.95	Proof	600.	—

e: Coin illustrated smaller than actual size.

ONE CENT, THE LEGACY OF THE PENNY, 2017.

This 5-coin set commemorates the 5th anniversary of the end of the penny's production. Also see page 556.

Small leaves design (1908)	Small leaves design (1911)
Designer and Engraver: George W. DeSaulles	Designer: W.H.J. Blakemore Obverse: Sir E.B. MacKennal

Two maple leaves design (1920)	Centennial design (1967)	Maple twig design (1982)
Designer: Fred Lewis	Designer: Alex Colville	Designer: G.E. Kruger-Gray
Engraver: Sir E.B. MacKennal	Engraver: Arnold Machin	Engraver: Arnold Machin

Designers:
    Obv.:   See illustrations
    Rev.:   See illustrations

Engravers:
    Obv.:   See illustrations
    Rev.:   See illustrations

Composition: 99.99% Ag, selective rose gold plating
Silver content: 157.6 g, 5.06 tr oz

	Small leaves design (1908)	Small leaves design (1911)	Two maple leaves design (1920)	Centennial design (1967)	Maple twig design (1982)
Weight:	62.67 g	62.67 g	31.39 g	31.39 g	31.39 g
Diameter:	54.0 mm	54.0 mm	38.0 mm	38.0 mm	38.0 mm
Thickness:	N/A				
Edge:	Reeded				
Die Axis:	↑↑				
Finish:	Proof				
Case of Issue:	Wooden collector's case with black beauty box. COA				

DATE	DESCRIPTION	QUANITY SOLD	ISSUE PRICE	FINISH	PR-69	PR-?
2017	Legacy of the Penny Set, Fine silver	1,946	709.95	Proof	600.	—

NE CENT, THE PENNY, FIVE OUNCE SILVER COIN – BIG COIN SERIES, 2017.

The 1957 Canadian Centennial circulation coins recall a momentous anniverary, these iconic coin designs make their return once more in this unning Big Coin series, beginning with one-cent coin designed by Alex Colville. Other coins in the set include a 5¢ coin (page 11), 10¢ coin (page 17), ¢ coin (page 57), 50¢ coin (page 88), $1 coin (page 130) and a $2 coin (page 144).

Designers and Engravers:

Obv.:	Susanna Blunt, Susan Taylor		
Rev.:	Alex Colville, RCM Staff		
Composition:	99.99% Ag		
Silver content:	157.6 g, 5.06 tr oz		
Weight:	157.6 g	**Edge:**	Reeded
Diameter:	65.25 mm	**Die Axis:**	↑↑
Thickness:	N/A	**Finish:**	Proof
Case of Issue:	Maroon clamshell with graphic beauty box, COA.		

DATE	DESCRIPTION	MINTAGE	ISSUE PRICE	FINISH	PR-69	PR-70
2017	Fine silver, (5 oz), The Penny	2,150	559.95	Proof	560.	—

ONE CENT DERIVATIVES

DATE	DESCRIPTION	QUANTITY SOLD	ISSUE PRICE	ISSUER	FINISH	MARKET VALUE
2003	**2003 Annual Mint Report**, One cent coin, selectively gold plated	7,746	19.95	RCM	PR-69	50.
2003	**Coronation Coin and Stamp Set**, two one cent coins, 1953 and 2003; two fifty cent coins, 2002 Jubilee and 2003 Uncrowned Portrait; two mint and two cancelled stamps of Her Majesty's Jubilee and Coronation; Presentation Case	14,743	22.95	RCM, CP	MS-65	25.

THREE CENTS

REE CENTS, 150TH ANNIVERSARY OF CANADA'S FIRST POSTAGE STAMP, 2001.

Sir Sandford Fleming's (1851) Three Pence Beaver was Canada's first postage stamp and a symbol of the transfer of postal authority from Britain to Canada.

Designers and Engravers:

Obv.:	Dora de Pédery-Hunt		
Rev.:	Sir Sandford Fleming, Cosme Saffioti		
Composition:	92.5% Ag, 7.5% Cu, 24-karat gold plate		
Silver content:	4.95 g, 0.159 tr oz		
Weight:	5.35 g	**Edge:**	Plain
Diameter:	21.3 mm	**Die Axis:**	↑↑
Thickness:	1.9 mm	**Finish:**	Proof
Case of Issue:	See Derivatives below		

DATE	DESCRIPTION	QUANTITY SOLD	ISSUE PRICE	FINISH	PR-69	PR-70
2001	Three Cent Beaver	59,573	N.I.I.	Proof	20.	—

THREE CENT DERIVATIVES

DATE	DESCRIPTION	QUANTITY SOLD	ISSUE PRICE	FINISH	PR-69	PR-70
2001	Three Cents, Medallion, Stamp set, Maroon leatherette case, COA	59,573	39.95	RCM, CP	PR-69	—

SPECIAL NOTE ON FINISHES

t is very important to understand the different finishes the Royal Canadian Mint uses on their various issues. These finishes are altered from time-me as the Mint develops new products.

For example, the brilliant relief against a parallel lined background finish first used on bullion coins was carried forward in 1996 to be used on the s contained in the specimen set.

n 2006 this finish was used on giftware coins such as the twenty-five cent coin issued to celebrate the 80th birthday of Queen Elizabeth II.

n 2010 a new specimen finish, brilliant relief against a laser-lined background, was used for the coins contained in the specimen set. There are now different specimen finishes being utilised on Canadian coinage.

Circulation and Brilliant Uncirculated (proof-like) finishes are another very confusing mixture of finishes, see page xvii for a further explanation.

FIVE CENTS

FIVE CENTS, ELIZABETH II PROOF, 1996-2018.

Starting in 1996 the five-cent coin issued in the proof set, previously struck from cupronickel, was now struck on a sterling silver planchet. The u... of sterling silver planchets was discontinued in 2011.

The year 2012 saw the introduction of the Premium Proof Set in which all coins were struck on fine silver planchets.

Standard Proof Sets were issued for 2012, 2014-2018. The five-cent coin in these sets was struck on a nickel planchet.

| Obverse 1996-2003 | Obverse 2004-2006, 2015-2018 Without Mint Logo | Obverse 2007-2014 With Mint Logo | Obverse 2017 With Canada 150 Logo | Reverse 1996-2018 Reverse | 2017 Living Traditions |

Designers:

Obv.:	1996-2003:	Dora de Pédery-Hunt
	2004-2017:	Susanna Blunt
Rev.:	1996-2016:	G. E. Kruger-Gray
	2017:	Gerald Gloade

Engravers:

Obv.:	1996-2003:	Dora de Pédery-Hunt
	2004-2017:	Susan Taylor
Rev.:	1996-2016:	Thomas Shingles

	Sterling Silver	Nickel	Fine Silver
Composition:	92.5% Ag, 7.5% Cu	100.% Ni	99.99% Ag
Silver content:	4.9 g, 0.158 tr oz	—	5.5 g, 0.177 tr oz
Weight:	5.35 g	3.95 g	5.5 g
Diameter:	21.3 mm	21.2 mm	21.0 mm
Thickness:	1.85 mm	1.85 mm	1.85 mm
Edge:	Plain	Plain	Plain
Die Axis:	↑↑	↑↑	↑↑
Finish:	Proof	Proof	Proof
Case of Issue:	Included in Proof Sets, see pages 546-550		

DATE	DESCRIPTION	COMP.	QUANTITY SOLD	ISSUE PRICE	FINISH	PR-69	PR-7
1996	Diademed Portrait / Beaver	Sterling	112,835	N.I.I.	Proof	15.	—
1997		Sterling	113,647	N.I.I.	Proof	15.	—
1998		Sterling	93,632	N.I.I.	Proof	15.	—
1999		Sterling	95,113	N.I.I.	Proof	15.	—
2000		Sterling	90,921	N.I.I.	Proof	18.	—
2001		Sterling	74,194	N.I.I.	Proof	20.	—
2002		Sterling	65,315	N.I.I.	Proof	20.	—
2003		Sterling	62,007	N.I.I.	Proof	20.	—
2004	Uncrowned Portrait / Beaver	Sterling	57,614	N.I.I.	Proof	20.	—
2005		Sterling	63,562	N.I.I.	Proof	20.	—
2006		Sterling	53,822	N.I.I.	Proof	20.	—
2007	Uncrowned Portrait, Mint Logo / Beaver	Sterling	37,413	N.I.I.	Proof	20.	—
2008		Sterling	38,630	N.I.I.	Proof	20.	—
2009		Sterling	27,549	N.I.I.	Proof	20.	—
2010		Sterling	32,342	N.I.I.	Proof	25.	—
2011		Sterling	32,910	N.I.I.	Proof	25.	—
2012		Nickel	27,254	N.I.I.	Proof	15.	—
2012	Premium Proof Set	Fine Silver	19,789	N.I.I.	Proof	25.	—
2013	Premium Proof Set	Fine Silver	20,182	N.I.I.	Proof	25.	—
2014		Nickel	11,251	N.I.I.	Proof	15.	—
2014	Premium Proof Set	Fine Silver	13,416	N.I.I.	Proof	25.	—
2015	Premium Proof Set	Fine Silver	20,000	N.I.I.	Proof	25.	—
2015		Nickel	20,000	N.I.I.	Proof	15.	—
2016	Premium Proof Set	Fine Silver	20,000	N.I.I.	Proof	25.	—
2016		Nickel	12,500	N.I.I.	Proof	15.	—
2017	Premium Proof Set, Beaver	Fine Silver	20,000	N.I.I.	Proof	25.	—
2017	Premium Proof Set, Living Traditions	Fine Silver	20,000	N.I.I.	Proof	25.	—
2017	Proof Set, Living Traditions	Nickel	25,000	N.I.I.	Proof	15	—
2017	Premium Proof Set 1967-2017	Fine Silver	20,000.	N.I.I.	Proof	25.	—
2018	Premium Proof Set	Fine Silver	20,000.	N.I.I.	Proof	25.	—
2018		Nickel	25,000.	N.I.I.	Proof	15.	—

Note: Quantity sold figures are identical to those listed for Proof Sets sold.

E CENTS, 90TH ANNIVERSARY OF THE ROYAL CANADIAN MINT, 1908-1998.

To commemorate the opening of the Royal Canadian Mint in 1908 a five-coin set was issued featuring the original reverse designs that appeared the 1908 coins, except the coins now feature the double date 1908-1998. The set was issued in two finishes, matte and mirror proof. The matte set t does not carry the country of origin "Canada." This error was corrected on the mirror proof issues.

Designers and Engravers:
Obv.: Dora de Pédery-Hunt
Rev.: Ago Aarand, G. W. DeSaulles
Composition: 92.5% Ag, 7.5% Cu
Silver content: 1.08 g, 0.035 tr oz
Finish: Matte Proof, Mirror Proof
Case of Issue: See Special Issue Proof Sets, page 551

Weight: 1.167 g
Diameter: 15.5 mm
Thickness: 1.0 mm
Edge: Reeded
Die Axis: ↑↑

DATE	DESCRIPTION	QUANTITY SOLD	ISSUE PRICE	FINISH	PR-68	PR-69
1998 (1908-)	90th Anniv. Royal Canadian Mint, Matte Proof	18,376	N.I.I.	Proof	20.	—
1998 (1908-)	90th Anniv. Royal Canadian Mint, Mirror Proof	24,893	N.I.I.	Proof	20.	—

E CENTS, LES VOLTIGEURS DE QUEBEC, 2000.

Les Voltigeurs regiment was formed in March 1862, and was headquartered in Quebec. In 1942 it provided an armoured regiment for the Canadian ces in World War II.

Designers and Engravers:
Obv.: Dora de Pédery-Hunt
Rev.: Susan Taylor
Composition: 92.5% Ag, 7.5% Cu
Silver content: 4.9 g, 0.158 tr oz
Finish: Proof
Case of Issue: Black leatherette clam style case, green insert and sleeve, encapsulated coin

Weight: 5.3 g
Diameter: Round: 21.3 mm
Thickness: 1.85 mm
Edge: Reeded
Die Axis: ↑↑

DATE	DESCRIPTION	QUANTITY SOLD	ISSUE PRICE	FINISH	PR-69	PR-70
2000	Les Voltigeurs de Québec	34,024	16.95	Proof	10.	—

E CENTS, ROYAL MILITARY COLLEGE OF CANADA, 2001.

The Royal Military College was established by an act of Parliament on May 26th, 1874. The college is located in Kingston, Ontario.

Designers and Engravers:
Obv.: Dora de Pédery-Hunt
Rev.: G. T. Locklin, Susan Taylor
Composition: 92.5% Ag, 7.5% Cu
Silver content: 4.9 g, 0.158 tr oz
Finish: Proof
Case of Issue: Black leatherette clam style case, green insert, encapsulated coin, multicoloured sleeve

Weight: 5.3 g
Diameter: Round: 21.3 mm
Thickness: 1.85 mm
Edge: Plain
Die Axis: ↑↑

DATE	DESCRIPTION	QUANTITY SOLD	ISSUE PRICE	FINISH	PR-69	PR-70
2001	Royal Military College of Canada	25,834	16.95	Proof	12.	—

E CENTS, 85TH ANNIVERSARY, BATTLE FOR VIMY RIDGE, 2002.

imy Ridge, France was the location of one of the major battles of World War I. It was taken and held by Canadian troops from April 9th to 12th, 1917.

Designers and Engravers:
Obv.: Dora de Pédery-Hunt
Rev.: S. A. Allward, Susan Taylor
Composition: 92.5% Ag, 7.5% Cu
Silver content: 4.9 g, 0.158 tr oz
Finish: Proof
Case of Issue: Black leatherette clam style case; maroon insert, encapsulated coin, multicoloured sleeve

Weight: 5.3 g
Diameter: Round: 21.3 mm
Thickness: 1.85 mm
Edge: Plain
Die Axis: ↑↑

ATE	DESCRIPTION	QUANTITY SOLD	ISSUE PRICE	FINISH	PR-69	PR-70
2002	85th Anniv. Battle for Vimy Ridge	22,646	16.95	Proof	28.	—

FIVE CENTS, 50TH ANNIVERSARY OF THE CORONATION OF QUEEN ELIZABETH II, 1953-2003.

Elizabeth II was crowned Queen on June 2nd, 1953, in Westminster Abbey, London, England.

Designers and Engravers:

Obv.:	M. Gillick, D. de Pédery-Hunt
Rev.:	G. E. Kruger-Gray, T. Shingles
Composition:	92.5% Ag, 7.5% Cu
Silver content:	4.9 g, 0.158 tr oz
Finish:	Proof
Case of Issue:	See Special Issue Proof Sets, page 552

Weight:	5.3 g
Diameter:	12-sided: 21.3 mm
Thickness:	1.85 mm
Edge:	Plain
Die Axis:	↑↑

DATE	DESCRIPTION	QUANTITY SOLD	ISSUE PRICE	FINISH	PR-69	PR-70
2003 (1953-)	50th Anniv. Coronation Queen Elizabeth II	21,537	N.I.I.	Proof	25.	—

FIVE CENTS, 60TH ANNIVERSARY, D-DAY LANDING, 1944-2004.

On June 6th, 1944, over 175,000 troops landed on the beaches of Normandy, along a fifty-mile front. Originally came in 2004 D-Day Nickel Medallion with CD Rom.

Designers and Engravers:

Obv.:	Susanna Blunt, Susan Taylor
Rev.:	Thomas Shingles, Christie Paquet
Composition:	92.5% Ag, 7.5% Cu
Silver content:	4.9 g, 0.158 tr oz
Finish:	Proof
Case of Issue:	See Derivatives, page 13

Weight:	5.3 g
Diameter:	12-sided: 21.3 mm
Thickness:	1.85 mm
Edge:	Plain
Die Axis:	↑↑

DATE	DESCRIPTION	QUANTITY SOLD	ISSUE PRICE	FINISH	PR-69	PR-7
2004 (1944-)	60th Anniv. D-Day, 1944-2004	20,019	N.I.I.	Proof	30.	—

FIVE CENTS, 60TH ANNIVERSARY OF VE-DAY, 1945-2005.

These coins were issued to celebrate the 60th anniversary of the victory over Nazi Germany in Europe. Peace was declared May 8th, 1945.

The selectively gold plated Victory five cent coin was issued in conjunction with the 2005 Annual Mint Report. This is the third coin in what wa be an annual series ending in 2008. The series was discontinued with the issue of the 2006 annual report. See the Five Cent Derivatives, page 1

Common Obverse	1945-2005 Victory	1945-2005 Victory Gold plated

Designers and Engravers:

Obv.:	T. H. Paget, Thomas Shingles
Rev.:	Thomas Shingles, Christie Paquet
Composition:	92.5% Ag, 7.5% Cu
Silver content:	4.9 g, 0.158 tr oz
Weight:	5.3 g
Diameter:	12-sided: 21.3 mm
Thickness:	1.85 mm
Edge:	Plain
Case of Issue:	See Derivatives, page 13

Die Axis:	↑↑
Finish:	Proof

DATE	DESCRIPTION	QUANTITY SOLD	ISSUE PRICE	FINISH	PR-69	PR-
2005 (1945-)	60th Anniv. VE-Day, 1945-2005	42,792	N.I.I.	Proof	15.	—
2005 (1945-)	60th Anniv. VE-Day, Selectively gold plated	6,065	N.I.I.	Proof	60.	—

FIVE CENTS, GEORGE V, STERLING SILVER, PROOF, 1935-2010.

This five-cent coin is from the Special Limited Edition Proof Set issued in 2010 to commemorate Emanuel Hahn's classic voyageur design w first appeared on the 1935 silver dollar.

Designers and Engravers:

Obv.:	Sir. E. B. MacKennal, RCM Staff
Rev.:	W. H. J. Blakemore, RCM Staff
Composition:	92.5% Ag, 7.5% Cu
Silver content:	4.95 g, 0.195 tr oz
Finish:	Proof
Case of Issue:	See Special Issue Proof Sets, page 553

Weight:	5.35 g
Diameter:	21.2 mm
Thickness:	1.85 mm
Edge:	Plain
Die Axis:	↑↑

DATE	DESCRIPTION	QUANTITY SOLD	ISSUE PRICE	FINISH	PR-69	PR-
2010 (1935-)	George V, Sterling Silver	4,996	N.I.I.	Proof	25.	—

VE CENTS, GEORGE V, STERLING SILVER, PROOF, 1911-2011.

This five-cent coin which carries the double date 1911-2011 is from the Special Edition Proof Set issued in 2011 to commemorate the 100th niversary of the striking of Canada's 1911 silver dollar.

Designers and Engravers:		**Weight:**	1.559 g
Obv.:	Sir E. B. MacKennal, RCM Staff	**Diameter:**	15.5 mm
Rev.:	Original design by L. C. Wyon,	**Thickness:**	1.0 mm
	Modified by W. H. J. Blakemore	**Edge:**	Reeded
Composition:	92.5% Ag, 7.5% Cu	**Die Axis:**	↑↑
Silver content:	1.442 g, 0.046 tr oz	**Finish:**	Proof
Case of Issue:	See Special Issue Proof Sets, page 553		

DATE	DESCRIPTION	QUANTITY SOLD	ISSUE PRICE	FINISH	PR-69	PR-70
2011 (1911-)	George V (1911), Sterling Silver	5,952	N.I.I.	Proof	25.	—

BIG COIN SERIES

/E CENTS, BIG COIN SET, 2015-2018.

This five-cent coin, which is part of the Big Coin Set started in 2015, features G.E. Kruger-Gray's enduring beaver design that first appeared on the
7 Canadian five-cent piece, with the 2017 coin having the reverse design by Alex Colville. Other coins in the set include a 10¢ coin (page 17), 25¢
1 (page 57), 50¢ coin (page 88), $1 coin (page 130) and a $2 coin (page 144).

igners and Engravers:		**Composition:**	
Obv.:	Susanna Blunt, Susan Taylor	2015:	99.99% Ag, Selectively gold plated
Rev.:	2015-2016:G.E. Kruger-Gray	2016:	99.99% Ag, Selectively coloured
	2017: Alex Colville	2017:	99.99% Ag, Selectively gold plated
	2018 G.E. Kruger-Gray	2019:	99.99% Ag, Selectively rose gold-plated
er content:	157.58 g, 5.06 tr oz		
ght:	157.6 g	**Edge:**	Reeded
neter:	65.25 mm	**Die Axis:**	↑↑
kness:	N/A	**Finish:**	Proof
e of Issue:	Maroon clam style case, black flocked insert, encapsulated coin, COA, custom box		

ATE	DESCRIPTION	QUANTITY SOLD	ISSUE PRICE	FINISH	PR-69	PR-70
2015	5¢ Big Coin	1,500	549.95	Proof	600.	—
2016	5¢ Big Coin	1,496	519.95	Proof	550.	—
2017	5¢ Big Coin	2,150	559.95	Proof	560.	—
2018	5¢ Big Coin	1,500	559.95	Proof	560.	—

:   Coins illustrated smaller than actual size.

LEGACY OF THE CANADIAN NICKEL

FIVE CENTS, LEGACY OF THE CANADIAN NICKEL, 2015.

This six coin set celebrates the history of the Canadian five-cent piece that was first minted in Canada after the Ottawa branch of the Royal Mint opened in 19 Prior to that, Canadian coins were struck at the Royal Mint in England or the Birmingham Mint in Birmingham, England. Featuring the effigies of reigning monarc at the time, the coins are larger than their original size. From originally containing sterling silver, to silver's removal from the coin in 1922, to an entirely-nic composition, and a later tombac alloy due to the war's need for nickel in the 1940s, the five cent coin's current plated steel composition has changed through the yea

| Obverse: King George V Designer: E.B. MacKennal Engraver: RCM Staff | The Crossed Maple Boughs Designer: W.H.J. Blakemore Engraver: RCM Staff | The Two Maple Leaves Designer: W.H.J. Blakemore Engraver: RCM Staff | Obverse: King George VI Designer: T.H. Paget Engraver: Thomas Shingles | The Victory Designer & Engraver: Thomas Shingles | The Identification c Nickel Des.: Stephan Trenl Engraver: Thomas Shingles |

| Obverse: Elizabeth II Designer: Arnold Machin Engraver: RCM Staff | The Centennial Five Cents Designer: Alex Colville Engraver: Myron Cook | | Obverse: Elizabeth II Designer: Susanna Blunt Engraver: Susan Taylor | The Beaver Designer: G.E. Kruger-Gray Engraver: RCM Staff |

Designers:
  Obv.: See obverse illustrations
  Rev.: See reverse illustrations
Composition: 99.99% Ag, Selectively gold plated
Silver Content: 31.83 g, 1.02 tr oz
Weight: 31.83 g
Diameter: 40.0 mm
Thickness: N/A
Case of Issue: Singly: Maroon leatherette clam style case, black flocked insert, encapsulated coin, COA
  Subscription: Six-hole wooden case, black flocked insert, encapsulated coins, COA

Engravers:
  Obv.: See obverse illustrations
  Rev.: See reverse illustrations
Edge: Reeded
Die Axis: ↑↑
Finish: Proof

DATE	DESCRIPTION	QUANTITY SOLD	ISSUE PRICE	FINISH	PR-69	PR-
2015	The Crossed Maple Boughs	6,690	109.95	Proof	90.	—
2015	The Two Maple Leaves	6,243	109.95	Proof	90.	—
2015	The Victory	6,251	109.95	Proof	90.	—
2015	The Identification of Nickel	5,595	109.95	Proof	90.	—
2015	The Centennial Five Cents	5,993	109.95	Proof	90.	—
2015	The Beaver	5,682	109.95	Proof	90.	—

ROYAL CANADIAN MINT COIN LORE: THE COINS THAT NEVER WERE

E CENTS, THE COINS THAT NEVER WERE – 3-COIN SET, 2018.

n 1936 Emanuel Hahn submitted several concepts for new circulation coinage, but most were set aside. Now, some of Hahn's "coins that never
e" are featured in a three-coin tribute set. In addition to the five-cent coin, the two twenty-five cent coins can be found on page 60.

Designers and Engravers:		Weight:	31.39 g
Obv.:	S. Blunt, S. Taylor	Diameter:	38 mm
Rev.:	Emanuel Otto Hahn	Thickness:	N/A
Composition:	99.99% Ag	**Edge:**	Reeded
Silver content:	31.39 g, 1.01 tr oz	**Die Axis:**	↑↑
Finish:	Reverse Proof		
Case of Issue:	Standard maroon clamshell with black beauty box, COA.		

DATE	DESCRIPTION	QUANTITY SOLD	ISSUE PRICE	FINISH	PR-69	PR-70
2018	The Coins That Never Were – 3-Coin Set	5,500	269.95	Reverse Proof	100.	—

FIVE CENT DERIVATIVES

DATE	DESCRIPTION	QUANTITY SOLD	ISSUE PRICE	ISSUER	FINISH	MARKET PRICE
004 (1944-)	**D-Day Five Cents**, 1944-2004; Bronze medallion, CD, Folder	20,019	29.95	RCM	PR-69	35.
005 (1945-)	VE-Day Five Cents, 1945-2005; Bronze medallion, Booklet	42,792	29.95	RCM	PR-69	15.
005 (1945-)	2005 Annual Mint Report, Five cent coin, selectively gold plated		24.95	RCM	PR-69	
	English	5,213				70.
	French	852				70.

TEN CENTS

TEN CENTS, ELIZABETH II PROOF, 1996-2018.

Starting in 1996 the ten-cent coin issued in the proof set, previously struck from cupronickel, was now struck on a sterling silver planchet. The of sterling silver planchets was discontinued in 2011.

The year 2012 saw the introduction of the Premium Proof Set in which all coins were struck on fine silver planchets.

Standard Proof Sets were issued for 2012-2017. The ten-cent coin in these sets was struck on a nickel planchet.

Obverse 1996-2003	Obverse 2004-2006, 2015-2018 Without Mint Logo	Obverse 2007-2014, 2018 With Mint Logo	Obverse 2017 With Canada 150 Logo	Reverse 1996-2018	Reverse 2017 Wings of Peace

Designers:

Obv.:	1996-2003:	Dora de Pédery-Hunt
	2004-2018:	Susanna Blunt
Rev.:		Emanuel Hahn
	2017:	Amy Choi

Engravers:

Obv.:	1996-2003:	Dora de Pédery-Hunt
	2004-2018:	Susan Taylor
Rev.:		Emanuel Hahn

	Sterling Silver	**Nickel**	**Fine Silver**
Composition:	92.5% Ag, 7.5% Cu	100.% Ni	99.99% Ag
Silver content:	2.15 g, 0.069 tr oz	—	2.5 g, 0.08 tr oz
Weight:	2.32 g	1.75 g	2.5 g
Diameter:	18.03 mm	18.05 mm	18.0 mm
Thickness:	1.7 mm	1.2 mm	1.2 mm
Edge:	Reeded	Reeded	Reeded
Die Axis:	↑↑	↑↑	↑↑
Finish:	Proof	Proof	Proof
Case of Issue:	Included in Proof Sets, see pages 546-550		

DATE	DESCRIPTION	COMP.	QUANTITY SOLD	ISSUE PRICE	FINISH	PR-69	PR
1996	Diademed Portrait / Bluenose	Sterling	112,835	N.I.I.	Proof	10.	—
1997		Sterling	113,647	N.I.I.	Proof	10.	—
1998		Sterling	93,632	N.I.I.	Proof	10.	—
1999		Sterling	95,113	N.I.I.	Proof	10.	—
2000		Sterling	90,921	N.I.I.	Proof	10.	—
2001		Sterling	74,194	N.I.I.	Proof	10.	—
2002		Sterling	65,315	N.I.I.	Proof	10.	—
2003		Sterling	62,007	N.I.I.	Proof	10.	—
2004	Uncrowned Portrait / Bluenose	Sterling	57,614	N.I.I.	Proof	10.	—
2005		Sterling	63,562	N.I.I.	Proof	10.	—
2006		Sterling	53,822	N.I.I.	Proof	10.	—
2007	Uncrowned Portrait, Mint Logo / Bluenose	Sterling	37,413	N.I.I.	Proof	10.	—
2008		Sterling	38,630	N.I.I.	Proof	10.	—
2009		Sterling	27,549	N.I.I.	Proof	10.	—
2010		Sterling	32,342	N.I.I.	Proof	20.	—
2011		Sterling	32,910	N.I.I.	Proof	20.	—
2012		Nickel	27,254	N.I.I.	Proof	20.	—
2012	Premium Proof Set	Fine Silver	19,789	N.I.I.	Proof	20.	—
2013	Premium Proof Set	Fine Silver	20,182	N.I.I.	Proof	20.	—
2014		Nickel	11,251	N.I.I.	Proof	10.	—
2014	Premium Proof Set	Fine Silver	13,416	N.I.I.	Proof	20.	—
2015	Premium Proof Set	Fine Silver	20,000	N.I.I.	Proof	20.	—
2015		Nickel	20,000	N.I.I.	Proof	10.	—
2016	Premium Proof Set	Fine Silver	20,000	N.I.I.	Proof	20.	—
2016		Nickel	12,500	N.I.I.	Proof	10.	—
2017	Premium Proof Set, Schooner	Fine Silver	20,000	N.I.I.	Proof	20.	—
2017	Premium Proof Set, Wings of Peace	Fine Silver	20,000	N.I.I.	Proof	20.	—
2017	Proof Set, Wings of Peace	Nickel	25,000	N.I.I.	Proof	10.	—
2017	Premium Proof Set, 1967-2017	Fine Silver	20,000	N.I.I.	Proof	20.	—
2018	Premium Proof Set,	Fine Silver	20,000	N.I.I.	Proof	20.	—
2018		Nickel	25,000	N.I.I	Proof	10.	—

Note: Quantity sold figures are identical to those listed for Proof Sets sold.

TEN CENTS, 500TH ANNIVERSARY OF CABOTO'S FIRST TRANSATLANTIC VOYAGE, 1997.

Giovanni Caboto (c.1450-c.1508) was an Italian navigator and explorer whose 1497 discovery of North America is commonly held to be the first voyage to the continent since those of the Vikings.

Designers and Engravers:	**Weight:** 2.4 g
Obv.: Dora de Pédery-Hunt	**Diameter:** 18.0 mm
Rev.: Donald H. Curley, Stan Witten	**Thickness:** 1.2 mm
Composition: 92.5% Ag, 7.5% Cu	**Edge:** Reeded
Silver content: 2.22 g, 0.071 tr oz	**Die Axis:** ↑↑
Finish: Proof	
Case of Issue: Clear plastic case with black insert, white sleeve. See Derivatives, page 18	

DATE	DESCRIPTION	QUANTITY SOLD	ISSUE PRICE	FINISH	PR-68	PR-69
1997	500th Anniv. of Caboto's Voyage	49,848	10.95	Proof	12.	—

TEN CENTS, 90TH ANNIVERSARY OF THE ROYAL CANADIAN MINT, 1908-1998.

First opened on January 2nd, 1908, the Ottawa Branch of the Royal Mint became the Royal Canadian Mint in 1931.

Designers and Engravers:	**Weight:** 2.32 g
Obv.: Dora de Pédery-Hunt	**Diameter:** 18.03 mm
Rev.: G. W. DeSaulles, RCM Staff	**Thickness:** 1.7 mm
Composition: 92.5% Ag, 7.5% Cu	**Edge:** Reeded
Silver content: 2.15 g, 0.069 tr oz	**Die Axis:** ↑↑
Finish: Matte Proof, Mirror Proof	
Case of Issue: See Special Issue Proof Sets, page 551	

DATE	DESCRIPTION	QUANTITY SOLD	ISSUE PRICE	FINISH	PR-68	PR-69
1998 (1908-)	Sterling silver, Matte Proof	18,376	N.I.I.	Proof	15.	—
1998 (1908-)	Sterling silver, Mirror Proof	24,893	N.I.I.	Proof	15.	—

TEN CENTS, 100TH ANNIVERSARY OF THE BIRTH OF THE CREDIT UNIONS IN NORTH AMERICA, 2000.

The first credit union in North America, The Caisse Populaire de Lévis in Quebec, began operation on January 23rd, 1901, with a ten-cent deposit.

Designers and Engravers:	**Weight:** 2.4 g
Obv.: Dora de Pédery-Hunt	**Diameter:** 18.0 mm
Rev.: Jean-Guy Lebel, W. Woodruff	**Thickness:** 1.2 mm
Composition: 92.5% Ag, 7.5% Cu	**Edge:** Reeded
Silver content: 2.22 g, 0.071 tr oz	**Die Axis:** ↑↑
Finish: Proof	
Case of Issue: Green printed card folder with encapsulated coin	

DATE	DESCRIPTION	QUANTITY SOLD	ISSUE PRICE	FINISH	PR-69	PR-70
2000	100th Anniv. Birth of Credit Unions in N.A.	69,791	9.95	Proof	8.	—

TEN CENTS, INTERNATIONAL YEAR OF THE VOLUNTEERS, 2001.

The United Nations declaration of International Year of the Volunteers gave cause for celebration for more than 7.5 million Canadian volunteers.

Designers and Engravers:	**Weight:** 2.4 g
Obv.: Dora de Pédery-Hunt	**Diameter:** 18.0 mm
Rev.: RCM Design, Stan Witten	**Thickness:** 1.2 mm
Composition: 92.5% Ag, 7.5% Cu	**Edge:** Reeded
Silver content: 2.22 g, 0.071 tr oz	**Die Axis:** ↑↑
Finish: Proof	
Case of Issue: Multicoloured printed card folder with encapsulated coin	

DATE	DESCRIPTION	QUANTITY SOLD	ISSUE PRICE	FINISH	PR-69	PR-70
2001	International Year of the Volunteers	40,634	14.95	Proof	8.	—

1. For the ten cent font varieties of 2007 (Curved and Straight 7) see page 517.
2. For the ten cent Finish variety from the 2010 Special Edition Specimen Set, see page 544.

TEN CENTS, 50TH ANNIVERSARY OF THE CORONATION OF QUEEN ELIZABETH II, 1953-2003.

Elizabeth II was crowned Queen June 2nd, 1953; her 50th anniversary was June 2nd, 2003.

Designers and Engravers:
Obv.:   Dora de Pédery-Hunt
Rev.:   Emanuel Hahn
Composition: 92.5% Ag, 7.5% Cu
Silver content: 2.15 g, 0.069 tr oz
Finish: Mirror Proof
Case of Issue: See Special Issue Proof Sets, page 551

Weight: 2.32 g
Diameter: 18.0 mm
Thickness: 1.7 mm
Edge: Reeded
Die Axis: ↑↑

DATE	DESCRIPTION	QUANTITY SOLD	ISSUE PRICE	FINISH	PR-69	PR-7
2003 (1953-)	50th Anniv. Coronation Queen Elizabeth II	21,537	N.I.I.	Proof	15.	—

TEN CENTS, 100TH ANNIVERSARY OF THE CANADIAN OPEN GOLF CHAMPIONSHIP, 2004.

The Canadian Open Golf Tournament was first played on the Royal Montreal Golf Club course in 1904. The tournament was won by the Eng player, John H. Oke.

Designers and Engravers:
Obv.:   Susanna Blunt, Susan Taylor
Rev.:   Cosme Saffioti
Composition: Nickel plated steel
Weight: 1.75 g
Case of Issue: See Derivatives, page 18

Diameter: 18.03 mm
Thickness: 1.2 mm
Edge: Reeded
Die Axis: ↑↑
Finish: Circulation

DATE	DESCRIPTION	QUANTITY SOLD	ISSUE PRICE	FINISH	MS-65 NC	MS-66 NC	MS- NC
2004	100th Anniv. of Canadian Open Golf Championship	39,486	N.I.I.	Circulation	12.	25.	—

TEN CENTS, GEORGE V, STERLING SILVER, PROOF, 1935-2010.

This ten-cent coin is from the Special Limited Edition Proof Set issued in 2010 to commemorate Emanuel Hahn's classic voyageur design w first appeared on the 1935 silver dollar.

Designers and Engravers:
Obv.:   Sir E. B. MacKennal
Rev.:   Original design by L. C. Wyon,
            Modified by W. H. J. Blakemore
Composition: 92.5% Ag, 7.5% Cu
Silver content: 2.22 g, 0.071 tr oz
Case of Issue: See Special Issue Proof Sets, page 551

Weight: 2.4 g
Diameter: 18.1 mm
Thickness: 1.1 mm
Edge: Reeded
Die Axis: ↑↑
Finish: Proof

DATE	DESCRIPTION	QUANTITY SOLD	ISSUE PRICE	FINISH	PR-69	PR-
2010 (1935-)	George V, Sterling Silver	4,996	N.I.I.	Proof	20.	—

TEN CENTS, GEORGE V, STERLING SILVER, PROOF, 1911-2011.

This ten-cent coin which carries the double date 1911-2011 is from the Special Edition Proof Set issued in 2011 to commemorate the anniversary of the striking of Canada's 1911 silver dollar.

Designers and Engravers:
Obv.:   Sir E. B. MacKennal
Rev.:   Original design by L. C. Wyon,
            Modified by W. H. J. Blakemore
Composition: 92.5% Ag, 7.5% Cu
Silver content: 2.22 g, 0.071 tr oz
Case of Issue: See Special Issue Proof Sets, page 551

Weight: 2.4 g
Diameter: 18.1 mm
Thickness: 1.1 mm
Edge: Reeded
Die Axis: ↑↑
Finish: Proof

DATE	DESCRIPTION	QUANTITY SOLD	ISSUE PRICE	FINISH	PR-69	PR
2011 (1911-)	George V, Sterling silver	5,952	N.I.I.	Proof	35.	—

BIG COIN SERIES

N CENTS, BIG COIN SET, 2015-2018.

The Big Coin Set started in 2015, features the classic Bluenose design for 2015, 2016 and 2018, which first appeared on the 1937 Canadian ten-t coin designed by Emanuel Hahn, and Alex Colville's 1967 design for the 2017 coin. Other coins in the set include a 5¢ coin (page 11), 25¢ coin ge 57), 50¢ coin (page 88), $1 coin (page 130) and a $2 coin (page 144).

gners and Engravers:

Obv.:	Susanna Blunt, Susan Taylor
Rev.:	Emanuel Hahn, Myron Cook,
	Alex Colville
	Emanuel Hahn

r content: 157.6 g, 5.06 tr oz
ht: 157.6 g
eter: 65.25 mm
kness: N/A
of Issue: Maroon clam style case, black flocked insert, encapsulated coin, COA, custom box

Composition:

2015:	99.99% Ag, Selectively gold plated
2016:	99.99% Ag, Selectively coloured on reverse
2017:	99.99% Ag, Selectively gold plated
2018:	99.99% Ag, Selectively rose gold-plated

Edge: Reeded
Die Axis: ↑↑
Finish: Proof

ATE	DESCRIPTION	QUANTITY SOLD	ISSUE PRICE	FINISH	PR-69	PR-70
015	10¢ Big Coin	1,483	549.95	Proof	550.	—
016	10¢ Big Coin	1,489	519.95	Proof	520.	—
017	10¢ Big Coin	2,150	559.95	Proof	560.	—
018	10¢ Big Coin	1,500	559.95	Proof	560.	—

Coins illustrated smaller than actual size.

TEN CENTS, LEGACY OF THE DIME, 2018.

The Legacy of the Dime set is a uique retrospective look at Canada's 10-cent circulation coin through the years, as struck by the Royal Canadian Mint.

1936 Dot
Reverse: W.H.J. Blakemore Obv.: Sir E.B. MacKennal

1947 Maple Leaf
Reverse: Emanuel Hahn Obverse: T.H. Paget

1967 Centennial
Reverse: Alex Colville
Obverse: Arnold Machin

2001 Year of the Volunteer
Reverse: RCM Staff
Obverse: Dora de Pédery-Hunt

2017 Wing of Peace)
Reverse: Amy Choi
Obverse: Susanna Blunt

Designers:		**Engravers:**
Obv.:	See illustrations	Obv.:	See illustrations
Rev.:	See illustrations	Rev.:	See illustrations

Composition: 99.99% Ag, selective gold plating
Silver content: 157.6 g, 5.06 tr oz

	1936 Dot	**1947 Maple Leaf**	**1967 Centennial**	**2001 Year of the Volunteer**	**2017 Wing of Pea**
Weight:	62.67 g	62.67 g	31.39 g	31.39 g	31.39 g
Diameter:	54.0 mm	54.0 mm	38.0 mm	38.0 mm	38.0 mm
Thickness:	N/A				
Edge:	Reeded				
Die Axis:	↑↑				
Finish:	Proof				
Case of Issue:	Wooden collector's case with black beauty box. COA				

DATE	DESCRIPTION	MINTAGE	ISSUE PRICE	FINISH	PR-69	PR
2018	Legacy of the Dime Set, Fine silver	3,000	709.95	Proof	710.	

TEN CENT DERIVATIVES

DATE	DESCRIPTION	QUANTITY SOLD	ISSUE PRICE	ISSUER	FINISH	MARK PRIC
1997	**John Caboto Ten Cents,** Sterling;. Canada 45¢ stamp; Italy 1300 Lira stamp; Set in multicoloured card folder	15,000	19.95	RCM, CP	PR-69	20
2000	**Bluenose Ten Cents,** Sterling; Two 46¢ stamps; Blue presentation case	15,000	19.95	RCM, CP	PR-69	20.
2001	**International Year of the Volunteers Ten Cents,** Thank You card and envelope	N/A	N/A	RCM	MS-65	10.
2004	**Ten Cent and Five Dollar Coins,** (100th Anniv. Canadian Open Golf Championship); Framed with two 48¢ circular stamps	18,750	49.95	RCM, CP	MS-65, PR-69	50
2004	**Canadian Open Championship Ten Cents,** Framed with two circular commemorative stamps, and a divot repair tool	20,736	21.49	RCM, CP	MS-65	20
2004	**Canadian Open Championship Ten Cents,** Canister also contains four commemorative stamps, a divot repair tool, three golf balls, five golf tees and a T-shirt	N/A	39.95	RCM, CP	MS-65	40

TWENTY-FIVE CENTS

TWENTY-FIVE CENTS, ELIZABETH II PROOF, 1996-2018.

Starting in 1996 the twenty-five-cent coin issued in the proof set, previously struck from cupronickel, was now struck on a sterling silver planchet.
The use of sterling silver planchets was discontinued in 2011.
The year 2012 saw the introduction of the Premium Proof Set in which all coins were struck on fine silver planchets.
Standard Proof Sets were issued for 2012, 2014-2018. The twenty-five cent coin in these sets was struck on a nickel planchet.

Obverse 1996-2003	Obverse 2004-2006, 2015-2018 Without Mint Logo	Obverse 2007-2014, 2018 With Mint Logo	Obverse 2018 With Canada 150 Logo	Reverse 1996-2018	Reverse 2017 Greener Future

Designers:
Obv.:   1996-2003:   Dora de Pédery-Hunt
        2004-2018:   Susanna Blunt
Rev.:   Emanuel Hahn
        2017:   Joelle Wong

Engravers:
Obv.:   1996-2003:   Dora de Pédery-Hunt
        2004-2018:   Susan Taylor
Rev.:   2017   Emanuel Hahn

Reverse
2017 Colour
Greener Future

	Sterling Silver	Nickel	Fine Silver
Composition:	92.5% Ag, 7.5% Cu	100.%	99.99% Ag
Silver content:	5.458 g, 0.175 tr oz	—	6.0 g, 0.193 tr oz
Weight:	5.9 g	4.4 g	6.0 g
Diameter:	23.9 mm	23.88 mm	23.9 mm
Thickness:	1.6 mm	1.62 mm	1.7 mm
Edge:	Reeded	Reeded	Reeded
Axis:	↑↑	↑↑	↑↑
Finish:	Proof	Proof	Proof
Place of Issue:	Included in Proof Sets, see pages 546-550		

DATE	DESCRIPTION	COMP.	QUANTITY SOLD	ISSUE PRICE	FINISH	PR-69	PR-70
1996	Diademed Portrait / Caribou	Sterling	112,835	N.I.I.	Proof	12.	—
1997		Sterling	113,647	N.I.I.	Proof	12.	—
1998		Sterling	93,632	N.I.I.	Proof	15.	—
1999		Sterling	95,113	N.I.I.	Proof	15.	—
2000		Sterling	90,921	N.I.I.	Proof	15.	—
2001		Sterling	74,194	N.I.I.	Proof	15.	—
2002		Sterling	65,315	N.I.I.	Proof	15.	—
2003		Sterling	62,007	N.I.I.	Proof	15.	—
2004	Uncrowned Portrait / Caribou	Sterling	57,614	N.I.I.	Proof	15.	—
2005		Sterling	63,562	N.I.I.	Proof	15.	—
2006		Sterling	53,822	N.I.I.	Proof	15.	—
2007	Uncrowned Portrait, Mint Logo / Caribou	Sterling	37,413	N.I.I.	Proof	15.	—
2008		Sterling	38,630	N.I.I.	Proof	15.	—
2009		Sterling	27,549	N.I.I.	Proof	15.	—
2010		Sterling	32,342	N.I.I.	Proof	20.	—
2011		Sterling	32,910	N.I.I.	Proof	20.	—
2012		Nickel	27,254	N.I.I.	Proof	20.	—
2012	Premium Proof Set	Fine Silver	19,789	N.I.I.	Proof	20.	—
2013	Premium Proof Set	Fine Silver	20,182	N.I.I.	Proof	20.	—
2014		Nickel	11,251	N.I.I.	Proof	15.	—
2014	Premium Proof Set	Fine Silver	13,416	N.I.I.	Proof	20.	—
2015	Premium Proof Set	Fine Silver	20,000	N.I.I.	Proof	20.	—
2015		Nickel	20,000	N.I.I.	Proof	15.	—
2016	Premium Proof Set	Fine Silver	20,000	N.I.I.	Proof	20.	—
2016		Nickel	12,500	N.I.I.	Proof	15.	—
2017	Premium Proof Set, Caribou	Fine Silver	20,000	N.I.I.	Proof	20.	—
2017	Premium Proof Set, Greener Future	Fine Silver	20,000	N.I.I.	Proof	20.	—
2017	Proof Set, Greener Future, Colour	Nickel	25,000	N.I.I.	Proof	15.	—
2017	Premium Proof Set 1967-2017	Fine Silver	20,000	N.I.I.	Proof	20.	—
2018	Premium Proof Set,	Fine Silver	20,000	N.I.I.	Proof	20.	—
2018		Nickel	25,000	N.I.I.	Proof	15.	—

Quantity sold figures are identical to those listed for Proof Sets sold.

125TH ANNIVERSARY OF CANADA, SILVER PROOF AND NICKEL UNCIRCULATED SETS, 1992.

Issued by the Royal Canadian Mint, in silver and nickel, the twelve different designs represent a familiar scene from each of the twelve provin and territories of Canada. This is the first issue of sterling silver twenty-five cent coins since 1919.

Also, a collection of nickel brilliant uncirculated coins mounted in a coloured map of Canada, with each twenty-five-cent coin placed in the province territory commemorated by its design was released October 7th, 1992. The Canada Day dollar which is the central point of a compass is listed on page 1

1867-1992
Obverse

Designers and Engravers:
Obv.: Dora de Pédery-Hunt, Ago Aarand
Rev.: See reverse illustrations

Composition:	Silver	Nickel
Silver content:	5.458 g	—
	0.175 tr oz	—
Weight:	5.9 g	5.05 g
Diameter:	23.8 mm	23.9 mm
Thickness:	1.7 mm	1.6 mm
Edge:	Reeded	Reeded
Die Axis:	↑↑	↑↑
Finish:	Proof	Circulation

Issue Price:

Individual proof silver:		$9.95
13-coin proof silver set:		$129.45
13 coin nickel set, "Map" holder:		$17.25

Quantity: Total individual silver coins: 651,812
Sold: Total silver sets: 84,397
Nickel sets, "Map" holder: 448,178

Case of Issue: (A) Royal blue flocked single coin case
(B) Royal blue flocked case, 13 coins.
Twelve 25¢ coins; one $1.00 coin

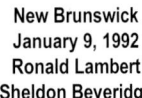

New Brunswick
January 9, 1992
Ronald Lambert
Sheldon Beveridge

Northwest
Territories
February 6, 1992
Beth McEachen

Newfoundland
March 5, 1992
Christopher
Newhook

Manitoba
April 7, 1992
Muriel Hope
Ago Aarand

Yukon
May 7, 1992
Libby Dulac
William Woodruff

Alberta
June 4, 1992
Mel Heath
William Woodru

Prince Edward
Island
July 7, 1992
N. Roe, S. Beveridge

Ontario
August 6, 1992
Greg Salmela
Susan Taylor

Nova Scotia
September 9, 1992
Bruce Wood
Terry Smith

Quebec
October 1, 1992
R. Bukauskas
Stan Witten

Saskatchewan
November 5, 1992
Brian Cobb
Terry Smith

British Columb
November 9, 19
Carla Egan
Sheldon Beveri

DATE	DESCRIPTION	PROOF STERLING SILVER		UNCIRCULATED NICKEL		
		PR-68	PR-69	MS-65 NC	MS-66 NC	MS-67 NC
1992	New Brunswick	15.	—	5.	10.	—
1992	Northwest Territories	15.	—	5.	10.	—
1992	Newfoundland	15.	—	5.	10.	—
1992	Manitoba	15.	—	5.	10.	—
1992	Yukon	15.	—	5.	10.	—
1992	Alberta	15.	—	5.	10.	—.
1992	Prince Edward Island	15.	—	5.	10.	—
1992	Ontario	15.	—	5.	10.	—
1992	Nova Scotia	15.	—	5.	10.	—
1992	Quebec	15.	—	5.	10.	—
1992	Saskatchewan	15.	—	5.	10.	—
1992	British Columbia	15.	—	5.	10.	—
1992	13 Coin Silver Proof Set	90.	—	*	*	*
1992	13 Coin Nickel Set with "Map" Holder	*	*	15.	—	—

...VENTY-FIVE CENTS, 125TH ANNIVERSARY MULE, 1867-1992.

A 1867-1992 obverse is muled with a Caribou reverse. The coin was reportedly issued in a Brilliant Uncirculated set of 1993.

Designers and Engravers:

Obv.:	Dora de Pédery-Hunt
Rev.:	Emanuel Hahn
Composition:	Nickel
Weight:	5.05 g
Diameter:	23.9 mm
Thickness:	1.6 mm	Edge: Reeded
Die Axis:	↑↑	Finish: Circulation

DATE	DESCRIPTION	MS-65
1992 (1867-)	Mule	Only two known

...VENTY-FIVE CENTS, 90TH ANNIVERSARY OF THE ROYAL CANADIAN MINT, 1908-1998.

...Issued to commemorate the opening of the Branch Mint in Ottawa, a five-coin set was struck featuring the same reverse designs as the original ...98 coins, except for the double date 1908-1998. The set was issued in two finishes, matte and mirror proof.

Designers and Engravers:

Obv.:	Dora de Pédery-Hunt
Rev.:	Ago Aarand, W. H. J. Blakemore
Composition:	92.5% Ag, 7.5% Cu
Silver content:	5.374 g, 0.173 tr oz
Weight:	.81 g	Edge: Reeded
Diameter:	23.6 mm	Die Axis: ↑↑
Thickness:	1.7 mm	Finish: See below
Case of Issue:	See Special Issue Proof Sets, page 551

DATE	DESCRIPTION	QUANTITY SOLD	ISSUE PRICE	FINISH	PR-68	PR-69
1998 (1908-)	90th Anniv. R.C. Mint, Matte Proof	18,376	N.I.I.	Matte Proof	25.	—
1998 (1908-)	90th Anniv. R.C. Mint, Mirror Proof	24,893	N.I.I.	Mirror Proof	25.	—

...LLENNIUM SILVER PROOF AND NICKEL UNCIRCULATED COMMEMORATIVE SETS, 1999.

...The twelve 25-cent nickel coins (circulation finish) of 1999 were issued along with a 1999 millennium medallion, inserted in a replica of a 1785 map of ...ada. Two different medallions were issued, one with a maple leaf obverse, the other carried the Nestlé logo; both have the common Royal Mint logo ...rse. They were only available in the millennium set. The set of twelve coins was also issued in sterling silver with a proof finish.

**1999
Obverse**

Designers and Engravers:		
Obv.:	Dora de Pédery-Hunt	
	Ago Aarand	
Rev.:	See reverse illustrations	

Composition:	Silver	Nickel
Silver content:	5.458 g	—
	0.175 tr oz	—
Weight:	5.9 g	5.05 g
Diameter:	23.88 mm	23.9 mm
Thickness:	1.7 mm	1.6 mm
Edge:	Reeded	Reeded
Die Axis:	↑↑	↑↑
Finish:	Proof	Circulation

Issue Price:

Individual proof silver:	$14.95
12 coin proof silver set:	$149.45
12 coin unc. nickel / RCM set:	$24.95
12 coin unc. nickel / Nestlé set:	$24.95

Quantity:	Total individual silver coins:	111,414
Sold:	Total silver sets:	60,245
	Total nickel sets:	1,499,973

Case of Issue: (A) Gold plastic single hole, oval case, royal blue flocked insert
(B) Gold plastic 12-hole, oval case, royal blue flocked insert

January	February	March	April	May	June
...Ka-Kin Poon	L. Springer	M. Lavoie	Ken Ojnak Ashevac	S. Minenok	G. Ho
...osme Saffioti	José Osio	Stan Witten	Sheldon Beveridge	William Woodruff	William Woodruff

MILLENNIUM SILVER PROOF AND NICKEL UNCIRCULATED COMMEMORATIVE SETS, 1999 (cont.).

| July
M. H. Sarkany
Stan Witten | August
A. Botelho
Cosme Saffioti | September
C. Bertrand
Stan Witten | October
J. E. Read
Sheldon Beveridge | November
B. R. Bacon
Stan Witten | December
J. L. P. Provenche
Stan Witten |

| DATE | DESCRIPTION | PROOF STERLING SILVER | | UNCIRCULATED NICKEL | | |
		PR-68	PR-69	MS-65 NC	MS-66 NC	MS-67 NC
1999	January, A Country Unfolds	15.	—	5.	10.	—
1999	February, Etched in Stone	15.	—	5.	10.	—
1999	March, The Log Drive	15.	—	5.	10.	—
1999	April, Our Northern Heritage	15.	—	5.	10.	—
1999	May, The Voyageurs	15.	—	5.	10.	—
1999	June, From Coast to Coast	15.	—	5.	10.	—
1999	July, A Nation of People	15.	—	5.	10.	—
1999	August, The Pioneer Spirit	15.	—	5.	10.	—
1999	September, Canada Through a Child's Eye	15.	—	5.	10.	—
1999	October, A Tribute to the First Nation	15.	—	5.	10.	—
1999	November, The Airplane Opens the North	15.	—	5.	10.	—
1999	December, This is Canada	15.	—	5.	10.	—
1999	12 Coin Silver Proof Set plus RCM Medallion	90.	—	*	*	*
1999	12 Coin Nickel Set plus RCM Medallion	*	*	12.	—	—
1999	12 Coin Nickel Set plus "Nestlé" Medallion	*	*	20.	—	—

Note: The PR-70 prices for individual twenty-cent coins are for examples that are certified. The PR-69 prices are for raw coins.

TWENTY-FIVE CENT MILLENNIUM MULES OF 1999.

It is in the 1999 millennium nickel set that the "No Denomination" coins of September and November are found. During the Fall of 1999, a Qu Elizabeth II obverse die became paired with the reverse dies of September and November millennium twenty-five cents coins creating two mules. interesting result of these pairings is that for the first time Canada has a non denominated legal tender coin.

| Queen Elizabeth II
No denomination
Obverse | 1999 September
Reverse Mule | 1999 November
Reverse Mule |

DATE	DESCRIPTION	MS-63 NC	MS-64 NC	MS-65 NC	MS-66 NC
1999	September, no denomination, Mule	100.	125.	175.	250.
1999	November, no denomination, Mule	100.	125.	175.	250.

TWENTY-FIVE CENT SOUVENIR MEDALLIONS OF 1999.

Along with the nickel souvenir sets two different medallions were issued: A Royal Canadian Mint medallion and a Nestlé Canada Inc. medallion.

| 1999 RCM Medallion Obv. | 1999 RCM Medallion Rev. | 1999 Nestlé Medallion Obv. | 1999 RCM Medallion Rev. |

DATE	DESCRIPTION	QUANTITY SOLD	ISSUE PRICE	FINISH	MS-65 NC	MS-66 NC	MS-67 NC
1999	RCM Medallion	N/A	N.I.I.	Uncirculated	6.	10.	—
1999	Nestlé Medallion	N/A	N.I.I.	Uncirculated	12.	15.	—

TWENTY-FIVE CENT STERLING SILVER SOUVENIR MEDALLION OF 1999-2000.

The 24-coin sterling silver set which was issued for the Chinese market in Hong Kong contains a 1999-2000 sterling silver medallion.

 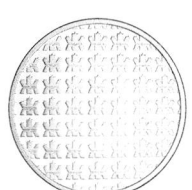

DATE	DESCRIPTION	QUANTITY SOLD	ISSUE PRICE	FINISH	PR-68	PR-69
1999-2000	Sterling Silver Medallion	N/A	N.I.I.	Proof	75.	—

MILLENNIUM SILVER PROOF AND NICKEL UNCIRCULATED COMMEMORATIVE SETS, 2000.

The 2000 Souvenir set was issued in sterling silver with a proof finish and in nickel with a circulation finish. The nickel set features 12 coins plus the 2000 commemorative medallion which was only issued with the souvenir set. The coins are displayed on an easel featuring an aerial photograph of Canada.

2000 Obverse

Designers and Engravers:			Issue Price:		
Obv.:	Dora de Pédery-Hunt		Individual proof silver:		$14.95
	Ago Aarand		12 coin proof silver set:		$149.45
Rev.:	See reverse illustrations		12 coin unc. nickel/RCM set:		$24.95
Composition:	Silver	Nickel	12 coin unc. nickel set/plastic case:		$49.55
Silver content:	5.458 g	—	Quantity:	Total silver sets:	37,940
	0.175 tr oz	—	Sold:	Total nickel sets:	876,041
Weight:	5.9 g	5.05 g			
Diameter:	23.9 mm	23.9 mm			
Thickness:	1.7 mm	1.6 mm			
Edge:	Reeded	Reeded			
Die Axis:	↑↑	↑↑			
Finish:	Proof	Uncirculated			
Case of Issue:	Silver:	(A) Black plastic single-hole, oval case, royal blue flocked insert			
		(B) Black plastic 12-hole, oval case, royal blue flocked insert			
		(C) Red plush presentation case, light brown insert, 24 coins, a 1999 and 2000 medallion. Issued for the Chinese market.			
	Nickel:	(A) 13 hole, Map of Canada. (B) 13 hole, plastic case			

January	February	March	April	May	June
...ald F. Warkentin	John Jaciw	Daryl Dorosz	Annie Wassef	Randy Trantau	Haver Demirer
José Osio	William Woodruff	Stan Witten	Stan Witten	José Osio	José Osio

MILLENNIUM SILVER PROOF AND NICKEL UNCIRCULATED COMMEMORATIVE SETS, 2000 (cont.).

July	August	September	October	November	December
Laura Paxton	W. S. Baker	Cezar Serbanescu	Jerik (Kong Tat) Hui	Kathy Vinish	Michelle Thibodea
Stan Witten	Susan Taylor	Cosme Saffioti	Susan Taylor	William Woodruff	José Osio

DATE	DESCRIPTION	PROOF STERLING SILVER		UNCIRCULATED NICKEL		
		PR-69	PR-70	MS-65 NC	MS-66 NC	MS-67 NC
2000	January, Pride	15.	—	5.	10.	—
2000	February, Ingenuity	15.	—	5.	10.	—
2000	March, Achievement	15.	—	5.	10.	—
2000	April, Health	15.	—	5.	10.	—
2000	May, Natural Legacy	15.	—	5.	10.	—
2000	June, Harmony	15.	—	5.	10.	—
2000	July, Celebration	15.	—	5.	10.	—
2000	August, Family	15.	—	5.	10.	—
2000	September, Wisdom	15.	—	5.	10.	—
2000	October, Creativity	15.	—	5.	10.	—
2000	November, Freedom	15.	—	5.	10.	—
2000	December, Community	15.	—	5.	10.	—
2000	12 Coin Silver Proof Set	90.	—	*	*	*
2000	12 Coin Nickel Set, RCM Medallion	*	*	10.	—	—
2000	12 Coin Nickel Set, Nestlé Medallion	*	*	15.	—	—

TWENTY-FIVE CENT SOUVENIR MEDALLIONS OF 2000.

Again in 2000 the nickel souvenir sets contained souvenir medallions. Two types were issued: The Royal Canadian Mint and Nestlé Canada Inc.

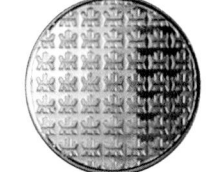

2000 Royal Canadian Mint Medallion   **2000 Nestle Medallion**

TWENTY-FIVE CENT MEDALLION MULE OF 2000.

In 2000 two dies were mismatched creating a mule. The obverse die of the February twenty-five cents is paired with the obverse die of the 2 medallion. The mule is found in the Medallion position of the 13-hole, Map of Canada Brilliant Uncirculated Set of 2000.

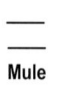

February Reverse   **February Obverse**   **Mule**   **Medallion Obverse**   **Medallion Reverse**

DATE	DESCRIPTION	QUANTITY SOLD	ISSUE PRICE	FINISH	MS-63 NC	MS-64 NC	MS-65 NC	MS-66 NC	MS N
2000	RCM Medallion	N.I.I.	—	Uncirculated	—	—	5.	8.	
2000	Nestlé Medallion	N.I.I.	—	Uncirculated	—	—	8.	15.	
2000	Coin / Medallion Mule	N.I.I.	—	Uncirculated	300.	500.	700.	—	

TWENTY-FIVE CENTS, CANADA'S FIRST COLOURISED COIN, 2000.

Issued to celebrate the year 2000, this was the first colourised coin issued by the Royal Canadian Mint.

Designers and Engravers:

Obv.:	Dora de Pédery-Hunt
Rev.:	Donald F. Warkentin, José Osio

Composition: Nickel
Weight: 5.05 g   **Edge:**   Reeded
Diameter: 23.9 mm   **Die Axis:** ↑↑
Thickness: 1.6 mm
Finish: Circulation, Colourised
Case of Issue: Blister packed on information card.

DATE	DESCRIPTION	QUANTITY SOLD	ISSUE PRICE	FINISH	MS-65 NC	MS-66 NC	MS-67 NC
2000	January, Pride, Colourised	49,719	8.95	Circulation	12.	20.	—

TWENTY-FIVE CENTS, CANADA DAY SERIES, 2000-2008.

The following series of twenty-five cent coins was issued to celebrate the Canada Day celebrations that took place during the last week of June, ding up to July 1st.

In 2004, four thousand six hundred and fifteen "Moose" coins were given to new Canadians during Canada Week Celebrations June 25th to July . Of the initial offering of 27,000, only 16,028 were sold in a "walking bundle" (see page 61).

ars:	2000	2001 to 2008
mposition:	1.00 nickel, Painted	Nickel plated steel, Painted
ight:	5.05 g	4.4 g
meter:	23.9 mm	23.9 mm
ckness:	1.6 mm	1.6 mm
ge:	Reeded	Reeded
Axis:	↑↑	↑↑
ish:	Uncirculated	2001 to 2008: Circulation
		2004: Circulation

se of Issue:	2000:	Blister packed on information card.
	2001:	Encapsulated coin fastened to an information card
	2002 to 2008:	Folder
	2004:	See Derivatives, page 60-61

0

igners and Engravers:

Obv.:   Dora de Pédery-Hunt
Rev.:   Laura Paxton, Stan Witten

1

igners and Engravers:

Obv.:   Dora de Pédery-Hunt
Rev.:   Silke Ware, William Woodruff

2003

Designers and Engravers:

Obv.:   Dora de Pédery-Hunt, Ago Aarand
Rev.:   Jade Pearen, Stan Witten

2004

Designers and Engravers:

Obv.:   Susanna Blunt, Susan Taylor
Rev.:   Cosme Saffiotti, Stan Witten

TWENTY-FIVE CENTS, CANADA DAY SERIES, 2000-2008 (cont.).

2002

Designers and Engravers:
Obv.:   Dora de Pédery-Hunt, Ago Aarand
Rev.:   Judith Chartier, Stan Witten

2005

Designers and Engravers:
Obv.:   Susanna Blunt, Susan Taylor
Rev.:   Stan Witten, Stan Witten

2006

Designers and Engravers:
Obv.:   Susanna Blunt, Susan Taylor
Rev.:   Stan Witten, Stan Witten

2004

Designers and Engravers:
Obv.:   Susanna Blunt, Susan Taylor
Rev.:   Nick Wooster, William Woodruff

2007

Designers and Engravers:
Obv.:   Susanna Blunt, Susan Taylor
Rev.:   José Osio

2008

Designers and Engravers:
Obv.:   Susanna Blunt, Susan Taylor
Rev.:   Stan Witten, Stan Witten

DATE/ COMP. MARK	DESCRIPTION	QUANTITY SOLD	ISSUE PRICE	FINISH	MS-65 NC
2000	Canada Day, Colourised, Celebration	26,106	8.95	Uncirculated	45.
2001P	Canada Day, Colourised	96,352	9.95	Uncirculated	8.
2002P (1952-)	Canada Day, Colourised	49,901	9.95	Uncirculated	12.
2003P	Canada Day, Colourised	63,511	9.95	Uncirculated	15.
2004P	Canada Day, Colourised	44,752	9.95	Uncirculated	12.
2004P	Canada Day, Citizenship/Moose	16,028	N.I.I.	Uncirculated	20.
2005P	Canada Day, Colourised	58,370	9.95	Uncirculated	12.
2006P	Canada Day, Colourised	30,328	9.95	Uncirculated	12.
2007	Canada Day, Colourised	27,743	9.95	Uncirculated	15.
2008	Canada Day, Colourised	11,538	9.95	Uncirculated	15.

TWENTY-FIVE CENTS, CANADA DAY, 2009, (GIFTWARE).

In 2009 the Royal Canadian Mint discontinued the standard Canada Day colourised twenty-five cent piece, changing it to a crown size coin, with no ation to the standard twenty-five-cent denomination.

Designers and Engravers:

Obv.:	Susanna Blunt, Susan Taylor
Rev.:	RCM Staff
Composition:	Nickel plated steel, Painted
Weight:	12.59 g
Diameter:	35.0 mm
Thickness:	2.0 mm
Edge:	Plain
Die Axis:	↑↑
Finish:	Specimen
Case of Issue:	Folder

DATE	DESCRIPTION	QUANTITY SOLD	ISSUE PRICE	FINISH	MS-65 NC
2009	Canada Day, Churchill	11,091	14.95	Specimen	20.

TWENTY-FIVE CENTS, 50TH ANNIVERSARY OF THE CORONATION OF QUEEN ELIZABETH II, 1953-2003.

This twenty-five-cent coin is from the Special Edition Proof Set issued in 2003 to commemorate the 50th anniversary of the Coronation of Queen Elizabeth II.

Designers and Engravers:

Obv.:	Mary Gillick, Thomas Shingles
Rev.:	Emanuel Hahn, Thomas Shingles
Composition:	92.5% Ag, 7.5% Cu
Silver content:	5.458 g, 0.175 tr oz
Weight:	5.9 g Edge: Reeded
Diameter:	23.9 mm Die Axis: ↑↑
Thickness:	1.6 mm Finish: Proof
Case of Issue:	See Special Issue Proof Sets, page 551

DATE	DESCRIPTION	QUANTITY SOLD	ISSUE PRICE	FINISH	PR-69	PR-70
2003 (1953-)	50th Anniv. Coronation Queen Elizabeth II	21,537	N.I.I.	Proof	20.	—

TWENTY-FIVE CENTS, CHRISTMAS DAY SERIES, COLOURISED, 2004-2010.

The twenty-five cents Christmas Day coins are issued as part of the Holiday Gift Set series, see page 531. The quantity sold figures shown are from number of Holiday Sets sold for that year. The last colourised twenty-five-cent coin in the Christmas Series was issued in 2010. The Holiday Gift s continued in 2011, however, the twenty-five-cent coin was no longer coloured, see pages 33-34.

Obverse With Mint Mark "P" 2004-2006	Obverse With RCM Logo 2007-2009	Obverse Without RCM Logo 2010	2004 Santa Claus José Osio	2005 Christmas Stocking José Osio
2006 Santa in Sleigh and Reindeer M. Hallam, J. Osio	2007 Christmas Tree RCM Staff	2008 Santa RCM Staff	2009 Santa Claus and Maple Leaves RCM Staff	2010 Santa Claus and Christmas Tree RCM Staff

TWENTY-FIVE CENTS, CHRISTMAS DAY SERIES, COLOURISED, 2004-2010 (cont.).

Designers and Engravers:

Obv.:	Susanna Blunt, Susan Taylor	**Diameter:**	23.9 mm
Rev.:	See reverse illustrations	**Edge:**	Reeded
Composition:	Nickel plated steel, Decal	**Thickness:**	1.6 mm
Weight:	4.4 g	**Die Axis:**	↑↑
Finish:	Circulation	**Case of Issue:**	See Holiday Gift Sets page 531

DATE/ COMP. MARK	DESCRIPTION	SOURCE	QUANTITY SOLD	ISSUE PRICE	FINISH	MS-65 NC
2004P	Santa Claus		62,777	N.I.I.	Uncirculated	25.
2005P	Christmas Stocking		72,831	N.I.I.	Uncirculated	12.
2006P	Santa in Sleigh and Reindeer	Available only from Holiday Gift Sets	99,258	N.I.I.	Uncirculated	12.
2007	Christmas Tree		66,267	N.I.I.	Uncirculated	15.
2008	Santa		42,344	N.I.I.	Uncirculated	15.
2009	Santa Claus and Maple Leaves		32,967	N.I.I.	Uncirculated	15.
2010	Santa Claus and Christmas Tree		10,870	N.I.I.	Uncirculated	15.

TWENTY-FIVE CENTS, SILVER POPPY, ROYAL CANADIAN MINT ANNUAL REPORT, SELECTIVELY GOLD PLATED, 2004.

This coin is the second in the Royal Canadian Mint Annual Report series. This series was cancelled in 2006.

Designers and Engravers:

Obv.:	Susanna Blunt, Susan Taylor		
Rev.:	Cosme Saffioti, Stan Witten		
Composition:	92.5% Ag, 7.5% Cu, Selectively gold plated		
Silver content:	5.458 g, 0.175 tr oz		
Weight:	5.9 g	**Edge:**	Reeded
Diameter:	23.9 mm	**Die Axis:**	↑↑
Thickness:	1.7 mm	**Finish:**	Proof
Case of Issue:	See Derivatives, page 60-61		

DATE	DESCRIPTION	QUANTITY SOLD	ISSUE PRICE	FINISH	PR-69	PR-7
2004	Poppy, selectively gold plated	12,677	N.I.I.	Proof	25.	—

TWENTY-FIVE CENTS, REMEMBRANCE DAY POPPY, COLOURISED, 2005 AND 2008, (GIFTWARE).

These twenty-five-cent coins were issued to commemorate Remembrance Day 2005 and 2008. They are encased in plastic bookmarks.

2005	**2008**

Designers and Engravers:

Obv.:	Susanna Blunt, Susan Taylor		
Rev.:	Cosme Saffioti, Stan Witten		
Composition:	Nickel plated steel, Colourised		
Weight:	4.4 g	**Edge:**	Reeded
Diameter:	23.9 mm	**Die Axis:**	↑↑
Thickness:	1.6 mm	**Finish:**	Circulation
Case of Issue:	See Derivatives, page 60-61		

DATE/ COMP. MARK	DESCRIPTION	SOURCE	QUANTITY SOLD	ISSUE PRICE	FINISH	MS-65 NC
2005P	Remembrance Day Poppy, Colourised	Bookmark	29,975	N.I.I.	Uncirculated	25.
2008	Remembrance Day Poppy, Colourised	Bookmark	489	12.95	Uncirculated	20.

Note: A colourised circulation Poppy coin was issued in 2004 to commemorate Remembrance Day 2004. See *Canadian Coins, Numismatic Issue Volume One.*

TWENTY-FIVE CENTS, 60TH ANNIVERSARY OF THE LIBERATION OF THE NETHERLANDS, 2005.

The Canadian Armed Forces played a leading role in the liberation of the Netherlands that was completed May 5th, 1945. This coin was issued in eight-coin, Brilliant Uncirculated set, by the Netherlands Mint.

Designers and Engravers:
Obv.:	Susanna Blunt, Susan Taylor
Rev.:	Peter Mossman, José Osio

Composition: 92.5% Ag, 7.5% Cu
Silver content: 5.458 g, 0.175 tr oz
Weight: 5.9 g   **Edge:** Reeded
Diameter: 23.9 mm   **Die Axis:** ↑↑
Thickness: 1.7 mm   **Finish:** Specimen
Case of Issue: See Derivatives, page 60-61

DATE	DESCRIPTION	QUANTITY SOLD	ISSUE PRICE	FINISH	SP-68	SP-69
2005	60th Year of Liberation	3,500	N.I.I.	Specimen	50.	—

TWENTY-FIVE CENTS, QUEBEC WINTER CARNIVAL, 2006 (GIFTWARE).

The Quebec Winter Carnival, the largest in North America, is held each year in Quebec City, Quebec.

Designers and Engravers:
Obv.:	Susanna Blunt, Susan Taylor
Rev.:	RCM Staff, Cecily Mok

Composition: Nickel plated steel, Painted
Weight: 4.4 g
Diameter: 23.9 mm   **Edge:** Reeded
Thickness: 1.6 mm   **Die Axis:** ↑↑
Finish: Circulation
Case of Issue: See Miscellaneous Gift Sets, page 537

DATE/ COMP. MARK	DESCRIPTION	SOURCE	QUANTITY SOLD	ISSUE PRICE	FINISH	MS-65 NC
2006P	Quebec Winter Carnival, Painted	Promo Gift Set	8,200	N.I.I.	Uncirculated	20.

TWENTY-FIVE CENTS, BREAST CANCER AWARENESS, 2006 (GIFTWARE).

This coin was issued to promote awareness for breast cancer. It is identical to the circulation issue, except the three outer ribbons and the central con are painted pink. This variety was issued encased in a plastic bookmark. Removal of the coin from the encased plastic is very difficult and may ult in the Awareness ribbons being damaged.

Designers and Engravers:
Obv.:	Susanna Blunt, Susan Taylor
Rev.:	C. Saffioti, S. Witten,K. Wachelko

Composition: Nickel plated steel, Painted
Weight: 4.4 g
Diameter: 23.9 mm   **Edge:** Reeded
Thickness: 1.6 mm   **Die Axis:** ↑↑
Finish: Circulation
Case of Issue: See Derivatives, page 60-61

DATE/ COMP. MARK	DESCRIPTION	SOURCE	QUANTITY SOLD	ISSUE PRICE	FINISH	MS-65 NC
2006P	Breast Cancer Awareness, Painted	Bookmark	40,911	N.I.I.	Uncirculated	50.

TWENTY-FIVE CENTS, QUEEN ELIZABETH II COMMEMORATIVES, 2006-2007 (GIFTWARE).

2006	2006	2007	2007
Obverse	80th Birthday	Obverse	60th Wedding Anniv.
	Queen Elizabeth II		Elizabeth II / Prince Philip
	Designer: Cosme Saffioti		Designer: R. R. Carmichael
	Engraver: Cecily Mok		Engraver: Cecily Mok

Designers:
  Obv.: Susanna Blunt
  Rev.: See reverse illustrations
Composition: Nickel plated steel, Decal
Weight: 12.61 g
Diameter: 35.0 mm
Finish: Specimen

Engravers:
  Obv.: Susan Taylor
  Rev.: See reverse illustrations
Thickness: 3.4 mm
Edge: Plain
Die Axis: ↑↑
Case of Issue: Blistered packed on information card

DATE	DESCRIPTION	QUANTITY SOLD	ISSUE PRICE	FINISH	SP-68	SP-6
2006 (1926-)	80th Birthday of Queen Elizabeth II	24,977	19.95	Specimen	18.	—
2007 (1947-)	60th Wedding Anniversary Elizabeth II and Prince Philip	15,235	21.95	Specimen	20.	—

TWENTY-FIVE CENTS, NHL HOCKEY SERIES (GIFTWARE), 2006-2007.
   The nine coloured twenty-five cent coins listed below are found in the NHL Team Gift Sets of 2006 and 2007, see page 532.

Designers:
  Obv.: Susanna Blunt
  Rev.: RCM Staff
Composition: Nickel plated steel, Decal
Weight: 4.4 g
Diameter: 23.9 mm
Finish: Circulation
Case of Issue: See NHL Team Gift Sets, page 532

Engravers:
  Obv.: Susan Taylor
  Rev.: RCM Staff
Thickness: 1.6 mm
Edge: Reeded
Die Axis: ↑↑

2006   HOCKEY SEASON, 2005-2006

Common Obverse	Montreal Canadiens	Ottawa Senators	Toronto Maple Leafs

DATE/ COMP. MARK	DESCRIPTION	SOURCE	QUANTITY SOLD	ISSUE PRICE	FINISH	MS N
2006P	Montreal Canadiens Logo	NHL Team	11,765	N.I.I.	Uncirculated	1
2006P	Ottawa Senators Logo	Gift	Included	N.I.I.	Uncirculated	1
2006P	Toronto Maple Leafs Logo	Sets	Included	N.I.I.	Uncirculated	1

TWENTY-FIVE CENTS, NHL HOCKEY SERIES (GIFTWARE), 2006-2007 (cont.).

07   HOCKEY SEASON, 2006-2007

Common Obverse

Calgary Flames

Edmonton Oilers

Montreal Canadiens

Ottawa Senators

Toronto Maple Leafs

Vancouver Canucks

DATE/ COMP. MARK	DESCRIPTION	SOURCE	QUANTITY SOLD	ISSUE PRICE	FINISH	MS-65 NC
2007	Calgary Flames Logo	Available only from NHL Team Gift Sets	1,082	N.I.I.	Uncirculated	15.
2007	Edmonton Oilers Logo		2,214	N.I.I.	Uncirculated	15.
2007	Montreal Canadiens Logo		4,091	N.I.I.	Uncirculated	25.
2007	Ottawa Senators Logo		2,474	N.I.I.	Uncirculated	15.
2007	Toronto Maple Leafs Logo		5,365	N.I.I.	Uncirculated	15.
2007	Vancouver Canucks Logo		1,526	N.I.I.	Uncirculated	15.

OCCASIONS SERIES

TWENTY-FIVE CENTS, OCCASIONS SETS, 2007-2013 (GIFTWARE).

In 2007 the Royal Canadian Mint continued their expansion into the giftware market with an issue of three new Occasion Gift Sets. The sets contain en circulation finish coins with the Caribou twenty-five cent coin being replaced with a coloured twenty-five-cent coin representing the occasion.

Common Obverse
2007-2008

Designers and Engravers:
Obv.:   Susanna Blunt, Susan Taylor
Rev.:   RCM Staff
Composition: Nickel plated steel, Decal
Weight: 4.4 g
Diameter: 23.9 mm
Thickness: 1.6 mm
Case of Issue: See Gift Sets, pages 528-530, 535-536
Edge: Reeded
Die Axis: ↑↑
Finish: Circulation

CASIONS - 2007

Balloons
Birthday Set

Bouquet
Wedding Set

Fireworks
Congratulations Set

Maple Leaf
Oh! Canada Set

Rattle
Baby Set

TWENTY-FIVE CENTS, OCCASIONS SETS, 2007 (GIFTWARE) PRICING TABLE.

DATE/ COMP. MARK	DESCRIPTION	SOURCE	QUANTITY SOLD	ISSUE PRICE	FINISH	MS-6 NC
2007	Balloons, Birthday Gift Set	Available only from Occasions Gift Sets	13,423	N.I.I.	Uncirculated	20.
2007	Bouquet, Wedding Gift Set		10,687	N.I.I.	Uncirculated	20.
2007	Fireworks, Congratulations Gift Set		9,671	N.I.I.	Uncirculated	30.
2007	Maple Leaf, Oh! Canada Gift Set		24,096	N.I.I.	Uncirculated	25.
2007	Rattle, Baby Gift Set		30,090	N.I.I.	Uncirculated	130.

OCCASIONS - 2008

Cake Wedding Set	Canadian Flag Oh! Canada Set	Party Hat Birthday Set	Teddy Bear Baby Set	Trophy Congratulations Set

DATE/ COMP. MARK	DESCRIPTION	SOURCE	QUANTITY SOLD	ISSUE PRICE	FINISH	MS-6 NC
2008	Cake, Wedding Gift Set	Available only from Occasions Gift Sets	7,404	N.I.I.	Uncirculated	40
2008	Canadian Flag, Oh! Canada Gift Set		30,567	N.I.I.	Uncirculated	30
2008	Party Hat, Birthday Gift Set		11,376	N.I.I.	Uncirculated	45
2008	Teddy Bear, Baby Gift Set		29,819	N.I.I.	Uncirculated	100
2008	Trophy, Congratulations Gift Set		6,821	N.I.I.	Uncirculated	60

OCCASIONS - 2009

Common Obverse With RCM Logo	Four Maple Leaves Oh! Canada Set	Teddy Bear Baby Set

DATE/ COMP. MARK	DESCRIPTION	SOURCE	QUANTITY SOLD	ISSUE PRICE	FINISH	MS- NC
2009	Four Maple Leaves, Oh! Canada Gift Set	Occasions Gift Sets	14,451	N.I.I.	Uncirculated	3
2009	Teddy Bear, Baby Gift Set		25,182	N.I.I.	Uncirculated	10

In 2009 only the Oh! Canada! and Baby giftware sets were issued. The other twenty-five cent Occasions coins were incorporated into gift cards, see page 34

OCCASIONS - 2010

For 2010, the Wedding Occasion twenty-five cent coin was moved back to the Wedding Gift Set series.

Common Obverse Without RCM Logo	Carriage Baby Set	Heart and Roses Wedding Set	Three Maple Leaves Oh! Canada Set

DATE/ COMP. MARK	DESCRIPTION	SOURCE	QUANTITY SOLD	ISSUE PRICE	FINISH	MS- N
2010	Carriage, Baby Gift Set	Occasions Gift Sets	27,048	N.I.I.	Uncirculated	3
2010	Heart and Roses, Wedding Gift Set		8,194	N.I.I.	Uncirculated	2
2010	Maple Leaves, Oh! Canada Gift Set		19,769	N.I.I.	Uncirculated	2

OCCASIONS SERIES (cont.).

WENTY-FIVE CENTS, OCCASIONS SETS, 2007-2013 (GIFTWARE) [cont.].

Beginning in 2011, the reverse designs on the twenty-five-cent coins contained in the Occasions Sets are die struck rather than illustrated with a decal.

**Common Obverse
2011-2012**

Designers:	
Obv.:	Susanna Blunt
Rev.:	Gary Taxali
Composition:	Nickel plated steel
Weight:	4.4 g
Diameter:	23.6 mm
Finish:	Circulation
Case of Issue:	See Gift Sets, pages 528-529, 531, 535-536

Engravers:	
Obv.:	Susan Taylor
Rev.:	See reverse illustrations
Thickness:	1.6 mm
Edge:	Reeded
Die Axis:	↑↑

CCASIONS - 2011

Baby's Feet Baby Set Engr.: Matt Bowen	Four Balloons Birthday Set Engr.: Stan Witten	Maple Leaf O Canada Set Engr.: Cecily Mok	Wedding Rings Wedding Set Engr.: Stan Witten	Snowflake Holiday Set Engr.: C. Paquet

DATE/ COMP. MARK	DESCRIPTION	SOURCE	QUANTITY SOLD	ISSUE PRICE	FINISH	MS-65 NC
2011	Baby's Feet, Baby Gift Set		38,576	N.I.I.	Uncirculated	110.
2011	Four Balloons, Birthday Gift Set	Occasions	21,173	N.I.I.	Uncirculated	15.
2011	Maple Leaf, O Canada Gift Set	Gift	22,475	N.I.I.	Uncirculated	15.
2011	Wedding Rings, Wedding Gift Set	Sets	20,461	N.I.I.	Uncirculated	15.
2011	Snowflake, Holiday Gift Set		41,666	N.I.I.	Uncirculated	15.

CCASIONS - 2012

The Occasions Sets issued in 2012 contain six coins (1¢, 5¢, 10¢, 25¢, $1 and $2). The use of the fifty-cent coin was discontinued.

Mobiles Baby Gift Set Engr.: C. Paquet	Ice Cream Cone and Balloons Birthday Gift Set Engr.: C. Paquet	Stylized Maple Leaves O Canada Set Engr.: C. Paquet	Wedding Rings and Heart Wedding Set Engr.: C. Paquet	Christmas Tree Ornaments Holiday Set Engr.: C. Paquet

DATE/ COMP. MARK	DESCRIPTION	SOURCE	QUANTITY SOLD	ISSUE PRICE	FINISH	MS-65 NC
2012	Mobiles, Baby Gift Set		43,920	N.I.I.	Uncirculated	20.
2012	Ice Cream Cone and Balloons, Birthday Set	Occasions	24,659	N.I.I.	Uncirculated	15.
2012	Stylized Maple Leaves, O Canada Gift Set	Gift	31,464	N.I.I.	Uncirculated	15.
2012	Wedding Rings and Heart, Wedding Gift Set	Sets	24,325	N.I.I.	Uncirculated	15.
2012	Christmas Tree Ornaments, Holiday Gift Set		26,404	N.I.I.	Uncirculated	15.

OCCASIONS SERIES (cont.).

TWENTY-FIVE CENTS, OCCASIONS SETS, 2007-2013 (GIFTWARE) [cont.].

The Occasions Sets issued in 2013 contain five coins (5¢, 10¢, 25¢, $1 and $2). The one-cent coin was discontinued in 2012.

Common Obverse

Designers:			**Engravers:**	
Obv.:	Susanna Blunt		Obv.:	Susan Taylor
Rev.:	Martin Coté		Rev.:	See reverse illustrations
Composition:	Nickel plated steel		**Thickness:**	1.6 mm
Weight:	4.4 g		**Edge:**	Reeded
Diameter:	23.9 mm		**Die Axis:**	↑↑
Finish:	Circulation			
Case of Issue:	See Gift Sets, pages 528-529, 531, 535-536			

OCCASIONS - 2013

Baby's Feet	Slice Birthday Cake	Maple Leaf	Wedding Rings	Holly Wreath
Baby Set	**Birthday Set**	**O Canada Set**	**Wedding Set**	**Holiday Set**
Engr.: Matt Bowen	Engr.: Stan Witten	Engr.: Stan Witten	Engr.: Matt Bowen	Engr.: Matt Bowen

DATE/ COMP. MARK	DESCRIPTION	SOURCE	QUANTITY SOLD	ISSUE PRICE	FINISH	MS-6 NC
2013	Baby's Feet, Baby Gift Set		53,708	N.I.I.	Uncirculated	50
2013	Slice of Birthday Cake, Birthday Gift Set	Occasions	22,678	N.I.I.	Uncirculated	15
2013	Maple Leaf, O Canada Gift Set	Gift	26,068	N.I.I.	Uncirculated	15
2013	Intertwined Wedding Rings, Wedding Set	Sets	20,317	N.I.I.	Uncirculated	15
2013	Holly Wreath, Holiday Gift Set		N/A	N.I.I.	Uncirculated	15

OCCASIONS CARDS WITH COINS

TWENTY-FIVE CENTS, CARDS WITH COINS, 2009-2010 (GIFTWARE).

In 2009 a series of four cards incorporating twenty-five cent Occasions (decal) coins was released into the gift market. The Cards With Coins series was discontinued in 2010.

Designers:		**Engravers:**	
Obv.:	Susanna Blunt	Obv.:	Susan Taylor
Rev.:	RCM Staff	Rev.:	RCM Staff
Composition:	Nickel plated steel, Decal	**Thickness:**	1.6 mm
Weight:	4.4 g	**Edge:**	Reeded
Diameter:	23.9 mm	**Die Axis:**	↑↑
Finish:	Circulation		
Case of Issue:	Folder		

CARDS WITH COINS - 2009

Common Obverse	Balloons, Streamers	Doves and Rings	Fireworks	Stylized Flower
With RCM Logo	**Birthday Card**	**Wedding Card**	**Congratulation Card**	**Thank You Card**

TWENTY-FIVE CENTS, CARDS WITH COINS, 2009 PRICING TABLE.

DATE	DESCRIPTION	QUANTITY SOLD	ISSUE PRICE	FINISH	MS-65 NC
2009	Balloons and Streamers, Birthday Card	9,663	9.95	Uncirculated	15.
2009	Doves and Rings, Wedding Card	7,571	9.95	Uncirculated	20.
2009	Fireworks, Congratulations Card	4,126	9.95	Uncirculated	15.
2009	Stylised Flower, Thank You Card	4,415	9.95	Uncirculated	15.

CARDS WITH COINS - 2010

Common Obverse Without RCM Logo	Flowers Thank You Card	Gift Box Birthday Card	Stars Congratulations Card

DATE	DESCRIPTION	QUANTITY SOLD	ISSUE PRICE	FINISH	MS-65 NC
2010	Flowers, Thank You Card	5,932	9.95	Uncirculated	10.
2010	Gift Box, Birthday Card	8,751	9.95	Uncirculated	10.
2010	Stars, Congratulations Card	5,693	9.95	Uncirculated	10.

TOOTH FAIRY GIFT CARDS

TWENTY-FIVE CENTS, TOOTH FAIRY GIFT CARDS, 2011-2012 (GIFTWARE).

In 2011 a new gift card theme was introduced. The Tooth Fairy Gift Card contains a "ready-to-fill" money envelope to place under a child's pillow to make the trade for the tooth.

Designers:		Engravers:	
Obv.:	Susanna Blunt	Obv.:	Susan Taylor
Rev.:	2011: RCM Staff	Rev.:	2011: Marcos Hallam
	2012: Gary Taxali		2012: Christie Paquet
Composition:	Nickel plated steel	Thickness:	1.6 mm
Weight:	4.4 g	Edge:	Reeded
Diameter:	23.9 mm	Die Axis:	↑↑
Finish:	Circulation		
Case of Issue:	Folder		

Common Obverse	2011	2012

DATE	DESCRIPTION	QUANTITY SOLD	ISSUE PRICE	FINISH	MS-65 NC
2011	Fairy	38,200	9.95	Uncirculated	15.
2012	Stylized Fairy	20,359	9.95	Uncirculated	15.

ISSUES OF THE VANCOUVER 2010 OLYMPIC WINTER GAMES

TWENTY-FIVE CENTS, VANCOUVER 2010 WINTER OLYMPIC GAMES, 2007-2008.

The painted maple leaf outlined twenty-five cent coins were co-issued with Petro Canada and encased in a collector card format. The coins are listed in issue date order. The Collector Cards though numbered 1 to 15 do not necessarily correspond to the issue date order. The Alpine Skiing painted reverse was issued with a 2007 and 2008 dated obverse.

**2007 Obverse
Olympic Games**

**2010
Olympic
Logo**

Designers and Engravers:

Obv.:	Susanna Blunt, Susan Taylor
Rev.:	See reverse illustrations
Composition:	Nickel plated steel, Painted
Weight:	4.4 g
Diameter:	23.9 mm
Thickness:	1.6 mm
Edge:	Reeded
Die Axis:	↑↑
Finish:	Circulation

**Curling
Des.: Glen Green
Engr.: C. Mok**

**Ice Hockey
Des.: Glen Green
Engr.: K. Wachelko**

**Biathlon
Des.: Glen Green
Engr.: K. Wachelko**

**Alpine Skiing
Des.: Glen Green
Engr.: RCM Staff**

**Ice Hockey
Bookmark and
Lapel Pin**

**Collector Card No. 4
2007 Alpine Skiing**

DATE	DESCRIPTION	QUANTITY SOLD	ISSUE PRICE	FINISH	MARKET VALUE
2007	Curling, Sport Card, Painted leaf	90,756	7.95	Circulation	15.
2007	Curling, Bookmark and Lapel Pin	5,332	9.95	Circulation	10.
2007	Ice Hockey, Sport Card, Painted leaf	100,839	7.95	Circulation	15.
2007	Ice Hockey, Bookmark and Lapel Pin	9,062	9.95	Circulation	10.
2007	Biathlon, Sport Card, Painted leaf	30,279	7.95	Circulation	15.
2007	Biathlon, Bookmark and Lapel Pin	Not issued	—	—	—
2007	Alpine Skiing, Sport Card, Painted leaf dated 2007	919	7.95	Circulation	30.
2007	Alpine Skiing, Bookmark and Lapel Pin	6,172	9.95	Circulation	10.
2008	Alpine Skiing, Sport Card, Painted leaf dated 2008	40,470	7.95	Circulation	15.

ISSUES OF THE VANCOUVER 2010 OLYMPIC WINTER GAMES (cont.).

TWENTY-FIVE CENTS, VANCOUVER 2010 WINTER OLYMPIC GAMES, 2008-2009.

2008 Obverse
Olympic Games

Snowboarding
Des.: Glen Green
Engr.: K. Wachelko

2010
Olympic
Logo

Designers and Engravers:
Obv.: Susanna Blunt, Susan Taylor
Rev.: See reverse illustrations
Composition: Nickel plated steel, Painted
Weight: 4.4 g
Diameter: 23.9 mm
Thickness: 1.6 mm
Edge: Reeded
Die Axis: ↑↑
Finish: Circulation

Freestyle Skiing
Des.: Glen Green
Engr.: C. Mok

Figure Skating
Des.: Glen Green
Engr.: C. Mok

Bobsleigh
Des.: Glen Green
Engr.: RCM Staff

Cross Country Skiing
Des.: Glen Green
Engr.: RCM Staff

Speed Skating
Des.: Glen Green
Engr.: K. Wachelko

Collector Card No. 6
Snowboarding

Snowboarding
Bookmark and
Lapel Pin

DATE	DESCRIPTION	QUANTITY SOLD	ISSUE PRICE	FINISH	MARKET VALUE
2008	Snowboarding, Sport Card, Painted leaf	40,771	7.95	Circulation	15.
2008	Snowboarding, Bookmark and Lapel Pin	5,150	9.95	Circulation	10.
2008	Freestyle Skiing, Sport Card, Painted leaf	35,447	7.95	Circulation	15.
2008	Freestyle Skiing, Bookmark and Lapel Pin	Not Issued	—	—	—
2008	Figure Skating, Sport Card, Painted leaf	16,479	7.95	Circulation	15.
2008	Figure Skating, Bookmark and Lapel Pin	6,047	9.95	Circulation	10.
2008	Bobsleigh, Sport Card, Painted leaf	1,383	7.95	Circulation	15.
2008	Bobsleigh, Bookmark and Lapel Pin	Not Issued	—	—	—
2009	Cross Country Skiing, Sport Card, Painted leaf	261	7.95	Circulation	15.
2009	Cross Country Skiing, Bookmark and Lapel Pin	Not Issued	—	—	—
2009	Speed Skating, Sport Card, Painted leaf	309	7.95	Circulation	15.
2009	Speed Skating, Bookmark and Lapel Pin	3,529	9.95	Circulation	10.

ISSUES OF THE VANCOUVER 2010 OLYMPIC WINTER GAMES (cont.).

TWENTY-FIVE CENTS, GOLDEN MOMENTS OLYMPIC COMMEMORATIVES, 2009.

The Golden Moments twenty-five cent coins were issued to commemorate the gold medals won at the Salt Lake City Winter Olympic Games by the Canadian men's and women's hockey teams in 2002, and the gold medal won by Cindy Klassen at the 2006 Turin Winter Olympic Games.

While three different commemorative designs are present, there are also three different major finish varieties within each design, making a total of nine major varieties in this series. Adding to the complication are two minor varieties within the Men's Ice Hockey colourised coins that of a raised and incused 2, making the grand total ten varieties.

Seven varieties are listed in Canadian Coins, 70th edition, Volume One, and six are listed here in Volume Two. The overlapping colourised varieties are duplicated in each volume.

The Men's Ice Hockey, colourised, raised 2 variety is NOT found in Petro Canada Sport Cards.

DESIGNS	FINISH VARIETIES	DIE VARIETIES
Men's Ice Hockey	Circulation	Raised 2 (See Volume One)
	Colourised	Incused 2
	Painted	Incused 2
Women's Ice Hockey	Circulation	None
	Colourised	None
	Painted	None
Cindy Klassen	Circulation	None
	Colourised	None
	Painted	None

Collector Card No. 12
Canadian Men's Ice Hockey Team

Collector Card No. 13
Canadian Women's Ice Hockey Team

Collector Card No. 14
Cindy Klassen Speed Skating

ISSUES OF THE VANCOUVER 2010 OLYMPIC WINTER GAMES (cont.).

TWENTY-FIVE CENTS, GOLDEN MOMENTS OLYMPIC COMMEMORATIVES, 2009 (cont.).

**Obverse
2009**

Designers and Engravers:
Obv.: Susanna Blunt, Susan Taylor
Rev.: Jason Bouwman, Susan Taylor
Composition: Nickel plated steel
Weight: 4.4 g   **Edge:** Reeded
Diameter: 23.9 mm   **Die Axis:** ↑↑
Thickness: 1.6 mm
Finish: 1. Circulation, Colourised
2. Brilliant Uncirculated, Painted

Men's Ice Hockey
Colourised Red

Colourised Leaf
Incused 2

Men's Ice Hockey
Painted Red

Painted Leaf
Incused 2

Women's Ice Hockey
Colourised Red

Colourised Leaf

Women's Ice Hockey
Painted Red

Painted Leaf

Cindy Klassen
Speed Skating
Colourised Red

Colourised Leaf

Cindy Klassen
Speed Skating
Painted Red

Painted Leaf

DATE	DESCRIPTION	SOURCE	QUANTITY SOLD	ISSUE PRICE	FINISH	MS-65
2009	Men's Ice Hockey, Incused "2", Colourised	Sport Card	N/A	7.95	Circulation	8.
2009	Men's Ice Hockey, Incused "2", Painted	Spec. Ed. Set	8,564	N.I.I.	PL	10.
2009	Women's Ice Hockey, Colourised	Sport Card	N/A	7.95	Circulation	8.
2009	Women's Ice Hockey, Painted	Sp. Ed. Set	8,564	N.I.I.	PL	10.
2009	Cindy Klassen, Speed Skating, Colourised	Sport Card	N/A	7.95	Circulation	8.
2009	Cindy Klassen, Speed Skating, Painted	Spec. Ed. Set	8,564	N.I.I.	PL	10.

ISSUES OF THE VANCOUVER 2010 PARALYMPIC WINTER GAMES

TWENTY-FIVE CENTS, VANCOUVER 2010 PARALYMPIC WINTER GAMES SPORT CARDS, 2007 AND 2009.

2007 Obverse Paralympic Games

2010 Paralympic Logo

Designers and Engravers:

Obv.:	Susanna Blunt, Susan Taylor
Rev.:	See reverse illustrations
Composition:	Nickel plated steel, Painted
Weight:	4.4 g
Diameter:	23.9 mm
Thickness:	1.6 mm
Edge:	Reeded
Die Axis:	↑↑
Finish:	Circulation

Wheelchair Curling Painted Leaf
Des.: Glen Green
Engr.: C. Mok

Ice Sledge Hockey Painted Leaf
Des.: Glen Green
Engr.: RCM Staff

25¢ Wheelchair Curling Mule

The Vancouver Olympic obverse was paired with the Paralympic Wheelchair Curling reverse to create a mule. The coin was not issued for circulation, but is found in the Vancouver 2010 Brilliant Uncirculated Sets of 2007, which were assembled in Ottawa. See page 520 for the set listing.

2007 Obverse with Olympic Logo

2007 Reverse Wheelchair Curling
Des.: Glen Green
Engr.: C. Mok

Collector Card No. 3
Wheelchair Curling

DATE	DESCRIPTION	QUANTITY SOLD	ISSUE PRICE	FINISH	MARKET VALUE
2007	Wheelchair Curling, Sport Card, Painted leaf	34,956	7.95	Circulation	15.
2007	Wheelchair Curling, Mule	N/A	N.I.I.	PL	550.
2009	Ice Sledge Hockey Sport Card, Painted leaf	N/A	7.95	Circulation	15.

NOTE ON TWENTY-FIVE CENT ISSUES

The Petro Canada sport card twenty-five cent issues of 2007, 2008 and 2009 have a painted outline of a maple leaf supporting a central design. There are twelve different designs. The painted coins were inserted into sport cards and bookmarks which were encased in a plastic film. This film all but impossible to remove without removing the painted outline from the coin.

ISSUES OF THE VANCOUVER 2010 OLYMPIC AND PARALYMPIC WINTER GAMES

TWENTY-FIVE CENTS, VANCOUVER 2010 OLYMPIC AND PARALYMPIC WINTER GAMES, SILVER PROOF SET, 2007-2009.

The twenty-five cent silver proof coins were issued in a presentation case. The set contains twelve coins and a one ounce sterling silver bar. Single of coins may only be obtained from a break up of this set.

Designers:		Engravers:	
Obv.:	Susanna Blunt	Obv.:	Susan Taylor
Rev.:	Glen Green	Rev.:	RCM Staff
Composition:	92.5% Ag, 7.5% Cu		
Silver content:	Single Coin: 5.365 g, 0.172 tr oz		
	Bar: 28.77 g, 0.925 tr oz	Thickness:	1.7 mm
	Set: 93.15 g, 3.0 tr oz	Edge:	Reeded
Weight:	5.8 g	Die Axis:	↑↑
Diameter:	23.6 mm	Finish:	Proof
Case of Issue:	Black leatherette clam case, 13-hole flocked insert, encapsulated coins, COA		

DATE	DESCRIPTION	QUANTITY SOLD	ISSUE PRICE	FINISH	PR-69	PR-70
2007	Curling	N.I.I.	—	Proof	20.	—
2007	Ice Hockey	N.I.I.	—	Proof	20.	—
2007	Wheelchair Curling	N.I.I.	—	Proof	20.	—
2007	Biathlon	N.I.I.	—	Proof	20.	—
2007	Alpine Skiing,	N.I.I.	—	Proof	20.	—
2008	Snowboarding	N.I.I.	—	Proof	20.	—
2008	Free Style Skiing	N.I.I.	—	Proof	20.	—
2008	Bobsleigh	N.I.I.	—	Proof	20.	—
2008	Figure Skating	N.I.I.	—	Proof	20.	—
2009	Cross Country Skiing	N.I.I.	—	Proof	20.	—
2009	Speed Skating	N.I.I.	—	Proof	20.	—
2009	Ice Sledge Hockey	N.I.I.	—	Proof	20.	—
—	Complete Set, 12 coins, 1 one ounce silver bar	3,172	199.95	Proof	200.	—

TWENTY-FIVE CENTS, VANCOUVER 2010 OLYMPIC WINTER GAMES MASCOTS, 2008, (GIFTWARE).

The three mascots, Miga and Quatchi for the Olympic Winter Games, and Sumi for the Paralympic Winter Games, appear on many souvenirs the Vancouver Winter Games.

Common Obverse

Miga

Quatchi

Sumi

Sumi Introduction Folder
"Meet The Vancouver 2010 Mascots!"

Designers:
Obv.:   Susanna Blunt
Rev.:   Design Team of the Vancouver Organising Committee
for the 2010 Olympic and Paralympic Games
Composition: Nickel plated steel, Decal
Weight: 4.4 g
Diameter: 23.9 mm
Finish: Circulation
Case of Issue: Introduction Folder "Meet The Vancouver 2010 Mascots!"

Engravers:
Rev.:   Susan Taylor
Rev.:   RCM Staff
Thickness: 1.6 mm
Edge: Reeded
Die Axis: ↑↑

DATE	DESCRIPTION	QUANTITY SOLD	ISSUE PRICE	FINISH	MARKE VALUE
2008	Miga	14,654	10.95	Uncirculated	25.
2008	Quatchi	15,310	10.95	Uncirculated	25.
2008	Sumi	15,333	10.95	Uncirculated	25.

TWENTY-FIVE CENT DERIVATIVES OF THE VANCOUVER 2010 OLYMPIC AND PARALYMPIC WINTER GAMES

DATE	DESCRIPTION	QUANTITY SOLD	ISSUE PRICE	FINISH	MARKE VALUE
2007	**Vancouver 2010 Coin Collector Card** (card only)	104,400	4.95	—	5.
2007	**Magnetic lapel pin**, Curling	3,118	9.95	Circulation	10.
2007	**Magnetic lapel pin**, Ice Hockey	3,158	9.95	Circulation	10.
2007	**Magnetic lapel pin**, Alpine Skiing	3,013	9.95	Circulation	10.
2008	**Magnetic lapel pin**, Snowboarding	6,095	9.95	Circulation	10.
2008	**Alpine Skiing**, Twenty-five cents, Painted and lapel pin	3,350	9.95	Circulation	10
2008	**Snowboarding**, Twenty-five cents, Painted and lapel pin	2,922	9.95	Circulation	10
2007-2010	**Magnetic Lapel Pin** for interchangeable sport coin	RCM	9.95	Circulation	10
2007-2010	**Green See Through Tin Can**, Magnetic lapel pin, 5 twenty-five cent coins of various sports	RCM	14.95	Circulation	15
2007-2010	**Green Tin Can** to hold the 15 Petro Canada Collector Cards	RCM	5.95	—	6

BIRDS OF CANADA SERIES

TWENTY-FIVE CENTS, COLOURISED BIRDS OF CANADA SERIES, 2007-2014 (GIFTWARE).
This series features popular Canadian birds as depicted by artists Arnold Nogy, Trevor Tennant and Tony Bianco.

2007 Common Obverse
With RCM Logo

Ruby-Throated Hummingbird

Red-Breasted Nuthatch

2008 Common Obverse
With RCM Logo

Downy Woodpecker

Northern Cardinal

2010 Common Obverse
Without RCM Logo

Goldfinch

Blue Jay

Designers:		**Engravers:**	
Obv.:	Susanna Blunt	Obv.:	Susan Taylor
Rev.:	Arnold Nogy	Rev.:	RCM Staff
Composition:	Nickel plated steel, Decal	**Thickness:**	2.0 mm
Weight:	12.61 to 13.0 g	**Edge:**	Plain
Diameter:	35.0 mm	**Die Axis:**	↑↑
Finish:	Specimen		
Case of Issue:	Maroon leatherette clam style case, black flocked insert, encapsulated coin, COA		

DATE	DESCRIPTION	QUANTITY SOLD	ISSUE PRICE	FINISH	SP-68	SP-69
2007	Ruby-Throated Hummingbird	17,174	24.95	Specimen	100.	—
2007	Red-Breasted Nuthatch	11,909	24.95	Specimen	280.	—
2008	Downy Woodpecker	14,282	24.95	Specimen	150.	—
2008	Northern Cardinal	11,604	24.95	Specimen	250.	—
2010	Goldfinch	13,991	24.95	Specimen	120.	—
2010	Blue Jay	13,965	24.95	Specimen	80.	—

TWENTY-FIVE CENTS, COLOURISED BIRDS OF CANADA SERIES, 2007-2014 (GIFTWARE) [cont.].

2011-2014 Common Obverse
Without RCM Logo

Black-capped Chickadee
Des.: Arnold Nogy

Barn Swallow
Des.: Arnold Nogy

Rose-Breasted Grosbeak
Des.: Arnold Nogy

Evening Grosbeak
Des.: Arnold Nogy

American Robin
Des.: Trevor Tennant

Barn Owl
Des.: Trevor Tennant

Eastern Meadowlark
Des.: Tony Bianco

Scarlet Tanager
Des.: Pierre Leduc

Designers:		**Engravers:**	
Obv.:	Susanna Blunt	Obv.:	Susan Taylor
Rev.:	See reverse illustrations	Rev.:	RCM Staff
Composition:	2011: Nickel plated steel, Decal	**Thickness:**	2.0 mm
	2012-2014: Cupronickel, Decal	**Edge:**	Plain
Weight:	12.61 to 13.0 g	**Die Axis:**	↑↑
Diameter:	35.0 mm	**Finish:**	Specimen
Case of Issue:	Maroon leatherette clam style case, black flocked insert, encapsulated coin, COA		

DATE	DESCRIPTION	QUANTITY SOLD	ISSUE PRICE	FINISH	SP-68	SP-
2011	Black-capped Chickadee	13,947	25.95	Specimen	50.	—
2011	Barn Swallow	14,000	25.95	Specimen	50.	—
2012	Rose-Breasted Grosbeak	19,897	29.95	Specimen	25.	—
2012	Evening Grosbeak	19,985	29.95	Specimen	25.	—
2013	American Robin	17,493	29.95	Specimen	30.	—
2013	Barn Owl	15,166	29.95	Specimen	25.	—
2014	Eastern Meadowlark	17,474	29.95	Specimen	30.	—
2014	Scarlet Tanager	12,182	29.95	Specimen	30.	—

™ENTY-FIVE CENTS, 90TH ANNIVERSARY OF THE END OF WORLD WAR I SET, 2008 (GIFTWARE).
These two twenty-five-cent pieces were issued in a 2008 commemorative set to mark the ninetieth anniversary of the end of WorldWar One. The mm crown-size coin depicts the Tomb of the Unknown Soldier at the NationalWar Memorial in Ottawa.
The standard 25-cent colourised Poppy coin was released into circulation during 2008. It was also incorporated into a bookmark that sold in the gift ™rket. A donation of $1.00 per bookmark sold was given to the Legion's Dominion Command Fund.

™08   TOMB OF THE UNKNOWN SOLDIER

Designers and Engravers:
Obv.:   Susanna Blunt, Susan Taylor
Rev.:   David Craig, Cecily Mok
Composition: Nickel plated steel
Weight: 12.61 g
Diameter: 35.0 mm
Thickness: 3.4 mm
Edge: Plain
Die Axis: ↑↑
Finish: Specimen

™08   COLOURISED POPPY

Specifications: See 2005 Colourised Poppy, page 27
Case of Issue:
(A)   Illustrated folder: Two coins, Serialised
(B)   Bookmark: Twenty-five cent coin only

DATE	DESCRIPTION	SOURCE	QUANTITY SOLD	ISSUE PRICE	FINISH	SP-68	MS-65 NC
2008	Tomb of the Unknown Soldier and Poppy	Folder	Incl. below	N.I.I.	Specimen	25.	—
2008	Poppy "Remembrance"	Folder	Incl. below	N.I.I.	Circulation	—	5.
2008	Set of Two Coins	Folder	10,167	24.95	—	—	25.
2008	Poppy, Bookmark	Bookmark	489	12.95	Circulation	—	15.

e: 1. While the finish on the Tomb of the Unknown Soldier, large size twenty-five cent coin, is listed by the Royal Canadian Mint as specimen, it certainly is not a specimen finish when compared with coins of their specimen set issues of 1996 to 2009.
2. The "quantity sold" figure is understated. The 2008 RCM Report omitted the quantity sold number for that year. That number should have been added to the 489 from the RCM Report for 2009.

™ENTY-FIVE CENTS, 100TH ANNIVERSARY OF ANNE OF GREEN GABLES©, 1908-2008 (GIFTWARE).
™his coin was issued to commemorate the 100th anniversary of Anne of Green Gables©, which was first published in 1908.

Designers and Engravers:
Obv.:   Susanna Blunt, Susan Taylor
Rev.:   Ben Stahl
Composition: Nickel plated steel, Decal
Weight: 12.61 g
Diameter: 35.0 mm
Thickness: 2.0 mm
Edge: Plain
Die Axis: ↑↑
Finish: Specimen
Case of Issue: Illustrated folder, Serialised

DATE	DESCRIPTION	QUANTITY SOLD	ISSUE PRICE	FINISH	SP-68	SP-69
2008 (1908-)	Anne of Green Gables©	32,795	19.95	Specimen	25.	—

TWENTY-FIVE CENTS, NOTRE-DAME-DU-SAGUENAY, 2009 (GIFTWARE).

The Lady of the Saguenay Fjord sits high on Cape Trinité in the majestic Saguenay Fjord, three hundred metres above sea level. The solid wood statue was designed by Louis Jobin in 1881.

Designers and Engravers:

Obv.:	Susanna Blunt, Susan Taylor
Rev.:	Promotion Saguenay, Susan Taylo
Composition:	Nickel plated steel, Decal
Weight:	11.7 g
Diameter:	35.0 mm
Thickness:	2.0 mm
Edge:	Plain
Die Axis:	↑↑
Finish:	Specimen
Case of Issue:	Coloured card

DATE	DESCRIPTION	QUANTITY SOLD	ISSUE PRICE	FINISH	SP-68	SP-69
2009	Notre-Dame-Du-Saguenay	16,653	14.95	Specimen	25.	—

TWENTY-FIVE CENTS, REMEMBRANCE DAY POPPIES, 2010 (GIFTWARE).

This twenty-five-cent coin is included in the Remembrance Day Collector Card. The card also has two die-cut holes to house the 2004 and 20 "Poppy" coins.

Designers and Engravers:

Obv.:	Susanna Blunt, Susan Taylor		
Rev.:	Cosme Saffioti, Stan Witten		
Composition:	Nickel plated steel, Colourised		
Weight:	4.4 g		
Diameter:	23.9 mm	**Edge:**	Reeded
Thickness:	1.6 mm	**Die Axis:**	↑↑
Finish:	Circulation		
Case of Issue:	See Derivatives, page 60-61		

DATE	DESCRIPTION	QUANTITY SOLD	ISSUE PRICE	FINISH	MS-65	MS-66	MS-
2010	Remembrance Day Poppies, colourised	21,738	N.I.I.	Uncirculated	5.	10.	—

TWENTY-FIVE CENTS, GEORGE V, STERLING SILVER, PROOF, 1935-2010.

This twenty-five-cent coin is from the Special Limited Edition Proof Set issued in 2010 to commemorate Emanuel Hahn's classic voyageur des which first appeared on the 1935 silver dollar.

Designers and Engravers:

Obv.:	Sir. E. B. MacKennal		
Rev.:	L. C. Wyon		
Composition:	92.5% Ag, 7.5% Cu		
Silver content:	5.458 g, 0.175 tr oz		
Weight:	5.9 g	**Edge:**	Reeded
Diameter:	23.9 mm	**Die Axis:**	↑↑
Thickness:	1.7 mm	**Finish:**	Proof
Case of Issue:	See Special Issue Proof Sets, page 496		

DATE	DESCRIPTION	QUANTITY SOLD	ISSUE PRICE	FINISH	PR-69	PR-
2010 (1935-)	George V, Sterling Silver	4,996	N.I.I.	Proof	30.	—

CANADIAN MYTHICAL CREATURES SET

TWENTY-FIVE CENTS, CANADIAN MYTHICAL CREATURES SET, 2011 (GIFTWARE).
This set features mythical Canadian animals as depicted by artist Emily S. Damstra.

Common Obverse	Sasquatch	Memphré	Mishepishu

Designers:		Engravers:	
Obv.:	Susanna Blunt	Obv.:	Susan Taylor
Rev.:	Emily S. Damstra	Rev.:	RCM Staff
Composition:	Nickel plated steel, Decal	Thickness:	2.0 mm
Weight:	12.61 to 13.0 g	Edge:	Plain
Diameter:	35.0 mm	Die Axis:	↑↑
Finish:	Specimen	Case of Issue:	Coloured folder

DATE	DESCRIPTION	QUANTITY SOLD	ISSUE PRICE	FINISH	SP-68	SP-69
2011	Sasquatch	12,321	24.95	Specimen	20.	—
2011	Memphré	5,811	24.95	Specimen	20.	—
2011	Mishepishu	5,831	24.95	Specimen	20.	—

TWENTY-FIVE CENTS, THE WEDDING CELEBRATION, HRH PRINCE WILLIAM AND MISS CATHERINE MIDDLETON, 2011 (GIFTWARE).
This coin was issued to commemorate the marriage of HRH Prince William and Miss Catherine Middleton on April 29th, 2011.

Designers and Engravers:	
Obv.:	Susanna Blunt, Susan Taylor
Rev.:	José Osio
Composition:	Nickel plated steel, Decal
Weight:	12.61 g
Diameter:	35.0 mm
Thickness:	2.0 mm
Edge:	Reeded
Die Axis:	↑↑
Finish:	Specimen
Case of Issue:	Illustrated folder

DATE	DESCRIPTION	QUANTITY SOLD	ISSUE PRICE	FINISH	SP-68	SP-69
2011	HRH Prince William and Miss Catherine Middleton	59,585	25.95	Specimen	15.	—

CANADA'S FLORA AND FAUNA SERIES

TWENTY-FIVE CENTS, CANADA'S FLORA AND FAUNA SERIES, 2011-2014 (GIFTWARE).

This series of coins is based on the flora and fauna of Canada's natural landscape. For similar series, see pages 269 and 466.

Common obverse

Designers and Engravers:

Obv.:	Susanna Blunt, Susan Taylor
Rev.:	See reverse illustrations
Composition:	2011: Nickel plated steel, Decal
	2012-2014: Cupronickel, Decal
Weight:	12.61 g
Diameter:	35.0 mm
Thickness:	1.9 to 2.0 mm
Case of Issue:	2011: Illustrated folder
	2012-2013: Maroon leatherette clam style case, black flocked insert, encapsulated coin, COA

Edge: Plain
Die Axis: ↑↑
Finish: Specimen

| Tulip with Ladybug
Designer: Cosme Saffioti
Engraver: RCM Staff | Aster with Bumble Bee
Designer: Maurice Gervais
Engraver: Cecily Mok | Purple Coneflower and
Eastern Tailed Blue Butterfly
Designer: Maurice Gervais
Engraver: RCM Staff | Water-lily and Leopard Fro
Designer: Maurice Gervais
Engraver: RCM Staff |

DATE	DESCRIPTION	QUANTITY SOLD	ISSUE PRICE	FINISH	SP-68	SP-6
2011	Tulip with Ladybug	15,777	24.95	Specimen	35.	—
2012	Aster with Bumble Bee	16,005	29.95	Specimen	25.	—
2013	Purple Coneflower and Eastern Tailed Blue Butterfly	14,459	29.95	Specimen	25.	—
2014	Water-lily and Leopard Frog	11,199	29.95	Specimen	25.	—

TWENTY-FIVE CENTS, 75TH ANNIVERSARY OF CANADIAN BROADCASTING CORPORATION / RADIO-CANADA, 2011 (GIFTWAF

Radio Canada's first broadcast was on November 2nd, 1936. The microphone depicted on the reverse of the coin was created by CBC/Ra Canada for the Royal Tour of King George VI and Queen Elizabeth in 1939. It was designed for outside broadcasts. Its special wind-resisting de represented a major technological advance of the time.

Designers and Engravers:

Obv.:	Susanna Blunt, Susan Taylor
Rev.:	Konrad Wachelko, Nick Martin
Composition:	Cupronickel
Weight:	12.61 g
Diameter:	35.0 mm
Thickness:	1.58 mm
Edge:	Reeded
Die Axis:	↑↑
Finish:	Specimen
Case of Issue:	Illustrated folder

DATE	DESCRIPTION	QUANTITY SOLD	ISSUE PRICE	FINISH	SP-68	SP-
2011	75th Anniversary of CBC/Radio-Canada	7,777	29.95	Specimen	15.	—

TWENTY-FIVE CENTS, WAYNE GRETZKY, 2011 (GIFTWARE).

Wayne Gretzky "The Great One", whose hockey jersey bore the number 99, is commemorated on this coin.

Designers and Engravers:
Obv.:	Susanna Blunt, Susan Taylor
Rev.:	Glen Green, RCM Staff
Composition:	Copper plated steel, Decal
Weight:	12.5 g
Diameter:	35.0 mm
Thickness:	1.9 mm
Edge:	Plain
Die Axis:	↑↑
Finish:	Specimen
Case of Issue:	Illustrated folder

DATE	DESCRIPTION	QUANTITY SOLD	ISSUE PRICE	FINISH	SP-68	SP-69
2011	Wayne Gretzky	13,263	34.99	Specimen	25.	—

TWENTY FIVE CENTS, GEORGE V, STERLING SILVER, PROOF, 1911-2011.

This twenty-five-cent coin which carries the double date 1911-2011 is from the Special Edition Proof Set issued in 2011 to commemorate the 100th anniversary of the striking of Canada's 1911 silver dollar.

Designers and Engravers:
Obv.:	Sir E. B. MacKennal
Rev.:	Original design by L. C. Wyon, Modified by W. H. J. Blakemore
Composition:	92.5% Ag, 7.5% Cu
Silver content:	5.46 g, 0.17 tr oz

Weight:	5.9 g	**Edge:**	Reeded
Diameter:	23.9 mm	**Die Axis:**	↑↑
Thickness:	1.7 mm	**Finish:**	Proof
Case of Issue:	See Special Issue Proof Sets, page 551		

DATE	DESCRIPTION	QUANTITY SOLD	ISSUE PRICE	FINISH	PR-69	PR-70
2011 (1911-)	George V, Sterling Silver	5,952	N.I.I.	Proof	20.	—

OUR LEGENDARY NATURE SET

TWENTY-FIVE CENTS, OUR LEGENDARY NATURE: CANADIAN CONSERVATION SUCCESSES, 2011.

These coins were issued to commemorate three species brought back from near extinction by Canadian Conversation methods. The Wood Bison, Orca Whale and Peregrine Falcon twenty-five-cent coins were issued as a three-coin set.

Common Obverse	Wood Bison	Orca Whale	Peregrine Falcon

Designers:
Obv.:	Susanna Blunt
Rev.:	RCM Staff
Composition:	92.5% Ag, 7.5% Cu, Painted
Silver content:	5.46 g, 0.17 tr oz

Engravers:
Obv.:	Susan Taylor
Rev.:	Cecily Mok

Weight:	5.9 g		
Diameter:	23.9 mm	**Edge:**	Reeded
Thickness:	1.5 mm	**Die Axis:**	↑↑
		Finish:	Proof
Case of Issue:	Three-hole maroon clam style case, black flocked insert, encapsulated coin, COA		

TWENTY-FIVE CENTS, OUR LEGENDARY NATURE: CANADIAN CONSERVATION SUCCESSES, 2011, PRICING TABLE.

DATE	DESCRIPTION	QUANTITY SOLD	ISSUE PRICE	FINISH	PR-69	PR-7(
2011	Wood Bison, Painted	—	N.I.I.	Proof	15.	—
2011	Orca Whale, Painted	—	N.I.I.	Proof	15.	—
2011	Peregrine Falcon, Painted	—	N.I.I.	Proof	15.	—
2011	Set of 3 coins	5,290	49.95	Proof	40.	—

TWENTY-FIVE CENTS, *RMS TITANIC*, 1912-2012 (GIFTWARE).

On April 10th, 1912, *RMS Titanic* set sail from England on her maiden voyage to North America. Shortly before midnight on April 14th, 1912, *R Titanic* struck an iceberg and sank shortly before dawn on the following morning. This coin was issued to remember the event.

Designers and Engravers:
Obv.: Susanna Blunt, Susan Taylor
Rev.: Yves Bérubé, RCM Staff
Composition: Cupronickel, Decal
Weight: 13.8 g
Diameter: 35.0 mm
Thickness: 2.0 mm
Edge: Plain
Die Axis: ↑↑
Finish: Specimen
Case of Issue: Illustrated folder

DATE	DESCRIPTION	QUANTITY SOLD	ISSUE PRICE	FINISH	SP-68	SP-6
2012 (1912-)	RMS Titanic	34,309	25.95	Specimen	25.	—

TWENTY-FIVE CENTS, 100TH ANNIVERSARY OF THE CALGARY STAMPEDE, 2012 (GIFTWARE).

This twenty-five-cent coin is part of a coin and stamp set issued to commemorate the 100th anniversary of the Calgary Stampede. A domestic and U.S. rate stamp are included in a colourful illustrated folder.

Designers and Engravers:
Obv.: Susanna Blunt, Susan Taylor
Rev.: Tony Bianco, Konrad Wachelko
Composition: Cupronickel, Decal
Weight: 13.9 g
Diameter: 35.0 mm
Thickness: 1.8 mm
Edge: Plain
Die Axis: ↑↑
Finish: Specimen
Case of Issue: See Derivatives, page 60-61

DATE	DESCRIPTION	QUANTITY SOLD	ISSUE PRICE	FINISH	SP-68	SP-(
2012	100th Anniversary of the Calgary Stampede	16,080	N.I.I.	Specimen	25.	—

PREHISTORIC CREATURES SERIES

TWENTY FIVE CENTS, PREHISTORIC CREATURES SERIES, 2012-2014 (GIFTWARE).
The coins in the Prehistoric Animal Series use a photo-luminescent technology (glow-in-the-dark) on the central image.

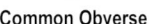

Common Obverse

2012
Pachyrhinosaurus Lakustai

Designers and Engravers:

Obv.:	Susanna Blunt, Susan Taylor
Rev.:	Julius T. Csotonyi, Cecily Mok
Composition:	Cupronickel, Photo-luminescent
Weight:	13.8 g
Diameter:	35.0 mm
Thickness:	1.9 to 2.0 mm
Finish:	Specimen
Case of Issue:	Maroon leatherette clam style case, black flocked insert, encapsulated coin, COA, custom coloured sleeve

Edge: Plain
Die Axis: ↑↑

2013
Quetzalcoatlus

2013
Tylosaurus Pembinensis

2014
Tiktaalik

DATE	DESCRIPTION	QUANTITY SOLD	ISSUE PRICE	FINISH	SP-68	SP-69
2012	Pachyrhinosaurus Lakustai	24,422	29.95	Specimen	80.	—
2013	Quetzalcoatlus	29,991	29.95	Specimen	25.	—
2013	Tylosaurus Pembinensis	29,458	29.95	Specimen	25.	—
2014	Tiktaalik	23,306	29.95	Specimen	25.	—

TWENTY-FIVE CENTS, 50TH ANNIVERSARY OF THE CANADIAN COAST GUARD, 2012 (GIFTWARE).
The CCGS Louis S. St. Laurent is depicted on this colourful twenty-five-cent coin. During a 1994 science expedition, the ship navigated through 0 kilometres of Arctic ice, visiting the North Pole as it made the first crossing of the Arctic Ocean from the Pacific to the Atlantic. It was a joint ada-US expedition with the USCGC Polar Sea. On August 22nd, 1994, the Louis S. St. Laurent was the first Canadian ship to reach the North Pole.

Designers and Engravers:

Obv.:	Susanna Blunt, Susan Taylor
Rev.:	Yves Bérubé, RCM Staff
Composition:	Cupronickel, Decal
Weight:	13.8 g
Diameter:	35.0 mm
Thickness:	1.9 mm
Edge:	Plain
Die Axis:	↑↑
Finish:	Specimen
Case of Issue:	Illustrated folder

DATE	DESCRIPTION	QUANTITY SOLD	ISSUE PRICE	FINISH	SP-68	SP-69
12	50th Anniversary of the Canadian Coast Guard	11,950	24.95	Specimen	20.	—

CANADIAN FOOTBALL LEAGUE SET

TWENTY-FIVE CENTS, CANADIAN FOOTBALL LEAGUE COIN AND STAMP SETS, 2012 (GIFTWARE).
These coin and stamp sets were issued by Canada Post to commemorate the 100th anniversary of the Canadian Football League. Each honours a CFL team with a twenty-five-cent coin and two commemorative stamps.

Common Obverse

Designers and Engravers:

Obv.:	Susanna Blunt, Susan Taylor
Rev.:	Filip Mroz of Bensimon Byrne, Marcos Hallam
Composition:	Cupronickel, Decal
Weight:	13.8 g
Diameter:	35.0 mm
Thickness:	2.0 mm
Edge:	Plain
Die Axis:	↑↑
Finish:	Specimen
Case of Issue:	See Derivatives, page 61

British Columbia Lions

Calgary Stampeders

Edmonton Eskimos

Hamilton Tiger Cats

Montreal Alouettes

Saskatchewan Roughriders

Toronto Argonauts

Winnipeg Blue Bombers

DATE	DESCRIPTION	QUANTITY SOLD	ISSUE PRICE	FINISH	SP-68	SP-
2012	British Columbia Lions	12,097	N.I.I.	Specimen	15.	—
2012	Calgary Stampeders	12,104	N.I.I.	Specimen	15.	—
2012	Edmonton Eskimos	12,120	N.I.I.	Specimen	15.	—
2012	Hamilton Tiger Cats	11,906	N.I.I.	Specimen	15.	—
2012	Montreal Alouettes	12,227	N.I.I.	Specimen	15.	—
2012	Saskatchewan Roughriders	15,700	N.I.I.	Specimen	15.	—
2012	Toronto Argonauts	12,434	N.I.I.	Specimen	15.	—
2012	Winnipeg Blue Bombers	12,214	N.I.I.	Specimen	15.	—

DUCKS OF CANADA SERIES

TWENTY-FIVE CENTS, DUCKS OF CANADA SERIES, 2013-2015 (GIFTWARE).

Common Obverse

This series celebrates the 75th anniversary of Ducks Unlimited Canada, an organization committed to the preservation and conservation of Canadian wetlands and its inhabitants.

| Mallard | Wood Duck | Northern Pintail | Harlequin Duck | Cinnamon Teal |

Designers:
Obv.: Susanna Blunt
Rev.: 2013-2014: Trevor Tennant
2015: Denis Mayer Jr.
Composition: Cupronickel, Decal
Weight: 13.5 g
Diameter: 35.1 mm
Thickness: 1.8 mm
Case of Issue: Maroon leatherette clam style case, black flocked insert, encapsulated coin, COA

Engravers:
Obv.: Susan Taylor
Rev.: RCM Staff

Edge: Plain
Die Axis: ↑↑
Finish: Specimen

DATE	DESCRIPTION	QUANTITY SOLD	ISSUE PRICE	FINISH	SP-68	SP-69
2013	Mallard	17,521	29.95	Specimen	25.	—
2013	Wood Duck	14,507	29.95	Specimen	25.	—
2014	Northern Pintail	11,031	29.95	Specimen	30.	—
2014	Harlequin Duck	6,592	29.95	Specimen	30.	—
2015	Cinnamon Teal	5,535	29.95	Specimen	30.	—

TWENTY-FIVE CENTS, HER MAJESTY QUEEN ELIZABETH II CORONATION, 2013 (GIFTWARE).

This coin was issued to commemorate the Coronation of Queen Elizabeth II. The reverse image features a detail from Canadian artist Phil Richard's 2012 official portrait of Her Majesty Queen Elizabeth II in celebration of her Diamond Jubilee.

Designers and Engravers:
Obv.: Susanna Blunt, Susan Taylor
Rev.: Phil Richards, RCM Staff
Composition: Cupronickel, Decal
Weight: 13.9 g
Diameter: 35.0 mm
Thickness: 1.9 mm
Edge: Plain
Die Axis: ↑↑
Finish: Specimen
Case of Issue: Maroon leatherette clam style case, black flocked insert, encapsulated coin, COA

DATE	DESCRIPTION	QUANTITY SOLD	ISSUE PRICE	FINISH	SP-68	SP-69
2013	HM Queen Elizabeth II Coronation	15,000	24.95	Specimen	30.	—

TWENTY-FIVE CENTS, BIRTH OF THE ROYAL INFANT, 2013 (GIFTWARE).
This coin was issued to commemorate the birth of Prince George of Cambridge, third in the line to the British throne.

Designers and Engravers:

Obv.:	Susanna Blunt, Susan Taylor
Rev.:	Laurie McGaw, Susan Taylor
Composition:	Cupronickel
Weight:	13.8 g
Diameter:	35.0 mm
Thickness:	1.9 mm
Edge:	Plain
Die Axis:	↑↑
Finish:	Specimen
Case of Issue:	Coloured folder

DATE	DESCRIPTION	QUANTITY SOLD	ISSUE PRICE	FINISH	SP-68	SP-6
2013	Birth of the Royal Infant	15,003	24.95	Specimen	20.	—

TWENTY-FIVE CENTS, THE EASTERN PRICKLY PEAR CACTUS, 2013 (GIFTWARE).
This is the first coin in a new series featuring Canadian flowers.

 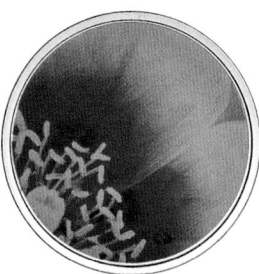

Designers and Engravers:

Obv.:	Susanna Blunt, Susan Taylor
Rev.:	Claudio D'Angelo, RCM Staff
Composition:	Cupronickel, Decal
Weight:	13.7 g
Diameter:	35.0 mm
Thickness:	1.9 mm
Edge:	Plain
Die Axis:	↑↑
Finish:	Specimen
Case of Issue:	Custom coloured cardboard box, encapsulated coin, COA

DATE	DESCRIPTION	QUANTITY SOLD	ISSUE PRICE	FINISH	SP-68	SP-6
2013	The Eastern Prickly Pear Cactus	7,189	24.95	Specimen	15.	—

TWENTY-FIVE CENTS, 2014 FIFA WORLD CUP™, 2014 (GIFTWARE).
In 2014 the FIFA World Cup™ was hosted by Brazil.

Designers and Engravers:

Obv.:	Susanna Blunt, Susan Taylor
Rev.:	Steve Hepburn, RCM Staff
Composition:	Cupronickel, Decal
Weight:	13.7 g
Diameter:	35.0 mm
Thickness:	1.9 mm
Edge:	Plain
Die Axis:	↑↑
Finish:	Specimen
Case of Issue:	Black and white clam style case, black flocked insert, encapsulated coin, COA, full colour sleeve

DATE	DESCRIPTION	QUANTITY SOLD	ISSUE PRICE	FINISH	SP-68	SP-
2014	2014 FIFA World Cup™	8,825	29.95	Specimen	25.	—

HAUNTED CANADA SERIES

WENTY-FIVE CENTS, HAUNTED CANADA, 2014-2016 (GIFTWARE).

There's a great tradition of storytelling across Canada, where many share a fascination with tales of unexplained apparitions, supernatural beings
and haunted places – even if some might send shivers down one's spine! The *Haunted Canada* series bring some of Canada's most beloved spooky
es to life.

Common Obverse

Designers and Engravers:

Obv.:	Susanna Blunt, Susan Taylor
Rev.:	RCM Staff
Composition:	Cupronickel, Lenticular
Weight:	13.8 g
Diameter:	35.0 mm
Thickness:	1.9 mm
Edge:	Plain
Die Axis:	↑↑
Finish:	Specimen
Case of Issue:	Maroon leatherette clam style case, black flocked insert, encapsulated coin, COA,

Ghost Bride

Brakeman

Bell Island

DATE	DESCRIPTION	QUANTITY SOLD	ISSUE PRICE	FINISH	SP-68	SP-69
2014	Ghost Bride	15,007	29.95	Specimen	75.	—
2015	Brakeman	15,175	29.95	Specimen	25.	—
2016	Bell Island	12,678	31.95	Specimen	30.	—

NATIONAL HOCKEY LEAGUE SET

TWENTY-FIVE CENTS, NATIONAL HOCKEY LEAGUE COIN AND STAMP SETS, 2014 (GIFTWARE).
These coin and stamp sets were issued by Canada Post. Each set honours a Canadian NHL team with a twenty-five-cent coin and t
commemorative stamps.

Common Obverse

Calgary Flames

Designers and Engravers:

Obv.:	Susanna Blunt, Susan Taylor
Rev.:	RCM Staff
Composition:	Cupronickel, Decal
Weight:	13.8 g
Diameter:	35.0 mm
Thickness:	2.0 mm
Edge:	Plain
Die Axis:	↑↑
Finish:	Specimen
Case of Issue:	See Derivatives, page 60-61

Edmonton Oilers

Montreal Canadiens

Ottawa Senators

Toronto Maple Leafs

Vancouver Canucks

Winnipeg Jets

DATE	DESCRIPTION	QUANTITY SOLD	ISSUE PRICE	FINISH	SP-68	SP-6
2014	Calgary Flames	5,721	25.95	Specimen	30.	–
2014	Edmonton Oilers	5,772	25.95.	Specimen	30.	–
2014	Montreal Canadiens	5,973	25.95	Specimen	35.	–
2014	Ottawa Senators	5,810	25.95	Specimen	30.	–
2014	Toronto Maple Leafs	5,970	25.95	Specimen	30.	–
2014	Vancouver Canucks	6,021	25.95	Specimen	30.	–
2014	Winnipeg Jets	5,925	25.95	Specimen	30.	–

BIG COIN SERIES

WENTY-FIVE CENTS, BIG COIN SET, 2015-2018.
The Big Coin Series started in 2015, features the classic Bluenose design for 2015, 2016 and 2018, which first appeared on the 1937 Canadian
-cent coin designed by Emanuel Hahn, with Alex Colville's 1967 design for the 2017 coin. Other coins in the set include a 1¢ coin (page 7), 5¢ coin
age 11), 10¢ coin (page 17), 50¢ coin (page 57), $1 coin (page 130) and a $2 coin (page 149).

signers and Engravers:

Obv.:	Susanna Blunt, Susan Taylor
Rev.:	Emanuel Hahn, Myron Cook
	Alex Colville
	Emanuel Hahn

er content: 157.58 g, 5.06 tr oz
ight: 157.6 g
meter: 65.25 mm
ckness: N/A

Composition:

2015:	99.99% Ag, Selectively gold plated
2016:	99.99% Ag, Selectively coloured on reverse
2017:	99.99% Ag, Selectively gold plated
2018:	99.95% Ag, Selectively rose gold-plated

Edge: Reeded
Die Axis: ↑↑
Finish: Proof

e of Issue: Maroon clam style case, black flocked insert, encapsulated coin, COA, custom box

DATE	DESCRIPTION	QUANTITY SOLD	ISSUE PRICE	FINISH	PR-69	PR-70
2015	25¢ Big Coin	1,491	549.95	Proof	600.	—
2016	25¢ Big Coin	1,484	519.95	Proof	520.	—
2017	25¢ Big Coin	1,855	559.95	Proof	560.	—
2018	25¢ Big Coin	1,500	559.95	Proof	560.	—

e: Coins illustrated smaller than actual size.

TWENTY-FIVE CENTS, LENTICULAR COIN, *BATMAN V SUPEMAN: DAWN OF JUSTICE*™, 2016.

Fearing the actions of a god-like super hero left unchecked, Gotham City's own formidable, forceful vigilante takes on Metropolis's most rever‍ modern-day saviour, while the world wrestles with what sort of hero it really needs. And with BATMAN™ and SUPERMAN™ at war with one anoth‍ a new threat quickly arises, putting mankind in greater danger than it's ever known before.

Designers and Engravers:

Obv.:	Susanna Blunt, Susan Taylor
Rev.:	DC Comics
Composition:	Cupronickel, Lenticular
Weight:	13.7 g
Diameter:	35 mm
Thickness:	N/A
Edge:	Plain
Die Axis:	↑↑
Finish:	Specimen
Case of Issue:	Custom presentation folder.

DATE	DESCRIPTION	QUANTITY SOLD	ISSUE PRICE	FINISH	SP-68	SP-69
2016	Dawn of Justice	27,120	29.95	Specimen	30.	—

TWENTY-FIVE CENTS, *STAR TREK*™: *ENTERPRISE*, 2016.

Beloved by millions, the originalf television series *Star Trek* has arguably helped shape the everyday lives of Canadians through its spirit of scien‍ innovation and discovery.

Designers and Engravers:

Obv.:	Susanna Blunt, Susan Taylor
Rev.:	RCM Staff
Composition:	Three-ply nickel finished plated steel
Weight:	12.61 g
Diameter:	35 mm
Thickness:	N/A
Edge:	Plain
Die Axis:	↑↑
Finish:	Specimen
Case of Issue:	Coin and stamp set, packaged in blister pack.

DATE	DESCRIPTION	QUANTITY SOLD	ISSUE PRICE	FINISH	SP-68	SP-6
2016	Enterprise	26,836	34.95	Specimen	35.	—

TWENTY-FIVE CENTS, LOVE MY CAT, 2017.

This special collectible is a meaningful way to celebrate that special bond between Canadians and their beloved felines, who seem to ask litt‍ return for their companionship.

Designers and Engravers:

Obv.:	Susanna Blunt
Rev.:	RCM Staff
Composition:	Three-ply nickel finished plated steel
Diameter:	35 mm
Thickness:	N/A
Edge:	Plain
Die Axis:	↑↑
Finish:	Specimen
Case of Issue:	Coin is set in blister in the card.

DATE	DESCRIPTION	QUANTITY SOLD	ISSUE PRICE	FINISH	SP-68	SP-6
2017	Love My Cat	16,529	31.95	Specimen	32.	—

VENTY-FIVE CENTS, LOVE MY DOG, 2017.

This special collectible is a meaningful way to celebrate that special bond between Canadians and their pet dogs, whose loving attention can turn en the worst day into a joyful reunion!

Designers and Engravers:
Obv.:	Susanna Blunt
Rev.:	RCM Staff

Composition: Three-ply nickel finished plated steel
Diameter: 35 mm
Thickness: N/A
Edge: Plain
Die Axis: ↑↑
Finish: Specimen
Case of Issue: Coin is set in blister in the card.

DATE	DESCRIPTION	QUANTITY SOLD	ISSUE PRICE	FINISH	SP-68	SP-69
2017	Love My Dog	16,761	31.95	Specimen	32.	—

VENTY-FIVE CENTS, LENTICULAR COIN, *THE JUSTICE LEAGUE*™, 2018.

Fueled by his restored faith in humanity and inspired by Superman's selfless act, Bruce Wayne enlists the help of his newfound ally, Diana Prince, ace an even greater enemy. Together, Batman and Wonder Woman work quickly to find and recruit a team of metahumans to stand against this vly awakened threat. But despite the formation of this unprecedented league of heroes—Batman, Wonder Woman, Aquaman, Cyborg and The sh—it may already be too late to save the planet from an assault of catastrophic proportions. Each package contains two cards! Your coin comes exclusive trading cards by Canadian artist Jason Fabok, with colours by Brad Anderson.

Designers and Engravers:
Obv.:	Susanna Blunt, Susan Taylor
Rev.:	Jason Fabak and Brad Anderson

Composition: Cupronickel, Lenticular
Weight: 12.3 g
Diameter: 35 mm
Thickness: N/A
Edge: Plain
Die Axis: ↑↑
Finish: Specimen
Case of Issue: Custom presentation folder.

DATE	DESCRIPTION	MINTAGE	ISSUE PRICE	FINISH	SP-68	SP-69
2018	*The Justice League*™	WSL	29.95	Specimen	30.	—

ROYAL CANADIAN MINT LORE: THE COINS THAT NEVER WERE

TWENTY-FIVE CENTS, THE COINS THAT NEVER WERE – 3-COIN SET, 2018.

In 1936 Emanuel Hahn submitted several concepts for new circulation coinage, but most were set aside. Now, some of Hahn's "coins that nev were" are featured in a three-coin tribute set. In addition to the twenty-five-cent coins, a five cent coin can be found on page 13.

Common Obverse

Polar Bear

Goose

Designers:		**Engravers:**	
Obv.:	Susanna Blunt	Obv.:	Susan Taylor
Rev.:	Emanuel Otto Hahn		
Composition:	99.99% Ag		
Silver content:	31.39 g, 1.01 tr oz		
Weight:	31.39 g	**Edge:**	Reeded
Diameter:	38 mm	**Die Axis:**	↑↑
Thickness:	N/A	**Finish:**	Reverse Proof
Case of Issue:	Standard maroon clamshell with black beauty box, COA.		

DATE	DESCRIPTION	MINTAGE	ISSUE PRICE	FINISH	PR-69	PR-7
2018	The Coins That Never Were – 3-Coin Set	5,500	269.95	Reverse Proof	270.	—

TWENTY-FIVE CENT DERIVATIVES

DATE	DESCRIPTION	QUANTITY SOLD	ISSUE PRICE	ISSUER	FINISH	MARKE PRICE
1999	**MILLENNIUM SET OF 12 CARDS** each containing a 1999 millennium twenty-five cent coin in a credit card format	N/A	N/A	RCM	MS-65	60
1999	**JANUARY** "A Country Unfolds"	N/A	N/A	RCM	MS-65	6
1999	**FEBRUARY** "Etched in Stone"	N/A	N/A	RCM	MS-65	6
1999	**MARCH** "The Log Drive"	N/A	N/A	RCM	MS-65	6
1999	**APRIL** "Our Northern Heritage"	N/A	N/A	RCM	MS-65	6
1999	**MAY** "The Voyageurs"	N/A	N/A	RCM	MS-65	6
1999	**JUNE** "From Coast to Coast"	N/A	N/A	RCM	MS-65	6
1999	**JULY** "A Nation of People"	N/A	N/A	RCM	MS-65	6
1999	**AUGUST** "The Pioneer Spirit"	N/A	N/A	RCM	MS-65	6
1999	**SEPTEMBER** "Canada Through a Child's Eye"	N/A	N/A	RCM	MS-65	6
1999	**OCTOBER** "A Tribute to the First Nation"	N/A	N/A	RCM	MS-65	6
1999	**NOVEMBER** "The Airplane Opens the North"	N/A	N/A	RCM	MS-65	6
1999	**DECEMBER** "This is Canada"	N/A	N/A	RCM	MS-65	6
2000	**MILLENNIUM SET 24** silver 25-cent coins, medallion and case	N/A	N/A	RCM	PR-69	200
2000	**MILLENNIUM SET OF 12 CARDS** each containing a 2000 millennium twenty-five cent coin in a credit card format	N/A	N/A	RCM	MS-65	66
2000	**JANUARY** - Pride "Tomorrow Today"	N/A	N/A	RCM	MS-65	6
2000	**FEBRUARY** - Ingenuity "Building for Tomorrow"	N/A	N/A	RCM	MS-65	6
2000	**MARCH** - Achievement "The Power to Excel"	N/A	N/A	RCM	MS-65	6
2000	**APRIL** - Health "Quest for a Cure"	N/A	N/A	RCM	MS-65	6
2000	**MAY** - Natural Legacy "Our Natural Treasures"	N/A	N/A	RCM	MS-65	6
2000	**JUNE** - Harmony "Hand in Hand"	N/A	N/A	RCM	MS-65	6
2000	**JULY** - Celebration "Celebrating our Future"	N/A	N/A	RCM	MS-65	6
2000	**AUGUST** - Family "The Ties That Bind"	N/A	N/A	RCM	MS-65	

TWENTY-FIVE CENT DERIVATIVES (cont.).

DATE	DESCRIPTION	QUANTITY SOLD	ISSUE PRICE	ISSUER	FINISH	MARKET PRICE
2000	**SEPTEMBER** - Wisdom "The Legacy"	N/A	N/A	RCM	MS-65	6.
2000	**OCTOBER** - Creativity "Expression For All Time"	N/A	N/A	RCM	MS-65	6.
2000	**NOVEMBER** - Freedom "Strong and Free"	N/A	N/A	RCM	MS-65	6.
2000	**DECEMBER** - Community "Canada in the World"	N/A	N/A	RCM	MS-65	6.
2000	**APRIL**, CIBC "Run For The Cure" Credit Card	N/A	N/A	RCM, CIBC	MS-65	6.
2000	**THE ADVENTURES OF ZAC AND PENNY MONEY** Set of twelve 2000 Millennium twenty-five cent coins in a display card; six booklets of stories and games	6,888	N/A	RCM	MS-65	20.
2004P	**WALKING BUNDLE** Twenty-five cent 'Moose' coin, T-shirt, Water bottle, Pouch	11,413	19.95	RCM	MS-65	30.
2004	**2004 ROYAL CANADIAN MINT ANNUAL REPORT** Twenty-five cent "Poppy" coin, sterling silver, selectively gold plated	12,677	24.95	RCM	PR-69	40.
2005P	**BOOKMARK** Twenty-five cent "Poppy" coin; Victory pin	29,975	12.95	RCM	MS-65	20.
2005	**60TH ANNIV. 1945-2005** Liberation Set, Netherlands	3,500	49.95	RCM	SP-68	60.
2006P	**BOOKMARK** Twenty-five cent "Breast Cancer" coin; painted; Lapel pin	40,911	13.95	RCM	MS-65	35.
2006	**CANADA DAY 2006,** Twenty-five cents, colourised; Four crayons and a colouring sheet	N/A	9.95	RCM	MS-65	15.
2007	**CANADA DAY,** Twenty-five cents, colourised coin, activity kit	N/A	9.95	RCM	MS-65	20.
2008	**CANADA DAY,** Twenty-five cents, colourised coin, activity kit	N/A	9.95	RCM	MS-65	15.
2009	**CANADA DAY,** Twenty-five cents, colourised coin, activity kit	N/A	14.95	RCM	MS-65	20.
2010	**REMEMBRANCE DAY COLLECTOR CARD,** includes 2010 twenty-five cent Remembrance Day coin; two die-cut holes for 2004 and 2008 twenty-five cent Poppy coins; postcard	21,738	9.95	RCM	MS-65	10.
2012	**TITANIC 100,** Twenty-five cent "Titanic" coin, White Star stock certificate, a re-created Titanic cancel, sheet of stamps, three Titanic postcards, leather-bound embossed album	10,000	140.95	RCM/CP	MS-65	75.
2012	**TITANIC PHILATELIC NUMISMATIC COVER,** Twenty-five cent coin, First Day Cover.	10,000	26.95	RCM/CP	MS-65	25.
2012	**CALGARY STAMPEDE COIN AND STAMP SET,** Twenty-five cents, colourised coin, a domestic rate and U.S. rate stamp	16,080	25.95	RCM/CP	SP-68	25.
2012	**CANADIAN FOOTBALL LEAGUE COIN AND STAMP SETS** Twenty-five cent coin, colourised, two commemorative stamps, coloured folder					
	British Columbia Lions	12,097	25.95	RCM/CP	SP-68	25.
	Calgary Stampeders	12,104	25.95	RCM/CP	SP-68	25.
	Edmonton Eskimos	12,120	25.95	RCM/CP	SP-68	25.
	Hamilton Tiger Cats	11,906	25.95	RCM/CP	SP-68	25.
	Montreal Alouettes	12,227	25.95	RCM/CP	SP-68	30.
	Saskatchewan Rough Riders	15,700	25.95	RCM/CP	SP-68	25.
	Toronto Argonauts	12,434	25.95	RCM/CP	SP-68	25.
	Winnipeg Blue Bombers	12,214	25.95	RCM/CP	SP-68	25.
2014	**NATIONAL HOCKEY LEAGUE COIN AND STAMP SETS** Twenty-five cent coin, colourised, two commemorative stamps, coloured folder					
	Calgary Flames	5,721	29.95	RCM/CP	SP-68	35.
	Edmonton Oilers	5,772	29.95	RCM/CP	SP-68	35.
	Montreal Canadiens	5,963	29.95	RCM/CP	SP-68	40.
	Ottawa Senators	5,810	29.95	RCM/CP	SP-68	35.
	Toronto Maple Leafs	5,969	29.95	RCM/CP	SP-68	35.
	Vancouver Canucks	5,986	29.95	RCM/CP	SP-68	35.
	Winnipeg Jets	5,925	29.95	RCM/CP	SP-68	35.
2016	*BATMAN V SPERMAN: DAWN OF JUSTICE* Twenty-five cent coin, 2 collectable trading cards	27,120	29.95	RCM	SP-68	30.
2016	*STAR TREK: ENTERPRISE **COIN AND STAMP SET**,* Twenty-five cent coin, 3 collectable stamps	26,836	34.95	RCM/CP	SP-68	35.

FIFTY CENTS

FIFTY CENTS, ELIZABETH II PROOF, 1996-2018.

Starting in 1996 the fifty-cent coin issued in the proof set, previously struck from cupronickel, was now struck on a sterling silver planchet. The u of sterling silver planchets was discontinued in 2011.

The year 2012 saw the introduction of the Premium Proof Set in which all coins were struck on fine silver planchets. Standard Proof Sets we issued for 2012, 2014-2017. The fifty-cent coin in these sets was struck on a nickel planchet. **Note:** Quantity sold figures are identical to those lis for Proof Sets sold.

Obverse
1996-2003

Obverse 2004-2006, 2015-2016
Without RCM Logo

Obverse 2007-2014, 2018
With RCM Logo

Reverse
1996-2018

Designers:
Obv.: 1996-2003: Dora de Pédery-Hunt
       2004-2018: Susanna Blunt
Rev.: 1996: Thomas Shingles
       1997-2016: C. Bursey-Sabourin
       2017: Heritage Canada contest

Engravers:
Obv.: 1996-2003: Dora de Pédery-Hunt
       2004-2018: Susan Taylor
Rev.: 1996:   Thomas Shingles
       1997-2016: William Woodruff

Reverse
2017
Canada 150

	Sterling Silver	Nickel	Fine Silver
Composition:	92.5% Ag, 7.5% Cu	100.%	99.99% Ag
Silver content:	8.603 g, 0.277 tr oz	—	9.4 g, 0.302 tr oz
Weight:	9.3 g	6.9 g	9.4 g
Diameter:	27.1 mm	27.13 mm	27.0 mm
Thickness:	1.9 mm	1.9 mm	2.0 mm
Edge:	Reeded	Reeded	Reeded
Die Axis:	↑↑	↑↑	↑↑
Finish:	Proof	Proof	Proof
Case of Issue:	Included in Proof Sets, pages 546-550		

DATE	DESCRIPTION	COMP	QUANTITY SOLD	ISSUE PRICE	FINISH	PR-69	PR-7
1996	Diademed Portrait / Arms of Canada	Sterling	112,835	N.I.I.	Proof	10.	—
1997		Sterling	113,647	N.I.I.	Proof	10.	—
1998		Sterling	93,632	N.I.I.	Proof	10.	—
1999		Sterling	95,113	N.I.I.	Proof	15.	—
2000		Sterling	90,921	N.I.I.	Proof	15.	—
2001		Sterling	74,194	N.I.I.	Proof	15.	—
2002		Sterling	65,315	N.I.I.	Proof	15.	—
2003		Sterling	62,007	N.I.I.	Proof	20.	—
2004	Uncrowned Portrait / Arms of Canada	Sterling	57,614	N.I.I.	Proof	20.	—
2005		Sterling	63,562	N.I.I.	Proof	15.	—
2006		Sterling	53,822	N.I.I.	Proof	15.	—
2007	Uncrowned Portrait, Mint Logo / Arms of Canada	Sterling	37,413	N.I.I.	Proof	15.	—
2008		Sterling	38,630	N.I.I.	Proof	15.	—
2009		Sterling	27,549	N.I.I.	Proof	15.	—
2010		Sterling	32,342	N.I.I.	Proof	15.	—
2011		Sterling	32,910	N.I.I.	Proof	15.	—
2012		Nickel	27,254	N.I.I.	Proof	15.	—
2012	Premium Proof Set	Fine Silver	19,789	N.I.I.	Proof	15.	—
2013	Premium Proof Set	Fine Silver	20,182	N.I.I.	Proof	15.	—
2014		Nickel	11,251	N.I.I.	Proof	15.	—
2014	Premium Proof Set	Fine Silver	13,416	N.I.I.	Proof	15.	—
2015	Premium Proof Set	Fine Silver	20,000	N.I.I.	Proof	15.	—
2015		Nickel	20,000	N.I.I.	Proof	15.	—
2016	Premium Proof Set	Fine Silver	20,000	N.I.I.	Proof	25.	—
2016		Nickel	20,000	N.I.I.	Proof	25.	—
2017	Premium Proof Set, Arms of Canada	Fine Silver	20,000	N.I.I.	Proof	25.	—
2017	Premium Proof Set, Canada 150 Logo	Fine Silver	20,000	N.I.I.	Proof	30.	—
2017	Proof Set, Canada 150 Logo	Nickel	25,000	N.I.I.	Proof	15.	—
2017	Premium Proof Set 1967-2017	Fine Silver	20,000	N.I.I.	Proof	25.	—
2018	Premium Proof Set	Fine Silver	20,000	N.I.I.	Proof	25.	—
2018		Nickel	25,000	N.I.I.	Proof	15.	

DISCOVERING NATURE SERIES, 1995-2000

FTY CENTS, BIRDS OF CANADA SET, 1995.
  The first set in the Discovering Nature Series commemorates birds that are native to Canada. This is the first of six sets totalling 24 coins. They are
e first sterling silver fifty cents to be issued since 1919.

Common Obverse

Designers:			Engravers:	
Obv.:	Dora de Pédery-Hunt		Obv.:	Dora de Pédery-Hunt
Rev.:	Coins 1 - 4: Jean-Luc Grondin		Rev.:	See reverse illustrations
	Coins 5 - 8: Dwayne Harty			

Composition: 92.5% Ag, 7.5% Cu
Silver content: 8.603 g, 0.277 tr oz
Weight: 9.3 g   **Edge:** Reeded
Diameter: 27.1 mm   **Die Axis:** ↑↑
Thickness: 2.1 mm   **Finish:** Proof
Case of Issue: Coins 1 - 4   Encapsulated coin in presentation box with illustrated booklet.
Coins 5 - 6   (A) Two coin set; encapsulated coins
(B) Four coin set; encapsulated coins

Coin No. 1	Coin No. 2	Coin No. 3	Coin No. 4
Atlantic Puffins	Whooping Crane	Gray Jays	White-tailed Ptarmigans
Sheldon Beveridge	Stan Witten	Sheldon Beveridge	Cosme Saffioti

FTY CENTS, LITTLE WILD ONES SET, 1996.
  The second set commemorates the young wildlife of Canada in their natural habitat.

Coin No. 5	Coin No. 6	Coin No. 7	Coin No. 8
Moose Calf	Wood Ducklings	Cougar Kittens	Black Bear Cubs
Ago Aarand	Sheldon Beveridge	Stan Witten	Sheldon Beveridge

DATE	COIN No.	DESCRIPTION	QUANTITY SOLD	ISSUE PRICE	FINISH	PR-68	PR-69
1995	1	Atlantic Puffins	Total	—	Proof	15.	—
1995	2	Whooping Crane	mintage	29.95	Proof	15.	—
1995	3	Gray Jays	all coins	—	Proof	15.	—
1995	4	White-tailed Ptarmigans	172,377	29.95	Proof	15.	—
1995	—	Set of 4 coins	—	56.95	Proof	45.	*
1996	5	Moose Calf	Total	—	Proof	15.	—
1996	6	Wood Ducklings	mintage	29.95	Proof	15.	—
1996	7	Cougar Kittens	all coins	—	Proof	15.	—
1996	8	Black Bear Cubs	206,552	29.95	Proof	15.	—
1996	—	Set of 4 coins	—	56.95	Proof	45.	*

te: Coins 1-2 and 3-4 were issued in two coin sets, issue price $29.95.

DISCOVERING NATURE SERIES, 1995-2000 (cont.).

FIFTY CENTS, CANADA'S BEST FRIENDS SET, 1997.

The 1997 set honours the friendship and loyalty of four of Canada's favourite canine companions.

Common Obverse

Designers:		
Obv.:	Dora de Pédery-Hunt	
Rev.:	Coins 9 - 12: Arnold A. Nogy	
	Coins 13 - 16: Pierre Leduc	
Composition:	92.5% Ag, 7.5% Cu	
Silver content:	8.603 g, 0.277 tr oz	
Weight:	9.3 g	
Diameter:	27.1 mm	
Thickness:	2.1 mm	
Case of Issue:	Encapsulated coin in presentation box, plus illustrated booklet.	

Engravers:	
Obv.:	Dora de Pédery-Hunt
Rev.:	See reverse illustrations
Edge:	Reeded
Die Axis:	↑↑
Finish:	Proof

Coin No. 9	Coin No. 10	Coin No. 11	Coin No. 12
Newfoundland	Nova Scotia Duck	Labrador Retriever	Canadian Eskimo Dog
William Woodruff	Tolling Retriever	Sheldon Beveridge	Cosme Saffioti
	Stan Witten		

FIFTY CENTS, CANADA'S OCEAN GIANTS SET, 1998.

The reverse designs of the 1998 set shows the grace and beauty of the whales that are seen off our coasts.

Coin No. 13	Coin No. 14	Coin No. 15	Coin No. 16
Killer Whale	Humpback Whale	Beluga Whale	Blue Whale
William Woodruff	Sheldon Beveridge	Cosme Saffioti	Stan Witten

DATE	COIN No.	DESCRIPTION	QUANTITY SOLD	ISSUE PRICE	FINISH	PR-68	PR-69
1997	9	Newfoundland	Total	19.95	Proof	15.	—
1997	10	Nova Scotia Duck Tolling Retriever	mintage	19.95	Proof	15.	—
1997	11	Labrador Retriever	all coins	19.95	Proof	15.	—
1997	12	Canadian Eskimo Dog	184,536	19.95	Proof	15.	—
1997	—	Set of 4 coins	—	59.95	Proof	50.	*
1998	13	Killer Whale	Total	19.95	Proof	15.	—
1998	14	Humpback Whale	mintage	19.95	Proof	15.	—
1998	15	Beluga Whale	all coins	19.95	Proof	15.	—
1998	16	Blue Whale	133,310	19.95	Proof	15.	—
1998	—	Set of 4 coins	—	59.95	Proof	50.	*

DISCOVERING NATURE SERIES, 1995-2000 (cont.).

FTY CENTS, CATS OF CANADA SET, 1999.

This set, issued in 1999, honours four species of domestic and wild felines found in Canada, a salute to our rich Canadian wildlife.

Common Obverse

Designers:		Engravers:	
Obv.:	Dora de Pédery-Hunt	Obv.:	Dora de Pédery-Hunt
Rev.:	Coins 17 - 20: John Crosby	Rev.:	See reverse illustrations
	Coins 21, 23: Jean-Luc Grondin		
	Coins 22, 24: Pierre Leduc		

Composition:	92.5% Ag, 7.5% Cu		
Silver content:	8.603 g, 0.277 tr oz		
Weight:	9.3 g	**Edge:**	Reeded
Diameter:	27.1 mm	**Die Axis:**	↑↑
Thickness:	2.1 mm	**Finish:**	Proof
Case of Issue:	Encapsulated coin in presentation box, plus illustrated booklet.		

Coin No. 17	Coin No. 18	Coin No. 19	Coin No. 20
Tonkinese	Lynx	Cymric	Cougar
Susan Taylor	Susan Taylor	Susan Taylor	Susan Taylor

FTY CENTS, CANADIAN BIRDS OF PREY, SET, 2000.

The sixth and last set of the series features the hunting birds indigenous to Canada.

Coin No. 21	Coin No. 22	Coin No. 23	Coin No. 24
Bald Eagle	Osprey	Great Horned Owl	Red-Tailed Hawk
William Woodruff	Susan Taylor	Susan Taylor	Stan Witten

DATE	COIN No.	DESCRIPTION	QUANTITY SOLD	ISSUE PRICE	FINISH	PR-68	PR-69
1999	17	Tonkinese	Total	19.95	Proof	25.	—
1999	18	Lynx	mintage	19.95	Proof	25.	—
1999	19	Cymric	all coins	19.95	Proof	25.	—
1999	20	Cougar	83,423	19.95	Proof	25.	—
1999	—	Set of 4 coins	—	59.95	Proof	75.	*
2000	21	Bald Eagle	Total	19.95	Proof	15.	—
2000	22	Osprey	mintage	19.95	Proof	15.	—
2000	23	Great Horned Owl	all coins	19.95	Proof	15.	—
2000	24	Red Tailed Hawk	123,628	19.95	Proof	15.	—
2000	—	Set of 4 coins	—	59.95	Proof	50.	*

CANADIAN SPORTS FIRSTS SERIES, 1998-2000

FIFTY CENTS, CANADIAN SPORTS FIRSTS SET, 1998.

A new sport series of sterling silver fifty cent coins began in 1998 with the issue of four coins, which continued in 1999 and 2000, making a total of 12 coins

Common Obverse

Designers:		**Engravers:**	
Obv.:	Dora de Pédery-Hunt	Obv.:	Dora de Pédery-Hunt
Rev.:	Coins 1 - 4: F. G. Peter	Rev.:	See reverse illustrations
	Coins 5 - 8: D. H. Curley		
Composition:	92.5% Ag, 7.5% Cu	**Thickness:**	2.1 mm
Silver content:	8.603 g, 0.277 tr oz	**Edge:**	Reeded
Weight:	9.3 g	**Die Axis:**	↑↑
Diameter:	27.1 mm	**Finish:**	Proof
Case of Issue:	Singles: Lithographed metal box, black flocked insert, encapsulated coin.		
	Set: Twelve coin metal container.		

Coin No. 1	Coin No. 2	Coin No. 3	Coin No. 4
First Official Amateur Figure Skating Championships, 1888 Sheldon Beveridge	First Canadian Ski Running/Ski Jumping Championships, 1898 Ago Aarand	First Overseas Can. Soccer Tour, 1888 Stan Witten, José Osio	Gilles Villeneuve Victory, Grand Prix of Canada for F1 Auto Racing, 1978 C. Saffioti, J. Osio

FIFTY CENTS, CANADIAN SPORTS FIRSTS SET, 1999.

The 1999 fifty-cent sterling silver coin set commemorates important dates in the history of Canadian sports. The designs reflect both the history of the sport and the growth and development into national pastimes.

Coin No. 5	Coin No. 6	Coin No. 7	Coin No. 8
1904-1999 First Canadian Open Golf Championship, 1904 William Woodruff	1874-1999 First Int'l Yacht Race Canada vs U.S.A. 1874 Stan Witten	1909-1999 First Grey Cup in Canadian Football, 1909 Cosme Saffioti	1891-1999 Invention of Basketball by Canadian James Naismith Sheldon Beveridge

DATE	COIN No.	DESCRIPTION	QUANTITY SOLD	ISSUE PRICE	FINISH	PR-68	PR-69
1998	1	First Official Amateur Figure Skating Chmpshp, 1888	Total	19.95	Proof	15.	—
1998	2	First Canadian Ski Running/Ski Jumping Chmpshp, 1898	mintage	19.95	Proof	15.	—
1998	3	First Overseas Canadian Soccer Tour, 1888	all coins	19.95	Proof	15.	—
1998	4	Gilles Villeneuve Victory, Grand Prix, F1 Auto Racing, 1978	56,428	19.95	Proof	15.	—
1998	—	Set of 4 coins	—	59.95	Proof	55.	*
1999	5	First Canadian Open Golf Chmpshp, 1904	Total	19.95	Proof	15.	—
1999	6	First Int'l Yacht Race between Canada and U.S.A., 1874	mintage	19.95	Proof	15.	—
1999	7	First Grey Cup in Canadian Football, 1909	all coins	19.95	Proof	15.	—
1999	8	Invention of Basketball by Canadian James Naismith, 1891	52,115	19.95	Proof	15.	—
1999	—	Set of 4 coins	—	59.95	Proof	55.	*

CANADIAN SPORTS FIRSTS SERIES, 1998-2000 (cont.).

FTY CENTS, CANADIAN SPORTS FIRSTS SET, 2000.

The 2000 fifty-cent sterling silver coin set celebrates the first competitions in Hockey, Curling, Steeplechase and Five Pin Bowling held in Canada. is is the last set in the twelve coin series.

Common Obverse

Designers:		Engravers:	
Obv.:	Dora de Pédery-Hunt	Obv.:	Dora de Pédery-Hunt
Rev.:	Brian Hughes	Rev.:	See reverse illustrations
Composition:	92.5% Ag, 7.5% Cu		
Silver content:	8.603 g, 0.277 tr oz		
Weight:	9.3 g	**Edge:**	Reeded
Diameter:	27.1 mm	**Die Axis:**	↑↑
Thickness:	2.1 mm	**Finish:**	Proof
Case of Issue:	Singles:	Lithographed metal box, black flocked insert, encapsulated coin.	
	Set:	Twelve coin metal case.	

Coin No. 9
1875-2000 First
Recorded Hockey Game
Stan Witten

Coin No. 10
1760-2000
Introduction of Curling
to North America
Cosme Saffioti

Coin No. 11
1840-2000 First
Steeplechase Race in
British North America
Susan Taylor

Coin No. 12
1910-2000 Birth
of the First 5-Pin
Bowling League
William Woodruff

DATE	COIN No.	DESCRIPTION	QUANTITY SOLD	ISSUE PRICE	FINISH	PR-69	PR-70
2000	9	First Recorded Hockey Game, 1875	Total	19.95	Proof	15.	—
2000	10	Introduction of Curling to North America, 1760	mintage	19.95	Proof	15.	—
2000	11	First Steeplechase Race in British North America, 1840	all coins	19.95	Proof	15.	—
2000	12	Birth of the First 5-Pin Bowling League, 1910	50,091	19.95	Proof	15.	—
2000	—	Set of 4 coins	—	59.95	Proof	55.	*

FIFTY CENT HISTORICAL COMMEMORATIVE SERIES, 1998-2008

FTY CENTS, 90TH ANNIVERSARY OF THE ROYAL CANADIAN MINT, 1908-1998.

Issued to commemorate the opening of the Royal Canadian Mint, a five-coin set was struck featuring the same reverse designs as the original 1908 ns, except for the double date 1908-1998. The set was issued in two finishes, matte and mirror proof.

Designers and Engravers:			
Obv.:	Dora de Pédery-Hunt		
Rev.:	Ago Aarand, W. H. J. Blakemore		
Composition:	92.5% Ag, 7.5% Cu		
Silver content:	10.749 g, 0.346 tr oz		
Weight:	11.62 g	**Edge:**	Reeded
Diameter:	29.7 mm	**Die Axis:**	↑↑
Thickness:	2.0 mm	**Finish:**	See below
Case of Issue:	See Special Issue Proof Sets, page 551		

DATE	DESCRIPTION	QUANTITY SOLD	ISSUE PRICE	FINISH	PR-68	PR-69
1998 (1908-)	90th Anniv. R.C. Mint	18,376	N.I.I.	Matte Proof	20.	—
1998 (1908-)	90th Anniv. R.C. Mint	24,893	N.I.I.	Mirror Proof	20.	—

FIFTY CENTS, 50TH ANNIVERSARY OF THE CORONATION OF QUEEN ELIZABETH II, 1953-2003.

This fifty-cent coin is from the Special Edition Proof Set issued in 2003 to commemorate the 50th anniversary of the Coronation of Queen Elizabeth

Designers and Engravers:
Obv.:	Mary Gillick
Rev.:	Thomas Shingles

Composition: 92.5% Ag, 7.5% Cu
Silver content: 10.749 g, 0.346 tr oz

Weight:	11.62 g	**Edge:**	Reeded
Diameter:	29.7 mm	**Die Axis:**	↑↑
Thickness:	1.9 mm	**Finish:**	Proof

Case of Issue: See Special Issue Proof Sets, page 496

DATE	DESCRIPTION	QUANTITY SOLD	ISSUE PRICE	FINISH	PR-69	PR-70
2003 (1953-)	50th Anniv. Coronation Queen Elizabeth II	21,537	N.I.I.	Proof	25.	—

FIFTY CENTS, COAT OF ARMS OF CANADA, 2004.

The Coat of Arms of Canada, which graced the George VI fifty-cent coin in 1937, has evolved over the years. This four-coin set, besides tracing the evolution, records the portrait changes of Elizabeth II.

1953-1964	**1953-1958**	**1965-1989**	**1959-1996**
1990-2003	**1959-1996**	**2003-2004**	**1997-2004**

Obverse Designers: Portraits
1953-1964	Mary Gillick
1965-1989	Arnold Machin
1990-2003	Dora de Pédery-Hunt
2003-2004	Susanna Blunt

Reverse Designers: Arms of Canada
1953 Small date:	G. E. Kruger-Gray
Large date:	Thomas Shingles
1954-1958	Thomas Shingles after G. E. Kruger-Gray
1959-1996	Thomas Shingles
1997-2004	C. Bursey-Sabourin

Composition: 92.5% Ag, 7.5% Cu
Silver content: 8.603 g, 0.277 tr oz

Weight:	9.3 g		
Diameter:	27.1 mm	**Edge:**	Reeded
Thickness:	2.1 mm	**Die Axis:**	↑↑
		Finish:	Proof

Case of Issue: Maroon leatherette case, black flocked interior, encapsulated coins, COA

DATE	DESCRIPTION	QUANTITY SOLD	ISSUE PRICE	FINISH	PR-69	PR-7
2004	Laureate Portrait	—	—	Proof	15.	—
2004	Tiara Portrait	—	—	Proof	15.	—
2004	Royal Diademed Portrait	—	—	Proof	15.	—
2004	Uncrowned Portrait	—	—	Proof	15.	—
2004	Total coins	12,230	—	Proof	—	*
2004	Total Sets	3,057	79.95	Proof	50.	*

FIFTY CENT HISTORICAL COMMEMORATIVE SERIES, 1998-2008 (cont.).

FTY CENTS, ROYAL CANADIAN MINT ANNUAL REPORT, SELECTIVELY GOLD PLATED, 2006.

This sterling silver gold-plated fifty-cent coin dated 2006 was issued in 2007 with the 2006 Royal Canadian Mint Annual Report. This was the last
ar a coin was combined with the Royal Canadian Mint Report.

Designers and Engravers:

Obv.:	Susanna Blunt, Susan Taylor
Rev.:	C. Bursey-Sabourin
Composition:	92.5% Ag, 7.5% Cu,
	Selectively gold plated
Silver content:	8.603 g, 0.277 tr oz
Weight:	9.3 g
Diameter:	27.1 mm	**Edge:**	Reeded
Thickness:	1.9 mm	**Die Axis:**	↑↑
Finish:	Proof
Case of Issue:	See Derivatives, page 90

DATE	DESCRIPTION	QUANTITY SOLD	ISSUE PRICE	FINISH	PR-69	PR-70
2006	RCM Annual Report	4,162	25.95	Proof	30.	—

FTY CENTS, 100TH ANNIVERSARY OF THE ROYAL CANADIAN MINT, 1908-2008.

This fifty-cent coin is from the Coin and Stamp Set issued in 2008 to commemorate the 100th anniversary of the Royal Canadian Mint. It was also
ued with the 2008 Royal Canadian Mint Centennial Book.

Designers and Engravers:

Obv.:	Susanna Blunt, Susan Taylor
Rev.:	RCM Staff
Composition:	92.5% Ag, 7.5% Cu
Silver content:	10.915 g, 0.351 tr oz
Weight:	11.8 g
Diameter:	29.7 mm	**Edge:**	Reeded
Thickness:	2.0 mm	**Die Axis:**	↑↑
Finish:	Proof
Case of Issue:	See Derivatives, page 90

DATE	DESCRIPTION	QUANTITY SOLD	ISSUE PRICE	FINISH	PR-69	PR-70
2008 (1908-)	100th Anniversary, Royal Canadian Mint	3,248	44.95	Proof	40.	—

CANADIAN FESTIVALS SERIES, 2001-2002

FIFTY CENTS, CANADIAN FESTIVALS SERIES, 2001-2002.
  The Royal Canadian Mint introduced a new series of sterling silver fifty-cent coins in 2001 commemorating Canadian Festivals. Each coin represen
a Canadian Province, Territory or Community, celebrating its culture, history and traditions with colourful festivals. The 13-coin set was issued o
three years, starting in 2001 and ending 2003. It was available by subscription in 2001 for $249.95 with coins being shipped as they became availab

ISSUES OF 2001

Common Obverse	Coin No. 1	Coin No. 2	Coin No. 3	Coin No. 4
	Quebec Winter Carnival	Toonik Tyme	Newfoundland and	Festival of Fathers
	(Quebec)	(Nunavut)	Labrador Folk Festival	(Prince Edward Islan
	S. Daigneault	J. Mardon, J. Osio	(Newfoundland)	B. Whiteway,
	S. Witten		D. Craig, C. Saffioti	W. Woodruff

ISSUES OF 2002

Coin No. 5	Coin No. 6	Coin No. 7	Coin No. 8	Coin No. 9
Annapolis Valley	Stratford Festival	Folklorama	Calgary Stampede	Squamish Days
Blossom Festival	of Canada	(Manitoba)	(Alberta)	Logger Sports
(Nova Scotia)	(Ontario)	William Woodruff	M. Grant, S. Witten	(British Columbia)
B. Ross, J. Osio	L. McGaw, S. Taylor			José Osio

Designers:			**Engravers:**	
Obv.:	Dora de Pédery-Hunt		Obv.:	Dora de Pédery-Hunt
Rev.:	See reverse illustrations		Rev.:	See reverse illustrations
Composition:	92.5% Ag, 7.5% Cu			
Silver content:	8.603 g, 0.277 tr oz			
Weight:	9.3 g		**Edge:**	Reeded
Diameter:	27.1 mm		**Die Axis:**	↑↑
Thickness:	2.1 mm		**Finish:**	Proof
Case of Issue:	(A) Singles: Multicoloured printed card folder with encapsulated coin.			
	(B) Thirteen coin set: Canadian Festivals subscription coffee table book.			

DATE	COIN	DESCRIPTION	QUANTITY SOLD	ISSUE PRICE	FINISH	PR-69	PR-7
2001	1	Quebec	2001 total	21.95	Proof	15.	—
2001	2	Nunavut	mintage	21.95	Proof	15.	—
2001	3	Newfoundland	all coins	21.95	Proof	15.	—
2001	4	Prince Edward Island	58,123	21.95	Proof	15.	—
2002	5	Nova Scotia 2002	2002 total	21.95	Proof	15.	—
2002	6	Ontario	mintage	21.95	Proof	15.	—
2002	7	Manitoba	all	21.95	Proof	15.	—
2002	8	Alberta	coins	21.95	Proof	15.	—
2002	9	British Columbia	61,900	21.95	Proof	15.	—

FIFTY CENTS, CANADIAN FESTIVALS SERIES, 2003

This is the third issue in the 13-coin set which commemorates festivals across Canada.

ISSUES OF 2003

| Common Obverse | Coin No. 10
Yukon Festival
(Yukon)
Ken Anderson
José Osio | Coin No. 11
Back to Batoche
(Saskatchewan)
David Hannan
Stan Witten | Coin No. 12
Great Northern
Arts Festival
(Inuvik)
Dawn Oman
Susan Taylor | Coin No. 13
Festival Acadien de
Caraquet
(New Brunswick)
Hudson Design Group
Susan Taylor |

Designers:
  Obv.:   Dora de Pédery-Hunt
  Rev.:   See reverse illustrations
Composition: 92.5% Ag, 7.5% Cu
Silver content: 8.603 g, 0.277 tr oz
Weight: 9.3 g
Diameter: 27.1 mm
Thickness: 2.1 mm
Case of Issue:

Engravers:
  Obv.:   Dora de Pédery-Hunt
  Rev.:   See reverse illustrations

Edge: Reeded
Die Axis: ↑↑
Finish: Proof

(A)   Singles: Multicoloured printed card folder with encapsulated coin.
(B)   Thirteen coin set: Canadian Festivals subscription coffee table book.

DATE	COIN No.	DESCRIPTION	QUANTITY SOLD	ISSUE PRICE	FINISH	PR-69	PR-70
2003	10	Yukon	2003 total	21.95	Proof	15.	—
2003	11	Saskatchewan	mintage	21.95	Proof	15.	—
2003	12	Inuvik	all coins	21.95	Proof	15.	—
2003	13	New Brunswick	26,451	21.95	Proof	15.	—
2001-2003	—	Set of 13 coins	—	249.95	Proof	150.	*

CANADA'S FOLKLORE AND LEGENDS SERIES

FIFTY CENTS, CANADA'S FOLKLORE AND LEGENDS SERIES, 2001-2002.
A new series of fifty-cent sterling silver coins celebrates Canadian Folklore and Legends. The official release date was April 11, 2001.

ISSUES OF 2001

Common Obverse

Coin No. 1
The Sled
Valentina Hotz-Entin
Susan Taylor

Coin No. 2
The Maiden's Cave
Peter Kiss
Susan Taylor

Coin No. 3
Les Petits Sauteux
Miyuki Tanobe
José Osio

ISSUES OF 2002

Coin No. 4
The Pig That Wouldn't
Get Over the Stile
Laura Jolicoeur
José Osio

Coin No. 6
Le Vaisseau Fantome
Colette Boivin
William Woodruff

Coin No. 5
Shoemaker in Heaven
Francine Gravel
Cosme Saffioti

Designers:		**Engravers:**
Obv.:	Dora de Pédery-Hunt	Obv.:	Dora de Pédery-Hunt
Rev.:	See reverse illustrations	Rev.:	See reverse illustrations

Composition: 92.5% Ag, 7.5% Cu
Silver content: 8.603 g, 0.277 tr oz
Weight: 9.3 g
Diameter: 27.1 mm
Thickness: 2.1 mm
Case of Issue: Multicoloured printed card folder with encapsulated coin.

Edge: Reeded
Die Axis: ↑↑
Finish: Proof

DATE	COIN No.	DESCRIPTION	QUANTITY SOLD	ISSUE PRICE	FINISH	PR-69	PR-7
2001	1	The Sled	Mintage	24.95	Proof	15.	—
2001	2	The Maiden's Cave	2001 coins	24.95	Proof	15.	—
2001	3	Les Petits Sauteux	28,979	24.95	Proof	15.	—
2002	4	The Pig That Wouldn't Get Over the Stile	Mintage 2002	24.95	·Proof	15.	—
2002	5	Shoemaker in Heaven	coins	24.95	Proof	15.	—
2002	6	Le Vaisseau Fantome	19,789	24.95	Proof	15.	—

CANADA'S GOLDEN FLOWER SERIES

TY CENTS, CANADA'S GOLDEN FLOWER SERIES, 2002-2007.

Beginning in 2002 the Royal Canadian Mint issued a series of sterling silver, selectively gold plated proof fifty-cent coins to commemorate different nts which had a floral theme.

**2002 and 2003
Common Obverse**

**2002
50th Anniversary of the
Canadian Tulip Festival
Anthony Testa
Stan Witten**

**2003
Golden Daffodil
Symbol of Hope
Christie Paquet
Stan Witten**

Designers and Engravers:

2002-2003		
	Obv.:	Dora de Pédery-Hunt
	Rev.:	See reverse illustrations
2004-2007		
	Obv.:	Susanna Blunt
		Susan Taylor
	Rev.:	See reverse illustration
Composition:		92.5% Ag, 7.5% Cu,
		22-karat gold plate on design
Silver content:		8.603 g, 0.277 tr oz
Weight:		9.3 g
Diameter:		27.1 mm
Thickness:		2.2 mm
Edge:		Reeded
Die Axis:		↑↑
Finish:		Proof

**2004 to 2007
Common Obverse**

**2004
Golden Easter Lily
Christie Paquet
Stan Witten**

**2005
Golden Rose
Christie Paquet**

**2006
Golden Daisy
Christie Paquet**

**2007
Golden Forget-Me-Not
Christie Paquet**

se of Issue:
2002-2004: Folders dated 2002, 2003 and 2004, encapsulated coin
2005-2006: Maroon plastic display case, black plastic insert, encapsulated coin, COA
2007: Maroon clam style case, black flocked insert, encapsulated coin, COA

DATE	DESCRIPTION	QUANTITÝ SOLD	ISSUE PRICE	FINISH	PR-69	PR-70
2002	Canadian Tulip Festival, 50th Anniversary	19,986	24.95	Proof	40.	—
2003	Golden Daffodil, Symbol of Hope	36,293	34.95	Proof	20.	—
2004	Golden Easter Lily	24,495	34.95	Proof	20.	—
2005	Golden Rose	17,418	34.95	Proof	30.	—
2006	Golden Daisy	18,190	36.95	Proof	40.	—
2007	Golden Forget-Me-Mot	10,845	38.95	Proof	50.	—

CANADIAN BUTTERFLY SERIES

FIFTY CENTS, CANADIAN BUTTERFLY SERIES, 2004-2006.
This series on Canada's butterflies contains the first hologram fifty-cent coin.

Common Obverse

Designers:			**Engravers:**	
Obv.:	Susanna Blunt		Obv.:	Susan Taylor
Rev.:	See reverse illustrations		Rev.:	See reverse illustrations
Composition:	92.5% Ag, 7.5% Cu, Selectively gold plated, Decal, Hologram			
Silver content:	8.603 g, 0.277 tr oz			
Weight:	9.3 g		**Edge:**	Reeded
Diameter:	27.1 mm		**Die Axis:**	↑↑
Thickness:	2.1 mm			
Finish:	Proof			
Case of Issue:	2004:	Red leatherette clam style case, black flocked insert, encapsulated coin, CC		
	2005-2006:	Maroon plastic display case, black plastic insert, encapsulated coin, CO		

2004
Canadian Tiger
Swallowtail Butterfly
Des.: Jianping Yan
Engr.: RCM Staff

2004
Canadian Clouded
Sulphur Butterfly
Des.: Susan Taylor
Engr.: Susan Taylor

2005
Monarch Butterfly
Des.: Susan Taylor
Engr.: Susan Taylor

2005
Spangled Fritillary
Butterfly
Des.: Jianping Yan
Engr.: Jianping Yan

2006
Short-tailed Swallowtail
Butterfly
Des.: Susan Taylor
Engr.: Susan Taylor

2006
Silvery Blue Butterfly
Des.: Jianping Yan
Engr.: Jianping Yan

DATE	DESCRIPTION	QUANTITY SOLD	ISSUE PRICE	FINISH	PR-69	PR-7
2004	Canadian Tiger Swallowtail Butterfly, Hologram	20,462	39.95	Proof	40.	—
2004	Canadian Clouded Sulphur Butterfly, Selectively gold plated	15,281	39.95	Proof	40.	—
2005	Monarch Butterfly, Decal	35,950	39.95	Proof	40.	—
2005	Spangled Fritillary Butterfly, Hologram	Incl. above	39.95	Proof	40.	—
2006	Short-tailed Swallowtail Butterfly, Decal	24,568	39.95	Proof	40.	—
2006	Silvery Blue Butterfly, Hologram	Incl. above	39.95	Proof	40.	—

SECOND WORLD WAR SERIES

TY CENTS, QUEST FOR PEACE AND FREEDOM DURING THE SECOND WORLD WAR, 2005.
The 60th anniversary of the end of World War II, 1945-2005, and the part Canada played, are commemorated in this six-coin sterling silver set. The
ns were issued one per month from May 2005 to October 2005.

Common Obverse

Designers:			Engravers:	
Obv.:	Susanna Blunt		Obv.:	Susan Taylor
Rev.:	Peter Mossman		Rev.:	See reverse illustrations
Composition:	92.5% Ag, 7.5% Cu			
Silver content:	8.603 g, 0.277 tr oz			
Weight:	9.3 g		**Edge:**	Reeded
Diameter:	27.1 mm		**Die Axis:**	↑↑
Thickness:	2.1 mm		**Finish:**	Specimen
Case of Issue:	Red leatherette case, black flocked insert, encapsulated coin, COA			

Battle of Britain
October 1940
Engr.: Stan Witten

Liberation of the
Netherlands
September 1944
Engr.: José Osio

Conquest of Sicily
August 1943
Engr.: RCM Staff

Battle of the Scheldt
November 1944
Engr.: RCM Staff

Raid on Dieppe
August 1942
Engr.: José Osio

Battle of the Atlantic
1939-1945
Engr.: Christie Paquet

DATE	DESCRIPTION	ISSUE DATE	QUANTITY SOLD	ISSUE PRICE	FINISH	SP-68	SP-69
2005	Battle of Britain	May	20,000	—	Specimen	25.	—
2005	Liberation of the Netherlands	June	20,000	—	Specimen	25.	—
2005	Conquest of Sicily	July	20,000	—	Specimen	25.	—
2005	Battle of the Scheldt	August	20,000	—	Specimen	25.	—
2005	Raid on Dieppe	September	20,000	—	Specimen	25.	—
2005	Battle of the Atlantic	October	20,000	—	Specimen	25.	—
2005	Set of 6 coins and display case	—	20,000	149.95	Specimen	130.	*

CANADIAN NHL HOCKEY SERIES

During the years 2005 to 2010 the Royal Canadian Mint issued many coins, mostly giftware, commemorating the Canadian teams of the Natio [cut off]
Hockey League.

FIFTY CENTS, NHL HOCKEY LEGENDS, 2005.

Hockey greats are commemorated in this legends series, issued in sets of four coins each: Jean Beliveau, Guy Lafleur, Jacques Plante and Maur [cut off]
Richard of the Montreal Canadiens, and Johnny Bower, Tim Horton, Darryl Sittler and Dave Keon of the Toronto Maple Leafs.

Common Obverse

Designers:
Obv.:   Susanna Blunt
Rev.:   RCM Staff
Composition: 92.5% Ag, 7.5% Cu, Painted
Silver content: 8.603 g, 0.277 tr oz
Weight: 9.3 g
Diameter: 27.1 mm
Thickness: 2.1 mm
Case of Issue: Maroon plastic display case, black plastic insert, encapsulated coin, COA

Engravers:
Obv.:   Susan Taylor
Rev.:   RCM Staff

Edge: Reeded
Die Axis: ↑↑
Finish: Specimen

2005 MONTREAL CANADIENS

Jean Beliveau

Guy Lafleur

Jacques Plante

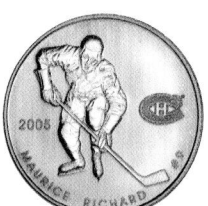
Maurice Richard

DATE	DESCRIPTION	QUANTITY SOLD	ISSUE PRICE	FINISH	SP-68	SP-6
2005	Jean Beliveau	N/A	N.I.I.	Specimen	35.	—
2005	Guy Lafleur	N/A	N.I.I.	Specimen	35.	—
2005	Jacques Plante	N/A	N.I.I.	Specimen	35.	—
2005	Maurice Richard	N/A	N.I.I.	Specimen	35.	—
2005	Set of 4 coins (Montreal)	N/A	99.95	Specimen	125.	*

2005 TORONTO MAPLE LEAFS

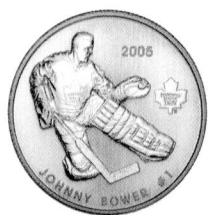
Johnny Bower

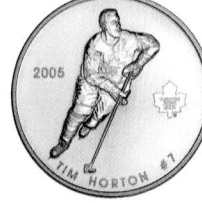
Tim Horton

Darryl Sittler

Dave Keon

DATE	DESCRIPTION	QUANTITY SOLD	ISSUE PRICE	FINISH	SP-68	SP-6
2005	Johnny Bower	N/A	N.I.I.	Specimen	25.	—
2005	Tim Horton	N/A	N.I.I.	Specimen	25.	—
2005	Darryl Sittler	N/A	N.I.I.	Specimen	25.	—
2005	Dave Keon	N/A	N.I.I.	Specimen	25.	—
2005	Set of 4 coins (Toronto)	N/A	99.95	Specimen	90.	*

Note: The Royal Canadian Mint Report of 2005 lists the quantity sold as 11,765 total sets.

CANADIAN NHL HOCKEY SERIES (cont.).

=TY CENTS, 2008-2009 NHL SEASON, 2009 (GIFTWARE).
  The fifty-cent issues for the 2008-2009 Hockey Season were embedded in an official NHL puck and then blister packed. Each coin has a lenticular
■al images) reverse which by rotating the coin transfers from the old to the new team logo.

■09   HOCKEY PUCKS

Common Obverse

Designers and Engravers:
Obv.:	Susanna Blunt, Susan Taylor
Rev.:	Logos of the NHL
Composition:	Nickel plated steel, Lenticular
Weight:	6.9 g
Diameter:	35.0 mm
Thickness:	2.0 mm
Edge:	Plain
Die Axis:	↑↑
Finish:	Specimen
Case of Issue:	Blister packaged

Calgary Flames

Edmonton Oilers

Montreal Canadiens

Ottawa Senators

Toronto Maple Leafs

Vancouver Canucks

DATE	DESCRIPTION	QUANTITY SOLD	ISSUE PRICE	FINISH	SP-68	SP-69
2009	Calgary Flames	270	24.95	Specimen	35.	—
2009	Edmonton Oilers	248	24.95	Specimen	35.	—
2009	Montreal Canadiens	1,266	24.95	Specimen	60.	—
2009	Ottawa Senators	310	24.95	Specimen	35.	—
2009	Toronto Maple Leafs	606	24.95	Specimen	35.	—
2009	Vancouver Canucks	318	24.95	Specimen	35.	—

CANADIAN NHL HOCKEY SERIES (cont.).

FIFTY CENTS, MONTREAL CANADIENS CENTENNIAL COIN SERIES, 1909-2009 (GIFTWARE).

The 100th anniversary of the Montreal Canadiens hockey club was commemorated in 2009 with six giftware fifty-cent coins displaying the hock jerseys worn by the Montreal players over the last 100 years. Each coin is sealed within a plastic sport card.

2009   MONTREAL CANADIENS CENTENNIAL

Common Obverse

Designers and Engravers:

Obv.:	Susanna Blunt, Susan Taylor
Rev.:	Logos of the NHL
Composition:	Nickel plated steel, Decal
Weight:	N/A
Diameter:	30.0 mm
Thickness:	N/A
Edge:	Plain
Die Axis:	↑↑
Finish:	Specimen
Case of Issue:	Collector Card

Coin No. 1	Coin No. 2	Coin No. 3
Montreal Canadiens	1945-1946	1915-1916
Home Jersey	Montreal Canadiens	Le Club de
	Road Jersey	Hockey Canadiens

Coin No. 4	Coin No 5	Coin No 6
1912-1913	1910-1911	1909-1910
"CAC"	Club Athletique	Club de Hockey
	Canadien	le Canadien

DATE	DESCRIPTION	QUANTITY SOLD	ISSUE PRICE	FINISH	SP-68	SP-6
2009 (1909-)	Montreal Canadiens Home Jersey	N/A	9.99	Specimen	15.	—.
2009 (1909-)	Montreal Canadiens Road Jersey	N/A	9.99	Specimen	15.	—.
2009 (1909-)	Le Club de Hockey Canadiens	N/A	9.99	Specimen	15.	—
2009 (1909-)	"CAC"	25,016	9.99	Specimen	15.	—
2009 (1909-)	Club Athletique Canadien	25,004	9.99	Specimen	15.	—
2009 (1909-)	Club de Hockey le Canadien	25,004	9.99	Specimen	15.	—.
2009 (1909-)	Complete Set, 6 coins and an album	496	59.95	Specimen	80.	*

Note: 1. Single Collector Cards were issued by Jean Coutu, while the Royal Canadian Mint issued only complete sets.
2. Quantity sold figures are incomplete due to year-end overruns.

CANADIAN NHL HOCKEY SERIES (cont.).

TY CENTS, 2009-2010 NHL SEASON, 2009-2010 (GIFTWARE).

Common Obverse

Designers and Engravers:
Obv.: Susanna Blunt, Susan Taylor
Rev.: RCM Staff
Composition: Nickel plated steel, Decal
Weight: 12.9 g
Diameter: 35.0 mm
Thickness: 2.0 mm
Edge: Plain
Die Axis: ↑↑
Finish: Specimen
Case of Issue: Tent Card

Calgary Flames

Edmonton Oilers

Montreal Canadiens

Ottawa Senators

Toronto Maple Leafs

Vancouver Canucks

DATE	DESCRIPTION	QUANTITY SOLD	ISSUE PRICE	FINISH	SP-68	SP-69
2009-2010	Calgary Flames	3,518	14.95	Specimen	18.	—
2009-2010	Edmonton Oilers	3,562	14.95	Specimen	18.	—
2009-2010	Montreal Canadiens	9,865	14.95	Specimen	18.	—
2009-2010	Ottawa Senators	3,293	14.95	Specimen	18.	—
2009-2010	Toronto Maple Leafs	5,981	14.95	Specimen	18.	—
2009-2010	Vancouver Canucks	3,563	14.95	Specimen	18.	—

HOLIDAY LENTICULAR SERIES

FIFTY CENTS, HOLIDAY LENTICULAR SERIES, 2007-2016 (GIFTWARE).

Designers and Engravers:

Obv.:	Susanna Blunt, Susan Taylor	
Rev.:	See reverse illustrations	

Composition:
	2007-2009:	Brass plated steel
	2010-2011:	Copper plated steel
	2012-2015:	Cupronickel
	2016:	Nickel-plated steel

Weight: 12.61 to 13.8 g
Diameter: 35.0 mm   **Edge:** Plain
Thickness: 2.0 mm   **Die Axis:** ↑↑
Finish: Specimen, Lenticular
Case of Issue:
  2007-2008, 2010-2014: Maroon leatherette clam style case black flocked insert, encapsulated coin, COA
  2009: Black leatherette clam style case, black flocked insert, encapsulated coin, COA

Obverse with RCM Logo
2007-2008

Obverse without RCM Logo
2009-2011

Obverse without RCM Logo
2012-2016

2007
Holiday Ornaments
Des.: C. Bursey-Sabourin

2008
Holiday Snowman
Des.: C. Bursey-Sabourin

2009
Holiday Toy Train
Des.: C. Bursey-Sabourin

2010 - Santa Claus and the
Red-nosed Reindeer
Des.: C. Bursey-Sabourin

2011
Gifts From Santa
Des.: C. Bursey-Sabourin

2012
Santa's Magical Visit
Des.: Tony Bianco

2013
Snowman
Des.: Tony Bianco

2014
Christmas Tree
Des.: Steve Hepburn

2015
Holiday Toy Box
Des.: Joel Kimmel

2016
Snow Angels
Des.: Joel Kimmel

TY CENTS, HOLIDAY LENTICULAR SERIES, 2007-2015 (GIFTWARE) PRICING TABLE:

DATE	DESCRIPTION	QUANTITY SOLD	ISSUE PRICE	FINISH	SP-68	SP-69
2007	Holiday Ornaments	16,989	25.95	Specimen	40.	—
2008	Holiday Snowman	21,679	25.95	Specimen	40.	—
2009	Holiday Toy Train	19,103	25.95	Specimen	40.	—
2010	Santa Claus and the Red-Nosed Reindeer	21,394	26.95	Specimen	30.	—
2011	Gifts from Santa	21,837	26.95	Specimen	30.	—
2012	Santa's Magical Visit	22,304	29.95	Specimen	30.	—
2013	Snowman	19,939	29.95	Specimen	30.	—
2014	Christmas Tree	19,945	29.95	Specimen	30.	—
2015	Holiday Tox Box	19,736	29.95	Specimen	30.	—
2016	Snow Angels	12,853	31.95	Specimen	32.	—

TRIANGULAR COIN SERIES

TY CENTS (triangular), MILK DELIVERY, 2008.

From the late 19th century to the middle of the 20th century milk and other dairy products were delivered to the home by a milkman who was paid a token previously purchased.

Designers and Engravers:
Obv.: Susanna Blunt, Susan Taylor
Rev.: RCM Staff, Christie Paquet
Composition: 92.5% Ag, 7.5% Cu, Enamel effect on reverse
Silver content: 18.50 g, 0.595 tr oz
Weight: 20.0 g   **Edge:** Interrupted serrations
Size: 36.0 x 34.1 mm   **Die Axis:** ↑↑
Thickness: 2.7 mm   **Finish:** Proof
Case of Issue: Maroon leatherette clam style case, black flocked insert, encapsulated coin, COA

TY CENTS (triangular), SIX STRING NATION GUITAR, 2009.

owi Taylor brought together the rich Canadian Heritage of materials to produce the Six String Nation Guitar. The guitar made its debut on Parliament during the 2006 Canada Day celebrations.

Designers and Engravers:
Obv.: Susanna Blunt, Susan Taylor
Rev.: RCM Staff, Christie Paquet
Composition: 75% Cu, 25% Ni, Selective hologram on reverse
Weight: 19.1 g   **Edge:** Interrupted serrations
Size: 36.0 x 34.1 mm   **Die Axis:** ↑↑
Thickness: 2.70 mm   **Finish:** Specimen
Case of Issue: Folder

DATE	DESCRIPTION	QUANTITY SOLD	ISSUE PRICE	FINISH	SP-68	SP-69	PR-69	PR-70
2008	Milk Delivery	24,448	49.95	Proof	—	—	30.	—
2009	Six String Nation Guitar	13,602	34.95	Specimen	35.	—	—	—

SPECIAL NOTE ON FINISHES

is very important to understand the different finishes the Royal Canadian Mint uses on their various issues. These finishes are altered from time-
ne as the Mint develops new products.

or example, the brilliant relief against a parallel lined background finish first used on bullion coins was carried forward in 1996 to be used on the
s contained in the specimen set.

2006 this finish was used on giftware coins such as the twenty-five cent coin issued to celebrate the 80th birthday of Queen Elizabeth II.

2010 a new specimen finish, brilliant relief against a laser-lined background, was used for the coins contained in the specimen set. There are now
ifferent specimen finishes being utilised on Canadian coinage.

rculation and Brilliant Uncirculated (proof-like) finishes are another very confusing mixture of finishes, see page xii for a further explanation.

VANCOUVER 2010 OLYMPIC AND PARALYMPIC WINTER GAMES

FIFTY CENTS, MASCOT COLLECTOR CARDS, 2010 (GIFTWARE).

Three mascots were adopted for the Vancouver 2010 Winter Games, Miga and Quatchi for the Olympic Games and Sumi for the Paralympic Games.

These crown-size fifty-cent coins are embedded in plastic within a collector card format. As with all embedded Royal Canadian Mint giftware, coins are very difficult to remove from their packaging without damaging the image on the coin.

Designers:		**Engravers:**	
Obv.:	Susanna Blunt	Obv.:	Susan Taylor
Rev.:	RCM Staff	Rev.:	RCM Staff
Composition:	Nickel plated steel, Decal	**Thickness:**	2.0 mm
Weight:	12.61 g	**Edge:**	Plain
Diameter:	35.0 mm	**Die Axis:**	↑↑
Finish:	Specimen		
Case of Issue:	Twelve collector cards were issued with the mascots in different sport poses. These coins are embedded in plastic.		

Comm(
Obvers

Coin No. 1
Miga Ice Hockey

Coin No. 2
Quatchi Ice Hockey

Coin No. 3
Sumi Paralympic
Ice Sledge Hockey

Coin No. 4
Quatchi and Miga
Figure Skating

Coin No. 5
Quatchi and Miga
Bobsleigh

Coin No. 6
Miga Ariels

Coin No. 7
Miga Skeleton

Coin No. 8
Quatchi Snowboard Cros

Coin No. 9
Miga Alpine Skiing

Coin No. 10
Sumi Paralympic
Alpine Skiing

Coin No.11
Quatchi Parallel
Giant Slalom

Coin No. 12
Miga Speed Skating

VANCOUVER 2010 OLYMPIC AND PARALYMPIC WINTER GAMES (cont.).

TY CENTS, MASCOT COLLECTOR CARDS, 2010 (GIFTWARE) PRICING TABLE.

DATE	CARD No.	DESCRIPTION	QUANTITY SOLD	ISSUE PRICE	FINISH	SP-68	SP-69
2010	1	Miga Ice Hockey	3,096	9.95	Specimen	15.	—
2010	2	Quatchi Ice Hockey	3,010	9.95	Specimen	15.	—
2010	3	Sumi Paralympic Ice Sledge Hockey	2,137	9.95	Specimen	15.	—
2010	4	Quatchi and Miga Figure Skating	2,981	9.95	Specimen	15.	—
2010	5	Quatchi and Miga Bobsleigh	2,119	9.95	Specimen	15.	—
2010	6	Miga Ariels	2,114	9.95	Specimen	15.	—
2010	7	Miga Skeleton	1,672	9.95	Specimen	15.	—
2010	8	Quatchi Snowboard Cross	2,090	9.95	Specimen	15.	—
2010	9	Miga Alpine Skiing	2,309	9.95	Specimen	15.	—
2010	10	Sumi Paralympic Alpine Skiing	1,902	9.95	Specimen	15.	—
2010	11	Quatchi Parallel Giant Slalom	1,730	9.95	Specimen	15.	—
2010	12	Miga Speed Skating	1,825	9.95	Specimen	15.	—
—	—	Collector Card Album	—	12.95	—	15.	*

TY CENTS, MASCOT HOCKEY PUCKS, 2010.

he Miga, Quatchi, and Sumi ice hockey coins were also issued embedded in NHL official hockey pucks.

Miga Ice Hockey

Quatchi Ice Hockey

Sumi Ice Hockey

gners:	Engravers:
Obv.: Susanna Blunt	Obv.: Susan Taylor
Rev.: RCM Staff	Rev.: RCM Staff
position: Nickel plated steel, Decal	Thickness: 2.0 mm
ht: 12.61 g	Edge: Plain
eter: 35.0 mm	Die Axis: ↑↑
h: Specimen	Case of Issue: Blister packaged

DATE	CARD No.	DESCRIPTION	QUANTITY SOLD	ISSUE PRICE	FINISH	SP-68	SP-69
010	1	Miga Ice Hockey	2,179	25.95	Specimen	20.	—
010	2	Quatchi Ice Hockey	2,524	25.95	Specimen	20.	—
010	3	Sumi Paralympic Ice Sledge Hockey	1,570	25.95	Specimen	20.	—

FIFTY CENTS, VANCOUVER 2010 OLYMPIC AND PARALYMPIC WINTER GAMES, 2010 (GIFTWARE).

This fifty-cent lenticular coin with images of the Vancouver skyline, and Inukshuk is found in the Vancouver 2010 Gold Collector's Set. It was iss in conjunction with Canada Post (see page 538).

Designers and Engravers:

Obv.:	Susanna Blunt, Susan Taylor
Rev.:	RCM Staff
Composition:	Nickel plated steel, Lenticular
Weight:	13.0 g
Diameter:	35.0 mm
Thickness:	2.0 mm
Edge:	Plain
Die Axis:	↑↑
Finish:	Specimen
Case of Issue:	See Collector Sets, page 538

DATE	DESCRIPTION	QUANTITY SOLD	ISSUE PRICE	FINISH	SP-68	SP-
2010	Lenticular Images of Vancouver and Inukshuk	11,384	N.I.I.	Specimen	40.	—

DINOSAUR EXHIBIT SET

FIFTY CENTS, DINOSAUR EXHIBIT LENTICULAR SET, 2010 (GIFTWARE).

The Royal Canadian Mint in conjunction with various Canadian Museums created this new set of lenticular coins featuring prehistoric dinos found in Canada.

Common Obverse	Daspletosaurus Torosus	Albertosaurus	Sinosauropteryx

Designers:

		Engravers:	
Obv.:	Susanna Blunt	Obv.:	Susan Taylor
Rev.:	RCM Staff	Rev.:	RCM Staff
Composition:	Brass-plated steel, Lenticular	**Thickness:**	2.0 mm
Weight:	12.9 g	**Edge:**	Plain
Diameter:	35.0 mm	**Die Axis:**	↑↑
Finish:	Specimen		
Case of Issue:	Folded panel containing six collector trading cards		

DATE	DESCRIPTION	QUANTITY SOLD	ISSUE PRICE	FINISH	SP-68	SP
2010	Daspletosaurus Torosus	11,652	24.95	Specimen	25.	—
2010	Albertosaurus	14,325	24.95	Specimen	25.	—
2010	Sinosauropteryx	19,865	24.95	Specimen	25.	—

FTY CENTS, 100TH ANNIVERSARY OF THE STRIKING OF CANADA'S 1911 SILVER DOLLAR, 1911-2011.

This fifty-cent coin which carries the double date 1911-2011 is from the Special Edition Proof Set issued in 2011 to commemorate the 100th iversary of the striking of Canada's 1911 silver dollar.

Designers and Engravers:

Obv.:	Sir E. B. MacKennal
Rev.:	Original design by L. C. Wyon, Modified by W. H. J. Blakemore

Composition: 92.5% Ag, 7.5% Cu
Silver content: 10.76 g, 0.345 tr oz

Weight:	11.629 g	**Edge:**	Reeded
Diameter:	29.7 mm	**Die Axis:**	↑↑
Thickness:	2.0 mm	**Finish:**	Proof

Case of Issue: See Special Issue Proof Sets, page 551

DATE	DESCRIPTION	QUANTITY SOLD	ISSUE PRICE	FINISH	PR-69	PR-70
2011 (1911-)	100th Anniv. Canada's 1911 Silver Dollar	5,952	N.I.I.	Proof	30.	—

FTY CENTS, WINNIPEG JETS, 2011-2012.

Designers and Engravers:

Obv.:	Susanna Blunt, Susan Taylor
Rev.:	William Woodruff, RCM Staff

Composition: Nickel plated steel

Weight:	7.0 g	**Edge:**	Reeded
Diameter:	27.1 mm	**Die Axis:**	↑↑
Thickness:	1.9 mm	**Finish:**	Uncirculated

Case of Issue: Colourised folder

DATE	DESCRIPTION	QUANTITY SOLD	ISSUE PRICE	FINISH	MS-65 NC
2011-2012	Winnipeg Jets	23,712	14.95	Circulation	10.

FTY CENTS, ROYAL CYPHER, THE QUEEN'S DIAMOND JUBILEE, 1952-2012 (GIFTWARE).

his coin which carries the double date 1952 2012 celebrates the Queen's Diamond Jubilee. The design is a reproduction of the Diamond Jubilee blem for Canada by the Royal Canadian Mint. The reverse design is a garland of maple leaves with the Queen's monogram and St. Edward's vn at the centre.

Designers and Engravers:

Obv.:	Susanna Blunt, Susan Taylor
Rev.:	Christie Paquet

Composition:	Silver-plated copper, Decal
Weight:	32.82 g
Diameter:	42.0 mm
Thickness:	3.0 mm
Edge:	Reeded
Die Axis:	↑↑
Finish:	Specimen
Case of Issue:	Colourised folder

DATE	DESCRIPTION	QUANTITY SOLD	ISSUE PRICE	FINISH	SP-68	SP-69
2012 (1952-)	Royal Cypher Queen's Diamond Jubilee	30,900	29.95	Specimen	20.	—

FIFTY CENTS, *RMS TITANIC*, 2012 (GIFTWARE).

This fifty-cent coin was issued to remember those who perished when *RMS Titanic* sank on April 15th, 1912.

Designers and Engravers:

Obv.:	Susanna Blunt, Susan Taylor
Rev.:	Yves Bérubé, Konrad Wachelko
Composition:	Silver-plated copper, Coloured
Weight:	32.82 g
Diameter:	42.0 mm
Thickness:	3.0 mm
Edge:	Reeded
Die Axis:	↑↑
Finish:	Proof
Case of Issue:	Maroon leatherette clam style case, black flocked insert, encapsulated coin,COA

DATE	DESCRIPTION	QUANTITY SOLD	ISSUE PRICE	FINISH	PR-69	PR
2012	*RMS Titanic*	14,997	34.95	Proof	70.	—

FIFTY CENTS, 75TH ANNIVERSARY OF SUPERMAN™: THEN AND NOW, COIN AND STAMP SET, 2013 (GIFTWARE).

This fifty-cent coin was issued to commemorate the 75th anniversary of Superman™.

Designers and Engravers:

Obv.:	Susanna Blunt, Susan Taylor
Rev.:	DC Comic/Warner Brothers, Nick Martin
Composition:	Cupronickel, Lenticular
Weight:	13.7 g
Diameter:	35.0 mm
Thickness:	2.0 mm
Edge:	Plain
Die Axis:	↑↑
Finish:	Specimen
Case of Issue:	See Derivatives page 90

DATE	DESCRIPTION	QUANTITY SOLD	ISSUE PRICE	FINISH	SP-68	SP
2013	Superman™: Then and Now	24,967	N.I.I.	Specimen	45.	—

FIFTY CENTS, BUTTERFLIES OF CANADA SERIES, CANADIAN TIGER SWALLOWTAIL, 2013 (GIFTWARE).

Featuring the Swallowtail as it rests on a dandelion, this fifty-cent coin is the first in the new Butterflies of Canada Series.

Designers and Engravers:

Obv.:	Susanna Blunt, Susan Taylor
Rev.:	Celia Godkin, Samantha Strath
Composition:	Silver-plated copper, Painted
Weight:	33.2 g
Diameter:	42.0 mm
Thickness:	3.2 mm
Edge:	Reeded
Die Axis:	↑↑
Finish:	Proof
Case of Issue:	Maroon leatherette clam style case, black flocked insert, encapsulated coin, COA

DATE	DESCRIPTION	QUANTITY SOLD	ISSUE PRICE	FINISH	PR-69	PR
2013	Canadian Tiger Swallowtail	11,851	34.95	Proof	25.	—

TY CENTS, LOST SHIPS IN CANADIAN WATERS: *RMS EMPRESS OF IRELAND*, 1914-2014 (GIFTWARE).
This coin commemorates the worst diaster in Canada's maritime history, the loss of the ill-fated *RMS Empress of Ireland*.

Designers and Engravers:

Obv.:	Susanna Blunt, Susan Taylor
Rev.:	Yves Bérubé, RCM Staff
Composition:	Silver plated copper, Decal
Weight:	32.82 g
Diameter:	42.0 mm
Thickness:	N/A
Edge:	Reeded
Die Axis:	↑↑
Finish:	Matte Proof
Case of Issue:	Maroon leatherette clam style case, black flocked insert, encapsulated coin, COA,

DATE	DESCRIPTION	QUANTITY SOLD	ISSUE PRICE	FINISH	PR-69	PR-70
2014 (1914-)	*RMS Empress of Ireland*	15,000	34.95	Matte Proof	35.	—

TY CENTS, 100 BLESSINGS OF GOOD FORTUNE, 2014 (GIFTWARE).

Designers and Engravers:

Obv.:	Susanna Blunt, Susan Taylor
Rev.:	Three Degrees Creative Group, RCM Staff
Composition:	Silver-plated copper
Weight:	32.5 g
Diameter:	42.0 mm
Thickness:	3.0 mm
Edge:	Reeded
Die Axis:	↑↑
Finish:	Proof, Coloured
Case of Issue:	Silver satin-like clam style case, black flocked insert, encapsulated coin, COA, red sleeve

DATE	DESCRIPTION	QUANTITY SOLD	ISSUE PRICE	FINISH	PR-69	PR-70
2014	100 Blessings of Good Fortune	5,900	34.95	Proof	25.	—

TY CENTS, TORONTO 2015™ PAN AM/PARAPAN AM GAMES: CELEBRATING EXCELLENCE, 2015.
Detailed engraving provides a showcase for the breathtaking combination of artistry and storytelling, resulting in a truly stunning numismatic version
e gold medals awarded at the TORONTO 2015 Pan Am/Parapan Am Games.

Designers and Engravers:

Obv.:	Susanna Blunt, Susan Taylor
Rev.:	Christi Belcourt
Composition:	Gold plated copper
Weight:	32.5 g
Diameter:	42.0 mm
Thickness:	N/A
Edge:	Reeded
Die Axis:	↑↑
Finish:	Proof
Case of Issue:	Maroon clamshell with custom beauty box.

DATE	DESCRIPTION	QUANTITY SOLD	ISSUE PRICE	FINISH	PR-69	PR-70
2015	Celebrating Excellence	4,556	44.95.	Proof	45.	—

BIG COIN SERIES

FIFTY CENTS, BIG COIN SET, 2015-2018.
The Big Coin Series started in 2015 features Thomas Shingles' Coat of Arms design first used in 1959 on the 2015, 2016 and 2018 issues, v the Howling Wolf design from the Centennial issue of 1967, designed by Alex Colville. For other coins in this set, see (pages 11, 17, 57, 130, 139)

Designers and Engravers:

Obv.:	Susanna Blunt, Susan Taylor
Rev.:	Thomas Shingles (2015, 2016, 2018)
	Alex Colville (2017)

Composition:

2015	99.99% Ag, Selectively gold plated
2016	99.99% Ag, Selectively coloured on reverse
2017	99.99% Ag, Selectively gold plated
2018	99.9% Ag, Selevely rose gold-plated

Silver content: 157.58 g, 5.06 tr oz
Weight: 157.6 g
Diameter: 65.25 mm
Thickness: N/A
Case of Issue: Maroon clam style case, black flocked insert, encapsulated coin, COA, custom box

Edge: Reeded
Die Axis: ↑↑
Finish: Proof

DATE	DESCRIPTION	QUANTITY SOLD	ISSUE PRICE	FINISH	PR-69	PR-
2015	50¢ Big Coin	1,499	549.95	Proof	600.	—
2016	50¢ Big Coin	1,497	519.95	Proof	520.	—
2017	50¢ Big Coin	2,150	559.95	Proof	560.	—
2018	50¢ Big Coin	1,500	559.95	Proof	560.	—

Note: Coins illustrated smaller than actual size.

~TY CENTS, 100TH ANNIVERSARY OF THE 1917 HALF-DOLLAR, 2017.

A collectible retrospective: This meticulously engraved coin revisits the reverse design that graced Canada's 50-cent coin until 1936.

Designers and Engravers:
Obv.:	Susanna Blunt, Susan Taylor
Rev.:	RCM Staff

Composition: 99.99% Ag, Selectively gold plated
Weight: 62.29 g
Diameter: 50.0 mm
Thickness: N/A
Edge: Reeded
Die Axis: ↑↑
Finish: Proof
Case of Issue: Wood case with graphic beauty box..

DATE	DESCRIPTION	MINTAGE	ISSUE PRICE	FINISH	PR-69	PR-70
2017	100th Anniversary of the 1917 Half-Dollar	4,000	194.95	Proof	240.	—.

~te: Coin illustrated smaller than actual size. This exclusive coin was only available to members of the Masters Club.

~TY CENTS, 75TH ANNIVERSARY OF THE 1943 HALF-DOLLAR, 2018.

This exclusive coin looks back at the half-dollar issued in 1943, which is re-created here in pure silver with a celebratory touch of gold plating.

Designers and Engravers:
Obv.:	Susanna Blunt, Susan Taylor
Rev.:	RCM Staff

Composition: 99.99% Ag, Selectively gold plated
Weight: 62.29 g
Diameter: 50.0 mm
Thickness: N/A
Edge: Reeded
Die Axis: ↑↑
Finish: Proof
Case of Issue: Wood case with graphic beauty box. COA.

DATE	DESCRIPTION	MINTAGE	ISSUE PRICE	FINISH	PR-69	PR-70
2018	75th Anniversary of the 1943 Half-Dollar	4,000	194.95	Proof	195.	—

~e: Coin illustrated smaller than actual size. This exclusive coin was only available to members of the Masters Club.

FIFTY CENT DERIVATIVES

DATE	DESCRIPTION	QUANTITY SOLD	ISSUE PRICE	ISSUER	FINISH	MARKET PRICE
1999	**MILLENNIUM SET OF 12 CARDS** each containing a 1999	N/A	N/A	RCM	MS-65	40
2001	**CANADA PROVINCIAL CREST** Credit Card Type	N/A	N/A	RCM	MS-65	8
2003	**CORONATION COIN AND STAMP SET** Two one cent coins, 1953 and 2003; Two fifty cent coins, 2002 Jubilee, 2003 Uncrowned Portrait; Two mint and two cancelled stamps of Her Majesty's Jubilee and Coronation; Presentation case	14,743	N/A	RCM	MS-65	30
2006	**ROYAL CANADIAN MINT ANNUAL REPORT** Fifty cent coin, Selectively gold plated	4,162	25.95	RCM	PR-69	35
2008	**100TH ANNIVERSARY COIN AND STAMP SET** Fifty cent coin, double-dated 1908-2008, fifty-two cent postage stamp, wooden presentation case, booklet	16,000	44.95	RCM/CP	PR-69	45
2008	**ROYAL CANADIAN MINT CENTENNIAL BOOK** Fifty cent coin, double-dated 1908-2008, postage stamp, 200-page book					
	English	136	99.95	RCM	PR-69	75
	French	46	99.95	RCM	PR-69	75
2010	**DASPLETOSAURUS TOROSUS** Fifty cent coin, six trading cards, folder	N/A	24.95	RCM	MS-65	35
2010	**ALBERTOSAURUS** Fifty cent coin, six trading cards, folder	N/A	24.95	RCM	MS-65	35
2010	**SINOSAUROPTERYX** Fifty cent coin, six trading cards, folder	N/A	24.95	RCM	MS-65	35
2012	**TITANIC 100**, Fifty cent coin, twenty-five cent coin, White Star stock certificate, a re-created Titanic cancel, sheet of stamps, three Titanic postcards, leather-bound embossed album	10,000	140.95	RCM/CP	MS-65	130
2012	**PHILATELIC NUMISMATIC COVER** Royal Cypher fifty cent coin, two dollar Diamond Jubilee stamp	10,000	25.95	RCM/CP	MS-65	25
2013	**75TH ANNIVERSARY OF SUPERMAN™: THEN AND NOW COIN AND STAMP SET**, Fifty cent coin, collectable stamp	25,038	29.75	RCM/CP	SP-68	50
2014	**BLESSING COIN AND STAMP COLLECTABLES** Fifty cent coin 100 Blessings of Good Fortune; Chinese stamp 120 fen, "Blossom of Fortune" (issue date Oct. 9, 2008).	N/A	38.88	RCM/CP	PR-69	30
2014	**RMS EMPRESS OF IRELAND COLLECTOR SET** Fifty-cent coin, two reproduction Empress postcards, domestic stamp, souvenir sheet international stamps, two first day covers, booklet.	15,000	99.95	RCM/CP	PR-69	100

ONE DOLLAR ISSUES

SILVER DOLLAR ISSUES, 1971-1989

Designers:		**Engravers:**	
Obv.:	See obverse illustrations	Obv.:	See obverse illustrations
Rev.:	See reverse illustrations	Rev.:	See reverse illustrations
Composition:	50% Ag, 50% Cu		
Silver content:	11.65 g, 0.375 tr oz		
Weight:	23.3 g	**Edge:**	Reeded
Diameter:	36.07 mm	**Die Axis:**	↑↑
Thickness:	2.95 mm	**Finish:**	Specimen

Case of Issue:

(A) Black leatherette clam style case, Coat of Arms, maroon and black insert
(B) Black leatherette clam case, Coat of Arms, white and black insert
(C) Blue leatherette clam style case, gilt RCMP crest, maroon and black insert
(D) Black leatherette clam style case, Coat of Arms, maroon and black plastic insert, encapsulated coin
(E) Blue leatherette clam style case, Coat of Arms, light blue insert with purple satin cloth printed "Library of Parliament - Bibliothèque Du Parlément 1876-1976
(F) Maroon leatherette case, Coat of Arms, maroon and black plastic insert, encapsulated coin
(G) Maroon velveteen case, Coat of Arms, maroon velveteen insert, encapsulated coin
(H) Black leatherette square case, Coat of Arms, maroon and black plastic insert, encapsulated coin, COA
(I) Black leatherette square case, maroon insert, encapsulated coin, COA
(J) Clear plastic outer case, black plastic insert, silver sleeve, encapsulated coin

OBVERSES 1971-1989

1971-1976, 1979-1984, 1986-1989	**1977**	**1978**	**1985**
Designer: A. Machin	**Designer: A. Machin**	**Designer: A. Machin**	**Designer: A. Machin**
Engraver: P. Brindley	**Engraver: RCM Staff**	**Engraver: RCM Staff**	**Engraver: P. Brindley**

REVERSES 1971-1989

1971	**1972**	**1973**
British Columbia Centennial	**Voyageur Design**	**R.C.M.P.**
Designer and Engraver:	**Designer: E. Hahn**	**Designer: P. Cedarberg**
P. Brindley	**Engraver: T. Smith**	**Engraver: P. Brindley**

1974
Winnipeg Centennial
Designer: P. Pederson
Engraver: P. Brindley

1975
Calgary Centennial
Designer: D. D. Paterson
Engraver: P. Brindley

1976
Library of Parliament
Designer and Engraver:
Walter Ott

1977
Silver Jubilee Elizabeth II
Designer: R. Lee
Engraver: A. Aarand

1978
11th Commonwealth Games
Designer: R. Taylor
Engraver: V. Coté

1979
Griffon Tricentennial
Designer: W. Schluep
Engraver: T. Smith

1980
Arctic Territories Centennial
Designer: D. D. Paterson
Engraver: W. Ott

1981
Trans-Canada Railway
Designer: C. Gorey
Engraver: W. Ott

1982
Regina Centennial
Designer: H. Brown
Engraver: W. Ott

1983
World University Games
Designer: C. Tietz
Engraver: W. Ott

1984
Toronto Sesquicentennial
Designer: D. J. Craig
Engraver: W. Ott

1985
National Parks Centennial
Designer: K. Rohlicek
Engraver: W. Ott

1986
Vancouver Centennial
Designer: E. J. Morrison
Engraver: V. Coté, W. Ott

1987
John Davis
Designer: C. Gorey
Engraver: V. Coté

1988
Saint-Maurice Ironworks
Designer: R. R. Carmichael
Engraver: S. Beveridge

1989
Mackenzie River Bicentenn
Designer: J. Mardon
Engraver: S. Beveridge

...VER DOLLAR SPECIMEN ISSUES, 1971-1980 PRICING TABLE.

...se of Issue:

(A)	Black leatherette clam style case, Coat of Arms, maroon and black insert
(B)	Black leatherette clam case, Coat of Arms, white and black insert
(C)	Blue leatherette clam style case, gilt RCMP crest, maroon and black insert
(D)	Black leatherette clam style case, Coat of Arms, maroon and black plastic insert, encapsulated coin
(E)	Blue leatherette clam style case, Coat of Arms, light blue insert with purple satin cloth printed "Library of Parliament - Bibliothèque Du Parlément 1876-1976
(F)	Maroon leatherette case, Coat of Arms, maroon and black plastic insert, encapsulated coin
(G)	Maroon velveteen case, Coat of Arms, maroon velveteen insert, encapsulated coin
(H)	Black leatherette square case, Coat of Arms, maroon and black plastic insert, encapsulated coin, COA
(I)	Black leatherette square case, maroon insert, encapsulated coin, COA
(J)	Clear plastic outer case, black plastic insert, silver sleeve, encapsulated coin

DATE	DESCRIPTION	CASE	QUANTITY SOLD	ISSUE PRICE	FINISH	SP-68	SP-69
1971 (1871-)	British Columbia Centennial	A	585,217	3.00	Specimen	15.	—
1971 (1871-)	British Columbia Centennial	B	Included	3.00	Specimen	20.	—
1972	Voyageur Design	A	341,581	3.00	Specimen	15.	—
1973 (1873-)	R.C.M.P.	A	904,723	3.00	Specimen	15.	—
1973 (1873-)	R.C.M.P.	C	Included	3.00	Specimen	25.	—
1974 (1874-)	Winnipeg Centennial	D	628,183	3.50	Specimen	15.	—
1975 (1875-)	Calgary Centennial, ↑↑ Medal Axis	D	833,095	3.50	Specimen	15.	—
1975 (1875-)	Calgary Centennial, ↑↓ Coinage Axis	D	Included	3.50	Specimen	Only one known	
1976 (1876-)	Library of Parliament	D	433,722	4.00	Specimen	15.	—
1976 (1876-)	Library of Parliament	E	Included	4.00	Specimen	25.	—
1977 (1952-)	Silver Jubilee Queen Elizabeth II	D	744,848	4.25	Specimen	15.	—
1977 (1952-)	Silver Jubilee Queen Elizabeth II	F	Included	—	Specimen	30.	—
1977 (1952-)	Silver Jubilee Queen Elizabeth II	G	Included	—	Specimen	30.	—
1978	Commonwealth Games, Edmonton	H	640,000	4.50	Specimen	15.	—
1979 (1679-)	Griffon Tricentennial	H	688,671	5.50	Specimen	15.	—
1980	Arctic Territories Centennial	H	389,564	22.00	Specimen	15.	—

...VER DOLLAR PROOF AND BRILLIANT UNCIRCULATED ISSUES, 1981-1989 PRICING TABLE.

...se of Issue: Proof: Black leatherette square case, maroon insert, encapsulated coin, COA
BU: Clear plastic outer case, black plastic insert, silver sleeve, encapsulated coin

DATE	DESCRIPTION	QUANTITY SOLD	ISSUE PRICE	FINISH	SP-68	SP-69	PR-68	PR-69
1981	Trans-Canada Railway Centennial	353,742	18.00	Proof	—	—	15.	—
1981	Trans-Canada Railway Centennial	148,647	14.00	BU	14.	—	—	—
1982 (1882-)	Regina Centennial	577,959	15.25	Proof	—	—	15.	—
1982 (1882-)	Regina Centennial	144,989	10.95	BU	14.	—	—	—
1983	World University Games	340,068	16.15	Proof	—	—	15.	—
1983	World University Games	159,450	10.95	BU	14.	—	—	—
1984 (1834-)	Toronto Sesquicentennial	571,563	17.50	Proof	—	—	15.	—
1984 (1834-)	Toronto Sesquicentennial	133,563	11.40	BU	14.	—	—	—
1985 (1885-)	National Parks Centennial	537,297	17.50	Proof	—	—	15.	—
1985 (1885-)	National Parks Centennial	162,873	12.00	BU	14.	—.	—	—
1986 (1886-)	Vancouver Centennial	496,418	18.00	Proof	—	—	15.	—
1986 (1886-)	Vancouver Centennial	124,574	12.25	BU	14.	—	—	—
1987 (1587-)	John Davis	405,688	19.00	Proof	—	—	15.	—
1987 (1587-)	John Davis	118,722	14.00	BU	14.	—	—	—
1988	Saint-Maurice Ironworks	259,230	20.00	Proof	—	—	16.	—
1988	Saint-Maurice Ironworks	106,702	15.00	BU	14.	—	—	—
1989	Mackenzie River Bicentennial	272,319	21.75	Proof	—	—	20.	—
1989	Mackenzie River Bicentennial	110,650	16.25	BU	14.	—	—	—

SILVER DOLLAR ISSUES, 1990-1991

1990-1991	1990	1991
Common Obverse	Henry Kelsey Tricentennial	175th Anniv. of the Frontenac
	Engraver: Ago Aarand	Engraver: Sheldon Beveridge

Designers:
Obv.:   Dora de Pédery-Hunt
Rev.:   D. J. Craig
Composition: 50% Ag, 50% Cu
Silver content: 11.65 g, 0.375 tr oz
Weight: 23.3 g
Diameter: 36.07 mm
Edge: Reeded

Engravers:
Obv.:   Dora de Pédery-Hunt
Rev.:   See reverse illustrations

Thickness: 2.95 mm
Die Axis: ↑↑
Finish: Proof or Brilliant Uncirculated

Case of Issue: **Proof:**   Black leatherette square case, maroon insert, encapsulated coin, COA
BU: Clear plastic outer case, black plastic insert, silver sleeve, encapsulated coin

DATE	DESCRIPTION SOLD	QUANTITY PRICE	ISSUE	FINISH	SP-68	SP-69	PR-68	PR-69
1990 (1690-)	Henry Kelsey Tricentennial	222,983	22.95	Proof	—	—	18.	—
1990 (1690-)	Henry Kelsey Tricentennial	85,763	16.75	BU	14.	20.	—	—
1991 (1816-)	175th Anniversary of the Frontenac	222,892	22.95	Proof	—	—	18.	—
1991 (1816-)	175th Anniversary of the Frontenac	82,642	16.75	BU	14.	20.	—	—

SILVER DOLLAR ISSUES, 1992-2002

signers:		**Engravers:**
Obv.:	Dora de Pédery-Hunt	Obv.:	Dora de Pédery-Hunt
Rev.:	See reverse illustrations	Rev.:	See reverse illustrations
mposition:	92.5% Ag, 7.5% Cu	**Thickness:**	2.95 mm
ver content:	23.29 g, 0.75 tr oz	**Edge:**	Reeded
eight:	25.175 g	**Die Axis:**	↑↑
ameter:	36.07 mm	**Finish:**	Proof or Brilliant Uncirculated

se of Issue: **1992-1997: Proof:** Black leatherette square case, maroon insert, encapsulated coin, COA
BU: Clear plastic outer case, black plastic insert, silver sleeve, encapsulated coin
1998-2002: Proof: Dark green clam display case, green insert, encapsulated coin, COA
BU: Multicoloured plastic slide case, encapsulated coin
1999: Proof: Multicoloured case, black insert, encapsulated coin, COA

1992-2002
Common Obverse

1992
Kingston to York Stagecoach
Designer: K. Smith
Engraver: S. Taylor

1993
100th Anniv. Stanley Cup
Designer: S. Sherwood
Engraver: S. Beveridge

1994
R.C.M.P. Northern Dog
Team Patrol
Designer: I. Sparkes
Engraver: A. Aarand

1995
325th Anniv. of the
Hudson's Bay Company
Designer: V. McIndoe
Engraver: S. Taylor

1996
200th Anniv. John McIntosh
Designer: R. Hill
Engraver: S. Beveridge

1997
25th Anniversary 1972
Canada/Russia Hockey Series
Designer: W. Burden
Engraver: S. Witten

1997
10th Anniv. of the
One Dollar Loon
Designer: J. Grondin
Engraver: S. Beveridge

1998
125th Anniv. R.C.M.P.
Designer: A. Halvorson
Engraver: S. Beveridge

1999
225th Anniversary of the
Voyage of Juan Perez
Designer: D. Craig
Engraver: S. Witten

1999
Int'l Year of Older Persons
Des.: S. Armstrong-Hodgson
Engr.: W. Woodruff

2000
Voyage of Discovery
Designer: D. F. Warkentin
Engraver: C. Saffioti

2001	2001	2002	2002
50th Anniv. of the National Ballet of Canada	90th Anniv. of the Striking of Canada's 1911 Silver Dollar	50th Anniversary Queen Elizabeth II's Accession to the Throne	Queen Elizabeth the Queen Mother
Designer: S. McKowen	Designer: RCM Staff	Designer: RCM Staff	Designer: RCM Staff
Engraver: S. Taylor	Engraver: C. Saffioti	Engraver: S. Taylor	Engraver: S. Taylor

DATE	DESCRIPTION	QUANTITY SOLD	ISSUE PRICE	FINISH	SP-68	SP-69	PR-68	PR-69
1992	Kingston to York Stagecoach	187,612	23.95	Proof	—	—	28.	—
1992	Kingston to York Stagecoach	78,160	17.50	BU	25.	—	—	—
1993 (1893-)	100th Anniv. of the Stanley Cup	294,314	23.95	Proof	—	—	30.	—
1993 (1893-)	100th Anniv. of the Stanley Cup	88,150	17.50	BU	25.	—	—	—
1994 (1969-)	R.C.M.P. Northern Dog Team Patrol	178,485	24.50	Proof	—	—	30.	—
1994 (1969-)	R.C.M.P. Northern Dog Team Patrol	65,295	17.95	BU	25.	—	—	—
1995	325th Anniv. Hudson's Bay Co.	166,259	24.50	Proof	—	—	30.	—
1995	325th Anniv. Hudson's Bay Co.	61,819	17.95	BU	25.	—	—	—
1996 (1796-)	200th Anniv. John McIntosh	133,779	29.95	Proof	—	—	30.	—
1996 (1796-)	200th Anniv. John McIntosh	58,834	19.95	BU	25.	—	—	—
1997 (1972-)	25th Anniv. Canada/Russia Hockey Series	184,965	29.95	Proof	—	—	30.	—
1997 (1972-)	25th Anniv. Canada/Russia Hockey Series	155,252	19.95	BU	25.	—	—	—
1997 (1987-)	10th Anniv. of the One Dollar Loon	24,995	49.95	Proof	—	—	80.	—
1998 (1873-)	125th Anniv. R.C.M.P.	130,795	29.95	Proof	—	—	30.	—
1998 (1873-)	125th Anniv. R.C.M.P.	81,376	19.95	BU	25.	—	—	—
1999 (1774-)	225th Anniv. Voyage Juan Perez	126,435	29.95	Proof	—	—	30.	—
1999 (1774-)	225th Anniv. Voyage Juan Perez	67,655	19.95	BU	25.	—	—	—
1999	International Year of Older Persons	24,976	49.95	Proof	—	—	45.	—
2000	Voyage of Discovery	121,575	29.95	Proof	—	—	30.	—
2000	Voyage of Discovery	62,975	19.95	BU	25.	—	—	—
2001 (1951-)	50th Anniv. National Ballet of Canada	89,390	30.95	Proof	—	—	30.	—
2001 (1951-)	50th Anniv. National Ballet of Canada	53,668	20.95	BU	25.	—	—	—
2001 (1911-)	90th Anniv. Canada's 1911 Silver Dollar	24,996	49.95	Proof	—	—	55.	—
2002 (1952-)	50th Anniv. Elizabeth II's Accession, Silver	29,688	33.95	Proof	—	—	30.	—
2002 (1952-)	50th Anniv. Elizabeth II's Accession, GP*	65,315	N.I.I.	Proof	—	—	60.	—
2002 (1952-)	50th Anniv. Elizabeth II's Accession, Silver	65,410	24.95	BU	25.	—	—	—
2002 (1900-)	Queen Elizabeth, the Queen Mother	9,994	49.95	Proof	—	—	225.	—

Note: GP* refers to Gold Plated

NE DOLLAR, 100TH ANNIVERSARY OF THE COBALT DISCOVERY, 1903-2003.

This coin marks 100 years since Fred LaRose, a blacksmith, threw his hammer at a fox, of course missing the fox, but striking a rock revealing a eaming vein of silver. This is the first issue of a pure silver (.9999 fine) dollar by the Royal Canadian Mint.

Designers and Engravers:

Obv.:	Dora de Pédery-Hunt
Rev.:	John Mardon, William Woodruff
Composition:	99.99% Ag
Silver content:	25.172 g, 0.809 tr oz
Weight:	25.175 g
Diameter:	36.07 mm
Thickness:	3.02 mm
Finish:	Proof or Brilliant Uncirculated
Proof:	Dark green clam case, green insert, encapsulated coin, COA
BU:	Multicoloured plastic slide case, encapsulated coin

		Edge:	Reeded
		Die Axis:	↑↑

DATE	DESCRIPTION	QUANTITY SOLD	ISSUE PRICE	FINISH	SP-68	SP-69	PR-69	PR-70
2003 (1903-)	100th Anniv. Cobalt Silver Discovery	88,536	36.95	Proof	—	—	32.	—
2003 (1903-)	100th Anniv. Cobalt Silver Discovery	51,130	28.95	BU	25.	—	—	—

OLD ONE DOLLAR, 50TH ANNIVERSARY QUEEN ELIZABETH II'S ACCESSION TO THE THRONE, 2003.

This undated gold issue is based on the 2002 reverse Accession design, and the new uncrowned obverse design for 2003. This gold dollar was sold eBay, September 25th, 2003, with 100% of the proceeds being donated to charities.

Designers and Engravers:

Obv.:	Susanna Blunt, Susan Taylor
Rev.:	RCM Staff, Susan Taylor
Composition:	99.99% Au
Gold content:	25.172 g, 0.809 tr oz
Weight:	25.175 g
Diameter:	36.07 mm
Thickness:	2.66 mm
Edge:	Reeded
Die Axis:	↑↑
Finish:	Proof
Case of Issue:	Not known

DATE	DESCRIPTION	QUANTITY SOLD	ISSUE PRICE	FINISH	SP-68	SP-69	PR-69	PR-70
2003	50th Anniv. Accession/Coronation of Elizabeth II, Gold	One	—	Proof			UNIQUE	

NE DOLLAR, 50TH ANNIVERSARY OF THE CORONATION OF QUEEN ELIZABETH II, 1953-2003.

This silver dollar is a reissue of the dollar first struck during the coronation year 1953. The design is differentiated by the double dates 1953-2003 the obverse, as opposed to the single date on the reverse of the 1953 dollar.

Designers and Engravers:

Obv.:	Mary Gillick, Thomas Shingles
Rev.:	Emanuel Hahn
Composition:	99.99% Ag
Silver content:	25.172 g, 0.809 tr oz
Weight:	25.175 g
Diameter:	36.07 mm
Thickness:	3.02 mm
Edge:	Reeded
Die Axis:	↑↑
Finish:	Proof
Case of Issue:	See Special Issue Proof Sets, page 551

DATE	DESCRIPTION	QUANTITY SOLD	ISSUE PRICE	FINISH	PR-69	PR-70
2003 (1953-)	50th Anniv. Coronation Elizabeth II	21,537	N.I.I.	Proof	70.	—

ONE DOLLAR, UNCROWNED PORTRAIT OF QUEEN ELIZABETH II, 2003.

This was a special edition dollar with the new obverse design for 2003, and the reverse honouring the "Voyageurs" design of Canada's first circulating silv
dollar. A fine gold (.9999) example of this design was struck by the Royal Canadian Mint and sold on eBay with the proceeds going to charities.

Designers and Engravers:

Obv.:	Susanna Blunt, Susan Taylor
Rev.:	Emanuel Hahn, RCM Staff
Composition:	Gold: 99.99% Au
Silver:	99.99% Ag
Bullion content:	Gold: 25.172 g, 0.809 tr oz
	Silver: 25.172 g, 0.809 tr oz
Weight:	Gold: 25.175 g, Silver: 25.175 g
Diameter:	36.07 mm
Thickness:	Gold: 2.66 mm
Silver:	3.02 mm
Edge:	Reeded
Die Axis:	↑↑
Finish:	Proof

Case of Issue: Gold: Unknown
Silver: Black leatherette clam case, maroon insert, encapsulated coin, COA

DATE	DESCRIPTION	QUANTITY SOLD	ISSUE PRICE	FINISH	PR-69	PR-70
2003	Uncrowned Portrait Queen Elizabeth II, Silver	29,586	51.95	Proof	35.	—
2003	Uncrowned Portrait Queen Elizabeth II, Gold	One	—	Proof		UNIQUE

ONE DOLLAR, 400TH ANNIVERSARY OF THE FIRST FRENCH SETTLEMENT IN NORTH AMERICA, 1604-2004.

In 1604 a tiny island, in what was to be called the St. Croix River, became the first French settlement in North America.
A 2004 Ile Sainte-Croix stamp and coin set was issued containing this silver dollar counterstamped with a fleur-de-lis privy mark.

Common Obverse	Proof	BU, with Privy Mark

Designers:

Obv.:	Susanna Blunt
Rev.:	R. R. Carmichael
Composition:	99.99% Ag
Silver content:	25.172 g, 0.809 tr oz
Weight:	25.175 g
Diameter:	36.07 mm
Thickness:	3.02 mm
Finish:	Proof or Brilliant Uncirculated

Engravers:

Obv.:	Susan Taylor
Rev.:	Stan Witten

Edge:	Reeded
Die Axis:	↑↑

Case of Issue:
(A)   Dark green leatherette clam case, green insert, encapsulated coin, COA
(B)   Multicoloured plastic slide case, encapsulated coin
(C)   Privy Mark Dollar, see Derivatives, page 129

DATE	DESCRIPTION	QUANTITY SOLD	ISSUE PRICE	FINISH	SP-68	SP-69	PR-69	PR-70
2004 (1604-)	First French Settlement	106,974	36.95	Proof	—	—	32.	—
2004 (1604-)	First French Settlement	42,582	28.95	BU	24.	34.	—	—
2004 (1604-)	First French Settlement, with Privy Mark	8,315	N.I.I.	BU	65.	—	—	—

NE DOLLAR, "THE POPPY" ARMISTICE DAY COMMEMORATIVE, 2004.

Throughout the world the poppy has become one of the most powerful symbols that honours the men and women who gave their lives for freedom.
or the circulation "Poppy" twenty-five-cent coin, see Canadian Coins, Volume One, Numismatic Issues.

Designers and Engravers:

Obv.:	Susanna Blunt, Susan Taylor
Rev.:	Cosme Saffioti, Stan Witten
Composition:	99.99% Ag
Silver content:	25.172 g, 0.809 tr oz
Weight:	25.175 g
Diameter:	36.07 mm **Edge:** Reeded
Thickness:	2.95 mm **Die Axis:** ↑↑
Finish:	Proof
Case of Issue:	Maroon leatherette clam style case, black flock insert, encapsulated coin, COA

DATE	DESCRIPTION	QUANTITY SOLD	ISSUE PRICE	FINISH	PR-69	PR-70
2004	"The Poppy" Armistice Day	24,527	49.95	Proof	50.	—

NE DOLLAR, 40TH ANNIVERSARY OF CANADA'S NATIONAL FLAG, 1965-2005.

The Canadian flag, which is composed of the symbolic maple leaf and the national colours first proclaimed in 1921, was raised for the first time
:bruary 15th, 1965, on Parliament Hill
The 2005 brilliant uncirculated silver dollar was also issued in a gift set which included an interactive CD Rom (see Derivatives, page 134).

	Proof	Proof, Selectively gold plated	Proof, Red enamel

:signers:		Engravers:	
Obv.:	Susanna Blunt	Obv.:	Susan Taylor
Rev.:	William Woodruff	Rev.:	William Woodruff
mposition:	99.99% Ag		
ver content:	25.172 g, 0.809 tr oz	**Thickness:**	3.02 mm
eight:	25.175 g	**Die Axis:**	↑↑
ameter:	36.07 mm	**Edge:**	Reeded
nish:	1. Proof		
	2. Proof, Selectively gold plated		
	3. Proof, Red enamel		
	4. Brilliant Uncirculated		
se of Issue:	Maroon plastic slide case, black plastic insert, encapsulated coin, COA		

DATE	DESCRIPTION	SOURCE	QUANTITY SOLD	ISSUE PRICE	FINISH	SP-68	SP-69	PR-69	PR-70
2005 (1965-)	Proof	Pr. Single	95,431	34.95	Proof	—	—	40.	—
2005 (1965-)	Proof, Selectively Gold plated	Pr. Set	63,562	N.I.I.	Proof	—	—	70.	—
2005 (1965-)	Proof, Red enamel	Pr. Single	4,898	99.95	Proof	—	—	240.	—
2005 (1965-)	Brilliant Uncirculated	BU Single	50,948	24.95	BU	24.	—	*	*

ONE DOLLAR, 150TH ANNIVERSARY OF THE VICTORIA CROSS, 2006.

In 1856 Queen Victoria Instituted the Victoria Cross medal. A total of 1,351 Victoria Cross medals have been awarded with 94 being awarded to Canadian

Proof   Proof, Selectively gold plated

Designers:
  Obv.:   Susanna Blunt
  Rev.:   RCM Staff
Composition: 99.99% Ag
Silver content: 25.172 g, 0.809 tr oz
Weight: 25.175 g
Diameter: 36.07 mm

Engravers:
  Obv.:   Susan Taylor
  Rev.:   RCM Staff

Thickness: 3.02 mm
Edge: Reeded
Die Axis: ↑↑

Finish: **1.** Proof   **2.** Proof, Selectively gold plated   **3.** Brilliant Uncirculated
Case of Issue: Maroon plastic slide case, black plastic insert, encapsulated coin, COA

DATE	DESCRIPTION	SOURCE	QUANTITY SOLD	ISSUE PRICE	FINISH	SP-68	SP-69	PR-69	PR-70
2006	Victoria Cross, Proof	Pr. Single	55,599	34.95	Proof	—	—	40.	—
2006	Victoria Cross, Proof, Selectively gold plated	Pr. Set	53,822	N.I.I.	Proof	—	—	75.	—
2006	Victoria Cross, Brilliant Uncirculated	BU Single	27,254	24.95	BU	25.	—	*	*

ONE DOLLAR, MEDAL OF BRAVERY, 2006.

The Canadian Medal of Bravery was established in 1972 and is awarded by the Governor General of Canada in recognition of "Acts of Bravery hazardous circumstances".

Proof   Proof, Red Enamel

Designers:
  Obv.:   Susanna Blunt
  Rev.:   Konrad Wachelko
Composition: 99.99% Ag
Silver content: 25.172 g, 0.809 tr oz
Weight: 25.175 g
Diameter: 36.07 mm

Engravers:
  Obv.:   Susan Taylor
  Rev.:   Konrad Wachelko

Thickness: 3.02 mm
Edge: Reeded
Die Axis: ↑↑

Finish: **1.** Proof **2.** Proof, Red enamel
Case of Issue: Maroon plastic slide case, black plastic insert, encapsulated coin, COA

DATE	DESCRIPTION	SOURCE	QUANTITY SOLD	ISSUE PRICE	FINISH	PR-69	PR-70
2006	Medal of Bravery	Pr. Single	8,343	54.95	Proof	60.	—
2006	Medal of Bravery, Red enamel	Pr. Single	4,999	99.95	Proof	140.	—

NE DOLLAR (HALF OUNCE), SILVER WOLF, 2006.

Designers and Engravers:

Obv.:	Susanna Blunt, Susan Taylor	
Rev.:	William Woodruff	

Composition: 99.99% Ag
Weight: 15.552 g, 0.50 tr oz
Diameter: 34.0 mm **Edge:** Reeded
Thickness: 2.1 mm **Die Axis:** ↑↑
Finish: Bullion
Case of Issue: Mylar Pouch

DATE	DESCRIPTION	QUANTITY SOLD	ISSUE PRICE	FINISH	MS-65	MS-66	MS-67
2006	$1 (½ oz), Silver Wolf	106,800	BV	Bullion	24.	32.	—

JE DOLLAR, THAYENDANEGEA, 2007.

Born in 1743, Thayendanegea (Joseph Brant) was a Mohawk Chief who fought along side the British during the American Revolution. Brant died
Canada, November 24th, 1807.

Proof	Proof, Selectively gold plated	Proof, Enamelled

signers:

Obv.:	Susanna Blunt
Rev.:	Laurie McGaw

mposition: 92.5% Ag, 7.5% Cu
ver content: 23.29 g, 0.749 tr oz
ight: 25.175 g
ameter: 36.07 mm
ish:
1. Proof
2. Proof, Selectively gold plated
3. Proof, Enamelled
4. Brilliant Uncirculated

se of Issue: (A) Proof, Enamelled: Maroon plastic slide case, black plastic insert, encapsulated coin, COA
(B) Proof / BU: Maroon leatherette clam style case, black flocked insert, encapsulated coin, COA

Engravers:

Obv.:	Susan Taylor
Rev.:	William Woodruff

Thickness: 3.02 mm
Edge: Reeded
Die Axis: ↑↑

DATE	DESCRIPTION	SOURCE	QUANTITY SOLD	ISSUE PRICE	FINISH	SP-68	SP-69	PR-69	PR-70
2007	Thayendanegea, Proof	Pr. Single	32,837	42.95	Proof	*	*	40.	—
2007	Thayendanegea, Proof, Selectively gold plated	Pr. Set	37,413	N.I.I.	Proof	*	*	70.	—
2007	Thayendanegea, Proof, Enamelled	Pr. Single	5,181	129.95	Proof	*	*	100.	—
2007	Thayendanegea, Brilliant Uncirculated	BU Single	16,378	34.95	BU	25.	—	*	*

ONE DOLLAR, CELEBRATION OF THE ARTS, 2007.

This coin was issued to commemorate the 50th anniversary of the founding of the Canada Council of the Arts.

Designers and Engravers:

Obv.:	Susanna Blunt, Susan Taylor		
Rev.:	Friedrich Peter, RCM Staff		
Composition:	92.5% Ag, 7.5% Cu		
Silver content:	23.29 g, 0.749 tr oz		
Weight:	25.175 g		
Diameter:	36.07 mm	**Edge:**	Reed
Thickness:	2.95 mm	**Die Axis:**	↑↑
Finish:	Proof		
Case of Issue:	Maroon plastic slide case, black plastic insert, encapsulated coin, COA		

DATE	DESCRIPTION	SOURCE	QUANTITY SOLD	ISSUE PRICE	FINISH	PR-69	PR-70
2007	Celebration of the Arts	Pr. Single	6,704	54.95	Proof	175.	—

ONE DOLLAR, 400TH ANNIVERSARY OF QUEBEC CITY, 1608-2008.

Founded in 1608 by Samuel de Champlain, Quebec City is one of the oldest cities in North America, and the only one north of Mexico with ramparts surrounding the Old City still intact.

Proof   Proof, Selectively gold plated

Designers:

Obv.:	Susanna Blunt
Rev.:	Suzanne Duranceau
Composition:	92.5% Ag, 7.5% Cu
Silver Content:	23.29 g, 0.749 tr oz
Weight:	25.175 g
Diameter:	36.07 mm
Thickness:	3.02 mm
Finish:	1. Proof
	2. Proof, Selectively gold plated
	3. Brilliant Uncirculated

Engravers:

Obv.:	Susan Taylor
Rev.:	Susan Taylor, Cecily Mok, Konrad Wachelko

Edge:	Reeded
Die Axis:	↑↑

Case of Issue: Maroon leatherette clam style case, black flocked insert, encapsulated coin, COA

DATE	DESCRIPTION	SOURCE	QUANTITY SOLD	ISSUE PRICE	FINISH	SP-68	SP-69	PR-69	PR-70
2008 (1608-)	Quebec City, Proof	Pr. Single	65,000	42.95	Proof	*	*	45.	—
2008 (1608-)	Quebec City, Proof, Selectively gold plated	Pr. Set	38,630	N.I.I.	Proof	*	*	75.	—
2008 (1608-)	Quebec City, Brilliant Uncirculated	BU Single	35,000	34.95	BU	28.	—	*	*

NE DOLLAR, CELEBRATING THE ROYAL CANADIAN MINT CENTENNIAL, 1908-2008.

The Ottawa Branch of the Royal Mint, London, struck their first coins on January 2nd, 1908. Control of the Ottawa Mint passed to Canada in 1931 d was renamed the Royal Canadian Mint.

Designers and Engravers:

Obv.:	Susanna Blunt, Susan Taylor
Rev.:	Jason Bouwman, José Osio
Composition:	92.5% Ag, 7.5% Cu, Selectively gold plated
Silver content:	23.29 g, 0.749 tr oz
Weight:	25.175 g
Diameter:	36.07 mm
Thickness:	3.1 mm
Finish:	Proof
Case of Issue:	Maroon leatherette clam style case, black flocked insert, encapsulated coin, COA

Edge: Reeded
Die Axis: ↑↑

DATE	DESCRIPTION	SOURCE	QUANTITY SOLD	ISSUE PRICE	FINISH	PR-69	PR-70
2008 (1908-)	Royal Canadian Mint Centennial	Pr. Single	15,000	59.95	Proof	160.	—

NE DOLLAR, "THE POPPY" ARMISTICE, 1918-2008.

A red poppy is worn every November 11th, in memory of our war veterans.

Designers and Engravers:

Obv.:	Susanna Blunt, Susan Taylor
Rev.:	Cosme Saffioti, Stan Witten
Composition:	92.5% Ag, 7.5% Cu
Silver content:	27.75 g, 0.892 tr oz
Weight:	30.0 g
Diameter:	36.2 mm
Thickness:	3.3 mm
Finish:	Proof
Case of Issue:	Maroon leatherette clam style case, black flocked insert, encapsulated coin, COA

Edge: Reeded
Die Axis: ↑↑

DATE	DESCRIPTION	SOURCE	QUANTITY SOLD	ISSUE PRICE	FINISH	PR-69	PR-70
2008 (1918-)	"The Poppy" Armistice	Pr. Single	4,994	139.95	Proof	150.	—

te: There is slight confusion in the Royal Canadian Mint's press release in which the finish on this coin is stated as "proof" in one section and "proof-like" in another. It is listed in this table as proof as that is the finish carried on the certificate of authenticity which accompanies the coins.

NE DOLLAR, 100TH ANNIVERSARY MONTREAL CANADIENS, 1909-2009.

The Montreal Canadiens, Montreal's hockey team, celebrated their 100th anniversary in 2009.

Designers and Engravers:

Obv.:	Susanna Blunt, Susan Taylor
Rev.:	Jason Bouwman, Konrad Wachelko
Composition:	92.5% Ag, 7.5% Cu, Selectively gold plated
Silver content:	23.29 g, 0.749 tr oz
Weight:	25.175 g
Diameter:	36.07 mm
Thickness:	3.1 mm
Case of Issue:	(A) Black leatherette clam style case, black flocked insert, encapsulated coin, COA (B) Acrylic stand

Edge: Reeded
Die Axis: ↑↑
Finish: Proof

DATE	DESCRIPTION	SOURCE	QUANTITY SOLD	ISSUE PRICE	FINISH	PR-69	PR-70
2009 (1909-)	Montreal Canadiens	Pr. Single	10,093	69.95	Proof	160.	—
2009 (1909-)	Montreal Canadiens	With stand	4,907	74.95	Proof	160.	—

ONE DOLLAR, 100TH ANNIVERSARY OF FLIGHT IN CANADA, 1909-2009.

J. A. Douglas McCurdy, a native of Baddeck, flew the Aerial Experiment Association's Silver Dart on February 23rd, 1909 over the frozen Bras d Lakes, in Nova Scotia. This was the first controlled flight in Canada and the British Empire.

	Proof	Proof, Selectively gold plated	Brilliant Uncirculated

Designers:
  Obv.:   Susanna Blunt
  Rev.:   Jason Bouwman
Composition: 92.5% Ag, 7.5% Cu
Silver content: 23.29 g, 0.749 tr oz
Weight: 25.175 g
Diameter: 36.07 mm
Thickness: 3.1 mm
Finish: 1. Proof
       2. Proof, Selectively gold plated
       3. Brilliant Uncirculated

Engravers:
  Obv.:   Susan Taylor
  Rev.:   William Woodruff

Edge: Reeded
Die Axis: ↑↑

Case of Issue: Maroon leatherette clam style case, black flocked insert, encapsulated coin, COA

DATE	DESCRIPTION	SOURCE	QUANTITY SOLD	ISSUE PRICE	FINISH	SP-68	SP-69	PR-69	PR-70
2009 (1909-)	Flight, Proof	Pr. Single	25,000	47.95	Proof	*	*	50.	—
2009 (1909-)	Flight, Proof, Selectively gold plated	Pr. Set	27,549	N.I.I.	Proof	*	*	75.	—
2009 (1909-)	Flight, Brilliant Uncirculated	BU Single	13,074	39.95	BU	30.	—	*	*

ONE DOLLAR, VANCOUVER 2010, THE SUN, 2010.

The Sun, representing life, abundance, healing and peace, has been the cornerstone in the cultures of Canada's many First Nation communitie

Designers and Engravers:
  Obv.:   Susanna Blunt, Susan Taylor
  Rev.:   Xwa lack tun (Ricky Harry), Cecily Mok
Composition: 92.5% Ag, 7.5% Cu
Silver content: 27.75 g, 0.892 tr oz
Weight: 30.0 g
Diameter: 36.2 mm   **Edge:** Plain
Thickness: 3.3 mm   **Die Axis:** ↑↑
Finish: Proof
Case of Issue: Black leatherette clam style case, black flocked insert, encapsulated coin, COA, Vancouver 2010 Olympic Winter Games theme sleeve

DATE	DESCRIPTION	SOURCE	QUANTITY SOLD	ISSUE PRICE	FINISH	PR-69	PR-70
2010	The Sun	Pr. Single	5,000	139.95	Proof	240.	—

⌐IE DOLLAR, 100TH ANNIVERSARY OF THE ROYAL CANADIAN NAVY, 1910-2010.

Founded in 1910 by the passage of the Naval Service Act, the Royal Canadian Navy served in three wars and many conflicts during the last 100 ⌐ars. *HMCS Sackville*, one of the original Flower Class Corvettes is portrayed on this commemorative silver dollar.

| | Proof | Proof, Selectively gold plated | Brilliant Uncirculated |

⌐signers		**Engravers:**	
Obv.:	Susanna Blunt	Obv.:	Susan Taylor
Rev.:	Yves Bérubé	Rev.:	Stan Witten

⌐mposition:	92.5% Ag, 7.5% Cu, Selectively gold plated		
⌐ver content:	23.29 g, 0.749 tr oz		
⌐ight:	25.175 g	**Edge:**	Reeded
⌐meter:	36.07 mm	**Die Axis:**	↑↑
⌐ckness:	3.0 mm	**Finish:**	Proof
⌐se of Issue:	Maroon leatherette clam style case, black flocked insert, encapsulated coin		

DATE	DESCRIPTION	SOURCE	QUANTITY SOLD	ISSUE PRICE	FINISH	SP-68	SP-69	PR-69	PR-70
2010 (1910-)	Proof	Pr. Single	29,141	52.95	Proof	*	*	45.	—
2010 (1910-)	Proof, Selectively gold plated	Pr. Set	32,342	N.I.I.	Proof	*	*	75.	—
2010 (1910-)	Brilliant Uncirculated	BU	12,946	46.95	BU	30.	—	*	*

⌐IE DOLLAR, 75TH ANNIVERSARY OF CANADA'S VOYAGEUR SILVER DOLLAR, 1935-2010.

The first circulating silver dollar was released in 1935. Emanuel Hahn's Voyageur design has become the classic symbol of Canada's silver dollars. ⌐s coin was also included in the 75th Anniversary of Canada's First Silver Dollar set, see page 553.

Designers and Engravers:			
Obv.:	Emanuel Hahn		
Rev.:	Percy Metcalfe		
Composition:	92.5% Ag, 7.5% Cu		
Silver content:	23.29 g, 0.749 tr oz		
Weight:	25.175 g	**Edge:**	Reeded
Diameter:	36.07 mm	**Die Axis:**	↑↑
Thickness:	3.0 mm	**Finish:**	Proof
Case of Issue:	Maroon leatherette clam style case, black flocked insert, encapsulated coin		

⌐ATE	DESCRIPTION	SOURCE	QUANTITY SOLD	ISSUE PRICE	FINISH	PR-69	PR-70
2010 (1935-)	75th Anniv. First Canadian Silver Dollar	Pr. Single	7,494	69.95	Proof	80.	—

ONE DOLLAR, ENAMELLED POPPY, 2010.

The poppy commemorated in the poem "In Flander's Fields" has become the flower of remembrance for Allied Service Personnel lost in battle.

Designers and Engravers:

Obv.:	Susanna Blunt, Susan Taylor
Rev.:	Christie Paquet, Christie Paquet
Composition:	92.5% Ag, 7.5% Cu, Red enamel
Silver content:	23.29 g, 0.749 tr oz
Weight:	25.175 g
Diameter:	36.07 mm **Edge:** Reed
Thickness:	3.1 mm **Die Axis:** ↑↑
Finish:	Proof
Case of Issue:	Maroon leatherette clam style case, black flocked insert, encapsulated coin, COA

DATE	DESCRIPTION	SOURCE	QUANTITY SOLD	ISSUE PRICE	FINISH	PR-69	PR-70
2010	Poppy, Enamelled	Pr. Single	4,907	139.95	Proof	180.	—

ONE DOLLAR, 100TH ANNIVERSARY OF THE STRIKING OF CANADA'S 1911 SILVER DOLLAR, 1911-2011.

This one dollar coin which carries the double date 1911-2011 is from the Special Edition Proof Set issued in 2011 to commemorate the 100 anniversary of the striking of Canada's 1911 silver dollar.

Designers and Engravers:

Obv.:	Sir E. B. MacKennal
Rev.:	W. H. J. Blakemore
Composition:	92.5% Ag, 7.5% Cu
Silver content:	23.29 g, 0.749 tr oz
Weight:	25.175 g
Diameter:	36.07 mm **Edge:** Reed
Thickness:	3.0 mm **Die Axis:** ↑↑
Finish:	Proof
Case of Issue:	See Special Issue Proof Sets, page 553

DATE	DESCRIPTION	SOURCE	QUANTITY SOLD	ISSUE PRICE	FINISH	PR-69	PR-70
2011 (1911-)	100th Anniv. Canada's 1911 Silver Dollar	Pr. Single	14,569	65.00	Proof	60.	—

ONE DOLLAR, 100TH ANNIVERSARY OF PARKS CANADA, 1911-2011.

The Dominion Parks Branch, known today as Parks Canada was founded in 1911. Parks Canada is the world's first system of national parks.

	Proof	**Proof, Selectively gold plated**	**Brilliant Uncirculated**

Designers:

Obv.:	Susanna Blunt
Rev.:	Luc Normandson
Composition:	92.5% Ag, 7.5% Cu
Weight:	25.175 g
Diameter:	36.07 mm
Thickness:	3.02 mm

Engravers:

Obv.:	Susan Taylor
Rev.:	Marcos Hallam
Silver Content:	23.29 g, 0.749 tr oz
Edge:	Reeded
Die Axis:	↑↑

Finish: **1.** Proof   **2.** Proof, Selectively gold plated   **3.** Brilliant Uncirculated
Case of Issue: Maroon leatherette clam style case, black flocked insert, encapsulated coin, COA

DATE	DESCRIPTION	SOURCE	QUANTITY SOLD	ISSUE PRICE	FINISH	SP-68	SP-69	PR-69	PR-7
2011 (1911-)	Parks Canada, Proof	Pr. Single	30,692	55.95	Proof	*	*	50.	—
2011 (1911-)	Parks Canada, Proof, Selectively gold plated	Pr. Set	32,910	N.I.I.	Proof	*	*	75.	—
2011 (1911-)	Parks Canada, Brilliant Uncirculated	BU Single	16,394	49.95	BU	35.	—	*	

—IE DOLLAR, 200TH ANNIVERSARY OF THE WAR OF 1812, 1812-2012.

The issue of these coins marks the two-hundredth anniversary of the first conflict between the American forces, and the English of Upper Canada, the —nch of Lower Canada, and the First Nations People who successfully defended against an American invasion. The conflict ran for three years, 1812-1814.

| | Proof | Proof, Selectively gold plated | Brilliant Uncirculated |

—signers:		Engravers:	
Obv.:	Susanna Blunt	Obv.:	Susan Taylor
Rev.:	Ardell Bourgeois	Rev.:	Konrad Wachelko
—mposition:	99.99% Ag	**Silver Content:**	23.17 g, 0.75 tr oz
—ight:	23.17 g	**Edge:**	Reeded
—meter:	35.9 mm	**Die Axis:**	↑↑
—ckness:	2.8 mm		
—ish:	1. Proof	2. Proof, Selectively gold plated	3. Brilliant Uncirculated
—se of Issue:	Maroon leatherette clam style case, black flocked insert, encapsulated coin, COA		

DATE	DESCRIPTION	SOURCE	QUANTITY SOLD	ISSUE PRICE	FINISH	SP-68	SP-69	PR-69	PR-70
2012 (1812-)	War of 1812, Proof	Pr. Single	39,569	59.95	Proof	*	*	40.	—
2012 (1812-)	War of 1812, Proof, Selectively gold plated Set	Prem. Pr.	19,789	N.I.I.	Proof	*	*	80.	—
2012 (1812-)	War of 1812, Brilliant Uncirculated	BU Single	19,623	54.95	BU	30.	—	*	*

—IE DOLLAR (¾ OUNCE), THE WAR OF 1812, 1812-2012.

Designers and Engravers:	
Obv.:	Susanna Blunt, Susan Taylor
Rev.:	Cathy Bursey-Sabourin, K. Wachelko
Composition:	99.99% Ag
Weight:	23.33 g, 0.50 tr oz
Diameter:	38.0 mm
Thickness:	2.4 mm
Edge:	Reeded
Die Axis:	↑↑
Finish:	Bullion
Case of Issue:	Tubes of 30

DATE	DESCRIPTION	QUANTITY SOLD	ISSUE PRICE	FINISH	MS-65	MS-66	MS-67
2012	$1 (¾ oz), The War of 1812	N/A	BV	Bullion	28.	35.	—

ONE DOLLAR, TWO LOONS, 2012.

This coin was issued to celebrate the 25th anniversary of the loon coin which replaced the one dollar bill in 1987.

Designers and Engravers:

Obv.:	Susanna Blunt, Susan Taylor
Rev.:	Richard Hunt, Cecily Mok
Composition:	99.99% Ag, Coloured
Silver content:	31.39 g, 1.00 tr oz
Weight:	31.39 g
Diameter:	38.0 mm
Thickness:	3.10 mm
Finish:	Proof

Edge: Ree
Die Axis: ↑↑

Case of Issue: Maroon leatherette clam style case, black flocked insert, encapsulated coin, COA, custom coloured sleeve

DATE	DESCRIPTION	SOURCE	QUANTITY SOLD	ISSUE PRICE	FINISH	PR-69	PR-70
2012	Two Loons	Pr. Single	9,965	109.95	Proof	110.	—

ONE DOLLAR, 100 YEARS OF THE CALGARY STAMPEDE, 2012.

First held in 1912, the Calgary Stampede is billed as the greatest outdoor show on earth.

Designers and Engravers:

Obv.:	Susanna Blunt, Susan Taylor
Rev.:	Steve Hepburn, Konrad Wachelko
Composition:	99.99% Ag
Silver content:	23.17 g, 0.75 tr oz
Weight:	23.17 g
Diameter:	36.07 mm
Thickness:	2.80 mm
Finish:	Proof

Edge: Ree
Die Axis: ↑↑

Case of Issue: Maroon leatherette clam style case, black flocked insert, encapsulated coin, COA, custom coloured sleeve

DATE	DESCRIPTION	SOURCE	QUANTITY SOLD	ISSUE PRICE	FINISH	PR-69	PR-70
2012	100 Years of the Calgary Stampede	Pr. Single	9,996	69.95	Proof	70.	—

ONE DOLLAR, THE 100TH GREY CUP, 2012.

The first Grey Cup game took place in 1909, with the University of Toronto defeating the Parkdale Canoe Club. There were 3,807 fans in attenda at the game which generated revenues of $2,616.40 for the Canadian Rugby Union.

Designers and Engravers:

Obv.:	Susanna Blunt, Susan Taylor
Rev.:	Filip Mroz of Bensimon Byrne, Konrad Wachelko
Composition:	99.99% Ag
Silver content:	23.17 g, 0.75 tr oz
Weight:	23.17 g
Diameter:	36.0 mm
Thickness:	2.75 mm
Finish:	Proof

Edge: Ree
Die Axis: ↑↑

Case of Issue: Maroon leatherette clam style case, bla flocked insert, encapsulated coin, COA, custom box

DATE	DESCRIPTION	SOURCE	QUANTITY SOLD	ISSUE PRICE	FINISH	PR-69	PR-70
2012	The 100th Grey Cup	Pr. Single	9,985	69.95	Proof	70.	—

NE DOLLAR, 100TH ANNIVERSARY OF THE CANADIAN ARCTIC EXPEDITION, 1913-2013.

In 1913, Canadian Prime Minister Sir Robert Borden commissioned an expedition, led by Manitoba-born ethnologist Vilhjalmur Stefansson, to
olore and map the western Canadian Arctic. Stefansson and zoologist Rudolph Anderson had travelled through the Far North the previous decade.
efansson planned to continue his earlier journey, but the government of Canada, recognizing the importance of the new sovereign territory, hosted
Expedition and broadened its mission significantly. A Northern Party led by Stefansson would undertake the mapping exercise while the Southern
rty led by Anderson would explore the geology, resources, and native inhabitants of the northern mainland.
The year 2013 saw the first fine silver dollar to be included in a Specimen Set.

| Brilliant Uncirculated | Proof | Proof, Selectively gold plated | Specimen |

signers:
  Obv.: Susanna Blunt
  Rev.: Bonnie Ross

mposition: 99.99% Ag
ver Content: 23.17g, 0.74 tr oz
ight: 23.17 g
meter: 36.07 mm
ish:
  1. Proof
  2. Proof, Selectively gold plated
se of Issue: Maroon leatherette clam style case, black flocked insert, encapsulated coin, COA

Engravers:
  Obv.: Susan Taylor
  Rev.: RCM Staff, Konrad Wachelko

Thickness: 2.8 mm
Edge: Reeded
Die Axis: ↑↑
  3. Specimen
  4. Brilliant Uncirculated

DATE	DESCRIPTION	SOURCE	QUANTITY SOLD	ISSUE PRICE	FINISH	SP-68	SP-69	PR-69	PR-70
2013 (1913-)	Canadian Arctic Expedition, Proof	Pr. Single	26,006	59.95	Proof	*	*	50.	—
2013 (1913-)	Canadian Arctic Expedition, Proof, Selectively gold plated	Pr. Set	20,494	N.I.I.	Proof	*	*	90.	—
2013 (1913-)	Canadian Arctic Expedition, Specimen	Sp. Set	9,787	N.I.I.	Specimen	35.	—	*	*
2013 (1913-)	Canadian Arctic Expedition, Brilliant Uncirculated	BU Single	13,325	54.95	BU	40.	—	*	*

JE DOLLAR, 250TH ANNIVERSARY OF THE END OF THE SEVEN YEARS WAR, 2013.

The Seven Years War (1756-1763) was the world's first global conflict extending far beyond North America to Europe, India and Africa. In North
erica the war was fought between the English, French, and the First Nations People.

Designers and Engravers:
  Obv.: Susanna Blunt, Susan Taylor
  Rev.: Tony Bianco, RCM Staff
Composition: 99.99% Ag
Silver content: 23.17 g, 0.74 tr oz
Weight: 23.17 g
Diameter: 36.0 mm   **Edge:** Reeded
Thickness: 2.75 mm   **Die Axis:** ↑↑
Finish: Proof
Case of Issue: Maroon leatherette clam style case, black flocked insert, encapsulated coin, COA, custom design box

DATE	DESCRIPTION	SOURCE	QUANTITY SOLD	ISSUE PRICE	FINISH	PR-69	PR-70
2013	250th Anniv. End of the Seven Years War	Pr. Single	10,004	69.95	Proof	60.	—

ONE DOLLAR, 60TH ANNIVERSARY OF THE KOREAN ARMISTICE AGREEMENT, 2013.

The reverse design on this coin is a reproduction of the Korean General Service Medal awarded to all troops who participated in the Korean W̶ during 1950-1958.

Designers and Engravers:

Obv.:	Susanna Blunt, Susan Taylor
Rev.:	Edward Carter Preston, Steven Stewart
Composition:	99.99% Ag
Silver content:	23.0 g, 0.74 tr oz
Weight:	23.0 g
Diameter:	36.0 mm
Thickness:	2.75 mm
Finish:	Maroon leatherette clam style case, blac̶ flocked insert, encapsulated coin, COA, custom design box

Edge: Reec̶
Die Axis: ↑↑

DATE	DESCRIPTION	SOURCE	QUANTITY SOLD	ISSUE PRICE	FINISH	PR-69	PR-70
2013	60th Anniv. Korean Armistice Agreement	Pr. Single	6,858	69.95	Proof	70.	—

ONE DOLLAR, 100TH ANNIVERSARY OF THE DECLARATION OF THE FIRST WORLD WAR, 2014.

The First World War began in August 1914 and ended November 1918. Thousands of Canadian men and women took part on the battlefields Europe.

Proof	**Proof, Selectively gold plated**	**Brilliant Uncirculated**

Designers:

Obv.:	Susanna Blunt
Rev.:	Bonnie Ross
Composition:	99.99% Ag
Silver Content:	22.8 g, .73 tr oz
Weight:	22.8 g
Diameter:	36.0 mm
Finish:	1. Proof
	2. Proof, Selectively gold plated
	3. Brilliant Uncirculated

Engravers:

Obv.:	Susan Taylor
Rev.:	Christie Paquet
Thickness:	2.8 mm
Edge:	Reeded
Die Axis:	↑↑

Case of Issue: Maroon leatherette clam style case, black flocked insert, encapsulated coin, COA

DATE	DESCRIPTION	SOURCE	QUANTITY SOLD	ISSUE PRICE	FINISH	SP-68	SP-69	PR-69	PR-7̶
2014	100th Anniv. Declaration WWI, Proof	Pr. Single	22,721	59.95	Proof	*	*	50.	—
2014	100th Anniv. Declaration WWI, Proof, Selectively gold plated	Prem. Pr. Set	13,416	N.I.I.	Proof	*	*	110.	—
2014	100th Anniv. Declaration WWI, Brilliant Uncirculated	BU Single	9,405	54.95	BU	45.	—	*	*

Note: Coins illustrated smaller than actual size.

E DOLLAR, 75TH ANNIVERSARY OF THE DECLARATION OF THE SECOND WORLD WAR, 1939-2014.

This limited edition silver dollar commemorating the declaration of World War Two, depicts the pivotal role women played in the Allied war effort as
build an Avro 683 Lancaster.

Designers and Engravers:

Obv.:	Susanna Blunt, Susan Taylor
Rev.:	Silvia Pecota, RCM Staff
Composition:	99.99% Ag
Silver content:	23.17 g, 0.74 tr oz
Weight:	23.17 g
Diameter:	36.07 mm
Thickness:	N/A
Finish:	Proof

Edge: Reeded
Die Axis: ↑↑

Case of Issue: Maroon leatherette clam style case, black flocked insert, encapsulated coin, COA

DATE	DESCRIPTION	SOURCE	QUANTITY SOLD	ISSUE PRICE	FINISH	PR-69	PR-70
2014 (1939-)	75th Anniv. Declaration Second World War	Pr. Single	7,017	69.95	Proof	70.	—

E DOLLAR, 50TH ANNIVERSARY OF THE CANADIAN FLAG, 1965-2015.

Celebrating the 50th anniversary of the Canadian flag, the proof, proof coloured, and brilliant uncirculated coins depict the symbolic power that the
adian flag has come to assume abroad and at home.

	Proof	Proof, Coloured Brilliant	Uncirculated

igners:

Obv.:	Susanna Blunt
Rev.:	John Mantha
mposition:	99.99% Ag
er Content:	23.17 g, 0.74 tr oz
ght:	23.17 g
meter:	36.07 mm
sh:	1. Proof
	2. Proof, Coloured
	3. Brilliant Uncirculated
e of Issue:	Maroon leatherette clam style case, black flocked insert, encapsulated coin, COA

Engravers:

Obv.:	Susan Taylor
Rev.:	RCM Staff

Thickness: 2.8 mm
Edge: Reeded
Die Axis: ↑↑

DATE	DESCRIPTION	SOURCE	QUANTITY SOLD	ISSUE PRICE	FINISH	SP-68	SP-69	PR-69	PR-70
2015 (1965-)	50th Anniv. of the Canadian Flag, Proof	Pr. Single	19,982	59.95	Proof	*	8	60.	—
2015 (1965-)	50th Anniv. of the Canadian Flag, Proof, Coloured	Prem. Pr.	14,006	N.I.I.	Proof	*	*	110.	—
2015 (1965-)	50th Anniv. of the Canadian Flag, Brilliant Uncirculated	BU Single	10,014	54.95	BU	50.	—	*	*

e: Coins illustrated smaller than actual size.

ONE DOLLAR, 100TH ANNIVERSARY OF *IN FLANDERS FIELDS*, 2015.

The year 2015 marked the 100th anniversary of the poem *In Flanders Fields*, which was written by Canadian physician Lieutenant Colonel J McCrae amid the horrors of the Second Battle of Ypres in May 1915.

Designers and Engravers:

Obv.:	Susanna Blunt, Susan Taylor
Rev.:	Tony Bianco

Composition: 99.99% Ag, with enamel
Silver content: 23.17 g, 0.74 tr oz

Weight:	23.17 g	**Edge:**	Ree
Diameter:	36.07 mm	**Thickness:**	N/A
Die Axis:	↑↑	**Finish:**	Proc

Case of Issue: Maroon clamshell with custom beauty b encapsulated coin, COA

DATE	DESCRIPTION	QUANTITY SOLD	ISSUE PRICE	FINISH	PR-69	PR-70
2015	*In Flanders Fields*	9,998	79.95	Proof	80.	—

RENEWED SILVER DOLLAR SERIES, 2015-2017

ONE DOLLAR, RENEWED SILVER DOLLAR SERIES, 2015-2017.

The Renewed Silver Dollar Series celebrates historic proof dollar designs. **Note:** This series was exclusively sold to the Mint Master's Club Members c

2015 The Voyager	**2016 Library of Parliament**	**2017 Parliament Building**
Obv.: Percy Metcalf Rev.: Emanuel Hahn	Obv.: Arnold Machin Rev.: Walter Ott	Obv.: Humphrey Paget Rev.: Emanuel H

Designers:

Obv.:	See illustrations
Rev.	See illustrations

Composition: 99.99% Ag, selective gold plating
Silver content: 62.67 g, 2.0 tr oz
Diameter: 54 mm (2015), 50 mm (2016-2017)
Thickness: N/A
Finish: Proof

Engravers:

Obv.:	See illustrations
Rev.:	See illustrations

Weight:	62.67 g - 62.69 g
Edge:	Reeded
Die Axis:	↑↑

Case of Issue: Maroon clamshell with custom beauty box, encapsulated coin, COA

DATE	DESCRIPTION	QUANTITY SOLD	ISSUE PRICE	FINISH	PR-69	PR-70
2015	The Voyageur	2,200	189.95	Proof	700.	—
2016	Library of Parliament	2,037	189.95	Proof	230.	—
2017	Commemorative Royal Visit, Parliament Building	4,000	194.95	Proof	195.	—

E DOLLAR, CELEBRATING CANADIAN ATHLETES, 2016.

Designers and Engravers:

Obv.:	Susanna Blunt, Susan Taylor
Rev.:	Three Degrees Creative Group
Composition:	99.99% Ag
Silver content:	23.17 g, 0.74 tr oz
Weight:	23.17 g
Diameter:	36.07 mm
Thickness:	N/A
Finish:	Proof
Case of Issue:	Maroon clamshell with black beauty box, encapsulated coin, COA

Edge: Reeded
Die Axis: ↑↑

DATE	DESCRIPTION	QUANTITY SOLD	ISSUE PRICE	FINISH	PR-69	PR-70
2016	Celebrating Canadian Athletes	5,328	79.95	Proof	75.	—

E DOLLAR, 150TH ANNIVERSARY OF THE TRANSLATLANTIC CABLE, 2016.

On July 27, 1866, a new era of global communication began as S.S. *Great Eastern* steamed into Heart's Content, Newfoundland, to complete a link
could relay messages quickly between the Old world and the New.

	Proof	Proof, Selectively gold plated	Proof, Coloured

igners:

Obv.:	Susanna Blunt
Rev.:	Yves Bérubé
nposition:	99.99% Ag
er content:	23.17 g, 0.74 tr oz
ght:	23.17 g
meter:	36.07 mm
ckness:	N/A
sh:	1. Proof
e of Issue:	Maroon clamshell with black beauty box, encapsulated coin, COA

Engravers:

Obv.:	Susan Taylor
Obv.:	RCM Staff

Edge: Reeded
Die Axis: ↑↑

2. Proof, Selectively gold plated   3. Brilliant Uncirculated

Note: Coins illustrated smaller than actual size.

ATE	DESCRIPTION	SOURCE	QUANTITY SOLD	ISSUE PRICE	FINISH	PR-69	PR-70
2016	150th Anniversary, Proof	Pr. Single	9,913	59.95	Proof	60.	—
2016	150th Anniversary, Proof, Selectively gold plated	Pr. Set	9,211	—	Proof	110.	—
2016	150th Anniversary, Proof, Coloured	Pr. Set	12,312	—	Proof	60.	—

150TH ANNIVERSARY OF CANADIAN CONFEDERATION

ONE DOLLAR, 150TH ANNIVERSARY OF CANADIAN CONFEDERATION, 2017.

Proof	Proof, Selectively gold plated

Designers:
   Obv.:   Susanna Blunt
   Rev.:   Rebecca Yanovskaya
Composition: 99.99% Ag
Silver content: 23.17 g, 0.74 tr oz
Weight: 23.17 g
Diameter: 36.07 mm
Thickness: N/A

Engravers:
   Obv.:   Susan Taylor

Edge: Reeded
Die Axis: ↑↑

Finish: **1.** Proof   **2.** Proof, Selectively gold plated   **3.** Brilliant Uncirculated
Case of Issue: Maroon clamshell with a standard black beauty box, encapsulated coin, COA

DATE	DESCRIPTION	SOURCE	QUANTITY SOLD	ISSUE PRICE	FINISH	PR-69	PR-70
2017	150th Anniversary of Canadian Confederation	PR Single	30,000	59.95	Proof	70.	—
2017	150th Anniversary of Canadian Confederation, Selectively gold plated	PR Set	8,017	234.95	Proof	130.	—

ONE DOLLAR, OUR HOME AND NATIVE LAND, 2017.

Common
Obverse

Designers and Engravers:
   Obv.:   Susanna Blunt, Susan Taylor
   Rev.:   Jamie Desrochers
Composition: 99.99% Ag
Silver content: 23.17 g, 0.74 tr oz
Weight: 23.17 g
Diameter: 36.07 mm   **Edge:**   Reeded
Thickness: N/A   **Die Axis:**   ↑↑
Finish: **1.** Proof   **2.** Proof, Selectively gold plated
               3. Proof, Coloured   **4.** SE Proof, Coloured
Case of Issue: Maroon clamshell with a standard black beauty box,
          with Canada 150 logo, COA

Proof	Proof, Selectively gold plated	Proof, Coloured	Special Editon Proof, Colou

DATE	DESCRIPTION	SOURCE	MINTAGE	ISSUE PRICE	FINISH	PR-69	PR-7
2017	Our Home and Native Land	Pr. Single	20,000	59.95	Proof	65.	
2017	Our Home and Native Land, Selectively gold plated	Pr. Set	20,000	—	Proof	140.	
2017	Our Home and Native Land, Coloured	Pr. Set	25,000	—	Proof	70.	
2017	Our Homeand Native Land, Coloured	SE Pr. Single	10,000	69.95	Proof	70.	

240TH ANNIVERSARY OF CAPTAIN COOK AT NOOTKA SOUND

E DOLLAR, 240TH ANNIVERSARY OF CAPTAIN COOK AT NOOTKA SOUND, 2018.

Commemorating the arrival of Captain James Cook at the summer village of the Nuu-chah-nulth people, at Nootka Sound, which drew more orers and traders to Canada's western shores.

| Common Obverse | Proof | Proof, Selectively gold plated | Special Edition Proof, Colour |

gners:
Obv.: Susanna Blunt
Rev.: John Horton

Engravers:
Obv.: Susan Taylor

position: 99.99% Ag
er content: 23.17 g, 0.74 tr oz
ght: 23.17 g
meter: 36.07 mm   **Edge:** Reeded
kness: N/A   **Die Axis:** ↑↑
sh: 1. Proof   2. Proof, Selectively gold plated   3. Brilliant Uncirculated
e of Issue: Maroon clamshell with a standard black beauty box, encapsulated coin, COA

DATE	DESCRIPTION	SOURCE	MINTAGE	ISSUE PRICE	FINISH	PR-69	PR-70
'018	240th Anniversary of Captain Cook at Nootka Sound	PR Single	20,000	59.95	Proof	60.	—
'018	240th Anniversary of Captain Cook at Nootka Sound, gold plated	PR Set	15,000	—	Proof	120.	—
'018	240th Anniversary of Caption Cook at Nootka Sound, colour	SP Proof Set	15,000	—	Proof	75.	—

E DOLLAR, 100TH ANNIVERSARY OF THE ARMISTICE OF THE FIRST WORLD WAR, 2018.

ovember 11, 1918: A date synonymous with peace and remembrance. The 2018 Special Edition Proof Dollar commemorates the centennial of rmistice of 1918.

Designers and Engravers:
Obv.: Susanna Blunt, Susan Taylor
Rev.: Jamie Desrochers
Composition: 99.99% Ag, Selective gold plating
Silver content: 23.17 g, 0.74 tr oz
Weight: 23.17 g
Diameter: 36.07 mm   **Edge:** Reeded
Thickness: N/A   **Die Axis:** ↑↑
Finish: Proof
Case of Issue: Standard maroon clamshell with black beauty box, COA

DATE	DESCRIPTION	MINTAGE	ISSUE PRICE	FINISH	PR-69	PR-70
2018	100th Anniversary of the Armistice of the First World War	15,000	69.95	Proof	70.	—

CASED NICKEL DOLLAR ISSUES, 1968-1984

At the start of 1968 the Royal Canadian Mint began the conversion from silver to nickel coinage. The first to participate was the Numismatic Department, which based in Hull, Quebec. The Hull Mint was opened circa 1965 to carry the increased demand for numismatic products which was overwhelming the Ottawa facili

The first full set of nickel coinage, the five, ten and fifty cents, and the one dollar coin are found in the Royal Canadian Mint's uncirculated set of 1968.

Nickel coinage is more difficult to strike than silver coinage, and the Mint needed to adjust their process. One of these adjustments was to reduce the size c fifty-cent and one dollar coins.

The finish on the coin was also a problem. The proof-like finish of silver was not as easily duplicated on nickel. Thus, the quality of finish varied from 1968 to when new presses for the Olympic Coin Program were put into use. The Mint did produce proof-like nickel coinage for their uncirculated sets, but not consiste for at times the standard of finish dropped to circulation. It is best to treat the finish for this period as "brilliant uncirculated" not proof-like, for even the experts difficulty determining the quality of the finish during this time period.

ONE DOLLAR, VOYAGEUR DESIGN, 1968 AND 1969.

A cased 1968 and 1969 nickel dollar was available from the Numismatic Department of the Mint during 1968-69, but the department did not aggress market this product until 1970. Thus the years 1968 and 1969 saw the development of the "cased dollar" line with the evolution of a "clam" style case.

Designers and Engravers:
Obv.:	Arnold Machin, Patrick Brindley
Rev.:	Raymond Taylor, Walter Ott

Composition: Nickel
Weight: 15.62 g
Diameter: 32.13 mm   **Edge:** Ree
Thickness: 2.3 mm   **Die Axis:** ↑↑
Finish: Brilliant Uncirculated
Case of Issue: Black leatherette, gold side trim, gilt Rc Canadian Mint Building crest, blue inte black insert, gilt Coat of Arms of Canad

DATE	DESCRIPTION	QUANTITY SOLD	ISSUE PRICE	FINISH	MS-65 NC	MS-66 NC	MS-67 NC
1968	Voyageur	N/A	N/A	BU	4.	8.	—
1968	Voyageur, Small Island	N/A	N/A	BU	20.	30.	—
1968	Voyageur, No Island	N/A	N/A	BU	10.	25.	—
1969	Voyageur	N/A	N/A	BU	4.	8.	—

ONE DOLLAR, MANITOBA CENTENNIAL, 1870-1970.

Canada's first commemorative nickel dollar has a special reverse featuring a prairie crocus in recognition of the centenary of Manitoba's entry Confederation. The finish on the cased dollar is brilliant uncirculated.

Designers and Engravers:
Obv.:	Arnold Machin, Patrick Brindley
Rev.:	Raymond Taylor, Walter Ott

Composition: Nickel
Weight: 15.62 g
Diameter: 32.13 mm   **Edge:** Re
Thickness: 2.3 mm   **Die Axis:** ↑
Finish: Brilliant Uncirculated

Case of Issue: (A) Black leatherette square case, gilt RCM crest, blue insert
(B) Maroon leatherette rectangular case, gold stamped crest of Canada, red interior, black insert
(C) Black leatherette rectangular case, gold stamped Japanese characters, Maple Leaf, Canada, red interior, black insert. Card insert. (Sold at the Canada pavilion in Japan, during 1970.)

DATE	DESCRIPTION	QUANTITY SOLD	ISSUE PRICE	FINISH	MS-65 NC	MS-66 NC	MS-6 NC
1970 (1870-)	Manitoba, Case A	349,120	2.00	BU	4.	8.	—
1970 (1870-)	Manitoba, Case B	Included	N/A	BU	10.	—	—
1970 (1870-)	Manitoba, Case C	Included	N/A	BU	10.	—	—

NE DOLLAR, BRITISH COLUMBIA CENTENNIAL, 1871-1971.

The nickel dollar for 1971 commemorates the entry in 1871 of British Columbia into Confederation. Its design is based on the arms of the province, with hield at the bottom and dogwood blossoms at the top. The design of the brilliant uncirculated nickel dollar is identical to that of the circulating issue.

Designers and Engravers:

Obv.:	Arnold Machin, Patrick Brindley
Rev.:	Thomas Shingles
Composition:	Nickel
Weight:	15.62 g
Diameter:	32.13 mm
Thickness:	2.3 mm
Finish:	Brilliant Uncirculated
Case of Issue:	Blue leatherette clam case, Coat of Arms of Canada, blue and black insert

Edge: Reeded
Die Axis: ↑↑

DATE	DESCRIPTION	QUANTITY SOLD	ISSUE PRICE	FINISH	MS-65 NC	MS-66 NC	MS-67 NC
1971 (1871-)	British Columbia Centennial	181,091	2.00	BU	4.	8.	—

NE DOLLAR, VOYAGEUR DESIGN, 1972.

The cased brilliant uncirculated nickel dollar issued by the numismatic department of the Royal Canadian Mint has the same design as the :ulating dollar with the exception of beads instead of denticles.

Designers and Engravers:

Obv.:	Arnold Machin, Patrick Brindley
Rev.:	Emanuel Hahn, Terry Smith
Composition:	Nickel
Weight:	15.62 g
Diameter:	32.13 mm
Thickness:	2.3 mm
Finish:	Brilliant Uncirculated
Case of Issue:	Blue leatherette clam case, Coat of Arms of Canada, blue and black insert

Edge: Reeded
Die Axis: ↑↑

DATE	DESCRIPTION	QUANTITY SOLD	ISSUE PRICE	FINISH	MS-65 NC	MS-66 NC	MS-67 NC
1972	Voyageur	143,392	2.00	BU	4.	8.	—

E DOLLAR, PRINCE EDWARD ISLAND CENTENNIAL, 1873-1973.

The 100th anniversary of the entry of Prince Edward Island into Confederation is commemorated with the reverse design depicting the provincial islature building in Charlottetown.

Designers and Engravers:

Obv.:	Arnold Machin, Patrick Brindley
Rev.:	Terry Manning, Walter Ott
Composition:	Nickel
Weight:	15.62 g
Diameter:	32.13 mm
Thickness:	2.3 mm
Finish:	Brilliant Uncirculated
Case of Issue:	Blue leatherette clam case, Coat of Arms of Canada, blue and black insert

Edge: Reeded
Die Axis: ↑↑

DATE	DESCRIPTION	QUANTITY SOLD	ISSUE PRICE	FINISH	MS-65 NC	MS-66 NC	MS-67 NC
973 (1873-)	Prince Edward Island Centennial	466,881	2.00	BU	4.	8.	—

ONE DOLLAR, WINNIPEG CENTENNIAL, 1874-1974.

The 100th anniversary of the establishment of Winnipeg, Manitoba, as a city is marked by the reverse of the 1974 dollar. The 1974 cased specim
silver dollar carries the same design, see page 92.

Designers and Engravers:

Obv.:	Arnold Machin, Patrick Brindley
Rev.:	Paul Pederson, Patrick Brindley
Composition:	Nickel
Weight:	15.62 g
Diameter:	32.13 mm **Edge:** Reed
Thickness:	2.3 mm **Die Axis:** ↑↑
Finish:	Brilliant Uncirculated
Case of Issue:	Blue leatherette clam case, Coat of Arms of Canada, blue and black insert

DATE	DESCRIPTION	QUANTITY SOLD	ISSUE PRICE	FINISH	MS-65 NC	MS-66 NC	MS-67 NC
1974 (1874-)	Winnipeg Centennial, Single Yoke	363,786	2.00	BU	4.	10.	—
1974 (1874-)	Winnipeg Centennial, Double Yoke #1	Included	2.00	BU	800.	—	—
1974 (1874-)	Winnipeg Centennial, Double Yoke #3	Included	2.00	BU	1,200.	—	—

ONE DOLLAR, VOYAGEUR DESIGN, 1975-1976.

With falling popularity, the cased nickel dollars were discontinued in 1976.

Designers and Engravers:

Obv.:	Arnold Machin, Patrick Brindley
Rev.:	Emanuel Hahn, Terry Smith
Composition:	Nickel
Weight:	15.62 g
Diameter:	32.13 mm **Edge:** Ree
Thickness:	2.3 mm **Die Axis:** ↑↑
Finish:	Specimen
Case of Issue:	Blue leatherette clam case, Coat of Arms of Canada, blue and black insert

DATE	DESCRIPTION	QUANTITY SOLD	ISSUE PRICE	FINISH	MS-65 NC	MS-66 NC	MS-67 NC
1975	Voyageur, Attached Jewel	88,102	2.50	BU	4.	10.	—
1976	Voyageur	74,209	2.50	BU	4.	10.	—

ONE DOLLAR, CONSTITUTION, 1867-1982

The reverse design of the 1982 nickel dollar commemorates Canada's Constitution. It features a faithful reproduction of the celebrated pain
Fathers of Confederation, with the inscription 1867 CONFEDERATION above the painting and CONSTITUTION 1982 beneath.

Designers and Engravers:

Obv.:	Arnold Machin, RCM Staff
Rev.:	Ago Aarand, RCM Staff
Composition:	Nickel
Weight:	15.62 g
Diameter:	32.13 mm **Edge:** Ree
Thickness:	2.3 mm **Die Axis:** ↑↑
Finish:	Specimen
Case of Issue:	Maroon square case with maple leaf log maroon insert, encapsulated coin

DATE	DESCRIPTION	QUANTITY SOLD	ISSUE PRICE	FINISH	SP-68	SP-69
1982 (1867-)	Constitution	107,353	9.75	Specimen	8.	—

E DOLLAR, 450TH ANNIVERSARY OF JACQUES CARTIER LANDING, 1534-1984.
The 450th year of Jacques Cartier's landing at Gaspé, Quebec, was honoured on July 24, 1984, by the issuing of a commemorative nickel dollar.

Designers and Engravers:

Obv.:	Arnold Machin, RCM Staff
Rev.:	Hector Greville, Victor Coté
Composition:	Nickel
Weight:	15.62 g
Diameter:	32.13 mm
Thickness:	2.3 mm
Finish:	Proof
Case of Issue:	Green velvet square case, green insert, encapsulated coin

	Edge:	Reeded
	Die Axis:	↑↑

DATE	DESCRIPTION	QUANTITY SOLD	ISSUE PRICE	FINISH	PR-69	PR-70
1984 (1534-)	450th Anniv. of Jacques Cartier Landing	87,776	9.75	Proof	8.	—

NOTES ON NICKEL AND BRONZE DOLLARS

 is important to remember the nickel dollar series 1968 to 1987 was issued, in most instances, for circulation (business strikes), however, they
e also issued as collector items either singly or in sets. This section, pages 116 to 119, lists only the single pliofilm pouched or cased nickel dollars
he period 1968 to 1984.

he term "proof-like" which applied to the silver dollars and sets of the period 1953-1967, was not carried forward to the nickel dollar coinage of
8-1987. Coins of the period 1968 to 1984 have a brilliant uncirculated finish.

ricing is based on third party, professionally graded coins. It is difficult for the average collector to determine the niceties between MS-65 (NC),
66 (NC) and MS-67 (NC). NC is non-circulating.

IS-65 (NC) pricing is based on the coin still being in its original packaging from the Mint. While MS-66 (NC) and MS-67 (NC) pricing is based on
coin being graded by a reputable third-party grading service.

NICKEL-BRONZE DOLLAR PROOF ISSUES, 1987-1995

ONE DOLLAR, LOON, 1987.

A proof striking of the loon dollar was issued by the numismatic department of the Royal Canadian Mint in 1987 commemorating the introduc￼ of the nickel-bronze dollar.

Designers and Engravers:

Obv.:	Arnold Machin, Patrick Brindley,
Rev.:	R. R. Carmichael, Terry Smith
Composition:	91.5% Ni, 8.5 Bronze
Weight:	7.0 g **Edge:** Plain
11-sided:	26.5 mm **Die Axis:** ↑↑
Thickness:	1.9 mm **Finish:** Proof
Case of Issue:	Royal blue velvet square case, blue insert, encapsulated coin

ONE DOLLAR, 125TH ANNIVERSARY OF CANADA, 1867-1992.

This coin was part of the "125" coin program by the numismatic department of the Royal Canadian Mint. This proof coin is the companion piec￼ the circulating issue of the same design.

Designers and Engravers:

Obv.:	Dora de Pédery-Hunt
Rev.:	Rita Swanson, Ago Aarand
Composition:	91.5% Ni, 8.5% Bronze
Weight:	7.0 g **Edge:** Plain
11-sided:	26.5 mm **Die Axis:** ↑↑
Thickness:	1.9 mm **Finish:** Proof
Case of Issue:	Royal blue velvet square case, blue insert, encapsulated coin

ONE DOLLAR, REMEMBRANCE, 1994.

The 1994 nickel Loon dollar depicts the War Memorial, built to commemorate the participation of all Canadians in the First World War. The mem￼ was rededicated in 1982 to include veterans of the Second World War and the Korean War.

Designers and Engravers:

Obv.:	Dora de Pédery-Hunt
Rev.:	Terry Smith, Ago Aarand
Composition:	91.5% Ni, 8.5% Bronze
Weight:	7.0 g **Edge:** Plain
11-sided:	26.5 mm **Die Axis:** ↑↑
Thickness:	1.9 mm **Finish:** Proof
Case of Issue:	Royal blue velvet square case, blue insert, encapsulated coin, COA

ONE DOLLAR, PEACEKEEPING, 1995.

This coin commemorates Canada's role in the United Nations peacekeeping forces. For the circulating issues see Canadian Coins, Volume O￼

Designers and Engravers:

Obv.:	Dora de Pédery-Hunt
Rev.:	J.K. Harman, R.G. Henriguez
	C. H. Oberlander, S. Taylor, A. Aarand
Composition:	91.5% Ni, 8.5% Bronze
Weight:	7.0 g **Edge:** Plain
11-sided:	26.5 mm **Die Axis:** ↑↑
Thickness:	1.9 mm **Finish:** Proof
Case of Issue:	Royal blue velvet square case, blue insert, encapsulated coin, COA

DATE	DESCRIPTION	QUANTITY SOLD	ISSUE PRICE	FINISH	PR-68	PR-69
1987	Loon, Nickel-Bronze	178,120	13.50	Proof	8.	—
1992 (1867)	125th Anniversary of Canada	24,227	19.95	Proof	10.	—
1994	Remembrance	54,524	19.95	Proof	10.	—
1995	Peacekeeping	43,293	17.95	Proof	10.	—

NICKEL-BRONZE DOLLAR SPECIMEN ISSUES, THE BIRD SERIES, 1997-2018

IE DOLLAR, BIRD SERIES, 1997-2018.

First released in 1997 as The Flying Loon to commemorate the 10th anniversary of the one dollar coin, the Bird Series of nickle-bronze dollar ecimen issues celebrates the diverse winged wildlife of Canada. Of note are the 2002 15th anniversary of the "Loonie" release, as well as the 2004 nada Goose dollar paying tribute to Jack Miner, an influential conservationist.

OBVERSES 1997, 2002, 2004-2018

Obverse 1997 Diademed Portrait	Obverse 2002 Diademed Portrait Double Date	Obverse 2004 Uncrowned Portrait With Date	Obverse 2004-2006, 2010-2018 Uncrowned Portrait	Obverse 2007-2009 Uncrowned Portrait With RCM Logo

REVERSES 1997, 2002, 2004-2018

1997 10th Ann. Loon Dollar Des.: J. Grondin Engr.: S. Beveridge	2002 15th Ann. Loon Dollar Des.: Dora de Pédery-Hunt Engr.: C. Saffioti	2004 Canada Goose Des. and Engr.: Susan Taylor	2004 Elusive Loon Des. and Engr.: Christie Paquet

2005 Tufted Puffin Des. and Engr.: Christie Paquet	2006 Snowy Owl Des.: G. Loates Engr.: RCM Staff	2007 Trumpeter Swan Des.: K. Burnett Engr.: C. Paquet	2008 Common Eider Des.: M. Dobson Engr.: S. Witten	2009 Great Blue Heron Des.: C. Jordison Engr.: J. Osio

2010 Northern Harrier Des.: A. Nogy Engr.: S. Taylor	2011 Great Grey Owl Des.: A. Nogy Engr.: C. Paquet	2012 25th Ann. Loon Dollar Des.: A. Nogy Engr.: S. Taylor	2013 Blue-Winged Teal Des.: G. Loates Engr.: M. Bowen	2014 Ferruginous Hawk Des.: T. Tennant Engr.: RCM Staff

ONE DOLLAR, BIRD SERIES, 1997-2018 (cont.).

2015	2016	2017	2018
Blue Jay	Tundra Swan	Snow Goose	Burrowing Owl
Des.: E. Spera	Des.: G. Scrimshaw	Des.: Derek C. Wicks	Des.: Pierre Girard
Engr.: RCM Staff	Engr.: RCM Staff	Engr.: RCM Staff	Engr.: RCM Staff

Designers:
Obv.:   1997, 2002: Dora de Pédery-Hunt
             2004-2018: Susanna Blunt
Rev.:   See reverse illustrations
Composition: 91.5% Ni, 8.5% Bronze
Weight: 7.0 g
11-sided: 26.5 mm
Thickness: 1.9 mm
Case of Issue: See Sets, pages 535, 541-543

Engravers:
Obv.:   1997, 2002: Dora de Pédery-Hunt
             2004-2018: Susan Taylor
Rev.:   See reverse illustrations

Edge: Plain
Die Axis: ↑↑
Finish: Specimen

DATE	DESCRIPTION	QUANTITY SOLD	ISSUE PRICE	FINISH	SP-68	SP-69
1997 (1987-)	10th Anniversary of the Loon Dollar	181,719	N.I.I.	Specimen	25.	—
2002 (1987-)	15th Anniversary of the Loon Dollar	67,672	N.I.I.	Specimen	30.	—
2004	Canada Goose	46,493	N.I.I.	Specimen	35.	—
2004	Elusive Loon	12,550	N.I.I.	Specimen	50.	—
2005	Tufted Puffin	39,818	N.I.I.	Specimen	50.	—
2006	Snowy Owl	39,935	N.I.I.	Specimen	50.	—
2007	Trumpeter Swan	27,056	N.I.I.	Specimen	45.	—
2008	Common Eider	21,227	N.I.I.	Specimen	45.	—
2009	Great Blue Heron	21,677	N.I.I.	Specimen	45.	—
2010	Northern Harrier	21,111	N.I.I.	Specimen	45.	—
2011	Great Grey Owl	25,665	N.I.I.	Specimen	50.	—
2012	25th Anniversary of the Loon Dollar	34,975	N.I.I.	Specimen	45.	—
2013	Blue-Winged Teal	28,884	N.I.I.	Specimen	45.	—
2014	Ferruginous Hawk	24,381	N.I.I.	Specimen	45.	—
2015	Blue Jay	22,739	N.I.I.	Specimen	45.	—
2016	Tundra Swan	21,565	N.I.I.	Specimen	45.	—
2017	Snow Goose	4,515	N.I.I.	Specimen	45.	—
2018	Burrowing Owl	30,000	N.I.I.	Specimen	40.	—

NOTE TO COLLECTORS

When the initials N.I.I. appear in the pricing table it indicates the coin was part of a set issued by the Royal Canadian Mint, and not issued individu
Coin designs that are found only in sets offered by the Royal Canadian Mint are listed individually by denomination, and date in Volume Two.

SP-68 / PR-69   This price is based on the item still being in the original package as sold by the Mint.
SP-69 / PR-70   This price is based on them item being graded by a reputable third-party grading company.

NICKEL-BRONZE DOLLAR PROOF ISSUES, 2002-2012

NE DOLLAR, CENTRE ICE LOON, 1987-2002.

A "Centre Ice" 22-karat gold-plated loon dollar coin was issued as part of a souvenir album entitled "Going For Gold." It was jointly offered by the yal Canadian Mint, Canada Post, and Maclean's Magazine to commemorate the Olympic gold medals for hockey won by the Canadian Men's and men's teams in the Salt Lake City Winter Olympic Games in 2002.

Designers and Engravers:

Obv.:	Dora de Pédery-Hunt
Rev.:	R. R. Carmichael, Cosme Saffioti
Composition:	91.5% Ni, 8.5% Bronze, Gold plated
Weight:	7.0 g
11-sided:	26.5 mm **Edge:** Plain
Thickness:	1.9 mm **Die Axis:** ↑↑
Finish:	Proof
Case of Issue:	See Derivatives, page 134

DATE	DESCRIPTION	QUANTITY SOLD	ISSUE PRICE	FINISH	PR-69	PR-70
2002 (1987-)	Centre Ice Loon, Gold-plated bronze	25,000	N.I.I.	Proof	50.	—

NE DOLLAR, 100TH ANNIVERSARY OF THE MONTREAL CANADIENS, 1909-2009.

Canada Post and the Royal Canadian Mint offered two different sets in 2009 for the 100th anniversary of the Montreal Canadiens:

1. Montreal Canadiens 100th Anniversary Pack which included a lacquered anniversary dollar and a lenticular souvenir sheet
2. Montreal Canadiens 100th Anniversary Set which included three different dollar coins (lacquered, painted Canadiens crest, and gold plated) plus a lenticular souvenir sheet.

Common Obverse	Lacquered	Painted Crest	Gold plated

signers:

Obv.:	Susanna Blunt
Rev.:	RCM Staff
mposition:	91.5% Ni, 8.5% Bronze
ight:	7.0 g
-sided:	26.5 mm
ish:	1. Circulation, Lacquered
	2. Circulation, Painted crest
	3. Circulation, Gold plated
se of Issue:	See Derivatives, page 134

Engravers:

Obv.:	Susan Taylor
Rev.:	Konrad Wachelko
Thickness:	2.0 mm
Die Axis:	↑↑
Edge:	Plain

DATE	DESCRIPTION	SOURCE	QUANTITY SOLD	ISSUE PRICE	FINISH	MS-65 NC	MS-66 NC
2009 (1909-)	Montreal Canadiens, Lacquered	Collector Set / Pack	N/A	N.I.I.	Lacquered	10.	—
2009 (1909-)	Montreal Canadiens, Painted crest	Collector Set	526	N.I.I.	Painted	50.	—
2009 (1909-)	Montreal Canadiens, Gold plated	Collector Set	9,500	N.I.I.	Gold plated	50.	—

ONE DOLLAR, 100TH ANNIVERSARY OF THE CANADIAN NAVY, 1910-2010.

An enlisted seaman of 1910, and a female officer of 2010, in front of *HMCS Halifax* the lead ship in the Navy's current fleet are depicted on th commemorative coin.

Designers and Engravers:

Obv.:	Susanna Blunt, Susan Taylor
Rev.:	Bonnie Ross, Stan Witten
Composition:	1. Nickel bronze
	2. Nickel bronze, Gold plated
Weight:	7.0 g
11-sided:	26.5 mm **Edge:** Plain
Thickness:	1.9 mm **Die Axis:** ↑↑
Finish:	Circulation
Case of Issue:	See Derivatives, page 134, and
	Special Edition Uncirculated Sets, page 521

DATE	DESCRIPTION	QUANTITY SOLD	ISSUE PRICE	FINISH	MS-65 NC	MS-66 NC
2010 (1910-)	Canadian Navy Centennial, Gold plated	10,085	19.95	Circulation	15.	—
2010 (1910-)	Canadian Navy Centennial	N/A	N.I.I.	Circulation	5.	—

ONE DOLLAR, 100TH ANNIVERSARY OF THE SASKATCHEWAN ROUGHRIDERS, 1910-2010.

Designers and Engravers:

Obv.:	Susanna Blunt, Susan Taylor
Rev.:	Saskatchewan Roughriders Football
	Club, RCM Staff
Composition:	1. Nickel bronze
	2. Nickel bronze, Gold plated
Weight:	7.0 g
11-sided:	26.5 mm **Edge:** Reeded
Thickness:	1.9 mm **Die Axis:** ↑↑
Finish:	Circulation
Case of Issue:	See Derivatives, page 134, and
	Special Edition Uncirculated Sets, page 521

DATE	DESCRIPTION	QUANTITY SOLD	ISSUE PRICE	FINISH	MS-65 NC	MS-66 NC
2010 (1910-)	Saskatchewan Roughriders, Gold plated	32,676	19.95	Circulation	12.	—
2010 (1910-)	Saskatchewan Roughriders	N/A	N.I.I.	Circulation	5.	—

ONE DOLLAR, 25TH ANNIVERSARY OF THE LOON DOLLAR, 1987-2012.

This coin was issued to celebrate the 25th anniversary of the loon dollar which was first introduced in 1987.

Designers and Engravers:

Obv.:	Susanna Blunt, Susan Taylor
Rev.:	R. R. Carmichael, RCM Staff
Composition:	Silver plated bronze plated steel
Weight:	7.0 g
11-sided:	26.5 mm **Edge:** Plain
Thickness:	1.9 mm **Die Axis:** ↑↑
Finish:	Circulation
Case of Issue:	See Derivatives, page 134

DATE	DESCRIPTION	QUANTITY SOLD	ISSUE PRICE	FINISH	MS-65 NC	MS-66 NC
2012 (1987-)	25th Anniversary of the Loon Dollar	8,890	N.I.I.	Circulation	25.	—

NOTE TO COLLECTORS

The Canadian Navy and Saskatchewan Roughriders uncirculated nickel-bronze dollars are also found in the 2010 Special Edition Uncircula Set, see page 521.

LOON STYLE NICKEL DOLLAR ISSUES, 2008-2010

▌E DOLLAR, 2007-2008 CANADIAN NHL HOCKEY SEASON, 2008 (GIFTWARE).

▌AD JERSEY CRESTS
This series of dollars is
▌nd in the NHL Teams Sets
▌e page 505).

Common obverse

Calgary Flames

Edmonton Oilers

Montreal Canadiens

Ottawa Senators

Toronto Maple Leafs

Vancouver Canucks

▌ME JERSEY CRESTS
This series of dollars is
▌nd embedded in official NHL
▌key pucks which are blister
▌kaged.

Common obverse

Calgary Flames

Edmonton Oilers

Montreal Canadiens

▌signers and Engravers:
Obv.:	Susanna Blunt, Susan Taylor
Rev.:	RCM Staff
▌nposition:	Nickel, Decal
▌ght:	7.0 g
▌sided:	26.5 mm
▌ckness:	1.9 mm
▌e:	Plain
▌ Axis:	↑↑
▌sh:	Uncirculated

Ottawa Senators

Toronto Maple Leafs

Vancouver Canucks

▌e of Issue:	**Road Jersey Crests:** Coloured folder
	Home Jersey Crests: Embedded in an official NHL puck, blister packaged

DATE	DESCRIPTION	SOURCE	QUANTITY SOLD	ISSUE PRICE	FINISH	MS-65 NC	MS-66 NC
2008	Calgary Flames, Road Jersey	NHL Set	N/A	N.I.I.	Uncirculated	20.	—
2008	Edmonton Oilers, Road Jersey	NHL Set	1,584	N.I.I.	Uncirculated	20.	—
2008	Montreal Canadiens, Road Jersey	NHL Set	2,659	N.I.I.	Uncirculated	35.	—
2008	Ottawa Senators, Road Jersey	NHL Set	1,633	N.I.I.	Uncirculated	20.	—
2008	Toronto Maple Leafs, Road Jersey	NHL Set	N/A	N.I.I.	Uncirculated	20.	—
2008	Vancouver Canucks, Road Jersey	NHL Set	1,302	N.I.I.	Uncirculated	20.	—
2008	Calgary Flames, Home Jersey	NHL Puck	1,304	15.95	Uncirculated	20.	—
2008	Edmonton Oilers, Home Jersey	NHL Puck	484	15.95	Uncirculated	20.	—
2008	Montreal Canadiens, Home Jersey	NHL Puck	62	15.95	Uncirculated	30.	—
2008	Ottawa Senators, Home Jersey	NHL Puck	775	15.95	Uncirculated	20.	—
2008	Toronto Maple Leafs, Home Jersey	NHL Puck	2,605	15.95	Uncirculated	20.	—
2008	Vancouver Canucks, Home Jersey	NHL Puck	1,160	15.95	Uncirculated	20.	—

ONE DOLLAR, 2008-2009 CANADIAN NHL HOCKEY SEASON, 2009 (GIFTWARE).

These nickel coloured dollar coins which feature the team logos are each embedded in a mini puck attached to a key chain. The key chain ald with a mini hockey stick and an informative insert card are enclosed in a blister pack.

Common Obverse

Calgary Flames

Edmonton Oilers

Montreal Canadiens

Ottawa Senators

Toronto Maple Leafs

Vancouver Canucks

Designers:		**Engravers:**	
Obv.:	Susanna Blunt	Obv.:	Susan Taylor
Rev.:	RCM Staff	Rev.:	RCM Staff
Composition:	Nickel, Decal		
Weight:	6.50 g	**Edge:**	Plain
11-sided:	26.5 mm	**Die Axis:**	↑↑
Thickness:	1.7 mm	**Finish:**	Uncirculated
Case of Issue:	Blister packaged, See Derivatives page 134		

DATE	DESCRIPTION	SOURCE	QUANTITY SOLD	ISSUE PRICE	FINISH	MS-65 NC	MS-6 NC
2009	Calgary Flames, Home Jersey	Mini Puck	73	24.95	Uncirculated	25.	—
2009	Edmonton Oilers, Home Jersey	Mini Puck	49	24.95	Uncirculated	25.	—
2009	Montreal Canadiens, Home Jersey	Mini Puck	326	24.95	Uncirculated	30.	—
2009	Ottawa Senators, Home Jersey	Mini Puck	95	24.95	Uncirculated	25.	—
2009	Toronto Maple Leafs, Home Jersey	Mini Puck	199	24.95	Uncirculated	25.	—
2009	Vancouver Canucks, Home Jersey	Mini Puck	101	24.95	Uncirculated	25.	—

Note: Mintage numbers are from the 2009 Royal Canadian Mint Annual Report. The 2008 and 2010 Annual Reports do not carry mintage numb for these coins.

NE DOLLAR, 2008-2009 CANADIAN NHL HOCKEY SEASON, 2009 (GIFTWARE) [cont.].

Road hockey jerseys folded in the shape of a heart are the central device on these nickel dollars. The coloured dollars are included in NHL Team ncirculated Sets for the 2008-2009 season, see page 532.

Common Obverse

Calgary Flames

Edmonton Oilers

Montreal Canadiens

Ottawa Senators

Toronto Maple Leafs

Vancouver Canucks

signers:		Engravers:	
Obv.:	Susanna Blunt	Obv.:	Susan Taylor
Rev.:	RCM Staff	Rev.:	RCM Staff
mposition:	Nickel, Decal		
eight:	7.0 g		
-sided:	26.5 mm	Edge:	Plain
ickness:	1.9 mm	Die Axis:	↑↑
se of Issue:	Blister packaged	Finish:	Uncirculated

DATE	DESCRIPTION	SOURCE	QUANTITY SOLD	ISSUE PRICE	FINISH	MS-65 NC	MS-66 NC
2009	Calgary Flames, Road Jersey	NHL Sets	382	24.95	Uncirculated	25.	—
2009	Edmonton Oilers, Road Jersey	NHL Sets	472	24.95	Uncirculated	25.	—
2009	Montreal Canadiens, Road Jersey	NHL Sets	4,857	24.95	Uncirculated	35.	—
2009	Ottawa Senators, Road Jersey	NHL Sets	387	24.95	Uncirculated	25.	—
2009	Toronto Maple Leafs, Road Jersey	NHL Sets	1,328	24.95	Uncirculated	25.	—
2009	Vancouver Canucks, Road Jersey	NHL Sets	794	24.95	Uncirculated	25.	—

NE DOLLAR, VANCOUVER 2010 LUCKY LOONIE, 2010.

This painted nickel dollar bearing the official emblem of the Vancouver 2010 Olympic Winter Games was used extensively in many giftware products e Derivatives, page 134). An identical variety in sterling silver, and with a proof finish, was issued as a Lucky Loonie, see page 128-129.

Designers and Engravers:

Obv.:	Susanna Blunt, Susan Taylor		
Rev.:	José Osio		
Composition:	Nickel, Painted		
Weight:	6.4 g		
11-sided:	26.5 mm	**Edge:**	Plain
Thickness:	1.9 mm	**Die Axis:**	↑↑
Finish:	Circulation		
Case of Issue:	See Derivatives, page 134		

DATE	DESCRIPTION	QUANTITY SOLD	ISSUE PRICE	FINISH	MS-65 NC	MS-66 NC
2010	Inukshuk, Vancouver 2010 Lucky Loonie, Painted	N/A	N.I.I.	Uncirculated	25.	—

LOON STYLE STERLING and FINE SILVER DOLLAR PROOF ISSUES, 2004-2018

ONE DOLLAR, STERLING SILVER AND FINE SILVER ISSUES, 2004-2018.

Issued in a proof finish, these uncirculated one-dollar coins commemorate the Olympics, occasions, and various historical and numismatic anniversaries.

Obverse P
2013-2016
"Plated"

OBVERSES 2004-2018

Obverse 2004 and 2006	Obverse 2006-2008	Obverse 2010	Obverse 2013-2016	Obverse 2017-2018

REVERSES 2004-2018

2004 Lucky Loonie Des.: R. R. Carmichael Engr.: RCM Staff	2006 Snowflake Des. and Engr.: Marcos Hallam	2006 Loon Settling Lucky Loonie Des.: RCM Staff Engr.: Cecily Mok	2006 Lullaby Loonie Des. and Engr.: Susan Taylor

2007 Baby Rattle Des.: RCM Staff Engr.: Cecily Mok	2007 "ABC" Building Blocks Des. and Engr.: Susan Taylor	2007-2008 Sterling Silver Loon Des.: R. R. Carmichael Engr.: Terry Smith	2008 Olympic Loon Dance Des. and Engr.: RCM Staff

2010 Anticipating The Game Des. and Engr.: José Osio	2012 (1987-) Silver, Gold Plated Loon Des.: R. R. Carmichael Engr.: RCM Staff	2012 25th Anniv. of Loonie Des.: R. R. Carmichael Engr.: RCM Staff	2012 25th Anniversary Lucky Loonie Des.: Emily Damstra Engr.: RCM Staff

NE DOLLAR, STERLING SILVER AND FINE SILVER ISSUES, 2004-2018 (continued).

2013-2018	2014	2016	2017
Silver, Gold Plated Loon	Lucky Loonie	Lucky Loonie	Connecting a Nation
Des.: R. R. Carmichael	Des.: Emily Damstra	Des.: Derek Wicks	Des.: Wesley Klassen
Engr.: RCM Staff	Engr.: RCM Staff	Engr.: RCM Staff	Engr.: RCM Staff

sigers
- Obv.: Susanna Blunt
- Rev.: See reverse illustrations

mposition: 2004-2010
92.5% Ag, 7.5% Cu, Painted

ver content: 6.475 g, 0.208 tr oz

eight: 7.0 g

sided: 26.5 mm

ickness: 1.7 to 1.9 mm

ge: Plain

e Axis: ↑↑

nish: Proof

Engravers:
- Obv.: Susan Taylor
- Rev.: See reverse illustrations

2012-2018
99.99% Ag

7.0 g, 0.225 tr oz to 8.1 g, .26 tr oz

7.0 to 8.1 g

26.5 mm

1.8 to 1.9

Plain

↑↑

Proof

se of Issue: Proof singles: Maroon leatherette clam style case, black flocked insert, encapsulated coin, COA
Proof single: 2010 Black leatherette clam style case, black flocked insert, encapsulated coin, COA Olympic themed sleeve

DATE	DESCRIPTION	SOURCE	QUANTITY SOLD	ISSUE PRICE	FINISH	MS-65 NC	MS-66 NC
2004	"Lucky Loonie", Painted	Proof. Single	19,994	39.95	Proof	45.	—
2006	Snowflake, Painted	Holiday Set, Blue folder	34,014	34.95	Proof	50.	—
2006	Loon Settling, Lucky Loonie, Painted	Pr. Single	19.973	39.95	Proof	40.	—
2006	Lullaby Loonie, Sterling silver	Folder and CD 1	8,225	29.95	Proof	150.	—
2006	Lullaby Loonie, Sterling silver	Keepsake Box Included		34.95	Proof	200.	—
2006	Lullaby Loonie, Sterling silver	CD and Picture Frame	Included	34.95	Proof	150.	—
2006	Lullaby Loonie, Sterling silver	Premium Baby Gift Set	Included	N.I.I.	Proof	200.	—
2007	Baby Rattle, Silver	Folder and CD	3,207	34.95	Proof	75.	—
2007	Baby Rattle, Gold plated	Premium Baby Gift Set	1,911	N.I.I	Proof	200.	—
2007	"ABC" Building Blocks	Keepsake Box	3,229	34.95	Proof	400.	—
2007	Sterling Silver Loon	Premium Wedding Gift Set	849	N.I.I.	Proof	100.	—
2008	Sterling Silver Loon	Premium Wedding Gift Set	N/A	N.I.I.	Proof	50.	—
2008	Sterling Silver Loon	Premium Baby Gift Set	N/A	N.I.I.	Proof	50.	—
2008	Sterling Silver Loon	Keepsake Box	N/A	N.I.I.	Proof	75.	—
2008	Sterling Silver Loon	CD and Picture Frame Holder	N/A	N.I.I.	Proof	50.	—
2008	Olympic Loon Dance, Painted	Proof. Single	52,987	49.95	Proof	40.	—
2010	Anticipating the Games, Painted	Proof. Single	13,285	54.95	Proof	50.	—
2012	Fine Silver, Gold Plated Premium	Proof Set	19,789	N.I.I.	Proof	70.	—
2012	25th Anniv. Loonie	Proof. Single	15,004	34.95	Proof	35.	—
2012	25th Anniv. Lucky Loonie, Painted	Proof. Single	19,982	39.95	Proof	40.	—
2013	Fine Silver, Gold Plated Premium	Proof Set	20,182	N.I.I.	Proof	35.	—
2014	Fine Silver, Gold Plated Premium	Proof Set	13,416	N.I.I.	Proof	35.	—
2014	Olympic Lucky Loonie, Painted	Proof. Single	14,449	39.95	Proof	40.	—
2015	Fine Silver, Gold Plated Premium	Proof Set	20,000	N.I.I.	Proof	35.	—
2016	Olympic Lucky Loonie	Proof Single	13,690	39.95	Proof	40.	—
2016	Fine Silver, Gold Plated Premium	Proof Set	20,000	N.I.I.	Proof	35.	—
2017	Fine Silver, Gold Plated Premium	Premium Proof Set	20,000	N.I.I.	Proof	40.	—
2017	Connecting a Nation, Gold Plated	Premium Proof Set	20,000	N.I.I.	Proof	50.	—
2017	Connecting a Nation	Proof Set	25,000	N.I.I.	Proof	15.	—
2018	Fine Silver, Gold Plated Premium	Proof Set	20,000	N.I.I.	Proof	35.	—

BIG COIN SERIES

ONE DOLLAR, BIG COIN SET, 2015-2018.

The Big Coin Series started in 2015, features Robert Carmichael's iconic loon design on the 2015, 2016 and 2018 coins, first used in 1987, with A Colville's 1967 design for the 2017 coin. The coins illustrated are smaller than actual size. For other coins in the set, see pages 11, 16, 56, 86, and 1

Designers and Engravers:

Obv.:	Susanna Blunt, Susan Taylor
Rev.:	Robert-Ralph Carmichael, RCM Staff
	Alex Colville
	Emanuel Hahn

Silver content: 157.58 g, 5.07 tr oz
Weight: 157.6 g
Diameter: 65.25 mm
Thickness: N/A
Case of Issue: Maroon clam style case, black flocked insert, encapsulated coin, COA, custom box

Composition:

2015:	99.99% Ag, Selectively gold plated
2016:	99.99% Ag, Selectively coloured on reverse
2017:	99.99% Ag, Selectively gold plated
2018	99.95% Ag, Selectively rose gold-plated

Edge: Reeded
Die Axis: ↑↑
Finish: Proof

DATE	DESCRIPTION	SOURCE	QUANTITY SOLD	ISSUE PRICE	FINISH	PR-69	PR-70
2015	$1 Big Coin, with gold plating	Pr. Single	1,500	549.95	Proof	700.	—
2016	$1 Big Coin, with colour	Pr. Single	1,500	519.95	Proof	550.	—
2017	$1 Big Coin, with gold plating	Pr. Single	2,111	549.95	Proof	600.	—
2018	$1 Big Coin, with rose gold-plating	Pr. Single	1,500	559.95	Proof	560.	—

Note: Coins illustrated smaller than actual size.

THREE-PLY BRASS-PLATED STEEL DOLLAR ISSUES, 2014-2018

NE DOLLAR, LOON, OCCASIONS SETS, 2014-2018.

These one dollar coins are from the Occasions and Holiday Gift Sets. See pages 528-529, 535-536.

esigners:
   Obv.:   Susanna Blunt
   Rev.:   See reverse illustrations
omposition: 3-ply brass plated steel
eight: 6.27 g
-sided: 26.5 mm
nish: Uncirculated

Engravers:
   Obv.:   Susan Taylor
   Rev.:   RCM Staff
Thickness: 1.9 mm
Edge: Plain
Die Axis: ↑↑
Case of Issue: Coloured folder

| Common Obverse 2014-2018 | Stork Born in 2014 Des.: Steven Stewart | Gifts and Balloons Happy Birthday 2014 Des.: Matt Bowen | Maple Leaf O Canada 2014 Des.: RCM Staff | Two Turtle Doves Married in 2014 Des.: RCM Staff |

| Reindeer 2014 Holiday Gift Set Des.: RCM Staff | Teddy Bear Born in 2015 Des.: RCM Staff | Three Balloons Happy Birthday 2015 Des.: RCM Staff | Large Maple Leaf O Canada 2015 Des.: Ali Giroux | Two Swans Married in 2015 Des.: RCM Staff |

| Snowflake 2015 Holiday Gift Set Des.: RCM Staff | Wedding Bells Married in 2016 Des.: Joel Kimmel | Large Maple Leaf O Canada 2016 Des.: Joel Kimmel | Building Blocks Born in 2016 Des.: Joel Kimmel | Cupcake, Party Hat, Present Happy Birthday 2016 Des.: Joel Kimmel |

| Holly and Pine Cone 2016 Holiday Gift Set Des.: Joel Kimmel | Hearts, Wedding Rings Married in 2017 Des.: RCM Staff | Large Maple Leaf O Canada 2017 Des.: RCM Staff | Rocking Horse Born in 2017 Des.: RCM Staff | Birthday Presents Happy Birthday 2017 Des.: RCM Staff |

ONE DOLLAR, LOON, OCCASIONS SETS, 2014-2018 (cont.).

| Ornaments and Holly 2017 Holiday Gift Set Des.: Joel Kimmel | Doves, Wedding Rings Married in 2018 Des.: RCM Staff | Two Large Maple Leaves & Keys O Canada 2018 Des.: RCM Staff | Crib & Teddy Bears Born in 2018 Des.: RCM Staff | Birthday Cake Happy Birthday 2018 Des.: RCM Staff |

DATE	DESCRIPTION	QUANTITY SOLD	ISSUE PRICE	FINISH	MS-65
2014	Stork, Born in 2014	54,122	N.I.I.	Uncirculated	20.
2014	Gifts and Balloons, Happy Birthday 2014	44,539	N.I.I.	Uncirculated	15.
2014	Maple Leaf, O Canada 2014	32,289	N.I.I.	Uncirculated	15.
2014	Two Turtle Doves, Married in 2014	35,742	N.I.I.	Uncirculated	15.
2014	Reindeer, Holiday Gift Set	31,951	N.I.I.	Uncirculated	15.
2015	Teddy Bear, Born in 2015	42,074	N.I.I.	Uncirculated	15.
2015	Three Balloons, Happy Birthday 2015	19,280	N.I.I.	Uncirculated	15.
2015	Large Maple Leaf, O Canada 2015	23,705	N.I.I.	Uncirculated	15.
2015	Two Swans, Married in 2015	18,427	N.I.I.	Uncirculated	15.
2015	Snowflake, 2015 Holiday Gift Set	32,994	N.I.I.	Uncirculated	15.
2016	Wedding Bells, Married in 2016	23,788	N.I.I.	Uncirculated	15.
2016	Large Maple Leaf, O Canada 2016	40,169	N.I.I.	Uncirculated	15.
2016	Building Blocks, Born in 2016	47,733	N.I.I.	Uncirculated	15.
2016	Cupcake, Party Hat, Present, Happy Birthday 2016	25,648	N.I.I.	Uncirculated	15.
2016	Holly and Pine Cone, 2016 Holiday Gift Set	23,696	N.I.I.	Uncirculated	15.
2017	Rose, Hearts, Wedding Rings, Married in 2017	14,145	N.I.I.	Uncirculated	15.
2017	Large Maple Leaf, O Canada 2017	20,652	N.I.I.	Uncirculated	15.
2017	Rocking Horse, Born in 2017	20,189	N.I.I.	Uncirculated	15.
2017	Birthday Presents, Happy Birthday 2017	14,149	N.I.I.	Uncirculated	15.
2017	Ornaments and Holly, 2017 Holiday Gift Set	N/A	N.I.I.	Uncirculated	17.
2018	Doves, Wedding Rings, Married in 2018	N/A	N.I.I.	Uncirculated	17.
2018	Two Large Maple Leaves, Maple Keys, O Canada 2018	N/A	N.I.I.	Uncirculated	17.
2018	Crib & Teddy Bears, Born in 2018	N/A	N.I.I.	Uncirculated	17.
2018	Birthday Cake, Happy Birthday 2018	N/A	N.I.I	Uncirculated	17.

E DOLLAR, ELIZABETH II PROOF, 2014.

This coin is from the 2014 Standard Proof Set.

Designers and Engravers:

Obv.:	Susanna Blunt, Susan Taylor
Rev.:	RCM Staff

Composition:	3-ply brass plated steel		
Weight:	6.27		
11-sided:	26.5 mm	**Edge:**	Plain
Thickness:	1.9 mm	**Die Axis:**	↑↑
Finish:	Proof		
Case of Issue:	See Proof Sets, page 550		

DATE	DESCRIPTION	SOURCE	QUANTITY SOLD	ISSUE PRICE	FINISH	PR-69	PR-70
2014	Elizabeth II Proof Coin	Pr. Set	11,251	N.I.I.	Proof	15.	—

E DOLLAR, 30TH ANNIVERSARY OF THE LOONIE, 1987-2017.

A special edition of the looinie is paired with the Voyageur design that was intended to appear on the one-dollar coin. It's a unique opportunity to w what is, next to what could have been – the coin that never was!

Common Obverse	Loon Designer: Robert-Ralph Carmichael	Voyageur Designer: Emanuel Hahn

signers:

Obv.:	Susanna Blunt
Rev.:	See reverse illustrations

mposition:	99.99% Ag
ight:	7.89 g
meter	26.5 mm
sh:	Proof

Engravers:

Obv.:	Susan Taylor

Thickness:	N/A
Die Axis:	↑↑
Edge:	Plain
Case of Issue:	Maroon clamshell with a black beauty box, COA

DATE	DESCRIPTION	MINTAGE	ISSUE PRICE	FINISH	PR-69	PR-70
2017 (1987-)	30th Anniversary of the Loonie 2-coin set	10,000	79.95	Proof	100.	—

ONE DOLLAR DERIVATIVES

DATE	DESCRIPTION	QUANTITY SOLD	ISSUE PRICE	ISSUER	FINISH	MARKE PRICE
1993	**Silver Dollar, 100th Anniversary of the Stanley Cup**, 43¢ Stanley Cup Commemorative Stamp	N/A	28.95	RCM, CP	MS-65	35
1997	**Silver Dollar, Canada/Russia Hockey**; Two 45¢ mint stamps; $5 phone card; Multicoloured folder	N/A	29.95	RCM, CP	MS-65	45
1997	**Silver Dollar, Canada/Russia Hockey**; Sterling silver pin	N/A	29.95	RCM	MS-65	30
1997	**Silver Dollar, Canada/Russia Hockey**; Print	N/A	24.95	RCM	MS-65	35
1997	**Silver Dollar, Canada/Russia Hockey**; Phone card/stamp set	N/A	N/A	RCM	MS-65	35
1998	**Loon Dollar**; Mint and cancelled one dollar stamps; Blue presentation case	N/A	17.99	RCM, CP	MS-65	10
1998	**Silver Dollar, 125th Anniv. R.C.M.P.**; Pin	N/A	29.95	RCM	MS-65	30
1999	**Silver Dollar, 225th Anniv. Juan Perez**; Journal Gift Set; Multicoloured folder	N/A	N/A	RCM, CP	MS-65	40
2000	**Loon Dollar**, Mint and cancelled one dollar stamps; Blue presentation case	N/A	17.99	RCM, CP	MS-65	10
2000	**Loon Dollar**, Encapsulated in a credit card	N/A	N/A	RCM	MS-65	5
2001	**Loon Dollar**, Encapsulated in a credit card	N/A	N/A	RCM	MS-65	5
2001	**Loon /Sacagawea Dollars**, Folder	N/A	N/A	RCM, USM	MS-65	10
2002	**Centre Ice Loon**, 22kt gold-plated bronze; block of four 48¢ stamps, Two Olympic Edition Macleans' magazines (one English, one French); "Going For Gold" Souvenir album, COA	25,000	54.95	RCM, CP, MM	PR-67	50
2004	**Silver Dollar, 2004 French Settlement with privy mark**; 2004 silver ¼ Euro; Canada 49¢ stamps, mint/cancelled; France .90 Euro stamps, mint/cancelled; Wooden presentation case, blue insert, encapsulated coins, COA	8,315	99.95	RCM, CP	MS-65	90
2004	**Elusive Loon with Privy Mark**, Mint and cancelled one dollar stamps; Wooden presentation case	12,550	25.22	RCM, CP	PR-67	50
2005	**Silver Dollar, 40th Anniversary of Canada's National Flag**, CD-Rom; Presentation folder	N/A	34.95	RCM	MS-65	35
2006	**Lucky Loonie Bookmark** "Celebrate the Legend"	10,095	N/A	RCM	MS-65	15
2008	**Nickel Bronze Lucky Loonie** embedded in Lucite	N/A	N/A	RCM	MS-65	15
2009	**Montreal Canadiens 100th Anniversary Pack**, 100th anniv. dollar coin and a lenticular souvenir sheet	15,473	19.95	RCM	MS-65	35
2009	**Montreal Canadiens 100th Anniversary Collector Set**, three one dollar coins (lacquered, coloured crest, gold plated),a sheet of three stamps, a lenticular souvenir sheet, 15 named retired jersey plaquettes, souvenir booklet	526	149.95	RCM	MS-65	150
2009	**NHL Canadian Team Crest Mini-Puck Mini-Stick Key Rings**, Colourised NHL team coin embedded in a mini puck key chain, 5" mini hockey stick	N/A	24.95	RCM	MS-65	25
2010	**Vancouver 2010 Colourised Nickel Bronze Lucky Loonie**, encapsulated and embedded in NHL puck; Blister packaged	30,396	19.95	RCM	MS-65	30
2010	**Sport Bag Tag**, colourised Vancouver 2010 Lucky Loonie dollar and lapel pin, green "See In Tin" container.	N/A	14.95	RCM	MS-65	30
2010	**Lanyard**, colourised Vancouver 2010 Lucky Loonie dollar	N/A	14.95	RCM	MS-65	35
2010	Hockey Player Lapel Pin Set, colourised 2010 Lucky Loonie dollar and six "hockey player" lapel pins.	N/A	N/A	RCM	MS-65	75
2010	**100th Anniversary Canadian Navy Coin and Stamp Set**, Gold plated nickel-bronze dollar; souvenir stamp sheet; 40-page booklet; square aluminum tin	20,000	39.95	RCM, CP	MS-65	25
2010	**100th Anniversary Saskatchewan Roughriders**, Gold plated nickel-bronze dollar; pop-up helmet packaging	N/A	19.95	RCM	MS-65	25
2012	**25th Anniversary of the Loonie Coin Card**, "Build Your Own" paper toy, Mini-book, Coin card	N/A	24.95	RCM	MS-65	25
2012	**CFL Ultimate Collector Set**, Grey Cup circulation loon style dollar, a special pane of nine commemorative stamps, a souvenir sheet featuring the eight CFL team logos, 100th Grey Cup 1 oz pure silver wafer, a replica Grey Cup, ten silver-edged collectable pins, souvenir booklet	8,000	199.95	RCM, CP	MS-65	150

Note: CP = Canada Post; MM = Maclean's Magazine; RCM = Royal Canadian Mint; USM = United States Mint

TWO DOLLARS

The first Canadian two dollar coin was issued in 1996 to replace the two dollar bank note which was then withdrawn from circulation. To mark this ─ent the Numismatic Department of the Royal Canadian Mint issued four different planchet varieties, in two different finishes.

▌WO DOLLARS, POLAR BEAR, 1996.
The 1996 two dollar Piedfort was not issued singly, but as part of a set. See the Two Dollar Derivatives, page 144.

| Obverse: Nickel / Bronze | Reverse: Nickel / Bronze | Obverse: Gold / Gold | Reverse: Gold / Gold |

▪signers:
  Obv.:   Dora de Pédery-Hunt
  Rev.:   Brent Townsend

Engravers:
  Obv.:   Dora de Pédery-Hunt
  Rev.:   Ago Aarand

▪mposition:	**Nickel Ring** 99.0% Ni 07.5% Cu	**Silver Ring** 92.5% Ag 77.6% Ag,	**White Gold Ring** 17.2% Au 5.2% Cu
	Bronze Core 92.0 % Cu 6.0% Al, 2.0% Ni	**Silver Gilt Core** 92.5% Ag 07.5% Cu	**Yellow Gold Core** 91.7% Au 04.1% Ag, 4.2% Cu
	Standard	**Standard**	**Piedford**	**Standard**
▪eight (g):	Ring 4.84 Core 2.46 Total 7.3	Ring 5.86 Core 2.97 Total 8.83	Ring 11.72 Core 5.94 Total 17.66	Ring 6.31 Core 5.09 Total 11.4
▪ntent: Gold	—	—	—	0.185 tr oz
** Silver**	—	0.263 tr oz	0.525 tr oz	0.164 tr oz
▪ameter (mm):	Ring 28.0 Core 16.8	Ring 28.1 Core 16.8	Ring 28.1 Core 16.8	Ring 28.0 Core 16.8
▪ickness (mm):	1.8	1.9	3.6	1.8
▪ge:	Interrupted serrations	Interrupted serrations	Interrupted serrations	Interrupted serrations
▪ Axis:	↑↑	↑↑	↑↑	↑↑
▪ish:	Specimen, Proof	Proof	Proof	Proof
▪se of Issue:	Nickel / Bronze, Specimen: Blue presentation folder Nickel / Bronze, Proof: Black leatherette case, blue insert, encapsulated coin, COA Silver / Gilt, Proof: Black suede case, blue insert, encapsulated coin, COA Gold / Gold, Proof: Blue suede case, blue insert, encapsulated coin, COA			

DATE	DESCRIPTION	QUANTITY SOLD	ISSUE PRICE	FINISH	SP-67	SP-68	PR-69	PR-70
1996	Nickel / Bronze, Blue folder	74,669	10.95	Specimen	8.	—	12.	*
1996	Nickel / Bronze, Black leatherette case	66,843 2	4.95	Proof	—	—	15.	—
1996	Silver / Gilt, Black suede case	N/A	N/A	Proof	—	—	20.	—
1996	Silver / Gilt, Piedfort, See Derivatives	11,526	N.I.I.	Proof	—	—	100.	—
1996	Gold / Gold, Blue case	5,000	299.95	Proof	—	—	375.	—

NOTE ON TWO DOLLAR ISSUES

1.   The blue presentation folder was printed "uncirculated" but the $2 coin has a specimen finish.
2.   Piedfort is a term used to describe a double thickness or essaie coin, usually struck for approval, see Derivatives page 144.

TWO DOLLARS, STERLING SILVER PROOF COINS, 1997-2011.

In 1997 the two-dollar coin was added to the proof set. The standard nickel/bronze composition was not used, instead planchets were made fr◆ sterling silver with a gold-plated core.

| Obverse 1997-2003 | Obverse 2004-2006 Without Mint Logo | Obverse 2007-2011 With Mint Logo | Reverse 1997-2011 |

Designers:
Obv.:   1997-2003: Dora de Pédery-Hunt
         2004-2011: Susanna Blunt
Rev.:   1997-2011: Brent Townsend
Composition: 92.5% Ag, 7.5% Cu
Silver content: 8.17 g, 0.263 tr oz
Weight: 8.83 g
Diameter: 28.1 mm
Thickness: 1.9 mm

Engravers:
Obv.:   1997-2003: Dora de Pédery-Hunt
         2004-2011: Susan Taylor
Rev.:   1997-2011: Ago Aarand

Edge: Interrupted serrations
Die Axis: ↑↑
Finish: Proof
Case of Issue: See Proof Sets, page 547-549

** Add in Jaime's $2 2010 No Ice variety

DATE	DESCRIPTION	QUANTITY SOLD	ISSUE PRICE	FINISH	PR-69	PR-70
1997	Diademed Portrait / Polar Bear; Sterling Silver	113,647	N.I.I.	Proof	20.	—
1998		93,632	N.I.I.	Proof	20.	—
1999		95,113	N.I.I.	Proof	20.	—
2000		90,921	N.I.I.	Proof	20.	—
2001		74,194	N.I.I.	Proof	20.	—
2002		65,315	N.I.I.	Proof	20.	—
2003		62,007	N.I.I.	Proof	20.	—
2004	Uncrowned Portrait / Polar Bear; Sterling Silver	57,614	N.I.I.	Proof	20.	—
2005		63,562	N.I.I.	Proof	20.	—
2006		53,822	N.I.I.	Proof	20.	—
2007	Uncrowned Portrait, Mint Logo / Polar Bear; Sterling Silver	37,413	N.I.I.	Proof	20.	—
2008		38,630	N.I.I.	Proof	20.	—
2009		27,549	N.I.I.	Proof	20.	—
2010		32,342	N.I.I.	Proof	20.	—
2011		32,910	N.I.I.	Proof	20.	—

Note: 1. Quantity sold figures are identical to those listed for Proof Sets sold.
2. Continuation from 2012 forward of the two-dollar Proof coins is listed on page 142. The break in the listing is due to a change in composition.

TWO DOLLARS, NUNAVUT, PROOF COMMEMORATIVE, 1999.

This coin commemorates the formation of Nunavut, Canada's third territory, in 1999. The design honours the native drum dance.

Obverse: Nickel / Bronze	Reverse: Nickel / Bronze	Obverse: Gold / Gold	Reverse: Gold / Gold

Designers:		Engravers:	
Obv.:	Dora de Pédery-Hunt	Obv.:	Dora de Pédery-Hunt
Rev.:	G. Arnaktauyok	Rev.:	Ago Aarand, José Osio

Composition:	Nickel Ring	Silver Ring	White Gold Ring
	99.0% Ni	92.5% Ag	17.2% Au
		07.5% Cu	77.6% Ag, 5.2% Cu
	Bronze Core	Silver Gilt Core	Yellow Gold Core
	92.0 % Cu	92.5% Ag	91.7% Au
	6.0% Al, 2.0% Ni	07.5% Cu	04.1% Ag, 4.2% Cu
	Standard	Standard	Standard
Weight (g):	Ring 4.84	Ring 5.86	Ring 6.31
	Core 2.46	Core 2.97	Core 5.09
	Total 7.3	Total 8.83	Total 11.4
Content: Gold	—	—	0.185 tr oz
Silver	—	0.263 tr oz	0.164 tr oz
Diameter (mm):	Ring 28.0	Ring 28.1	Ring 28.0
	Core 16.8	Core 16.8	Core 16.8
Thickness (mm):	1.8	1.9	1.8
Edge:	Interrupted	Interrupted	Interrupted
	serrations	serrations	serrations
Die Axis:	↑↑	↑↑	↑↑
Finish:	Brilliant Uncirculated,	Proof	Proof
	Specimen		

Case of Issue:	Nickel / Bronze, Brilliant Uncirculated: Blue presentation folder
	Nickel / Bronze, Specimen: Maple wood case, encapsulated coin, window box
	Silver / Gilt, Proof: Green leatherette case, black insert, encapsulated coin, COA
	Gold / Gold, Proof: Antique case, black insert, encapsulated coin, COA

DATE	DESCRIPTION	SOURCE	QUANTITY SOLD	ISSUE PRICE	FINISH	AS ISSUED
1999	Nickel / Bronze	BU Set	N/A	N/A	BU	10.
1999	Nickel / Bronze	Specimen Set, Maple wood case	20,000	N/A	Specimen	20.
1999	Silver / Gilt	Proof Set, Single	39,873	24.95	Proof	25.
1999	Gold / Gold	Single Case	4,298	299.95	Proof	375.

VARIETIES OF 1999.

Three different reverse dies were used to produce the three different finishes on the 1999 Nunavut commemorative two dollar coins.

1.   Reverse Circulation Die: Raised narrow ring encircling the join between the ring and the core.
2.   Reverse Specimen Die: Raised wide ring encircling the join between the ring and the core.
3.   Reverse Proof Die: No encircling ring between the ring and the core.

Reverse	**Reverse**	**Reverse**
Narrow Ring	**Wide Ring**	**No Ring**
Brilliant Uncirculated	**Specimen Dies**	**Proof Dies**
Dies		

Two varieties of brilliant uncirculated sets were produced in 1999. The standard set, where the $2 coin was produced with a pair of brilli... uncirculated dies, and the Mule variety where the $2 coin was produced with an obverse brilliant uncirculated die and a reverse proof die. See pa... 516 for the listings of the 1999 brilliant uncirculated sets.

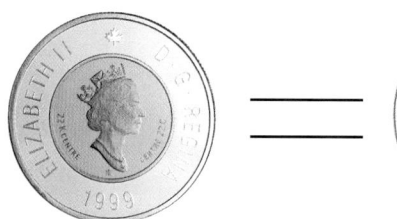

Nickel/bronze, no ring reverse mule

DATE	DESCRIPTION	QUANTITY SOLD	ISSUE PRICE	FINISH	SP-67	SP-68	PR-68	PR-69
1999	Mule from Brilliant Uncirculated Sets	Unknown	N.I.I.	BU	275.	—	—	—

TWO DOLLARS, PATH OF KNOWLEDGE COMMEMORATIVE, 2000.

The mother polar bear passes to her cubs the lesson of survival on the Arctic ice floes.

Obverse Nickel / Bronze	Reverse Nickel / Bronze	Obverse Gold / Gold	Reverse Gold / Gold

Designers:
Obv.:   Dora de Pédery-Hunt
Rev.:   Tony Bianco

Engravers:
Obv.:   Dora de Pédery-Hunt
Rev.:   Cosme Saffioti

Composition:	**Nickel Ring** 99.0% Ni	**Silver Ring** 92.5% Ag 07.5% Cu	**White Gold Ring** 17.2% Au 77.6% Ag, 5.2% Cu
	Bronze Core 92.0 % Cu 6.0% Al, 2.0% Ni	**Silver Gilt Core** 92.5% Ag 07.5% Cu	**Yellow Gold Core** 91.7% Au 04.1% Ag, 4.2% Cu
	Standard	Standard	Standard
Weight (g):	Ring 4.84 Core 2.46 Total 7.3	Ring 5.86 Core 2.97 Total 8.83	Ring 6.31 Core 5.09 Total 11.4
Content: Gold	—	—	0.185 tr oz
Silver	—	0.263 tr oz	0.164 tr oz
Diameter (mm):	Ring 28.0 Core 16.8	Ring 28.1 Core 16.8	Ring 28.0 Core 16.8
Thickness (mm):	1.8	1.9	1.8
Edge:	Interrupted serrations	Interrupted serrations	Interrupted serrations
Axis:	↑↑	↑↑	↑↑
Finish:	Brilliant Uncirculated, Specimen	Proof	Proof

Case of Issue: Nickel / Bronze, Specimen: Maple wood case, encapsulated coin, sleeve
Silver / Gilt, Proof: Green leatherette case, black insert, encapsulated coin, COA
Gold / Gold, Proof: Antique case, black insert, encapsulated coin, COA

DATE	DESCRIPTION	SOURCE	QUANTITY SOLD	ISSUE PRICE	FINISH	AS ISSUED
2000	Nickel / Bronze, wood case	BU Set	186,985	15.95	BU	10.
2000	Nickel / Bronze	Specimen Single	1,500	N/A	Specimen	20.
2000	Nickel / Bronze	Specimen Set	N/A	34.95	Specimen	20.
2000	Silver / Gilt Silver	Proof Single	39,768	24.95	Proof	25.
2000	Gold / Gold	Proof Single	5,881	299.95	Proof	375.

TWO DOLLARS, POLAR BEAR, 2000-2001.

Designers and Engravers:
Obv.:	Dora de Pédery-Hunt
Rev.:	Brent Townsend, Ago Aarand

Composition: Bronze
Ring:	99.0% Nickel
Core:	92.0% Cu, 6.0% Al, 2.0% Ni

Weight: Ring: 4.84 g, Core: 2.46 g
Total weight: 7.3 g
Diameter: Ring: 28.5 mm, Core: 16.8 mm
Thickness: 1.8 mm
Edge: Interrupted serrations
Die Axis: ↑↑   **Finish:** Specimen
Case of Issue: Maple wood case, encapsulated coin, sleeve

DATE	DESCRIPTION	QUANTITY SOLD	ISSUE PRICE	FINISH	SP-68	SP-69
2000	Nickel / Bronze, wood case	20,000	N/A	Specimen	20.	—
2001	Nickel / Bronze, wood case	20,000	N/A	Specimen	20.	—

TWO DOLLARS, PROUD POLAR BEAR, STERLING SILVER, 2004.

Issued jointly by the Royal Canadian Mint and Canada Post, the $2 Proud Polar Bear Stamp and Coin Set contains the first single metal two d
Canadian coin. The set comprises mint and cancelled $2.00 stamps, along with the $2.00 sterling silver coin. The two dollar coin is unusual in th
carries two maple leaf privy marks.

Designer and Engravers:
Obv.:	Susanna Blunt, Susan Taylor
Rev.:	Stan Witten

Composition: 92.5% Ag, 7.5% Cu
Silver content: 8.14 g, 0.262 tr oz
Weight:	8.8 g	**Edge:**	Reeded
Diameter:	28.0 mm	**Die Axis:**	↑↑
Thickness:	1.7 mm	**Finish:**	Proof
Case of Issue:	See Derivatives, page 139		

DATE	DESCRIPTION	QUANTITY SOLD	ISSUE PRICE	FINISH	PR-69	PR-70
2004	Proud Polar Bear, Sterling silver	12,607	N.I.I.	Proof	40.	—

TWO DOLLARS, 10TH ANNIVERSARY, GOLD, 1996-2006.

This gold two dollar coin does not carry the karat marks similar to the previous gold issues of 1996, 1999 and 2000.

Designers and Engravers:
Obv.:	Susanna Blunt, Susan Taylor
Rev.:	Brent Townsend, Ago Aarand

Composition:
Yellow Gold Ring: 91.7% Au, 4.1% Ag, 4.2% Cu
White Gold Core: 17.5% Au, 77.6 Ag, 5.2% Cu
Gold content: Gold: 10.352 g, 0.333 tr oz
Silver: 3.151 g, 0.101 tr oz
Weight: Ring: 10.62 g, Core: 3.6 g
Total: 14.22 g
Diameter: Ring: 28.0 mm, Core: 16.8 mm
Thickness: 1.8 mm
Edge: Interrupted serrations
Die Axis: ↑↑   **Finish:** Proof
Case of Issue: Maroon clam style case, black insert,
encapsulated coin, COA

DATE	DESCRIPTION	QUANTITY SOLD	ISSUE PRICE	FINISH	PR-69	PR-70
2006 (1996-)	Yellow gold ring / White gold core	2,068	399.95	Proof	600.	—

WO DOLLARS, CHURCHILL REVERSE, RCM LOGO, 1996-2006.

In 2006 a contest was held to name a new polar bear design to appear on the 10th anniversary two dollar coin. The name "Churchill" was the winner. e 10th anniversary coin has the double dates above the Queen's portrait and the Royal Mint logo below.

Designers and Engravers:
- Obv.: Susanna Blunt, Susan Taylor
- Rev.: Tony Bianco, Stan Witten

Composition:
- Ring: 99.9% Ni
- Core: 92.0% Cu, 6.0% Al, 2.0% Ni

Weight: 7.3 g
Diameter: Ring: 28.0 mm, Core: 16.8 mm
Thickness: 1.8 mm
Edge: Interrupted serrations **Die Axis:** ↑↑
Finish: Brilliant Uncirculated
Case of Issue: See Special Uncirculated Sets, page 519

DATE	DESCRIPTION	QUANTITY SOLD	ISSUE PRICE	FINISH	MS-65 NC	MS-66 NC
2006 (1996-)	"Churchill" Polar Bear	31,636	N.I.I.	BU	10.	—

YOUNG WILDLIFE SERIES

WO DOLLARS, OUNG WILDLIFE SERIES, 2010-2015.

These two dollar coins are from the ecial Edition Specimen Sets.

Common Obverse   **2010 Lynx Kittens**   **2011 Elk Calf**

2012 Wolf Cubs   **2013 Black Bear Cubs**   **2014 Baby Rabbits**   **2015 Baby Racoons**

signers:
- Obv.: Susanna Blunt
- Rev.: 2010-2012: Christie Paquet
  2013: Glen Loates; 2014: Pierre Leduc

Engravers:
- Obv.: Susan Taylor
- Rev.: 2010-2012: Christie Paquet
  2013: Eric Boyer; 2014: RCM Staff

mposition:
- Ring: 99.9% Ni
- Core: 92.0% Cu, 6.0% Al, 2.0% Cu

eight: 7.5 g
ge: Interrupted serrations
ish: Specimen; Brilliant portrait, frosted relief lined background

Diameter:
- Ring: 28.0 mm
- Core: 16.8 mm

Thickness: 1.9 mm
Die Axis: ↑↑
Case of Issue: See Special Edition Specimen Sets, page 544

DATE	DESCRIPTION	QUANTITY SOLD	ISSUE PRICE	FINISH	SP-68	SP-69
2010	Lynx Kittens	14,790	N.I.I.	Specimen	45.	—
2011	Elk Calf	13,899	N.I.I.	Specimen	70.	—
2012	Wolf Cubs	14,968	N.I.I.	Specimen	45.	—
2013	Black Bear Cubs	17,218	N.I.I.	Specimen	45.	—
2014	Baby Rabbits	11,886	N.I.I.	Specimen	45.	—
2015	Baby Racoons	8,504	N.I.I.	Specimen	45.	—

TWO DOLLARS, ELIZABETH II, FINE SILVER, GOLD PLATED INNER CORE, PROOF, 2012-2018

During 2012 and 2014 the Mint produced two varieties of proof set, a Premium Set in which the planchets used are of fine silver, and a Standa
Set, of which the planchets used are of the standard alloys. In 2017, a glow-in-the-dark version was created to celebrate Canada 150.

| Obverse: 2012 With Mint Logo | Obverse: 2013-2016 With No Mint Logo | Obverse: 2017 With Canada 150 Logo | Common Reverse 2012-2018 | Reverse: 2017 Dance of the Spirits Des.: Timothy Hsia |

Designers:
 Obv.: Susanna Blunt
 Rev.: Tony Bianco
   Premium - Fine Silver
Composition: Outer ring: Fine silver
   Inner Core: Gold plated, 99.99% Ag,
Silver content: 9.0 g, 0.289 tr oz
Weight: 9.0 g
Diameter: Ring: 28.0 mm
   Core: 16.8 mm
Thickness: 1.80 mm
Edge: Interrupted serrations
Die Axis: ↑↑
Finish: Proof
Case of Issue: See Proof and Premium Proof Sets, page 549-550

Engravers:
 Obv.: Susan Taylor
 Rev.: Stan Witten
Standard - Nickel Brass
Outer ring: Three-ply nickel finish plated steel
Inner Core: Brass-plated aluminum bronze

6.99 g
Ring: 28.0 mm
Core: 16.8 mm
1.80 mm
Interrupted serrations
↑↑
Proof

Reverse: 2017
Colourised
Dance of the Spirits
Des.: Timothy Hsia

DATE	DESCRIPTION	COMPOSITION	QUANTITY SOLD	ISSUE PRICE	FINISH	PR-69	PR-70
2012	Elizabeth II	Nickel brass	27,254	N.I.I.	Proof	15.	—
2012	Elizabeth II	Fine silver	19,789	N.I.I.	Proof	35.	—
2013	Elizabeth II	Fine silver	20,338	N.I.I.	Proof	35.	—
2014	Elizabeth II	Nickel brass	11,251	N.I.I.	Proof	15.	—
2014	Elizabeth II	Fine silver	13,416	N.I.I.	Proof	35.	—
2015	Elizabeth II	Fine silver	20,000	N.I.I.	Proof	35.	—
2015	Polar Bear, Proof Set	Nickel brass	20,000	N.I.I.	Proof	15.	—
2016	Elizabeth II	Fine silver	20,000	N.I.I.	Proof	35.	—
2016	Polar Bear, Proof Set	Nickel brass	20,000	N.I.I.	Proof	15.	—
2017	Polar Bear, Premium Proof Set	Fine silver	20,000	N.I.I.	Proof	45.	—
2017	Dance of the Spirits, Proof Set	Fine silver	20,000	N.I.I.	Proof	45.	—
2017	Dance of the Spirits (colourised), Proof Set	Nickel brass	25,000	N.I.I.	Proof	25.	—
2018	Polar Bear, Proof Set	Nickel brass	25,000	N.I.I.	Proof	15.	—
2018	Polar Bear, Premium Proof Set	Fine silver	20,000	N.I.I.	Proof	35.	—

TWO DOLLAR SILVER COINS

O DOLLARS (¾ OUNCE), DEVIL'S BRIGADE, 2013.

Designers and Engravers:

Obv.:	Susanna Blunt, Susan Taylor
Rev.:	Ardell Bourgeois, Cecily Mok
Composition:	99.99% Ag
Weight:	23.33 g, 0.50 tr oz
Diameter:	38.07 mm
Thickness:	2.4 mm
Edge:	Reeded
Die Axis:	↑↑
Finish:	Bullion
Case of Issue:	Tubes of 30

DATE	DESCRIPTION	QUANTITY SOLD	ISSUE PRICE	FINISH	MS-65	MS-66	MS-67
2013	$2 (¾ oz), Devil's Brigade	N/A	BV	Bullion	32.	45.	65.

O DOLLAR BULLION ISSUES, 2015-2017.

Designers and Engravers:

Obv.:	Susanna Blunt, Susan Taylor
Rev.:	Pierre Leduc, Stan Witten
Composition:	99.99% Ag
Weight:	23.33 g, 0.75 tr oz
Diameter:	38.1 mm
Thickness:	2.4 mm
Edge:	Reeded
Die Axis:	↑↑
Finish:	Bullion, Radial lines
Case of Issue:	Tubes of 30

DATE	DESCRIPTION	MINTAGE	ISSUE PRICE	FINISH	MS-65	MS-66	MS-67
2015	$2 (¾ oz), Grey Wolf	300,000	BV	Bullion	25.	30.	—
2015	$2 (1/2 oz), Calgary Stampede	N/A	BV	Bullion	20.	25.	—
2015	$2 (1/2 oz), Eagle	N/A	BV	Bullion	24.	30.	—
2016	$2 (1/2 oz), Eagle	N/A	BV	Bullion	24.	30.	—
2016	$2 (3/4 oz), Howling Wolves	1,000,000	BV	Bullion	26.	30.	—
2017	$2 (3/4 oz), Howling Wolves	N/A	BV	Bullion	22.	26.	—

BIG COIN SERIES

TWO DOLLARS, BIG COIN SERIES, 2015-2018.

These two-dollar coins, which are part of the Big Coin started started in 2015, features Brent Townsend's iconic polar bear design first introduce 1996. Other coins in the set include a 5¢ coin (page 11), 10¢ coin (page 17), 25¢ coin (page 57), 50¢ coin (page 88), and $1 coin (page 130).

Designers and Engravers:	**Composition:**
Obv.: Susanna Blunt, Susan Taylor	2015: 99.99% Ag, Selectively gold plated
Rev.: Robert-Ralph Carmichael, RCM Staff	2016: 99.99% Ag, Selectively coloured on reverse
Silver content: 157.58 g, 5.07 tr oz	
Weight: 157.6 g	**Edge:** Reeded
Diameter: 65.25 mm	**Die Axis:** ↑↑
Thickness: N/A	**Finish:** Proof
Case of Issue: Maroon clam style case, black flocked insert, encapsulated coin, COA, custom box	

DATE	DESCRIPTION	COMPOSITION	QUANTITY SOLD	ISSUE PRICE	FINISH	PR-69	PR-70
2015	$2 Big Coin	Silver	1,488	549.95	Proof	600.	—
2016	$2 Big Coin	Silver	1,469	519.95	Proof	520.	—
2018	$2 Big Coin	Silver	1,500	559.95	Proof	560.	—

Note: Coins illustrated smaller than actual size.

TWO DOLLAR DERIVATIVES

The following single coins, coin and note sets, or coin and stamp sets, are based on the numismatic two dollar coins.

DATE	DESCRIPTION	QUANTITY SOLD	ISSUE PRICE	ISSUER	FINISH	MARK PRIC'
1996	**Two Dollar Coin, Specimen;** $2 Regular bank note; Blue folder	91,427	29.95	RCM	SP-66	2!
1996	**Encapsulated Two Dollar Coin, Proof;** Encapsulated $2 BRX Replacement note; Blue presentation case	27,103	79.95	RCM	PR-69	3!
1996	**Encapsulated Two Dollar Coin, Piedfort;** Encapsulated pair of uncut $2 BRX replacement notes; Blue/green presentation case	11,526	179.95	RCM	PR-69	11!
1996	**Two Dollar Coin, Brilliant Uncirculated;** $2 regular issue note; 45¢ mint stamp; Blue/green presentation case	N/A	N/A	RCM, CP	MS-65	2(
1998W	**Two Dollar Coin;** Mint and cancelled $2 stamps; Blue presentation case	N/A	N/A	RCM, CP	MS-65	2(
1999	**Two Dollar Nunavut Coin;** Mint and cancelled 46¢ stamps; Blue presentation case	N/A	17.95	RCM, CP	MS-65	2(
2000W	**Two Dollar Coin;** Mint and cancelled $2 stamps; Blue presentation case	20,000	19.99	RCM, CP	MS-65	2(
2000	**Two Dollar Coin, "Path of Knowledge" (Three Bears);** Credit card-like holder	N/A	N/A	RCM	MS-65	
2001	**Two Dollar Coin;** Credit card-like holder	N/A	N/A	RCM	MS-65	
2004	**Two Dollar Proud Polar Bear Coin;** Mint and cancelled $2 stamps; Wooden presentation case	12,607	29.95	RCM, CP	PR-69	5!
2016	**Two Dollar 4-Coin Set,** 20 Years in the Minting Includes one uncut 2-dollar banknote sheet from 1986 series.	150	11,499.95	RCM	PR-69	10,50(

THREE DOLLARS

REE DOLLARS, THE BEAVER, SQUARE, 2006.

Designers and Engravers:

Obv.:	Susanna Blunt, Cosme Saffioti
Rev.:	Cosme Saffioti, Cosme Saffioti

Composition: 92.50% Ag, 7.50% Cu
plated in 24kt gold
Silver content: 10.84 g, 0.349 tr oz
Weight: 11.72 g
Size: 27.0 x 27.0 mm   **Edge:** Plain
Thickness: 1.80 mm   **Die Axis:** ↑↑
Finish: Specimen
Case of Issue: Maroon plastic slide case, black plastic
insert, encapsulated coin, COA

DATE	DESCRIPTION	QUANTITY SOLD	ISSUE PRICE	FINISH	SP-68	SP-69
2006	The Beaver	20,000	45.95	Specimen	75.	—

REE DOLLARS, RETURN OF THE TYEE, 2010.

Salmon has long been the essential food source of the Northwest Coast people. The largest species of Pacific salmon is the Chinook, or black
mon, called the Tyee (King) by the First Nation People. Two tyee are arranged in a circle, representing the "Circle of Life."

Designers and Engravers:

Obv.:	Susanna Blunt, Susan Taylor
Rev.:	Jody Broomfield, Christie Paquet

Composition: 99.99% Ag, Selectively plated in pink
and yellow gold
Silver content: 7.96 g, 0.256 tr oz
Weight: 7.96 g
Diameter: 27.0 mm   **Edge:** Reeded
Thickness: 1.9 mm   **Die Axis:** ↑↑
Finish: Proof
Case of Issue: Maroon leatherette clam style case, black
flocked insert, encapsulated coin, COA

DATE	DESCRIPTION	QUANTITY SOLD	ISSUE PRICE	FINISH	PR-69	PR-70
2010	Return of the Tyee	8,301	54.95	Proof	50.	—

ROYAL CANADIAN MINT MARKS ON COINS

"P" is a composition mark for coins struck on multi-ply plated (nickel or copper on steel) planchets

"W" is the mint mark for coins struck at the Winnipeg Mint.

The "Circle M" is the Royal Canadian Mint logo

CANADA'S WILDLIFE CONSERVATION SERIES

THREE DOLLARS, CANADA'S WILDLIFE CONSERVATION SERIES, SQUARE, 2010-2011.

| Common Obverse | Barn Owl
Engr.: Christie Paquet | Polar Bear
Engr.: Stan Witten | Orca Whale
Engr.: José Osio | Black-Footed Ferret
Engr.: K. Wachelko |

Designers:
  Obv.:   Susanna Blunt
  Rev.:   Jason Bouwman
Composition: 92.50% Ag; 7.50% Cu, Gold plated
Silver content: 11.1 g, 0.357 tr oz
Weight: 12.0 g
Size: 27.1 x 27.1 mm
Thickness: 2.0 mm
Case of Issue: Maroon leatherette clam style case, black flocked insert, encapsulated coin, COA

Engravers:
  Obv.:   Susan Taylor
  Rev.:   See reverse illustrations
Edge: Plain
Die Axis: ↑↑
Finish: Specimen

DATE	DESCRIPTION	QUANTITY SOLD	ISSUE PRICE	FINISH	SP-68	SP-69
2010	Barn Owl	10,578	59.95	Specimen	40.	—
2010	Polar Bear	8,544	59.95	Specimen	40.	—
2011	Orca Whale	10,698	62.95	Specimen	40.	—
2011	Black-Footed Ferret	8,237	62.95	Specimen	40.	—

THREE DOLLARS, FAMILY SCENE, 2011.

Designers and Engravers:
  Obv.:   Susanna Blunt, Susan Taylor
  Rev.:   Andrew Qappik, RCM Staff
Composition: 99.99% Ag, Selectively plated in pink and yellow gold
Silver content: 7.96 g, 0.256 tr oz
Weight: 7.96 g   **Edge:**   Reeded
Diameter: 27.0 mm   **Die Axis:**   ↑↑
Thickness: 2.0 mm   **Finish:**   Proof
Case of Issue: Maroon leatherette clam style case, black flocked insert, encapsulated coin, COA

DATE	DESCRIPTION	QUANTITY SOLD	ISSUE PRICE	FINISH	PR-69	PR-70
2011	Family Scene	6,687	64.95	Proof	40.	—

BIRTH STONE COLLECTION

THREE DOLLARS, BIRTH STONE COLLECTION, 2011 (GIFTWARE).

Common Obverse

Designers and Engravers:

Obv.:	Susanna Blunt, Susan Taylor
Rev.:	Christie Paquet

Composition: 99.99% Ag, Swarovski element
Silver content: 7.96 g, 0.25 tr oz

Weight:	7.96 g	**Edge:**	Reeded
Diameter:	27.0 mm	**Die Axis:**	↑↑
Thickness:	1.8 mm	**Finish:**	Proof

Case of Issue: Maroon leatherette clam style case, black flocked insert, encapsulated coin, COA

January - Garnet

February - Amethyst

March - Aquamarine

April - Diamond

May - Emerald

June - Alexandrite

July - Ruby

August - Peridot

September - Sapphire

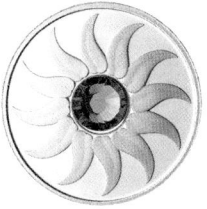

October - Tourmaline

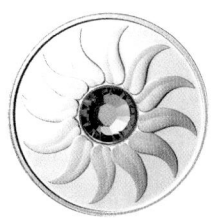

November - Topaz

December - Zircon

DATE	DESCRIPTION	QUANTITY SOLD	ISSUE PRICE	FINISH	PR-69	PR-70
2011	January - Garnet	2,534	64.95	Proof	50.	—
2011	February - Amethyst	2,571	64.95	Proof	50.	—
2011	March - Aquamarine	2,560	64.95	Proof	50.	—
2011	April - Diamond	2,528	64.95	Proof	50.	—
2011	May - Emerald	2,915	64.95	Proof	50.	—
2011	June - Alexandrite	2,724	64.95	Proof	50.	—
2011	July - Ruby	3,073	64.95	Proof	50.	—
2011	August - Peridot	2,673	64.95	Proof	50.	—
2011	September - Sapphire	2,717	64.95	Proof	50.	—
2011	October - Tourmaline	2,593	64.95	Proof	50.	—
2011	November - Topaz	2,870	64.95	Proof	50.	—
2011	December - Zircon	2,879	64.95	Proof	50.	—
2011	Set of 12 coins	—	—	Proof	600.	*

BIRTH STONE COLLECTION (cont.).

THREE DOLLARS, BIRTH STONE COLLECTION, 2012 (GIFTWARE).

Common Obverse

Designers and Engravers:

Obv.:	Susanna Blunt, Susan Taylor
Rev.:	Maurice Gervais, Konrad Wachelko

Composition: 99.99% Ag, Swarovski element
Silver content: 7.96 g, 0.25 tr oz

Weight:	7.96 g	**Edge:**	Reeded
Diameter:	27.0 mm	**Die Axis:**	↑↑
Thickness:	1.8 mm	**Finish:**	Proof

Case of Issue: 12-holed black clam style case, black flocked insert, encapsulated coin, COA, grey sleeve

January - Garnet

February - Amethyst

March - Aquamarine

April - Diamond

May - Emerald

June - Alexandrite

July - Ruby

August - Peridot

September - Sapphire

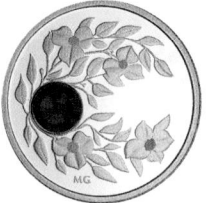

October - Tourmaline

November - Topaz

December - Zircon

DATE	DESCRIPTION	QUANTITY SOLD	ISSUE PRICE	FINISH	PR-69	PR-70
2012	January - Garnet	1,926	64.95	Proof	50.	—
2012	February - Amethyst	2,017	64.95	Proof	50.	—
2012	March - Aquamarine	2,229	64.95	Proof	50.	—
2012	April - Diamond	2,181	64.95	Proof	50.	—
2012	May - Emerald	2,613	64.95	Proof	50.	—
2012	June - Alexandrite	2,135	64.95	Proof	50.	—
2012	July - Ruby	2,464	64.95	Proof	50.	—
2012	August - Peridot	2,193	64.95	Proof	50.	—
2012	September - Sapphire	2,334	64.95	Proof	50.	—
2012	October - Tourmaline	2,094	64.95	Proof	50.	—
2012	November - Topaz	2,060	64.95	Proof	50.	—
2012	December - Zircon	2,230	64.95	Proof	50.	—
2012	Set of 12 coins	200	779.40	Proof	600.	*

REE DOLLARS, HUMMINGBIRD WITH MORNING GLORY, 2013 (GIFTWARE).

The ruby-throated hummingbird depicted on this coin is one of Canada's most common hummingbird species. Measuring 2.75 to 3.5 inches and ghing three to four grams, it is about the size of a large moth.

Designers and Engravers:

Obv.:	Susanna Blunt, Susan Taylor
Rev.:	Yves Bérubé, José Osio

Composition: 99.99% Ag, Siam red Swarovski crystal element
Silver content: 8.06 g, 0.257 tr oz
Weight: 8.0 g
Diameter: 27.0 mm   **Edge:** Reeded
Thickness: 2.0 mm   **Die Axis:** ↑↑
Finish: Reverse Proof
Case of Issue: Maroon leatherette clam style case, black flocked insert, encapsulated coin, COA, custom sleeve

DATE	DESCRIPTION	QUANTITY SOLD	ISSUE PRICE	FINISH	PR-69	PR-70
2013	Hummingbird with Morning Glory	7,392	69.95	Proof	50.	—

CANADA'S ANIMAL ARCHITECTS SERIES

REE DOLLARS, CANADA'S ANIMAL ARCHITECTS SERIES, 2013-2014 (GIFTWARE).

Common Obverse	**Bee and Hive** **Des.: Yves Bérubé**	**Spider and Web** **Des.: Yves Bérubé**	**(Monarch) Caterpillar** **and Chrysalis** **Des.: Trevor Tennant**

** signers:**

Obv.:	Susanna Blunt
Rev.:	See reverse illustrations

mposition: 99.99%, Ag, Painted
er content: 7.96 g, 0.256 tr oz
ight: 7.96 g
meter: 26.9 mm
ckness: 1.9 - 2.0 mm
e of Issue: Maroon leatherette clam style case, black flocked insert, encapsulated coin, COA

Engravers:

Rev.:	Susan Taylor
Rev.:	Susan Taylor

Edge: Reeded
Die Axis: ↑↑
Finish: Proof

DATE	DESCRIPTION	QUANTITY SOLD	ISSUE PRICE	FINISH	PR-69	PR-70
2013	Bee and Hive	9,993	69.95	Proof	50.	—
2014	Spider and Web	5,431	69.95	Proof	50.	—
2014	Caterpillar and Chrysalis	5,827	69.95	Proof	50.	—

REE DOLLARS, FISHING, 2013.

Designers and Engravers:

Obv.:	Susanna Blunt, Susan Taylor
Rev.:	John Mantha, Steven Stewart

Composition: 99.99% Ag
Silver content: 7.96 g, 0.256 tr oz
Weight: 7.96 g
Diameter: 26.9 mm   **Edge:** Reeded
Thickness: 1.8 mm   **Die Axis:** ↑↑
                      Finish: Proof
Case of Issue: Maroon leatherette clam style case, black flocked insert, encapsulated coin, COA

DATE	DESCRIPTION	QUANTITY SOLD	ISSUE PRICE	FINISH	PR-69	PR-70
2013	Fishing	14,985	34.95	Proof	25.	—

THREE DOLLARS, MISS CANADA: AN ALLEGORY, 2013.

Miss Canada, a visual representation of national value and identity, who first appeared after confederation in 1867.

Designers and Engravers:
Obv.:	Susanna Blunt, Susan Taylor
Rev.:	Laurie McGaw, José Osio

Composition: Bronze
Weight: 19.2 g
Diameter: 35.75 mm
Thickness: 2.7 mm
Edge: Plain
Die Axis: ↑↑
Finish: Proof
Case of Issue: Maroon leatherette clam style case, black flocked insert, encapsulated coin, COA

DATE	DESCRIPTION	QUANTITY SOLD	ISSUE PRICE	FINISH	PR-69	PR-70
2013	Miss Canada: An Allegory	11,232	34.95	Proof	30.	—

THREE DOLLARS, MARTIN SHORT PRESENTS CANADA, 2013.

Designers and Engravers:
Obv.:	Susanna Blunt, Susan Taylor
Rev.:	Tony Bianco, RCM Staff

Composition: 99.99% Ag
Silver content: 7.96 g, 0.256 tr oz

Weight:	7.96 g	**Edge:**	Reeded
Diameter:	26.9 mm	**Die Axis:**	↑↑
Thickness:	1.8 mm	**Finish:**	Proof

Case of Issue: Maroon leatherette clam style case, black flocked insert, encapsulated coin, COA, custom case

DATE	DESCRIPTION	QUANTITY SOLD	ISSUE PRICE	FINISH	PR-69	PR-70
2013	Martin Short Presents Canada	5,923	49.95	Proof	25.	—

THREE DOLLARS, MAPLE LEAF IMPRESSION, 2013.

The impression of a large maple leaf is framed by 100 smaller maple leaves, creating a three dimensional illusion. The design was also issued the red and green coloured twenty dollar coins (see page 265).

Designers and Engravers:
Obv.:	Susanna Blunt, Susan Taylor
Rev.:	José Osio, RCM Staff

Composition: 99.99% Ag
Silver content: 7.96 g, 0.256 tr oz

Weight:	7.96 g		
Diameter:	27.0 mm	**Edge:**	Reeded
Thickness:	1.8 mm	**Die Axis:**	↑↑
Finish:	Proof		

Case of Issue: Maroon leatherette clam style case, black flocked insert, encapsulated coin, COA

DATE	DESCRIPTION	QUANTITY SOLD	ISSUE PRICE	FINISH	PR-69	PR-70
2013	Maple Leaf Impression	9,820	59.95	Proof	45.	—

REE DOLLARS, 100TH ANNIVERSARY OF CANADIAN ARCTIC EXPEDITION: LIFE IN THE NORTH, 2013.

Celebrating the 100th anniversary of the historic arctic expedition led by Vilhjalmur Stefansson and Rudolph Anderson, this three dollar coin's
erse was designed by Kinngait Nunavut artist Tim Pitsiulak to celebrate life in the north. This coin's design was also released on the twenty-five cent
n in the Special Edition Uncirculated Set 2013-2014 (see page 523).

Designers and Engravers:

Obv.:	Susanna Blunt, Susan Taylor
Rev.:	Tim Pitsiulak, RCM Staff

Composition: 99.99% Ag
Silver content: 7.96 g, 0.256 tr oz

Weight:	7.96 g	**Edge:**	Reeded
Diameter:	26.85 mm	**Die Axis:**	↑↑
Thickness:	1.8 mm	**Finish:**	Proof

Case of Issue: Maroon leatherette clam style case, black flocked insert, encapsulated coin, COA

DATE	DESCRIPTION	QUANTITY SOLD	ISSUE PRICE	FINISH	PR-69	PR-70
2013	Life in the North	4,492	34.95	Proof	30.	—

REE DOLLARS, JEWEL OF LIFE, 2014.

Featuring the artistry of Quebec actor, singer and jewellery designer Caroline Néron, this three dollar coin combines Swarovski crystals to depict
silhouette of a tree in winter.

 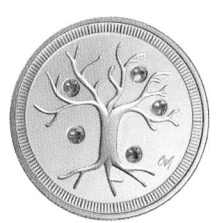

Designers and Engravers:

Obv.:	Susanna Blunt, Susan Taylor
Rev.:	Caroline Néron, Konrad Wachelko

Composition: 99.99% Ag, Selectively gold plated, Swarovski elements
Silver content: 7.96 g, 0.256 tr oz

Weight:	7.96 g		
Diameter:	27.0 mm	**Edge:**	Reeded
Thickness:	1.8 mm	**Die Axis:**	↑↑
Finish:	Proof		

Case of Issue: Maroon leatherette clam style case, black flocked insert, encapsulated coin, COA, custom beauty box

DATE	DESCRIPTION	MINTAGE	ISSUE PRICE	FINISH	PR-69	PR-70
2014	Jewel of Life	15,000	59.95	Proof	50.	—

REE DOLLARS, "WAIT FOR ME, DADDY", 2014.

Based on the iconic 1940 photograph taken in British Columbia by photographer Claude Dettloff, this three dollar coin commemorates the 75th
versary of the declaration of the Second World War.

Designers and Engravers:

Obv.:	Susanna Blunt, Susan Taylor
Rev.:	Claude Dettloff, RCM Staff

Composition: 99.99% Ag
Silver content: 7.96 g, 0.256 tr oz

Weight:	7.96 g	**Edge:**	Reeded
Diameter:	27.0 mm	**Die Axis:**	↑↑
Thickness:	N/A	**Finish:**	Matte Proof

Case of Issue: Maroon leatherette clam style case, black flocked insert, encapsulated coin, COA

DATE	DESCRIPTION	QUANTITY SOLD	ISSUE PRICE	FINISH	PR-69	PR-70
2014	"Wait For Me, Daddy"	6,374	44.95	Matte Proof	45.	—

THREE DOLLARS, 50TH ANNIVERSARY OF THE CANADIAN FLAG, 1965-2015.

This coin commemorates the Canadian flag, Canada's symbolic icon of multilingualism and diversity.

Designers and Engravers:
Obv.:   Susanna Blunt, Susan Taylor
Rev.:   RCM Staff
Composition: 99.99% Ag, Coloured
Silver content: 7.96 g, 0.256 tr oz
Weight: 7.96 g   **Edge:**   Reeded
Diameter: 27.0 mm   **Die Axis:**   ↑↑
Thickness: N/A   **Finish:**   Proof
Case of Issue: Maroon leatherette clam style case, black flocke insert, encapsulated coin, COA, custom box

DATE	DESCRIPTION	QUANTITY SOLD	ISSUE PRICE	FINISH	PR-69	PR-70
2015 (1965-)	50th Anniversary of the Canadian Flag	14,998	29.95	Proof	35.	—

THREE DOLLARS, 400TH ANNIVERSARY OF SAMUEL DE CHAMPLAIN IN HURONIA, 2015.

The year 2015 marks the 400th anniversary of Samuel de Champlain's voyage of discovery through Huronia.

Designers and Engravers:
Obv.:   Susanna Blunt
Rev.:   Laurie McGaw
Composition: 99.99% Ag
Silver content: 7.96 g, 0.256 tr oz
Weight: 7.96 g   **Edge:**   Reeded
Diameter: 27 mm   **Die Axis:**   ↑↑
Thickness: N/A   **Finish:**   Proof
Case of Issue: Maroon leatherette clam style case, black flocke insert, encapsulated coin, COA, custom box

DATE	DESCRIPTION	QUANTITY SOLD	ISSUE PRICE	FINISH	PR-69	PR-70
2015	400th Anniversary of Samuel de Champlain in Huronia	4,292	29.95	Proof	30.	—

THREE DOLLARS, 100TH ANNIVERSARY OF *IN FLANDERS FIELDS*, 2015.

The year 2015 marks the 100th anniversary of the poem *In Flanders Fields*.

Designers and Engravers:
Obv.:   Susanna Blunt
Rev.:   Laurie McGaw
Composition: 99.99% Ag
Silver content: 7.96 g, 0.256 tr oz
Weight: 7.96 g   **Edge:**   Reeded
Diameter: 27.0 mm   **Die Axis:**   ↑↑
Thickness: N/A   **Finish:**   Matte Pr
Case of Issue: Maroon leatherette clam style case, black flocke insert, encapsulated coin, COA, custom box

DATE	DESCRIPTION	QUANTITY SOLD	ISSUE PRICE	FINISH	PR-69	PR-70
2015	100th Anniversary of *In Flanders Fields*	14,810	29.95	Matte Proof	35.	—

THREE DOLLARS, QUEEN ELIZABETH ROSE, 2016.

Designers and Engravers:
Obv.:   Susanna Blunt
Rev.:   Claudio D'Angelo
Composition: 99.99% Ag
Silver content: 7.96 g, 0.256 tr oz
Weight: 7.96 g   **Edge:**   Reeded
Diameter: 27 mm   **Die Axis:**   ↑↑
Thickness: N/A   **Finish:**   Proof
Case of Issue: Maroon leatherette clam style case, black flocke insert, encapsulated coin, COA, custom box

DATE	DESCRIPTION	QUANTITY SOLD	ISSUE PRICE	FINISH	PR-69	PR-70
2016	Queen Elizabeth Rose	9,999	44.95	Proof	55.	—

REE DOLLARS, MAPLE LEAF QUARTET, 2017.

Like pieces of a puzzle, Canada and its history have been shaped by the many who have come together to define this nation through its people. In spirit, the RCM has introduced a quartet of coins whose individual images come together to form a single, complete image of a proud Canadian icon.

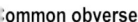

:ommon obverse

Designers and Engravers:
Obv.:   Susanna Blunt
Rev.:   Celia Godkin
Composition: 99.99% Ag
Silver content: 11.85 g, 0.381 tr oz
Weight: 11.85 g (each)   **Edge:**   Plain
Diameter: 27 x 27 mm (each)   **Die Axis:**   ↑↑
Thickness: N/A   **Finish:**   Reverse Proof
Case of Issue: Presented in a clamshell case with a graphic beauty box.

DATE	DESCRIPTION	MINTAGE	ISSUE PRICE	FINISH	PR-69	PR-70
2017	Silver Maple Leaf Quartet	4,527 (each)	204.95	Reverse Proof	205.	—

REE DOLLARS, HEART OF OUR NATION, 2017.

This coin is filled with inspiring symbols, and even if you haven't seen or experienced them all, you'll likely notice they all feel like "home" – Canada, ch and ever-changing combination of people, histories and aspirations that come together with the maple leaf at their heart.

Designers and Engravers:
Obv.:   Susanna Blunt
Rev.:   Laurie McGaw
Composition: 99.99% Ag
Silver content: 7.96 g, 0.256 tr oz
Weight: 7.96 g   **Edge:**   Reeded
Diameter: 27 mm   **Die Axis:**   ↑↑
Thickness: N/A   **Finish:**   Specimen
Case of Issue: Folder with easel back.

DATE	DESCRIPTION	MINTAGE	ISSUE PRICE	FINISH	SP-68	SP-69
2017	Heart Of Our Nation	W.S.L.	19.95	Specimen	20.	—

REE DOLLARS, CELEBRATION OF LOVE, 2017.

A 6mm heart-shpaed Swarovski® Branded crystal adds a distinctive sparkle to this coin.

Designers and Engravers:
Obv.:   Susanna Blunt
Rev.:   Joel Kimmel
Composition: 99.99% Ag
Silver content: 7.96 g, 0.256 tr oz
Weight: 7.96 g   **Edge:**   Reeded
Diameter: 27 mm   **Die Axis:**   ↑↑
Thickness: N/A   **Finish:**   Proof
Case of Issue: Premium graphic case.

DATE	DESCRIPTION	MINTAGE	ISSUE PRICE	FINISH	PR-69	PR-70
2017	Celebration of Love	17,500	54.95	Proof	55.	—

THREE DOLLARS, THE SPIRIT OF CANADA, 2017.

Designers and Engravers:
Obv.:	Susanna Blunt
Rev.:	Steve Hepburn

Composition: 99.99% Ag
Silver content: 7.96 g, 0.256 tr oz
Weight: 7.96 g   **Edge:** Reeded
Diameter: 27 mm   **Die Axis:** ↑↑
Thickness: N/A   **Finish:** Specimen
Case of Issue: Folder-style packaging with pop-out easel back.

DATE	DESCRIPTION	QUANTITY SOLD	ISSUE PRICE	FINISH	SP-68	SP-69
2017	The Spirit of Canada	33,983	19.95	Specimen	20.	—

THREE DOLLARS, 100TH ANNIVERSARY OF THE BATTLE OF VIMY RIDGE, 2017.

The Battle of Vimy Ridge (April 9, 1917) marks the beginning of its rise to independent greatness — born of valour and sacrifice on the battlefie
where the Canadian National Vimy Memorial now stands, this coin commemorates the 100th anniversaray of Canada's historic battle.

Designers and Engravers:
Obv.:	Susanna Blunt
Rev.:	Laurie McGaw

Composition: 99.99% Ag
Silver content: 7.96 g, 0.256 tr oz
Weight: 7.96 g   **Edge:** Reeded
Diameter: 27 mm   **Die Axis:** ↑↑
Thickness: N/A   **Finish:** Specimen
Case of Issue: Folder-style packaging with pop-out easel back.

DATE	DESCRIPTION	MINTAGE	ISSUE PRICE	FINISH	SP-68	SP-69
2017	100th Anniversary of the Battle of Vimy Ridge	W.S.L.	19.95	Specimen	20.	—

THREE DOLLARS, 100TH ANNIVERSARY OF THE TORONTO MAPLE LEAFS™, 2017.

In 1917, the Toronto Maple Leafs™ were born. This coin embodies the enduring spirit of Leafs™ Nation — a passion that united people on and
the ice, and inspired young and old alike to carve fond memories on winter ice.

Designers and Engravers:
Obv.:	Susanna Blunt
Rev.:	Steven Rosati

Composition: 99.99% Ag
Silver content: 7.96 g, 0.256 tr oz
Weight: 7.96 g   **Edge:** Reeded
Diameter: 27 mm   **Die Axis:** ↑↑
Thickness: N/A   **Finish:** Matte Pr
Case of Issue: Folder-style packaging with pop-out easel back.

DATE	DESCRIPTION	MINTAGE	ISSUE PRICE	FINISH	PR-69	PR-7
2017	100th Anniversary of the Toronto Maple Leafs	W.S.L.	34.95	Matte Proof	35.	—

Note: W.S.L. = While Supplies Last.

2017 ZODIAC SERIES

REE DOLLARS, *ZODIAC* SERIES, 2017.

The zodiac has a long, rich history that dates back to Hellenic and Babylonian civilizaitons, which astrology and astronomy were viturally inseparable. day, its 12 signs entertain, intrigue or inspire millions of people worldwide, who find hope or guidance in the cyclical alignment of the stars and nets! The stars align in the *2017 Zodiac* series, which features sparkling Swarovski® crystal embellshiments within a coloured rendition of the zodiac.

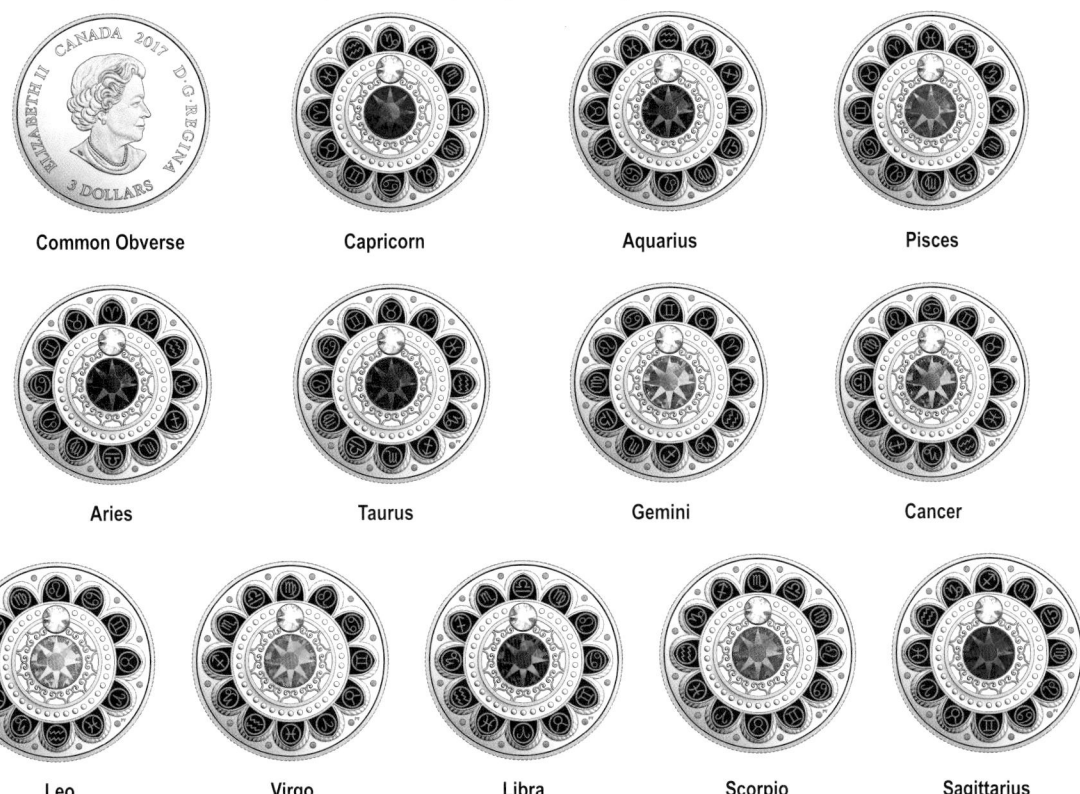

Common Obverse	Capricorn	Aquarius	Pisces
Aries	Taurus	Gemini	Cancer
Leo	Virgo	Libra	Scorpio	Sagittarius

		Engravers:	
signers:		Rev.:	Susan Taylor
Obv.:	Susanna Blunt	Rev.:	Susan Taylor
Rev.:	Pandora Young		

mposition: 99.99%, Ag,
ver content: 7.96 g, 0.256 tr oz
ight: 7.96 g
meter: 27 mm
ckness: N/A
se of Issue: Maroon clamshell with black beauty box.

Edge: Reeded
Die Axis: ↑↑
Finish: Proof

DATE	DESCRIPTION	QUANTITY SOLD	ISSUE PRICE	FINISH	PR-69	PR-70
2017	Capricorn	2,286	54.95	Proof	55.	—
2017	Aquarius	1,000	54.95	Proof	55.	—
2017	Pisces	5,500	54.95	Proof	55.	—
2017	Aries	5,500	54.95	Proof	55.	—
2017	Taurus	5,500	54.95	Proof	55.	—
2017	Gemini	5,500	54.95	Proof	55.	—
2017	Cancer	5,500	54.95	Proof	55.	—
2017	Leo	5,500	54.95	Proof	55.	—
2017	Virgo	5,500	54.95	Proof	55.	—
2017	Libra	5,500	54.95	Proof	55.	—
2017	Scorpio	5,500	54.95	Proof	55.	—
2017	Sagittarius	5,500	54.95	Proof	55.	—

MAPLE LEAF QUARTET

THREE DOLLARS, MAPLE LEAF QUARTET, THIRTY YEARS, (1988-2018).

Introduced in 1988, the Royal Canadian Mint's Silver Maple Leaf (SML) coin remains one of the most recognized and sought-after investment piec in the world. This selectively rose gold-plated quartet is a tribute to the SML's solitary maple leaf as a true mark of excellence.

Common obverse

Designers and Engravers:
Obv.:   Susanna Blunt
Rev.:   Pierre Leduc
Composition: 99.99% Ag, Selective rose gold-plated
Silver content: 11.85 g, 0.381 tr oz
Weight: 11.85 g (each)   **Edge:** Plain
Diameter: 27 x 27 mm (each)   **Die Axis:** ↑↑
Thickness: N/A   **Finish:** Reverse Pro
Case of Issue: Maroon clamshell
case with a black beauty box.

DATE	DESCRIPTION	QUANTITY SOLD	ISSUE PRICE	FINISH	PR-69	PR-70
2018	Silver Maple Leaf Quartet, Thirty Years (1988-2018)	6,500 (each)	204.95	Reverse Proof	205.	—

TEACHINGS FROM GRANDMOTHER MOON SERIES

THREE DOLLARS, TEACHINGS FROM GRANDMOTHER MOON, 2018.

Canada's Indigenous people view every aspect of nature as a living relation that plays an active role in their lives, and Grandmother Moon is ev present, making 13 appearances throughout the year as she watches over Mother Earth's children and lights up their paths.

Spirit Moon is a time to honour the stillness and reflect upon our place within creation; Bear Moon teaches us patience and to honour the vision qu that began in the fall; Sugar Moon brings us the maple sap that begins to flow; Sucker Moon brings the sucker fish back to the stream, and teaches how to become healed healers; Flower Moon puts nature's life-giving energy on full display, and reminds us that we too, are part of this sacred web of l

Common Obverse

Designers and Engravers:
Obv.:   Susanna Blunt, Susan Taylor
Rev.:   Frank Polson, Susan Taylor
Composition: 99.99%, Ag, Painted
Silver content: 7.96 g, 0.256 tr oz
Weight: 7.96 g   **Edge:** Reeded
Diameter: 27 mm   **Die Axis:** ↑↑
Thickness: N/A   **Finish:** Proof
Case of Issue: Maroon leatherette clam style case,
black flocked insert, encapsulated coin, COA

Spirit Moon

Bear Moon

Sugar Moon

Sucker Moon

Flower Moon

DATE	DESCRIPTION	MINTAGE	ISSUE PRICE	FINISH	PR-69	PR-70
2018	Spirit Moon	4,000	49.95	Proof	50.	—
2018	Bear Moon	4,000	49.95	Proof	50.	—
2018	Sugar Moon	4,000	49.95	Proof	50.	—
2018	Sucker Moon	4,000	49.95	Proof	50.	—
2018	Flower Moon	4,000	49.95	Proof	50.	—

REE DOLLARS, CELEBRATION OF LOVE, 2018.

Three clear-coloured Swarovski® crystal elements add elegance and a timeless beauty to the revese. The application of selective colour adds a utifully rich, red hue to the two engraved roses.

Designers and Engravers:
Obv.:	Susanna Blunt
Rev.:	Anna Bucciarelli

Composition: 99.99% Ag
Silver content: 7.96 g, 0.256 tr oz

Weight:	7.96 g	**Edge:**	Reeded
Diameter:	27 mm	**Die Axis:**	↑↑
Thickness:	N/A	**Finish:**	Proof

Case of Issue: Premium graphic box.

DATE	DESCRIPTION	MINTAGE	ISSUE PRICE	FINISH	PR-69	PR-70
2018	Celebration of Love	15,000	54.95	Proof	55.	—

REE DOLLARS, CARIBOU, 2018.

Designers and Engravers:
Obv.:	Susanna Blunt
Rev.:	Steve McPhee

Composition: 99.99% Ag
Silver content: 7.96 g, 0.256 tr oz

Weight:	7.96 g	**Edge:**	Reeded
Diameter:	27 mm	**Die Axis:**	↑↑
Thickness:	N/A	**Finish:**	Specimen

Case of Issue: Folder-style packaging with pop-out easel back.

DATE	DESCRIPTION	MINTAGE	ISSUE PRICE	FINISH	SP-68	SP-69
2018	Caribou	W.S.L.	19.95	Specimen	20.	—

e: W.S.L. = While Supplies Last.

FOUR DOLLARS

DINOSAUR COLLECTION

FOUR DOLLARS, DINOSAUR COLLECTION, 2007-2010.

Over 65 million years ago Alberta and Saskatchewan were covered by a great subtropical inland sea, home to more than thirty-five dinosa species. There are five coins in this series.

Obverse 2007-2010
With RCM Logo

Designers:		Engravers:	
Obv.:	Susanna Blunt	Obv.:	Susan Taylor
Rev.:	Kerri Burnett	Rev.:	See reverse illustrations

Composition: 99.99% Ag, Selective aging effect
Silver content: 15.87 g, 0.510 tr oz
Weight: 15.87 g   **Edge:** Reeded
Diameter: 34.0 mm   **Die Axis:** ↑↑
Thickness: 2.1 mm   **Finish:** Proof
Case of Issue: Maroon leatherette clam style case, black flocked insert, encapsulated coin, COA

2007
Parasaurolophus
Engraver: Christie Paquet

2008
Triceratops
Engraver: Konrad Wachelko

2009
Tyrannosaurus Rex
Engraver: Marcos Hallam

2010
Dromaeosaurus
Engraver: Cecily Mok

Obverse 2010
Without RCM Logo

2010
Euoplocephalus Tutus
Engraver: Christie Paquet

DATE	DESCRIPTION	QUANTITY SOLD	ISSUE PRICE	FINISH	PR-69	PR-70
2007	Parasaurolophus	14,946	39.95	Proof	75.	—
2008	Triceratops	13,046	39.95	Proof	75.	—
2009	Tyrannosaurus Rex	13,572	39.95	Proof	50.	—
2010	Dromaeosaurus	8,982	42.95	Proof	45.	—
2010	Euoplocephalus Tutus	6,256	49.95	Proof	45.	—

OUR DOLLARS, HANGING THE STOCKINGS, 2009.

The link between stockings and Christmas began to emerge with the legend of Saint Nicholas, when he dropped three small bags of gold down the imney and into the stockings of the three daughters of a poor man, to help with their dowries.

Designers and Engravers:
Obv.:	Susanna Blunt, Susan Taylor
Rev.:	Tony Bianco, RCM Staff

Composition: 99.99% Ag
Silver content: 15.87 oz, 0.510 tr oz
Weight: 15.87 g
Diameter: 34.0 mm
Thickness: 2.0 mm
Edge: Reeded
Die Axis: ↑↑
Finish: Proof
Case of Issue: Maroon leatherette clam style case, black flocked insert, encapsulated coin, COA

DATE	DESCRIPTION	QUANTITY SOLD	ISSUE PRICE	FINISH	PR-69	PR-70
2009	Hanging The Stockings	6,011	42.95	Proof	40.	—

OUR DOLLARS, WELCOME TO THE WORLD, 2011.

This design is also featured on the twenty-five-cent coins contained in the Baby Gift Sets for 2011 and 2013 (see pages 33-34). It is also featured the $10 silver issue of 2012-2015 (see page 199).

Designers and Engravers:
Obv.:	Susanna Blunt, Susan Taylor
Rev.:	José Osio, Matt Bowan

Composition: 99.99% Ag
Silver content: 15.87 oz, 0.510 tr oz
Weight: 15.87 g
Diameter: 34.0 mm
Thickness: 2.2 mm
Edge: Reeded
Die Axis: ↑↑
Finish: Proof
Case of Issue: Black leatherette clam style case, black flocked insert, encapsulated coin, COA

DATE	DESCRIPTION	QUANTITY SOLD	ISSUE PRICE	FINISH	PR-69	PR-70
2011	Welcome to the World	7,059	59.95	Proof	150.	—

THE HEROES OF 1812 SERIES

FOUR DOLLARS, THE HEROES OF 1812 SERIES, 2012-2013.

The War of 1812 was one of the fundamental turning points in Canada's history. It profoundly influenced British North America's (Canada's) sen of identity uniting French and English-speaking inhabitants and Aboriginal communities against an American invasion.

| Obverse | Tecumseh
Engr.: Nick Martin | Sir Isaac Brock
Engr.: Matt Bowen | Charles-Michel
de Salaberry
Engr.: Steven Stewart | Laura Secord
Engr.: Samantha Strath |

Designers:
Obv.:   Susanna Blunt
Rev.:   Bonnie Ross
Composition: 99.99% Ag, Coloured
Silver content: 7.96 g, 0.255 tr oz
Weight: 7.96 g
Diameter: 27.0 mm
Thickness: 1.8 mm
Case of Issue: Maroon leatherette clam style case, black flocked insert, encapsulated coin, COA, custom coloured box

Engravers:
Obv.:   Susan Taylor
Rev.:   See reverse illustrations

Edge: Reeded
Die Axis: ↑↑
Finish: Proof

DATE	DESCRIPTION	QUANTITY SOLD	ISSUE PRICE	FINISH	PR-69	PR-70
2012	Tecumseh	7,521	49.95	Proof	35.	—
2012	Sir Isaac Brock	6,980	49.95	Proof	35.	—
2013	Charles-Michel de Salaberry	5,383	49.95	Proof	35.	—
2013	Laura Secord	5,104	49.95	Proof	35.	—

Note: These Heroes of 1812 four dollar coins, plus the Battle of Chateuguay kilo silver coin, were issued as a five-coin set. They were issued in a custom wooden maple wood box, limited to an issue of 80 sets.

FIVE DOLLARS

√E DOLLARS, NORMAN BETHUNE COMMEMORATIVE, 1998.

In 1998 the Royal Canadian Mint produced a $5 silver coin to commemorate the 60th anniversary of Dr. Norman Bethune's arrival in China. The ▪n was issued as part of a two-coin set in conjunction with China Gold Coin Incorporation (CGCI).

signers:
  Obv.:   Dora de Pédery-Hunt
  Rev.:   Harry Chan

Engravers:
  Obv.:   Dora de Pédery-Hunt
  Rev.:   Ago Aarand, Stan Witten

▪se of Issue: Brown plastic two-hole red insert, encapsulated coin, COA, box cover in Chinese brocade

MINT	COMPOSITION	WEIGHT (G)	SILVER CONTENT	DIAMETER	THICKNESS	EDGE	DIE AXIS
CGCI	99.99% silver	31.10	31.10 g, 1.00 tr oz	40.0	3.2 mm	Reeded	↑↑
RCM	99.99% silver	31.39	31.39 g, 1.01 tr oz	38.0	3.3 mm	Reeded	↑↑

DATE	DESCRIPTION	QUANTITY SOLD	ISSUE PRICE	FINISH	PR-68	PR-69
1998	Bethune - CGCI	N.I.I.	—	Proof	45.	—
1998	Bethune - RCM	N.I.I.	—	Proof	45.	—
1998	Set of 2 coins	65,831	98.00	Proof	80.	*

FIVE DOLLARS, THE VIKING SETTLEMENT, 1999.

This coin commemorates the Viking landing at L'Anse-aux-Meadows, Newfoundland, circa 1000 A.D. Norway issued a 20-Kroner coin in 1999 a commemorating the same Viking Landing. These two coins were offered as a set.

1999 Obverse	Canada $5		1999 Obverse	Norway 20 Kroner
Designer and Engraver:	Designer: D. Curley		Designer and Engraver:	Designer and Engraver:
Dora de Pédery-Hunt	Engraver: S. Witten		Unknown	Unknown

Composition: 81.0% Cu, 9.0% Ni, 10.0 Zi
Weight: 9.9 g
Diameter: 27.0 mm
Thickness: 2.5 mm
Case of Issue: Oval imitation resin stone case, two-holes, brown insert, encapsulated coins, printed cardboard outer sleeve.

Edge: Plain
Die Axis: ↑↑
Finish: Proof

DATE	DESCRIPTION	QUANTITY SOLD	ISSUE PRICE	FINISH	PR-68	PR-69
1999	Canada $5	—	—	Proof	30.	—
1999	Norway 20 Kroner	—	—	Proof	30.	—
1999	Set of 2 coins	28,450	N/A	Proof	50.	*

FIVE DOLLARS, 100TH ANNIVERSARY OF THE FIRST WIRELESS TRANSMISSION, 2001.

On December 12th, 1901, Gugliemo Marconi (1874-1937) successfully transmitted the first wireless message across the Atlantic from Poldhu Cornwall, England, to Signal Hill in St. John's, Newfoundland. To commemorate this anniversary, the Royal Canadian Mint in conjunction with the Ro Mint issued this two-coin set.

2001 Obverse	Canada $5		2001 Obverse	British £2
Designer and Engraver:	Designer and Engraver:		Des.: I. Rank-Bradley	Des.: Royal Mint Staff
Dora de Pédery-Hunt	Cosme Saffioti		Engraver: Robert Evans	Engraver: Robert Evans

Composition: Coin: 92.5% Ag, 7.5% Cu
Cameo: 24-karat gold plated

Coin: 92.5% Ag, 7.5% Cu
Outer circle: Plated 22kt gold
Inner disc: 92.5% Ag, 7.5% Cu

Silver Content: 15.69 g, 0.504 tr oz   22.2 g, 0.714 tr oz
Weight: 16.96 g   24.0 g
Diameter: 28.4 mm   28.4 mm
Thickness: N/A   N/A
Edge: Reeded   Lettering
Die Axis: ↑↑   ↑↑
Finish: Proof
Case of Issue: Brown resin oval case with a Marconi stamp on upper lid, brown flocked insert, encapsulated coin, COA, brown printed cardboard box

DATE	DESCRIPTION	QUANTITY SOLD	ISSUE PRICE	FINISH	PR-69	PR-70
2001	Canada $5	—	—	Proof	30.	—
2001	U.K. £2	—	—	Proof	30.	—
2001	Set of 2 coins	15,011	99.95	Proof	50.	*

VE DOLLARS, 2006 F.I.F.A.™ WORLD CUP, 2003.

The Canadian Soccer Association, founded in 1912, has been affiliated with the Federation International de Football Association since 1913. The 06 World Cup championship was held in Germany.

Designers and Engravers:

Obv.:	Susanna Blunt, Susan Taylor
Rev.:	Urszula Walerzak, José Osio

Composition: 99.99% Ag
Silver content: 31.30 g, 1.01 tr oz
Weight: 31.3 g
Diameter: 38.0 mm
Thickness: 3.1 mm
Edge: Reeded
Die Axis: ↑↑
Finish: Proof
Case of Issue: Black case, black flocked insert, encapsulated coin, COA, multicoloured sleeve

DATE	DESCRIPTION	QUANTITY SOLD	ISSUE PRICE	FINISH	PR-69	PR-70
2003	2006 F.I.F.A.™ World Cup	21,542	39.95	Proof	40.	—

VE DOLLARS, 100TH ANNIVERSARY OF THE CANADIAN OPEN CHAMPIONSHIP, 2004

Issued jointly by the Royal Canadian Mint and Canada Post to celebrate the 100th Anniversary of the tournament, this limited edition framed set ntains both a five-dollar note and a ten-cent coin. These coins were issued in various combinations.

Designers and Engravers:

Obv.:	Susanna Blunt, Susan Taylor
Rev.:	Cosme Saffioti

Composition: 99.99% Ag
Silver content: 27.90 g, 0.90 tr oz
Weight: 27.9 g
Diameter: 38.0 mm
Thickness: 3.0 mm
Edge: Reeded
Die Axis: ↑↑
Finish: Proof
Case of Issue: See Derivatives, page 179

DATE	DESCRIPTION	QUANTITY SOLD	ISSUE PRICE	FINISH	PR-69	PR-70
2004	100th Anniv. Canadian Open Championship	18,750	N.I.I.	Proof	45.	—

ote: N.I.I. denotes Not Issued Individually.

CANADIAN WILDLIFE SERIES

FIVE DOLLARS, CANADIAN WILDLIFE SERIES, 2004-2006.

These five dollar coins were part of a coin and stamp set series which was issued jointly by the Royal Canadian Mint and Canada Post to p homage to Canada's diverse wildlife. See Derivatives, page 179.

2004
The Majestic Moose
Obv. Designer: Susanna Blunt
Obv. Engraver: Susan Taylor
Rev. Designer: D. Preston-Smith
Rev. Engraver: Stan Witten

2005 Common Obverse
Designer: Susanna Blunt
Engraver: Susan Taylor

White-tailed Deer and Fawn
Designer: Xerxes Irani
Engraver: José Osio

The Atlantic Walrus and Calf
Designer: Pierre Leduc
Engraver: José Osio

2006 Common Obverse
Designer: Susanna Blunt
Engraver: Susan Taylor

Peregrine Falcon and Nestlings
Designer: Dwayne Harty
Engraver: José Osio

Sable Island Horse and Foal
Designer: N/A
Engraver: Christie Paquet

Composition:	99.99% Ag	**Thickness:**	3.0 mm
Silver content:	28.0 g, 0.9 tr oz	**Edge:**	Reeded
Weight:	28.0 g	**Die Axis:**	↑↑
Diameter:	38.0 mm	**Finish:**	Proof
Case of Issue:	See Derivatives, page 179		

DATE	DESCRIPTION	QUANTITY SOLD	ISSUE PRICE	FINISH	PR-69	PR-70
2004	The Majestic Moose	12,822	N.I.I.	Proof	90.	—
2005	White-tailed Deer and Fawn	6,439	N.I.I.	Proof	45.	—
2005	The Atlantic Walrus and Calf	5,519	N.I.I.	Proof	45.	—
2006	Peregrine Falcon and Nestlings	7,226	N.I.I.	Proof	45.	—
2006	Sable Island Horse and Foal	10,108	N.I.I.	Proof	45.	—

VE DOLLARS, 60TH ANNIVERSARY OF THE END OF THE SECOND WORLD WAR, 2005.

In the six years of conflict Canada had enlisted more than one million men and women in His Majesty's Armed Forces. Of these, more than 45,000 ve their lives in the cause of peace. A $50 gold version was also issued (see page 434).

| Obverse | Reverse | Reverse with Maple Leaf Privy Mark |

signers:		Engravers:	
Obv.:	Susanna Blunt	Obv.:	Susan Taylor
Rev.:	Peter Mossman	Rev.:	Christie Paquet
mposition:	99.99% Ag		
ver content:	31.50 g, 1.01 tr oz		
eight:	31.5 g	Edge:	Reeded
ameter:	38.0 mm	Die Axis:	↑↑
ickness:	3.2 mm	Finish:	See below
se of Issue:	Maroon plastic display case, black plastic insert, encapsulated coin, COA		

DATE	DESCRIPTION	QUANTITY SOLD	ISSUE PRICE	FINISH	68	69	70
2005	60th Anniv. WWII	25,000	39.95	Specimen	45.	60.	—
2005	60th Anniv. WWII with Maple Leaf Privy Mark	10,000	N.I.I.	Proof	—	70.	—

VE DOLLARS, COMMEMORATING THE CENTENNIAL OF THE PROVINCES OF ALBERTA AND SASKATCHEWAN, 2005.

Common Obverse	Alberta Centennial	Saskatchewan Centennial
Designer: Susanna Blunt	Designer: Michelle Grant	Designer: Paulett Sapergia
Engraver: Susan Taylor	Engraver: Stan Witten	Engraver: José Osio

mposition:	99.99% Ag		
ver content:	25.20 g, 0.81 tr oz		
ight:	25.2 g	Edge:	Reeded
ameter:	36.0 mm	Die Axis:	↑↑
ickness:	3.1 mm	Finish:	Proof
se of Issue:	Maroon plastic display case, black plastic insert, encapsulated coin, COA		

DATE	DESCRIPTION	QUANTITY SOLD	ISSUE PRICE	FINISH	PR-69	PR-70
2005	Alberta Centennial	20,000	49.95	Proof	40.	—
2005	Saskatchewan Centennial	20,000	49.95	Proof	40.	—

FIVE DOLLARS, BREAST CANCER AWARENESS, 2006.

Designers and Engravers:

Obv.:	Susanna Blunt, Susan Taylor
Rev.:	Christie Paquet, Christie Paquet

Composition: 99.99% Ag, Painted
Silver content: 25.17 g, 0.81 tr oz
Weight: 25.175 g
Diameter: 36.1 mm
Thickness: 3.1 mm
Edge: Reeded
Die Axis: ↑↑
Finish: Proof
Case of Issue: Maroon plastic display case, black plastic insert, encapsulated coin, COA

DATE	DESCRIPTION	QUANTITY SOLD	ISSUE PRICE	FINISH	PR-69	PR-70
2006	Breast Cancer Awareness, Painted	11,048	59.95	Proof	50.	—

FIVE DOLLARS, CANADIAN FORCES SNOWBIRDS, 2006.

Designers and Engravers:

Obv.:	Susanna Blunt, Susan Taylor
Rev.:	Jianping Yan, RCM Staff

Composition: 99.99% Ag, Double hologram
Silver content: 25.17 g, 0.81 tr oz
Weight: 25.175 g
Diameter: 36.1 mm
Thickness: 3.1 mm
Edge: Reeded
Die Axis: ↑↑
Finish: Proof
Case of Issue: See Derivatives, page 179

DATE	DESCRIPTION	QUANTITY SOLD	ISSUE PRICE	FINISH	PR-69	PR-70
2006	Canadian Forces Snowbirds, Double hologram	10,034	N.I.I.	Proof	40.	—

FIVE DOLLARS, 80TH ANNIVERSARY OF CANADA IN JAPAN, 2009.

The legation of Japan opened in Ottawa in 1928, and in 1929 Canada established its mission in Tokyo. With a mintage of 27,872 worldwide, o 5,000 coins were for sale in Canada.

Designers and Engravers:

Obv.:	Susanna Blunt, Susan Taylor
Rev.:	José Osio

Composition: 92.5% Ag, 7.5% Cu
Silver content: 23.29 g, 0.75 tr oz
Weight: 25.175 g
Diameter: 36.1 mm
Thickness: 3.1 mm
Edge: Reeded
Die Axis: ↑↑
Finish: Proof
Case of Issue: Maroon leatherette clam style case, black flocked insert, encapsulated coin, COA

DATE	DESCRIPTION	QUANTITY SOLD	ISSUE PRICE	FINISH	PR-69	PR-70
2009 (1929-)	80th Anniversary of Canada in Japan	27,872	N/A	Proof	50.	—

CANADIAN WILDLIFE SERIES (BULLION ISSUES)

VE DOLLARS (1 ounce), CANADIAN WILDLIFE SERIES (BULLION ISSUES), 2011-2017.
 The TimberWolf first appeared as the reverse design on the 2006 half-ounce silver maple and, then again in 2007 on the gold fifty-cent issue. These tings also include the bullion Birds of Prey Series.

2011-2017 Common Obverse (except for date)

Designers and Engravers:

Obv.:	Susanna Blunt, Susan Taylor
Rev.:	See reverse illustrations
Composition:	99.99% Ag
Weight:	31.11 g, 1.00 tr oz
Diameter:	38.0 mm
Thickness:	3.0 mm
Edge:	Reeded
Die Axis:	↑↑
Finish:	Bullion
Case of Issue:	Mylar pouch
Note:	Smaller than actual size.

2011 Timber Wolf
es. and Eng.: William Woodruff

2011 Grizzly
Des. and Eng.: William Woodruff

2012 Moose
Des. and Eng.: William Woodruff

2012 Cougar
Des. and Eng.: José Osio

2013 Pronghorn Antelope
Designer and Engraver:
Emily Damstra

2013 Wood Bison
Designer: Emily Damstra
Engraver: Christie Paquet

2014 Peregrine Falcon
Designer: Emily Damstra
Engraver: RCM Staff

2014 Bald Eagle
Designer: Emily Damstra
Engraver: RCM Staff

2015 Red Tailed Hawk
Designer: Emily Damstra
Engraver: RCM Staff

2015 Great Horned Owl
Designer and Engraver:
RCM Staff

2016 Peregrine Falcon
Designer and Engraver:
RCM Staff

2017 Bald Eagle
Designer and Engraver:
RCM Staff

FIVE DOLLARS (1 ounce), CANADIAN WILDLIFE SERIES (BULLION ISSUES), 2011-2017, PRICING TABLE.

DATE	DESCRIPTION	QUANTITY SOLD	ISSUE PRICE	FINISH	MS-65	MS-66
2011	Timber Wolf	1,000,000	BV	Bullion	40.	—
2011	Grizzly	1,000,000	BV	Bullion	30.	—
2012	Moose	1,000,000	BV	Bullion	30.	—
2012	Cougar	1,000,000	BV	Bullion	30.	—
2013	Pronghorn Antelope	1,000,000	BV	Bullion	30.	—
2013	Wood Bison	1,000,000	BV	Bullion	30.	—
2014	Peregrine Falcon	1,000,000	BV	Bullion	30.	—
2014	Bald Eagle	1,000,000	BV	Bullion	30.	—
2015	Red Tailed Hawk	1,000,000	BV	Bullion	30.	—
2015	Great Horned Owl	1,000,000	BV	Bullion	30.	—
2016	Peregrine Falcon	1,000,000	BV	Bullion	30.	—
2017	Bald Eagle	1,000,000	BV	Bullion	30.	—

CALENDAR IN THE SKY SERIES

FIVE DOLLARS, CALENDAR IN THE SKY SERIES, 2011-2012.

This series depicts the Full Moons of the Algonquin people. The first coin in the series, Full Buck Moon, is also known as Thunder Moon or Summ' Moon. The second coin, Full Hunter's Moon, is also known as Travel Moon or Dying Moon. The third coin, Full Wolf's Moon, is also known as Sn¢ Moon or Old Moon. The April full moon known as the Pink Moon, is a tribute to the pink flowers such as the wild ground phlox depicted on the coin th' appears in the springtime.

Common Obverse

Designers and Engravers:
Obv.:   Susanna Blunt, Susan Taylor
Rev.:   John Mantha, Cecily Mok
Composition: Outer ring: 92.50% Ag, 0.75% Cu
Inner core obverse: 92.50% Ag, 0.75% Cu
Inner core reverse: Niobium
Silver content: 6.56 g, 0.21 tr oz
Weight: 8.5 g (including 1.4 g Niobium)   **Edge:**   Interrupted serrations
Diameter: 28.0 mm   **Die Axis:** ↑↑
Thickness: 1.8 mm   **Finish:**   Proof
Case of Issue: Maple wood display case, black flocked insert, encapsulated coin, COA

Full Buck Moon

Full Hunter's Moon

Full Wolf Moon

Full Pink Moon

DATE	DESCRIPTION	QUANTITY SOLD	ISSUE PRICE	FINISH	PR-69	PR-70
2011	Full Buck Moon	6,412	119.95	Proof	75.	—
2011	Full Hunter's Moon	5,446	119.95	Proof	75.	—
2012	Full Wolf Moon	7,496	121.95	Proof	110.	—
2012	Full Pink Moon	7,238	121.95	Proof	75.	—
—	Set of 4 coins	—	487.50	Proof	300.	*

VE DOLLARS, 25TH ANNIVERSARY OF THE RICK HANSEN MAN-IN-MOTION TOUR, 1987-2012.

This coin was issued to commemorate the 25th anniversary of Rick Hansen's Man-in-Motion world tour between March 1985 and May 1987. Hansen vered more than 40,000 km through thirty-four countries on four continents during the 26-month trek. He raised $26,000,000 for spinal cord research.

Designers and Engravers:

Obv.:	Susanna Blunt, Susan Taylor
Rev.:	Chris Reid, Rosina Li, Christie Paquet
Composition:	99.99% Ag
Silver content:	23.17 g, 0.74 tr oz
Weight:	23.17 g
Diameter:	36.0 mm
Thickness:	2.8 mm

Edge:	Reeded
Die Axis:	↑↑
Finish:	Proof

Case of Issue: Maroon leatherette clam style case, black flocked insert, encapsulated coin, COA, custom sleeve

DATE	DESCRIPTION	QUANTITY SOLD	ISSUE PRICE	FINISH	PR-69	PR-70
2012 (1987-)	Rick Hansen	3,409	69.95	Proof	35.	—

VE DOLLARS, GEORGINA POPE, 2012.

In 1899 Georgina Pope was one of four volunteer nurses who travelled to South Africa to assist British troops during the South African War. Each ~se was given the rank of lieutenant in the military.

Designers and Engravers:

Obv.:	Susanna Blunt, Susan Taylor
Rev.:	Laurie McGaw, Susan Taylor, Matt Bowen
Composition:	99.99% Ag
Silver content:	23.17 g, 0.74 tr oz
Weight:	23.17 g
Diameter:	36.0 mm
Thickness:	2.7 mm

Edge:	Reeded
Die Axis:	↑↑
Finish:	Proof

Case of Issue: Maroon leatherette clam style case, black flocked insert, encapsulated coin, COA

DATE	DESCRIPTION	QUANTITY SOLD	ISSUE PRICE	FINISH	PR-69	PR-70
2012	Georgina Pope	3,154	69.95	Proof	40.	—

VE DOLLARS, DEVIL'S BRIGADE, 2013.

During World War II Canada joined forces with the United States to create the First Special Service Force.

Designers and Engravers:

Obv.:	Susanna Blunt, Susan Taylor
Rev.:	Ardell Bourgeois, Cecily Mok
Composition:	99.99% Ag
Silver content:	23.0 g, 0.74 tr oz
Weight:	23.0 g
Diameter:	36.00 mm
Thickness:	2.8 mm

Edge:	Reeded
Die Axis:	↑↑
Finish:	Proof

Case of Issue: Maroon leatherette clam style case, black flocked insert, encapsulated coin, COA

DATE	DESCRIPTION	QUANTITY SOLD	ISSUE PRICE	FINISH	PR-69	PR-70
2013	Devil's Brigade	7,255	59.95	Proof	60.	—

ABORIGINAL TRADITION OF HUNTING SERIES

FIVE DOLLARS, ABORIGINAL TRADITION OF HUNTING SERIES, 2013-2015.

This series honours the rich heritage of Aboriginal hunting from a boy's inaugural hunt (coin one) to the Cree geese hunting in spring (coin four).

Common Obverse

Designers and Engravers:

Obv.:	Susanna Blunt, Susan Taylor
Rev.:	Darlene Gait
	See Reverse illustrations
Composition:	99.99% Ag
Silver content:	22.9 g, 0.736 tr oz
Weight:	22.9 g
Diameter:	36.0 mm
Thickness:	2.8 mm

Edge: Reeded
Die Axis: ↑↑
Finish: Proof

Case of Issue: Maroon leatherette clam style case, black flocked insert, encapsulated coin, COA

Deer	**Bison**	**Hunting in Harmony (The Seal)**	**Canada Goose**
Designer: Darlene Gait	Designer: Darlene Gait	Designer: Darlene Gait	Designer: Tim Whiskeychan
Engraver: Christie Paquet	Engraver: Eric Boer	Engraver: RCM Staff	Engraver: RCM Staff

DATE	DESCRIPTION	QUANTITY SOLD	ISSUE PRICE	FINISH	PR-69	PR-70
2013	Deer	4,758	69.95	Proof	50.	—
2013	Bison	1,726	69.95	Proof	50.	—
2014	Hunting in Harmony (The Seal)	2,751	69.95	Proof	50.	—
2014	Canada Goose	2,554	69.95	Proof	50.	—

CONTEMPORARY ABORIGINAL ART SET

FIVE DOLLARS, CONTEMPORARY ABORIGINAL ART SET, 2013.

This set honours contemporary Aboriginal art.

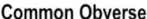

Common Obverse	**Mother and Baby Ice Fishing**	**Father Ice Fishing**

Designers:

Obv.:	Susanna Blunt
Rev.:	Ulaayu Pilurtuut
Composition:	99.99% Ag, Niobium
Silver content:	8.5 g, 0.273 tr oz
Weight:	8.5 g (including 1.4 g Niobium)
Diameter:	28.0 mm
Thickness:	1.8 mm

Engravers:

Obv.:	Susan Taylor
Rev.:	Alex Tirabasso

Edge: Interrupted serrations
Die Axis: ↑↑
Finish: Proof

Case of Issue: Black leatherette clam style case, black flocked insert, encapsulated coin, COA

DATE	DESCRIPTION	QUANTITY SOLD	ISSUE PRICE	FINISH	PR-69	PR-70
2013	Mother and Baby Ice Fishing	4,791	139.95	Proof	90.	—
2013	Ice Fishing Father	2,968	139.95	Proof	90.	—

IVE DOLLARS, ROYAL INFANT TOYS, 2013.

Designers and Engravers:
Obv.:	Susanna Blunt, Susan Taylor
Rev.:	Laurie McGaw, Samantha Strath

Composition: 99.99% Ag, Selectively gold plated
Silver content: 23.17 g, 0.75 tr oz
Weight: 23.17 g   **Edge:** Reeded
Diameter: 36.0 mm   **Die Axis:** ↑↑
Thickness: 2.7 mm   **Finish:** Proof
Case of Issue: Maroon leatherette clam style case, black flocked insert, encapsulated coin, COA custom box

DATE	DESCRIPTION	QUANTITY SOLD	ISSUE PRICE	FINISH	PR-69	PR-70
2013	Royal Infant Toys	9,739	74.95	Proof	50.	—

HISTORICAL DESIGNS ON CANADIAN BANK NOTE SERIES

IVE DOLLARS, CANADIAN BANK NOTES SERIES, 2013-2015.
This series depicts the colourful vignettes used on early Canadian bank notes.

Common Obverse

Seascape Themed Vignette
Engr.: Matt Bowen

Designers and Engravers:
Obv.:	Susanna Blunt, Susan Taylor
Rev.:	RCM Staff, See reverse illustrations

Composition: 99.99% Ag
Silver content: 23.0 g, 0.74 tr oz
Weight: 23.0 g
Diameter: 36.0 mm
Thickness: 2.8 mm
Edge: Reeded
Die Axis: ↑↑
Finish: Proof
Case of Issue: Maroon clam style case, black flocked insert, encapsulated coin, COA, custom box

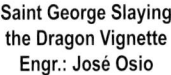

**Saint George Slaying
the Dragon Vignette
Engr.: José Osio**

**Lion on the Mountain
Vignette
Engr.: RCM Staff**

**Canadian Banknote
Vignette
Engr.: RCM Staff**

DATE	DESCRIPTION	QUANTITY SOLD	ISSUE PRICE	FINISH	PR-69	PR-70
2013	Seascape Theme Vignette (Canadian Bank of Commerce 1888 $20)	7,155	69.95	Proof	60.	—
2014	Saint George Slaying the Dragon Vignette (1859 Bank of Western Canada $5)	8,497	69.95	Proof	60.	—
2014	Lion on the Mountain Vignette (Northern Crown Bank)	7,560	69.95	Proof	60.	—
2015	Canadian Banknote Vignette (1929 Barclay's Bank $5)	3,695	69.95	Proof	60.	—

FIVE DOLLARS, ALICE MUNRO, 2014.

Canadian author Alice Munro, whose short stories are revered the world over, was the recipient of the 2013 Nobel Prize in Literature.

Designers and Engravers:

Obv.:	Susanna Blunt, Susan Taylor
Rev.:	Laurie McGaw, RCM Staff

Composition: 99.99% Ag
Silver content: 23.17 g, 0.74 tr oz

Weight:	23.17 g	**Edge:**	Reeded
Diameter:	36.0 mm	**Die Axis:**	↑↑
Thickness:	2.7 mm	**Finish:**	Proof

Case of Issue: Maroon leatherette clam style case, black flocked insert, encapsulated coin, COA

DATE	DESCRIPTION	QUANTITY SOLD	ISSUE PRICE	FINISH	PR-69	PR-70
2014	Alice Munro	4,587	69.95	Proof	45.	—

FIVE DOLLARS, 100TH ANNIVERSARY OF THE CANADIAN EXPEDITIONARY FORCE, 2014.

This coin was issued to pay tribute to those who served in the regiments, battalions and ancillary units of the Canadian Expeditionary Force (CE during the First World War.

Designers and Engravers:

Obv.:	Susanna Blunt, Susan Taylor
Rev.:	Scott Waters, RCM Staff

Composition: 99.99% Ag
Silver content: 23.17 g, 0.74 tr oz

Weight:	23.17 g	**Edge:**	Reeded
Diameter:	36.0 mm	**Die Axis:**	↑↑
Thickness:	2.7 mm	**Finish:**	Proof

Case of Issue: Maroon leatherette clam style case, black flocked insert, encapsulated coin, COA

DATE	DESCRIPTION	QUANTITY SOLD	ISSUE PRICE	FINISH	PR-69	PR-70
2014	100th Anniversary of the Canadian Expeditionary Force	6,384	64.95	Proof	60.	—

FIVE DOLLARS, PRINCESS TO MONARCH, 2014.

In celebration of the United Kingdom's longest-reigning monarch Queen Elizabeth II, this coin's reverse features an interpretation of a 19 photograph in which Princess Elizabeth is seen inspecting the troops in Fredericton, New Brunswick.

Designers and Engravers:

Obv.:	Susanna Blunt, Susan Taylor
Rev.:	Trevor Tennant, RCM Staff

Composition: 99.99% Ag
Silver content: 23.17 g, 0.74 tr oz

Weight:	23.17 g	**Edge:**	Reeded
Diameter:	36.0 mm	**Die Axis:**	↑↑
Thickness:	2.7 mm	**Finish:**	Proof

Case of Issue: Maroon leatherette clam style case, black flocked insert, encapsulated coin, COA

DATE	DESCRIPTION	QUANTITY SOLD	ISSUE PRICE	FINISH	PR-69	PR-70
2014	Princess to Monarch	2,821	64.95	Proof	55.	—

Note: This is one coin of a twenty-four coin set issued by twelve different Commonwealth countries.

FLOWERS IN CANADA SET

/E DOLLARS, FLOWERS IN CANADA SET, 2014.

Featuring the art of Bert Liverance on the coins' reverses, this set of three coins uses a niobium insert to capture some of the beauty seen in ᴘada's flowers.

Common Obverse	Tulip	Rose	Poinsettia

ᴅsigners:
Obv.:	Susanna Blunt	**Engravers:**	
Rev.:	Bert Liverance	Obv.:	Susan Taylor
ᴍposition:	99.99% Ag, Niobium	Rev.:	RCM Staff
ᴇight:	9.0 g (including 1.4 g Niobium)	**Silver content:**	9.0 g, 0.289 tr oz
ᴍmeter:	28.0 mm	**Edge:**	Interrupted serrations
ᴋckness:	N/A	**Die Axis:**	↑↑
ᴅse of Issue:	Maroon clam style case, black flocked insert, encapsulated coin, COA	**Finish:**	Proof

DATE	DESCRIPTION	QUANTITY SOLD	ISSUE PRICE	FINISH	PR-69	PR-70
2014	Tulip	4,046	139.95	Proof	100.	—
2014	Rose	2,977	139.95	Proof	100.	—
2014	Poinsettia	2,565	139.95	Proof	100.	—

/E DOLLARS (1 ounce), FIVE BLESSINGS, 2014.

Common Obverse	2014 Proof Finish, Coloured	2014 Bullion Finish

ᴅsigners:
Obv.:	Susanna Blunt	**Engravers:**	
Rev.:	RCM Staff	Obv.:	Susan Taylor
ᴍposition:	99.99% Ag	Rev.:	RCM Staff
ᴇight:	31.39 g, 1.01 tr oz	**Edge:**	Reeded
ᴍmeter:	38.0 mm	**Die Axis:**	↑↑
ᴋckness:	3.2 mm	**Finish:**	Proof, coloured; Bullion
ᴅse of Issue:	Proof: Maroon leatherette clam style case, black flock insert, encapsulated coin, COA		
	Bullion: Unknown		

DATE	DESCRIPTION	QUANTITY SOLD	ISSUE PRICE	FINISH	SP-68	SP-69	PR-69	PR-70
2014	Five Blessings, Proof, Colourised	4,559	99.95	Proof	*	*	100.	—
2014	Five Blessings, Bullion Finish	N/A	BV	Bullion	35.	45.	*	*

FIVE DOLLARS, YEAR OF THE SHEEP, 2015.

This coin celebrates the Chinese New Year and the wealth, warmth and prosperity that the Year of the Sheep ushers in.

Designers and Engravers:

Obv.:	Susanna Blunt, Susan Taylor		
Rev.:	Simon Ng, RCM Staff		
Composition:	99.99% Ag		
Silver content:	23.17 g, 0.74 tr oz		
Weight:	23.17 g	**Edge:**	Reeded
Diameter:	36.0 mm	**Die Axis:**	↑↑
Thickness:	N/A	**Finish:**	Proof
Case of Issue:	Maroon leatherette clam style case, black flocked insert, encapsulated coin, COA		

DATE	DESCRIPTION	QUANTITY SOLD	ISSUE PRICE	FINISH	PR-69	PR-70
2015	Year of the Sheep	7,975	74.95	Proof	70.	—

CORNELIUS KRIEGHOFF 200TH ANNIVERSARY SET

FIVE DOLLARS, CORNELIUS KRIEGHOFF 200TH ANNIVERSARY SET, 2015.

This set of three coins celebrates the 200th anniversary of the birth of Cornelius Krieghoff, one of Canada's most well-known artists depicting 1 century life among French-Canadian settlers and First Nations peoples.

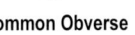
Common Obverse   *Hunter in Winter*   *Moccasin Seller Crossing the St. Lawrence at Quebec City*   *Indian Wigwam in Lower Canada*

Designers:

		Engravers:	
Obv.:	Susanna Blunt	Obv.:	Susan Taylor
Rev.:	Cornelius Krieghoff	Rev.:	RCM Staff
Composition:	99.99% Ag	**Thickness:**	N/A
Silver content:	23.17 g, 0.74 tr oz	**Edge:**	Reeded
Weight:	23.17 g	**Die Axis:**	↑↑
Diameter:	36.07 mm	**Finish:**	Proof
Case of Issue:	Three-hole red wooden lacquered box, black flocked insert, encapsulated coin, COA		

DATE	DESCRIPTION	QUANTITY SOLD	ISSUE PRICE	FINISH	PR-69	PR-70
2015	Hunter in Winter	123	N.I.I.	Proof	70.	—
2015	Moccasin Seller Crossing the St. Lawrence at Quebec City	131	N.I.I.	Proof	70.	—
2015	Indian Wigwam in Lower Canada	131	N.I.I.	Proof	70.	—
2015	Set of 3 coins	1,803	199.95	Proof	175.	*

E DOLLARS, POLAR BEAR AND CUB, 2015.

Designers and Engravers:
Obv.:	Susanna Blunt, Susan Taylor
Rev.:	Germaine Arnaktauyok

Composition:	99.99% Ag		
Silver content:	31.39 g, 1.01 tr oz		
Weight:	31.39 g	**Edge:**	Reeded
Diameter:	36.0 mm	**Die Axis:**	↑↑
Thickness:	N/A	**Finish:**	Proof
Case of Issue:	Maroon leatherette clam style case, black beauty, COA		

DATE	DESCRIPTION	QUANTITY SOLD	ISSUE PRICE	FINISH	PR-69	PR-70
2015	Polar Bear and Cub	3,585	89.95	Proof	90.	—

E DOLLARS, TODAY'S MONARCH, YESTERYEAR'S PRINCESS, 2015.

As the UK's longest-reigning monarch, Elizabeth II's unexpected role as queen was undoubtedly shaped by her experiences as a princess during Second World War.

Designers and Engravers:
Obv.:	Susanna Blunt, Susan Taylor
Rev.:	Trevor Tennant

Composition:	99.99% Ag		
Silver content:	23.17 g, 0.74 tr oz		
Weight:	23.17 g	**Edge:**	Reeded
Diameter:	36.07 mm	**Die Axis:**	↑↑
Thickness:	N/A	**Finish:**	Proof
Case of Issue:	Maroon leatherette clam style case, black flocked insert, encapsulated coin, COA		

DATE	DESCRIPTION	QUANTITY SOLD	ISSUE PRICE	FINISH	PR-69	PR-70
2015	Today's Monarch, Yesteryear's Princess	1,865	64.95	Proof	60.	—

E DOLLARS (1 ounce), BULLION SUPERMAN SHIELD, 2016.

Designers and Engravers:
Obv.:	Susanna Blunt, Susan Taylor
Rev.:	DC Comics

Composition:	99.99% Ag
Weight:	31.1 g, 1.0 tr oz
Diameter:	38.0 mm
Thickness:	3.3 mm
Edge:	Reeded
Die Axis:	↑↑
Finish:	Bullion
Case of Issue:	Plastic tubes of 25 coin

DATE	DESCRIPTION	QUANTITY SOLD	ISSUE PRICE	FINISH	MS-65	MS-66
2016	$5 (1 oz), Superman Shield	N/A	BV	Bullion	30.	—

BIRTH STONE COLLECTION

FIVE DOLLARS, BIRTH STONE COLLECTION, 2016 (GIFTWARE).

Common Obverse

Designers and Engravers:
Obv.:	Susanna Blunt, Susan Taylor
Rev.:	Three Degrees Creative Group

Composition: 99.99% Ag, Swarovski element
Silver content: 7.96 g, 0.25 tr oz
Weight: 7.96 g
Diameter: 27.0 mm
Thickness: 1.8 mm
Case of Issue: Maroon leatherette clam style case, black flocked insert, encapsulated coin, COA

Edge: Reeded
Die Axis: ↑↑
Finish: Proof

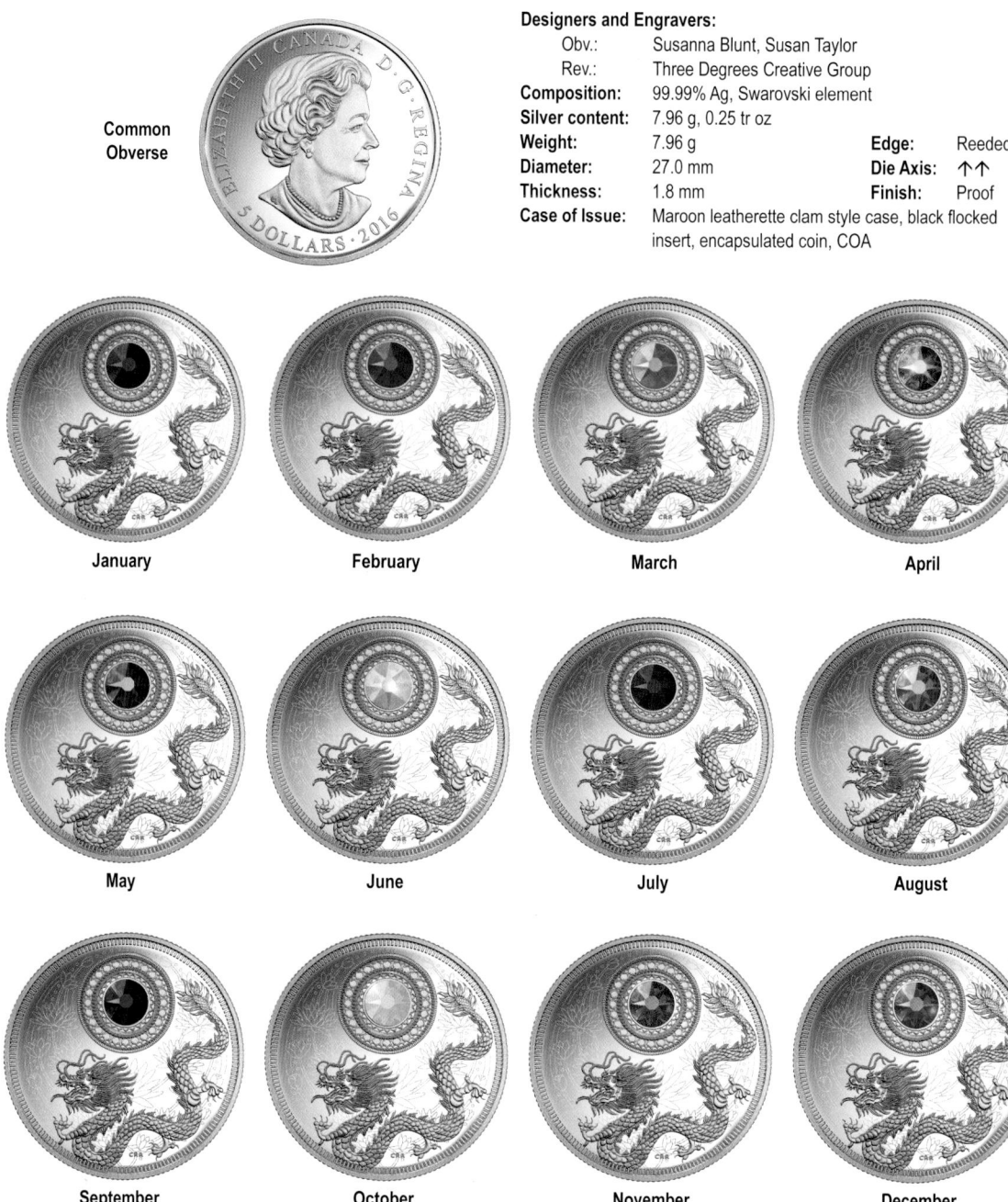

January   February   March   April

May   June   July   August

September   October   November   December

E DOLLARS, BIRTH STONE COLLECTION, 2016 (GIFTWARE), PRICING TABLE.

DATE	DESCRIPTION	QUANTITY SOLD	ISSUE PRICE	FINISH	PR-69	PR-70
2016	January	3,000	49.95	Proof	70.	—
2016	February	3,001	49.95	Proof	70.	—
2016	March	3,000	49.95	Proof	50.	—
2016	April	2,900	49.95	Proof	45.	—
2016	May	3,000	49.95	Proof	45.	—
2016	June	2,993	49.95	Proof	45.	—
2016	July	2,999	49.95	Proof	45.	—
2016	August	2,974	49.95	Proof	45.	—
2016	September	2,990	49.95	Proof	45.	—
2016	October	2,994	49.95	Proof	45.	—
2016	November	2,983	49.95	Proof	45.	—
2016	December	2,973	49.95	Proof	45.	—

BULLION PREDATOR SERIES

E DOLLARS (1 ounce), PREDATOR SERIES, 2016-2017.

ommon
Obverse

2016
Cougar

2017
Lynx

igners:
  Obv.:   Susanna Blunt
  Rev.:   Emily Damstra
nposition: 99.99% Ag
ght: 31.1 g, 1.0 tr oz
meter: 38.0 mm
kness: 3.3 mm
e of Issue: Plastic tubes of 25 coin

Engravers:
  Obv.:   Susan Taylor

Edge: Reeded
Die Axis: ↑↑
Finish: Bullion

DATE	DESCRIPTION	MINTAGE	ISSUE PRICE	FINISH	MS-65	MS-66
2016	$5 (1 oz), Cougar	50,000	BV	Bullion	30.	—
2017	$5 (1 oz), Lynx	50,000	BV	Bullion	30.	—

E DOLLARS, PROUDLY CANADIAN, 2017
his unique coin features a dynamic Canadian flag surrounded by brightly coloured fireworks. The flag and fireworks glow in the dark!

Designers and Engravers:
  Obv.:   Susanna Blunt
  Rev.:   Tony Bianco
Composition: 99.99% Ag
Silver content: 7.96 g, 0.256 tr oz
Weight: 7.96 g
Diameter: 27.0 mm
Thickness: N/A
Case of Issue: Folder with easel back.

Edge: Reeded
Die Axis: ↑↑
Finish: Specimen

DATE	DESCRIPTION	MINTAGE	ISSUE PRICE	FINISH	SP-68	SP-69
2017	Proudly Canadian	N/D	29.95	Specimen	30.	—

BIRTHSTONE SERIES

FIVE DOLLARS, BIRTHSTONES, 2018.

Like a kaleidoscope of ornate shapes and patterns, the mandala is a spellbinding representation of symmetry, harmony and unity! Art, astronomy geometry intersect in this monthly Birthstone Series, which features a colourful henn-inspired motif and a Swarovoski® crystal that adds vibrant symbol

Common Obverse   January   February

March   April   May   June

Designers:		Engravers:	
Obv.:	Susanna Blunt	Obv.:	Susan Taylor
Rev.:	Pandora Young	Rev.:	Susan Taylor
Composition:	99.99% Ag	**Silver content:**	7.96 g, 0.256 tr oz
Weight:	7.96 g	**Edge:**	Reeded
Diameter:	27 mm	**Die Axis:**	↑↑
Thickness:	N/A	**Finish:**	Proof
Case of Issue:	Maroon clamshell with black beauty box, COA		

DATE	DESCRIPTION	MINTAGE	ISSUE PRICE	FINISH	PR-69	PR-7
2018	January	4,000	54.95	Proof	55.	—
2018	February	4,000	54.95	Proof	55.	—
2018	March	4,000	54.95	Proof	55.	—
2018	April	4,000	54.95	Proof	55.	—
2018	May	4,000	54.95	Proof	55.	—
2018	June	4,000	54.95	Proof	55.	—

FIVE DOLLARS, HEARTS AGLOW, 2018

Designers and Engravers:			
Obv.:	Susanna Blunt		
Rev.:	Jose Osio		
Composition:	99.99% Ag		
Silver content:	7.96 g, 0.256 tr oz		
Weight:	7.96 g	**Edge:**	Reeded
Diameter:	27.0 mm	**Die Axis:**	↑↑
Thickness:	N/A	**Finish:**	Specim
Case of Issue:	Folder with easel back.		

DATE	DESCRIPTION	MINTAGE	ISSUE PRICE	FINISH	SP-68	SP-6
2018	Hearts Aglow	W.S.L.	29.95	Specimen	30.	—

FIVE DOLLAR DERIVATIVES

DATE	DESCRIPTION	QUANTITY SOLD	ISSUE PRICE	ISSUER	FINISH	MARKET PRICE
2004	**Five Dollar Coin** Majestic Moose. Two $5 stamps (one mint, one cancelled), COA, Wooden presentation case	12,822	39.95	RCM, CP	PR-69	90.
2004	**Five Dollar and Ten Cent Coins** Canadian Open Championship. Two commemorative stamps (one mint, one cancelled), two golf tees, RCM medallion, Framed, COA	18,750	49.99	RCM, CP	PR-69	60.
2005	**Allied Forces Silver Proof Set**, six coins: Australia, Canada, Russia, U.S.A. and U.K.	10,000	£245.	RCM, BRM	PR-69	400.
2005	**Five Dollar Coin** White-tailed Deer and Fawn. Two $1 stamps (one mint, one cancelled), COA, Wooden presentation case.	6,439	49.55	RCM, CP	PR-69	40.
2005	**Five Dollar Coin** Atlantic Walrus and Calf. Two $1 stamps (one mint, one cancelled), COA, Wooden presentation case.	5,519	49.55	RCM, CP	PR-69	40.
2006	**Five Dollar Coin** Peregrine Falcon and Nestlings.. Two $2 stamps (one mint, one cancelled), COA, Wooded presentation case.	7,226	49.55	RCM, CP	PR-69	45.
2006	**Five Dollar Coin** Sable Island Horse and Foal. Two $2 stamps (one mint, one cancelled), COA, Wooded presentation case.	10,108	49.55	RCM, CP	PR-69	45.
2006	**Five Dollar Coin Snowbirds**. Four 51¢ stamps (two mint, two on a "uniquely cancelled" souvenir sheet); Booklet; Numbered plaque; Metallic box	10,034	59.95	RCM, CP	PR-69	40.

FIVE AND TEN DOLLARS

MONTREAL SUMMER OLYMPIC GAMES, SILVER ISSUES, 1973-1976.

In 1976, Montreal, Quebec, hosted the XXI Olympiad. To commemorate and help finance Canada's first Olympics, the federal government agre to produce a series of twenty-eight silver and two gold coins (see page 440 for the $100 gold coins). There are seven series of silver coins. Each se has two $5 and two $10 coins, making a total of fourteen coins of each denomination. Each series depicts different Olympic themes on the reve and has a common design (except for the date) on the obverse. The date on the coins is usually the year of minting. Orders for the Olympic coins w accepted up to the end of December 1976, so a small unit continued to function into 1977 on the Olympic Coin Program. Mintage by series was ne recorded, but the annual reports of the Royal Canadian Mint give the following figures by year: 1973 - 537,898 $10, 543,098 $5; 1974 - 3,949,878 $ 3,981,140 $5; 1975 - 4,952,433 $10, 3,970,000 $5; 1976 - 3,970,514 $10, 3,775,259 $5. These figures do not necessarily coincide with the actual p office sales figures for the coins.

The Olympic coins were offered to the collector in two finishes, brilliant uncirculated and proof. The uncirculated issues were packaged and offe for sale in four different formats: (1) encapsulated (single coins only in styrene crystal capsules); (2) encapsulated one-coin "standard" case (sir coins in black case with red interior); (3) encapsulated four-coin "custom" set (two $5 and two $10 coins by series in black case with gold trim and insert); and (4) encapsulated four-coin "prestige" set (two $5 and two $10 coins by series in matte black leatherette case with blue insert).

The proof coins were only offered in sets, and the "deluxe" case of issue was made of Canadian white birch with a specially tanned steer hide co with a black insert. All coins in the set are encapsulated.

Because of the fluctuating price of silver during the years of the program (1973 to 1976), the original issue prices varied somewhat from serie series.

SERIES I TO VII

The following information is common to all twenty-eight $5.00 and $10.00 silver coins. Naturally, the date changes with the year of issue.

SPECIFICATIONS

FIVE DOLLARS

Composition:	92.5% Ag, 7.5% Cu
Silver content:	22.48 g, 0.72 tr oz
Weight:	24.30 g
Diameter:	38.0 mm
Thickness:	2.4 mm
Edge:	Reeded
Die Axis:	↑↑
Finish:	Proof and Circulation
Case of Issue:	See above

TEN DOLLARS

Composition:	92.5% Ag, 7.5% Cu
Silver content:	44.95 g, 1.44 tr oz
Weight:	48.60 g
Diameter:	45.0 mm
Thickness:	3.2 mm
Edge:	Reeded
Die Axis:	↑↑
Finish:	Proof and Circulation
Case of Issue:	See above

Original Issue Prices

PACKAGE TYPE	SERIES I	SERIES II	SERIES III-VII
$5 Encapsulated	6.00	7.50	8.00
$10 Encapsulated	12.00	15.00	15.75
Set of 4 Encapsulated	36.00	45.00	47.50
$5 in Standard Case	7.50	9.00	9.00
$10 in Standard Case	14.00	17.00	17.00
Set of 4 in Standard Case	43.00	52.00	52.00
Custom Set	45.00	55.00	55.00
Prestige Set	50.00	60.00	60.00
Deluxe Proof Set	72.50	82.50	82.50

MONTREAL SUMMER OLYMPIC GAMES — SERIES I

1973 $10 Obverse
Designer: Arnold Machin
Engraver: Patrick Brindley

Coin No. 1
Map of the World
Reverse design was
photochemically etched

Coin No. 3
Montreal Skyline
Ago Aarand

1973 $5 Obverse
Designer: Arnold Machin
Engraver: Patrick Brindley

Coin No. 2
Map of North America
Reverse design was
photochemically etched

Coin No. 4
Kingston and Sailboats
Terrence Smith

...me:	Geographic
...cial Release Date:	December 13, 1973. The Series I issuing period began in late 1973 and was carried over into 1974.
...signer of Reverse:	Georges Huel, worked by invitation.
...erse Engravers:	See above
...ue Price:	See page 180
...sh:	Proof and circulation

DATE	DESCRIPTION	QUANTITY SOLD	FINISH	MS-65	MS-66	MS-67/PR-68	PR-69
1973	$5 Map of North America	537,898	Circulation	20.	25.	—	*
1973	$5 Map of North America	Included	Proof	—	—	25.	—
1973	$5 Kingston and Sailboats	Included	Circulation	20.	25.	—	*
1973	$5 Kingston and Sailboats	Included	Proof	—	—	25.	—
1973	$10 Map of the World	543,098	Circulation	40.	50.	—	*
1973	$10 Map of the World	Included	Proof	—	—	50.	—
1973	$10 Montreal Skyline	Included	Circulation	40.	50.	—	—
1973	$10 Montreal Skyline	Included	Proof	—	—	50.	—

...e: Mintage numbers are simply estimates based on the 1974-1976 Royal Canadian Mint reports.

MONTREAL SUMMER OLYMPIC GAMES — 1973-1974 Mule

During the latter half of 1974, a dated obverse die - possibly made in advance for the Series II coins - was paired inadvertently with a Series I reve[rse] die of the Map of the World resulting in the production and release of a Series I-Series II mule dated 1974. The 1973-1974 Mule was found in the 19[..] four-coin custom sets, and mostly those with a European release location.

DATE	DESCRIPTION	QUANTITY SOLD	FINISH	MS-65	MS-66	MS-67
1973-74	$10 1974 Obverse - 1973 Map Reverse	Unknown	Circulation	350.	450.	—

NOTE TO COLLECTORS

1. The 1976 Montreal Summer Olympic Games were financed by the sale of five and ten dollar sterling silver coins issued over a four-year period (1973-1976). The volume of coins soon overcame any collector demand. Their value is based on face, or intrinsic value, whichever is greater. Currently, the intrinsic value is the driving force, and this will vary day-to-day with the silver market.

2. A quantity of Series One coins was issued in Styrofoam rolls to the banks for circulation. For these coins see *Canadian Coins, Volume One*. The remainders of Series One coins, and coins from Series Two through Seven were encapsulated. They are assigned a grade of MS-65 or PR-69. To obtain a higher grade the coin must be removed from the capsule and graded by a reputable grading company.

INTRINSIC VALUE OF MONTREAL OLYMPIC COINS AT VARIOUS SILVER VALUES

PRICE OF SILVER	$5	$10	FOUR COIN SET
$20.00	$14.40	$28.80	$84.40
$25.00	$18.00	$36.00	$108.00
$30.00	$21.60	$43.20	$129.60
$35.00	$25.20	$50.40	$151.10
$40.00	$28.80	$57.60	$172.80
$45.00	$32.40	$64.80	$194.40
$50.00	$36.00	$72.00	$216.00
$55.00	$39.60	$79.20	$237.60
$60.00	$43.20	$86.40	$259.20
$65.00	$46.80	$93.60	$280.80
$70.00	$50.40	$100.80	$302.40
$75.00	$54.00	$108.00	$324.00
$80.00	$57.60	$115.20	$345.60
$85.00	$61.20	$122.40	$367.20
$90.00	$65.80	$131.60	$394.80
$95.00	$69.40	$138.80	$416.40
$100.00	$73.00	$146.00	$438.00

MONTREAL SUMMER OLYMPIC GAMES — SERIES II

1974 $10 Obverse
Designer: Arnold Machin
Engraver: Patrick Brindley

Coin No. 5
Head of Zeus
Patrick Brindley

Coin No. 7
Temple of Zeus
Walter Ott

1974 $5 Obverse
Designer: Arnold Machin
Engraver: Patrick Brindley

Coin No. 6
Athlete with Torch
Patrick Brindley

Coin No. 8
Olympic Rings and Wreath
Walter Ott

eme:	Olympic Motifs
icial Release Date:	September 16, 1974
signer of Reverse:	Anthony Mann, winner of an invitational competition.
verse Engravers:	See above
ue Price:	See page 180
ish:	Proof and circulation

DATE	DESCRIPTION	QUANTITY SOLD	FINISH	MS-65	MS-66	MS-67/PR-68	PR-69
1974	$5 Athlete with Torch	1,990,570	Circulation	20.	25.	—	*
1974	$5 Athlete with Torch	Included	Proof	—	—	25.	—
1974	$5 Olympic Rings and Wreath	Included	Circulation	20.	25.	—	*
1974	$5 Olympic Rings and Wreath	Included	Proof	—	—	25.	—
1974	$10 Head of Zeus	1,974,939	Circulation	40.	50.	—	*
1974	$10 Head of Zeus	Included	Proof	—	—	50.	—
1974	$10 Temple of Zeus	Included	Circulation	40.	50.	—	*
1974	$10 Temple of Zeus	Included	Proof	—	—	50.	—

MONTREAL SUMMER OLYMPIC GAMES — SERIES III

1974 $10 Obverse
Designer: Arnold Machin
Engraver: Patrick Brindley

Coin No. 9
Lacrosse
Walter Ott

Coin No. 11
Cycling
Ago Aarand

1974 $5 Obverse
Designer: Arnold Machin
Engraver: Patrick Brindley

Coin No. 10
Canoeing
Patrick Brindley

Coin No. 12
Rowing
Terrence Smith

Theme: Early Canadian Sports
Official Release Date: April 16, 1975
Designer of Reverse: Ken Danby, winner of an invitational competition.
Engravers: See above
Issue Price: See page 180
Finish: Proof and circulation

DATE	DESCRIPTION	QUANTITY SOLD	FINISH	MS-65	MS-66	MS-67/PR-68	PR-69
1974	$5 Canoeing	1,990,570	Circulation	20.	25.	—	*
1974	$5 Canoeing	Included	Proof	—	—	25.	—
1974	$5 Rowing	Included	Circulation	20.	25.	—	*
1974	$5 Rowing	Included	Proof	—	—	25.	—
1974	$10 Lacrosse	1,974,939	Circulation	40.	50.	—	*
1974	$10 Lacrosse	Included	Proof	—	—	50.	—
1974	$10 Cycling	Included	Circulation	40.	50.	—	*
1974	$10 Cycling	Included	Proof	—	—	50.	—

MONTREAL SUMMER OLYMPIC GAMES — SERIES IV

1975 $10 Obverse
Designer: Arnold Machin
Engraver: Patrick Brindley

Coin No. 13
Men's Hurdles
Patrick Brindley

Coin No. 15
Women's Shot Put
Patrick Brindley

1975 $5 Obverse
Designer: Arnold Machin
Engraver: Patrick Brindley

Coin No. 14
Marathon
Walter Ott

Coin No. 16
Women's Javelin
Walter Ott

eme:	Olympic Track and Field Sports
ficial Release Date:	August 12, 1975
signer of Reverse:	Leo Yerxa, winner of an invitational competition.
gravers:	See above
ue Price:	See page 180
ish:	Proof and circulation

DATE	DESCRIPTION	QUANTITY SOLD	FINISH	MS-65	MS-66	MS-67/PR-68	PR-69
1975	$5 Marathon	1,985,000	Circulation	20.	25.	—	*
1975	$5 Marathon	Included	Proof	—	—	25.	—
1975	$5 Women's Javelin	Included	Circulation	20.	25.	—	*
1975	$5 Women's Javelin	Included	Proof	—	—	25.	—
1975	$10 Men's Hurdles	2,476,217	Circulation	40.	50.	—	*
1975	$10 Men's Hurdles	Included	Proof	—	—	50.	—
1975	$10 Women's Shot Put	Included	Circulation	40.	50.	—	*
1975	$10 Women's Shot Put	Included	Proof	—	—	50.	—

MONTREAL SUMMER OLYMPIC GAMES — SERIES V

1975 $10 Obverse
Designer: Arnold Machin
Engraver: Patrick Brindley

Coin No. 17
Paddling
Reverse design was
photochemically etched

Coin No. 19
Sailing
Reverse design was
photochemically etched

1975 $5 Obverse
Designer: Arnold Machin
Engraver: Patrick Brindley

Coin No. 18
Diving
Reverse design was
photochemically etched

Coin No. 20
Swimming
Reverse design was
photochemically etched

Theme: Olympic Summer Sports
Official Release Date: December 1, 1975
Designer of Reverse: Lynda Cooper, winner of an open national competition.
Engravers: See above
Issue Price: See page 180
Finish: Proof and circulation

DATE	DESCRIPTION	QUANTITY SOLD	FINISH	MS-65	MS-66	MS-67/PR-68	PR-69
1975	$5 Diving	1,985,000	Circulation	20.	25.	—	*
1975	$5 Diving	Included	Proof	—	—	25.	—
1975	$5 Swimming	Included	Circulation	20.	25.	—	*
1975	$5 Swimming	Included	Proof	—	—	25.	—
1975	$10 Paddling	2,476,216	Circulation	40.	50.	—	*
1975	$10 Paddling	Included	Proof	—	—	50.	—
1975	$10 Sailing	Included	Circulation	40.	50.	—	*
1975	$10 Sailing	Included	Proof	—	—	50.	—

MONTREAL SUMMER OLYMPIC GAMES — SERIES VI

1976 $10 Obverse
Designer: Arnold Machin
Engraver: Patrick Brindley

Coin No. 21
Field Hockey
Reverse design was
photochemically etched

Coin No. 23
Soccer
Reverse design was
photochemically etched

1976 $5 Obverse
Designer: Arnold Machin
Engraver: Patrick Brindley

Coin No. 22
Fencing
Reverse design was
photochemically etched

Coin No. 24
Boxing
Reverse design was
photochemically etched

eme:	Olympic Team and Body Contact Sports
ficial Release Date:	March 1, 1976
signer of Reverse:	Shigeo Fukada, winner of an open international competition.
gravers:	See above
ue Price:	See page 180
ish:	Proof and circulation

DATE	DESCRIPTION	QUANTITY SOLD	FINISH	MS-65	MS-66	MS-67/PR-68	PR-69
1976	$5 Fencing	1,887,630	Circulation	20.	25.	—	*
1976	$5 Fencing	Included	Proof	—	—	25.	—
1976	$5 Boxing	Included	Circulation	20.	25.	—	*
1976	$5 Boxing	Included	Proof	—	—	25.	—
1976	$10 Field Hockey	1,985.257	Circulation	40.	50.	—	*
1976	$10 Field Hockey	Included	Proof	—	—	50.	—
1976	$10 Soccer	Included	Circulation	40.	50.	—	*
1976	$10 Soccer	Included	Proof	—	—	50.	—

MONTREAL SUMMER OLYMPIC GAMES — SERIES VII

1976 $10 Obverse
Designer: Arnold Machin
Engraver: Patrick Brindley

Coin No. 25
Olympic Stadium
Ago Aarand

Coin No. 27
Olympic Velodrome
Terrence Smith

1976 $5 Obverse
Designer: Arnold Machin
Engraver: Patrick Brindley

Coin No. 26
Olympic Village
Sheldon Beveridge

Coin No. 28
Olympic Flame
Walter Ott

Theme: Olympic Games Souvenir Designs
Official Release Date: June 1, 1976
Designer of Reverse: Elliott John Morrison, winner of an invitational competition.
Engravers: See above
Issue Price: See page 180
Finish: Proof and circulation

DATE	DESCRIPTION	QUANTITY SOLD	FINISH	MS-65	MS-66	MS-67/PR-68	PR-69
1976	$5 Olympic Village	1,887,629	Circulation	20.	25.	—	*
1976	$5 Olympic Village	Included	Proof	—	—	25.	—
1976	$5 Olympic Flame	Included	Circulation	20.	25.	—	*
1976	$5 Olympic Flame	Included	Proof	—	—	25.	—
1976	$10 Olympic Stadium	1,985,257	Circulation	40.	50.	—	*
1976	$10 Olympic Stadium	Included	Proof	—	—	50.	—
1976	$10 Olympic Velodrome	Included	Circulation	40.	50.	—	*
1976	$10 Olympic Velodrome	Included	Proof	—	—	50.	—

EIGHT DOLLARS

GHT DOLLARS, GREAT GRIZZLY, 2004.

Designers and Engravers:

Obv.:	Susanna Blunt, Susan Taylor
Rev.:	Alain Leduc, Susan Taylor
Composition:	99.99% Ag
Silver content:	28.8 g, 0.925 tr oz
Weight:	28.8 g
Diameter:	39.0 mm
Thickness:	2.8 mm
Edge:	Reeded
Die Axis:	↑↑
Finish:	Proof
Case of Issue:	See Derivatives, page 194

DATE	DESCRIPTION	QUANTITY SOLD	ISSUE PRICE	FINISH	PR-69	PR-70
2004	Great Grizzly	12,942	N.I.I.	Proof	70.	—

GHT DOLLARS, 120TH ANNIVERSARY OF THE CANADIAN PACIFIC RAILWAY, 2005.

A set of two eight-dollar coins was issued in 2005. One honours the Chinese workers in Canada for their enormous contributions; the other mmemorates the opening of the Transcontinental Railway in 1885.

Railway Bridge   **Chinese Memorial**

signers:			**Engravers:**	
Obv.:	Susanna Blunt		Obv.:	Susan Taylor
Rev.:	RCM Staff		Rev.:	José Osio
mposition:	99.99% Ag with gold plated inner core			
ver content:	32.15 g, 1.03 tr oz			
eight:	32.15 g		**Edge:**	Reeded
ameter:	40.0 mm		**Die Axis:**	↑↑
ickness:	3.0 mm		**Finish:**	Proof
se of Issue:	Two-hole maroon leatherette clam style case, black flocked insert, encapsulated coin, COA			

DATE	DESCRIPTION	QUANTITY SOLD	ISSUE PRICE	FINISH	PR-69	PR-70
2005	Railway Bridge	—	N.I.I.	Proof	55.	—
2005	Chinese Memorial	—	N.I.I.	Proof	55.	—
2005	Set of 2 coins	9,892	120.00	Proof	90.	*

EIGHT DOLLARS, THE SHAPE OF TRADE IN ANCIENT CHINA, 2007.

Designers and Engravers:

Obv.:	Susanna Blunt, Susan Taylor
Rev.:	Harvey Chan, Cecily Mok
Composition:	99.99% Ag
Silver content:	25.18 g, 0.81 tr oz
Weight:	25.18 g
Diameter:	36.1 mm
Thickness:	2.9 mm
Edge:	Reeded
Die Axis:	↑↑
Finish:	Proof
Case of Issue:	Maroon clam style case, black flocked insert, encapsulated coin, COA

DATE	DESCRIPTION	QUANTITY SOLD	ISSUE PRICE	FINISH	PR-69	PR-70
2007	Ancient China	19,996	49.95	Proof	50.	—

CHINESE HISTORY AND TRADITIONS SERIES

EIGHT DOLLARS, MAPLE OF LONG LIFE, 2007.

Designers and Engravers:

Obv.:	Susanna Blunt, Susan Taylor
Rev.:	Jianping Yan, RCM Staff
Composition:	99.99% Ag, Hologram
Silver content:	25.18 g, 0.81 tr oz
Weight:	25.18 g
Diameter:	36.1 mm
Thickness:	2.9 mm
Edge:	Reeded
Die Axis:	↑↑
Finish:	Proof
Case of Issue:	Maroon clam style case, black flocked insert, encapsulated coin, COA

DATE	DESCRIPTION	QUANTITY SOLD	ISSUE PRICE	FINISH	PR-69	PR-70
2007	Maple of Long Life	12,427	45.95	Proof	50.	—

EIGHT DOLLARS, MAPLE OF WISDOM, 2009.

Designers and Engravers:

Obv.:	Susanna Blunt, Susan Taylor
Rev.:	Simon Ng, RCM Staff
Composition:	92.5% Ag, 7.5% Cu, Hologram and crystal
Silver content:	23.40 g, 0.752 tr oz
Weight:	25.3 g
Diameter:	36.1 mm
Thickness:	3.0 mm
Edge:	Reeded
Die Axis:	↑↑
Finish:	Proof
Case of Issue:	Maroon clam style case, black flocked insert, encapsulated coin, COA

DATE	DESCRIPTION	QUANTITY SOLD	ISSUE PRICE	FINISH	PR-69	PR-70
2009	Maple of Wisdom	7,273	88.88	Proof	90.	—

CHINESE HISTORY AND TRADITIONS SERIES (cont.).

GHT DOLLARS, MAPLE OF STRENGTH, 2010.

Designers and Engravers:

Obv.:	Susanna Blunt, Susan Taylor
Rev.:	Simon Ng, Cecily Mok
Composition:	92.5% Ag, 7.5% Cu, Hologram
Silver content:	23.40 g, 0.752 tr oz
Weight:	25.3 g
Diameter:	36.1 mm
Thickness:	3.0 mm
Finish:	Proof
Case of Issue:	Maroon clam style case, black flocked insert, encapsulated coin, COA

Edge: Reeded
Die Axis: ↑↑

DATE	DESCRIPTION	QUANTITY SOLD	ISSUE PRICE	FINISH	PR-69	PR-70
2010	Maple of Strength	5,138	88.88	Proof	100.	—

GHT DOLLARS, DRAGON DANCE, 2016.

Designers and Engravers:

Obv.:	Susanna Blunt, Susan Taylor
Rev.:	Harvey Chan
Composition:	99.99% Ag
Silver content:	7.96 g, 0.25 tr oz
Weight:	7.96
Diameter:	27 mm
Thickness:	N/A
Finish:	Matte Proof
Case of Issue:	Maroon clam style case, black flocked insert, encapsulated coin, COA

Edge: Reeded
Die Axis: ↑↑

DATE	DESCRIPTION	QUANTITY SOLD	ISSUE PRICE	FINISH	PR-69	PR-70
2016	Dragon Dance	19,990	29.95	Matte Proof	30.	—

GHT DOLLARS, TIGER AND DRAGON YN AND YANG, 2016.

Designers and Engravers:

Obv.:	Susanna Blunt, Susan Taylor
Rev.:	Charles Vinh
Composition:	99.99% Ag
Silver content:	20.86 g, 0.67 tr oz
Weight:	20.86 g
Diameter:	36 mm
Thickness:	N/A
Finish:	Proof
Case of Issue:	Maroon clam style case, black flocked insert, encapsulated coin, COA

Edge: Reeded
Die Axis: ↑↑

DATE	DESCRIPTION	QUANTITY SOLD	ISSUE PRICE	FINISH	PR-69	PR-70
2016	Tiger and Dragon Yin and Yang	6,886	98.88	Proof	100.	—

te: For other coins in the Chinese History and Traditions Series see page 238.

EIGHT DOLLARS, LION DANCE, 2017.

Designers and Engravers:

Obv.:	Susanna Blunt, Susan Taylor
Rev.:	Simon Ng

Composition: 99.99% Ag
Silver content: 7.96 g, 0.25 tr oz
Weight: 7.96 g
Diameter: 27 mm   **Edge:** Reeded
Thickness: N/A   **Die Axis:** ↑↑
Finish: Matte Proof
Case of Issue: Maroon clamshell with black beauty bc

DATE	DESCRIPTION	MINTAGE	ISSUE PRICE	FINISH	PR-69	PR-70
2017	Lion Dance	30,000	29.95	Matte Proof	30.	—

CANADIAN WILDLIFE SERIES, 2013-2017

EIGHT DOLLARS (1½ ounce), CANADIAN WILDLIFE SERIES, 2013-2017.

Obverse 2013-2014	2013 Polar Bear Designer: A. Germain Engraver: S. Stewart	2014 Arctic Fox Designer: Maurice Gervais Engraver: Konrad Wachelko

2015-2017 Obverse With Radial Lines (RL)	2015 Polar Bear and Cub Designer: G. Arnaktauyok Engraver: RCM Staff	2016 Snow Falcon Designer: Stan Witten Engraver: RCM Staff	2017 Grizzly Bear Designer: Pierre Leduc Engraver: RCM Staff

Designers:

Obv.:	Susanna Blunt
Rev.:	See reverse illustrations

Composition: 99.99% Ag
Weight: 46.65 g, 1.5 tr oz
Diameter: 38.1 mm
Thickness: 4.5 mm
Case of Issue: Bullion: Plastic tubes
Proof: Maroon leatherette clam style case, black flocked insert, encapsulated coin, COA

Engravers:

Obv.:	Susan Taylor
Rev.:	See reverse illustrations

Edge: Reeded
Die Axis: ↑↑
Finish: See pricing table

EIGHT DOLLARS (1½ ounce), CANADIAN WILDLIFE SERIES, 2013-2017, PRICING TABLE.

DATE	DESCRIPTION	QUANTITY SOLD	ISSUE PRICE	FINISH	MS-65	MS-66	PR-69	PR-70
2013	$8 (1½ oz) Polar Bear, Bullion	N/A	BV	Bullion	50.	—	*	*
2013	$8 (1½ oz) Polar Bear, Proof	9,684	124.95	Proof	—	—	130.	—
2014	$8 (1½ oz) Arctic Fox, Bullion	N/A	BV	Bullion	50.	—	*	*
2014	$8 (1½ oz) Arctic Fox, Proof	7,500	124.95	Proof	—	—	130.	—
2015	$8 (1½ oz) Polar Bear and Cub, Bullion	N/A	BV	Bullion	50.	—	*	*
2015	$8 (1½ oz) Polar Bear and Cub, Proof	N/A	134.95	Proof	—	—	135.	—
2016	$8 (1½ oz), Snow Falcon	N/A	BV	Bullion	50.	—	*	*
2017	$8 (1½ oz), Grizzly Bear, Bullion	N/A	BV	Bullion	50.	—	*	*

EIGHT DOLLARS (1¼ ounce), CANADIAN SILVER BISON, 2015-2016.

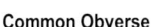

Common Obverse

2015 Canadian Silver Bison

2016 Canadian Silver Bison

Designers:		Engravers:	
Rev.:	RCM Staff		
Composition:	99.99% Ag		
Weight:	38.88 g, 1.25 tr oz	Edge:	Reeded
Thickness:	4.1 mm	Die Axis:	↑↑
Diameter:	38.0 mm	Finish:	Bullion, Radial lines
Case of Issue:	Plastic tubes		

DATE	DESCRIPTION	QUANTITY SOLD	ISSUE PRICE	FINISH	MS-65	MS-66
2015	$8 (1¼ oz), Canadian Silver Bison	500,000	BV	Bullion	40.	—
2016	$8 (1¼ oz), Canadian Silver Bison	N/A	BV	Bullion	40.	—

EIGHT DOLLARS, *FENG SHUI* GOOD LUCK CHARMS, 2017.

Designers and Engravers:

Obv.:	Susanna Blunt, Susan Taylor
Rev.:	Charles Vinh
Composition:	99.99% Ag
Silver content:	20.86 g, 0.67 tr oz
Weight:	20.86 g
Diameter:	36 mm
Thickness:	N/A
Finish:	Proof
Case of Issue:	Maroon clam style case, black flocked insert, encapsulated coin, COA

Edge:	Reeded
Die Axis:	↑↑

DATE	DESCRIPTION	MINTAGE	ISSUE PRICE	FINISH	PR-69	PR-70
2017	*Feng Shui* Good Luck Charms	6,888	98.88	Proof	100.	—

EIGHT DOLLARS, DRAGON LUCK, 2018.

Designers and Engravers:

Obv.:	Susanna Blunt, Susan Taylor
Rev.:	Simon Ng
Composition:	99.99% Ag
Silver content:	7.96 g, 0.25 tr oz
Weight:	7.96
Diameter:	27 mm
Thickness:	N/A
Finish:	Matte Proof
Case of Issue:	Maroon clamshell with black beauty box, COA

Edge: Reeded
Die Axis: ↑↑

DATE	DESCRIPTION	MINTAGE	ISSUE PRICE	FINISH	PR-69	PR-70
2018	Dragon Luck	20,000	29.95	Matte Proof	30.	—

EIGHT DOLLARS, CHINESE BLESSEINGS, 2018.

Designers and Engravers:

Obv.:	Susanna Blunt, Susan Taylor
Rev.:	Aries Cheung
Composition:	99.99% Ag
Silver content:	47.35 g, 1.52 tr oz
Weight:	47.35 g
Diameter:	49.8 x 28.6 mm
Thickness:	N/A
Finish:	Proof
Case of Issue:	Maroon clamshell with black beauty box, COA

Edge: Reeded
Die Axis: ↑↑

DATE	DESCRIPTION	MINTAGE	ISSUE PRICE	FINISH	PR-69	PR-70
2018	Chinese Blessings	5,888	159.95	Proof	160.	—

EIGHT DOLLAR DERIVATIVES

DATE	DESCRIPTION	QUANTITY SOLD	ISSUE PRICE	ISSUER	FINISH	MARKET PRICE
2004	**Eight Dollar Great Grizzly**; Two postage stamps; Wooden presentation case	12,942	48.88	RCM, CP	Proof	75.

TEN DOLLARS

EN DOLLARS, YEAR OF THE VETERAN, 2005.

Designers and Engravers:
Obv.:	Susanna Blunt, Susan Taylor
Rev.:	Elaine Goble, Susan Taylor

Composition: 99.99% Ag
Silver content: 25.175 g, 0.81 tr oz
Weight: 25.175 g
Diameter: 36.1 mm
Thickness: 3.1 mm
Edge: Reeded
Die Axis: ↑↑
Finish: Proof
Case of Issue: Maroon plastic case, black plastic insert, encapsulated coin, COA

DATE	DESCRIPTION	QUANTITY SOLD	ISSUE PRICE	FINISH	PR-69	PR-70
2005	Year of the Veteran	6,549	49.95	Proof	35.	—

EN DOLLARS, COMMEMORATING THE VISIT OF POPE JOHN PAUL II TO CANADA, 2005.

 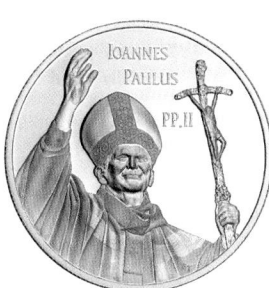

Designers and Engravers:
Obv.:	Susanna Blunt, Susan Taylor
Rev.:	Susan Taylor, Susan Taylor

Composition: 99.99% Ag
Silver content: 25.175 g, 0.81 tr oz
Weight: 25.175 g
Diameter: 36.1 mm
Thickness: 3.1 mm
Edge: Reeded
Die Axis: ↑↑
Finish: Proof
Case of Issue: Maroon plastic case, black plastic insert, encapsulated coin, COA

DATE	DESCRIPTION	QUANTITY SOLD	ISSUE PRICE	FINISH	PR-69	PR-70
2005	Pope John Paul II	24,716	49.95	Proof	55.	—

ote: In 2005 a set containing both the $10 silver and $75 gold (see page 435) coins was issued to commemorate the visit to Canada of Pope John Paul II. This may have been a special presentation set as only nine were issued.

EN DOLLARS, FORTRESS OF LOUISBOURG, NATIONAL HISTORIC SERIES, 2006.

Designers and Engravers:
Obv.:	Susanna Blunt, Susan Taylor
Rev.:	Marcos Hallam

Composition: 99.99% Ag
Silver content: 25.175 g, 0.81 tr oz
Weight: 25.175 g
Diameter: 36.1 mm
Thickness: 3.1 mm
Edge: Reeded
Die Axis: ↑↑
Finish: Proof
Case of Issue: Maroon plastic case, black plastic insert, encapsulated coin, COA

DATE	DESCRIPTION	QUANTITY SOLD	ISSUE PRICE	FINISH	PR-69	PR-70
2006	Fortress of Louisbourg	5,544	49.95	Proof	35.	—

TEN DOLLARS, BLUE WHALE, 2010.

This is the last coin and stamp set in the Canadian Wildlife Series which was co-produced by the Royal Canadian Mint and Canada Post.

Designers and Engravers:

Obv.:	Susanna Blunt, Susan Taylor
Rev.:	Pierre Leduc, Stan Witten
Composition:	92.50% Ag, 7.50% Cu
Silver content:	25.70 g, 0.826 tr oz
Weight:	27.78 g
Diameter:	40.0 mm
Thickness:	2.7 mm
Edge:	Reeded
Die Axis:	↑↑
Finish:	Proof
Case of Issue:	See Derivatives page 229

DATE	DESCRIPTION	QUANTITY SOLD	ISSUE PRICE	FINISH	PR-69	PR-70
2010	Blue Whale	9,719	N.I.I.	Proof	70.	—

TEN DOLLARS, 75TH ANNIVERSARY OF THE FIRST BANK NOTES ISSUED BY THE BANK OF CANADA, 1935-2010.

The reverse design on this coin is a reproduction of the allegory that appeared on the original 1935 ten-dollar bank note; a seated woma surrounded by a variety of farm produce to symbolise the harvest.

Designers and Engravers:

Obv.:	Susanna Blunt, Susan Taylor		
Rev.:	Susan Taylor, Susan Taylor		
Composition:	99.99% Ag		
Silver content:	15.90 g, 0.511 tr oz		
Weight:	15.90 g		
Diameter:	34.0 mm		
Thickness:	2.2 mm	Die Axis:	↑↑
Edge:	Reeded	Finish:	Proof
Case of Issue:	Maroon leatherette clam style case, black flock insert, encapsulated coin, COA		

DATE	DESCRIPTION	QUANTITY SOLD	ISSUE PRICE	FINISH	PR-69	PR-70
2010 (1935-)	75th Anniv. of First Notes Issued by Bank of Canada	6,818	54.95	Proof	45.	—

TEN DOLLARS, HIGHWAY OF HEROES, 2011.

Designers and Engravers:

Obv.:	Susanna Blunt, Susan Taylor		
Rev.:	Major C. Gauthier/S. Witten, S. Witten		
Composition:	99.99% Ag		
Silver content:	15.87 g, 0.510 tr oz		
Weight:	15.87 g		
Diameter:	34.0 mm		
Thickness:	2.0 mm	Die Axis:	↑↑
Edge:	Reeded	Finish:	Proof
Case of Issue:	Maroon leatherette clam style case, black flocked insert, encapsulated coin COA		

DATE	DESCRIPTION	QUANTITY SOLD	ISSUE PRICE	FINISH	PR-69	PR-70
2011	Highway of Heroes	7,732	69.95	Proof	50.	—

BOREAL FOREST SET

EN DOLLARS, BOREAL FOREST SET, 2011.

The year 2011 was declared the International Year of Forests by the United Nations, a time to celebrate the important role forests play in our lives.

Common Obverse

Designers:		**Engravers:**	
Obv.:	Susanna Blunt	Obv.:	Susan Taylor
Rev.:	Corrine Hunt	Rev.:	See reverse illustrations
Composition:	99.99% Ag		
Silver content:	15.87 g, 0.510 tr oz		
Weight:	15.87 g	**Edge:**	Reeded
Diameter:	34.0 mm	**Die Axis:**	↑↑
Thickness:	2.0 mm	**Finish:**	Proof
Case of Issue:	Maroon leatherette clam style case, black flocked insert encapsulated coin, COA		

Orca Whale	Peregrine Falcon	Wood Bison	Boreal Forest
Engraver: Cecily Mok	Engraver: Marcos Hallam	Engraver: Konrad Wachelko	Engraver: Marcos Hallam

DATE	DESCRIPTION	QUANTITY SOLD	ISSUE PRICE	FINISH	PR-69	PR-70
2011	Orca Whale	3,131	69.95	Proof	45.	—
2011	Peregrine Falcon	3,014	69.95	Proof	45.	—
2011	Wood Bison	3,063	69.95	Proof	45.	—
2011	Boreal Forest	3,292	69.95	Proof	45.	—

EN DOLLARS, WINTER TOWN, 2011.

Designers and Engravers:		
Obv.:	Susanna Blunt, Susan Taylor	
Rev.:	Virginia Boulay, RCM Staff	
Composition:	99.99% Ag, Coloured	
Silver content:	15.87 g, 0.510 tr oz	
Weight:	15.87 g	
Diameter:	34.0 mm	**Edge:** Reeded
Thickness:	2.0 mm	**Die Axis:** ↑↑
Finish:	Proof	
Case of Issue:	Maroon leatherette clam style case, black flocked insert, encapsulated coin, COA	

DATE	DESCRIPTION	QUANTITY SOLD	ISSUE PRICE	FINISH	PR-69	PR-70
2011	Winter Town	4,103	69.95	Proof	45.	—

TEN DOLLARS, LITTLE SKATERS, 2011.

Designers and Engravers:

Obv.:	Susanna Blunt, Susan Taylor
Rev.:	Virginia Boulay, Christie Paquet
Composition:	99.99% Ag, Coloured
Silver content:	15.87 g, 0.510 tr oz
Weight:	15.87 g
Diameter:	34.0 mm **Edge:** Reeded
Thickness:	2.0 mm **Die Axis:** ↑↑
Finish:	Proof
Case of Issue:	Maroon leatherette clam style case, black flocked insert, encapsulated coin COA

DATE	DESCRIPTION	QUANTITY SOLD	ISSUE PRICE	FINISH	PR-69	PR-70
2011	Little Skaters	3,663	69.95	Proof	40.	—

TEN DOLLARS, YEAR OF THE DRAGON, 2012.

Designers and Engravers:

Obv.:	Susanna Blunt, Susan Taylor
Rev.:	Three Degrees Creative Group Inc., Konrad Wachelko
Composition:	99.99% Ag
Silver content:	15.87 g, 0.510 tr oz
Weight:	15.87 g
Diameter:	33.9 mm **Edge:** Reeded
Thickness:	2.0 mm **Die Axis:** ↑↑
Finish:	Specimen
Case of Issue:	Red cardboard pocket, red envelope, encapsulated coin, COA

DATE	DESCRIPTION	QUANTITY SOLD	ISSUE PRICE	FINISH	SP-68	SP-69
2012	Year of the Dragon	51,128	29.95	Specimen	25.	—

TEN DOLLARS, *RMS TITANIC*, 2012.

This coin was issued for the 100th anniversary of the sinking of *RMS Titanic* on her maiden voyage.

Designers and Engravers:

Obv.:	Susanna Blunt, Susan Taylor
Rev.:	Yves Bérubé, Konrad Wachelko
Composition:	99.99% Ag
Silver content:	15.87 g, 0.510 tr oz
Weight:	15.87 g
Diameter:	33.9 mm **Edge:** Reeded
Thickness:	2.0 mm **Die Axis:** ↑↑
Finish:	Proof
Case of Issue:	Maroon leatherette clam style case, black flocked insert, encapsulated coin COA

DATE	DESCRIPTION	QUANTITY SOLD	ISSUE PRICE	FINISH	PR-69	PR-70
2012	*RMS Titanic*	20,000	64.95	Proof	60.	—

EN DOLLARS, *HMS SHANNON*, 1812-2012.

The Leda-class frigate, *HMS Shannon*, was launched from Finsbury, England, in 1806. Captain Philip Broke led his vessel to many victories against French during the Napoleonic Wars. When tensions rose in the autumn of 1811, *HMS Shannon* sailed to North America.

Designers and Engravers:

Obv.:	Susanna Blunt, Susan Taylor
Rev.:	Bonnie Ross, Christie Paquet
Composition:	99.99% Ag, Selectively gold plated
Silver content:	15.87 g, 0.510 tr oz
Weight:	15.87 g
Diameter:	34.0 mm **Edge:** Reeded
Thickness:	2.1 mm **Die Axis:** ↑↑
Finish:	Proof
Case of Issue:	Black leatherette clam style case, black flocked insert, encapsulated coin, COA, custom coloured box

DATE	DESCRIPTION	QUANTITY SOLD	ISSUE PRICE	FINISH	PR-69	PR-70
2012 (1812-)	*HMS Shannon*	9,970	64.95	Proof	65.	—

EN DOLLARS, PRAYING MANTIS, 2012.

Designers and Engravers:

Obv.:	Susanna Blunt, Susan Taylor
Rev.:	Robert Ganz, Konrad Wachelko
Composition:	99.99% Ag
Silver content:	15.87 g, 0.510 tr oz
Weight:	15.87 g
Diameter:	34.0 mm **Edge:** Reeded
Thickness:	2.1 mm **Die Axis:** ↑↑
Finish:	Proof
Case of Issue:	Black leatherette clam style case, black flocked insert, encapsulated coin, COA, custom coloured sleeve

DATE	DESCRIPTION	QUANTITY SOLD	ISSUE PRICE	FINISH	PR-69	PR-70
2012	Praying Mantis	5,727	69.95	Proof	35.	—

EN DOLLARS, WELCOME TO THE WORLD, 2012-2018.

This design is also featured on the twenty-five-cent coins contained in the Baby Gift Sets for 2011 and 2013 (see pages 33-34). It is also featured the $4 silver issue of 2011 (see page 159).

 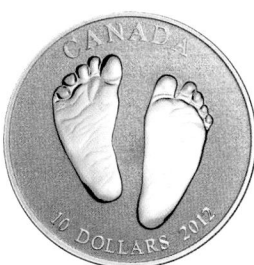

Designers and Engravers:

Obv.:	Susanna Blunt, Susan Taylor
Rev.:	José Osio, Matt Bowan
Composition:	99.99% Ag
Silver content:	15.87 g, 0.510 tr oz
Weight:	15.87 g
Diameter:	34.0 mm **Edge:** Reeded
Thickness:	2.1 mm **Die Axis:** ↑↑
Finish:	See pricing table
Case of Issue:	Maroon leatherette clam style case, black flocked insert, encapsulated coin, COA, custom sleeve

DATE	DESCRIPTION	QUANTITY SOLD	ISSUE PRICE	FINISH	PR-69	PR-70
2012	Welcome to the World, Reverse Proof	9,999	59.95	Rev Proof	110.	—
2013	Welcome to the World, Proof	14,916	59.95	Proof	90.	—
2014	Welcome to the World, Matte Proof	14,994	59.95	Matte Proof	90.	—
2015	Born in 2015, Reverse Proof	14,996	59.95	Rev Proof	90.	—
2016	Welcome to the World	19,905	59.95	Rev. Proof	90.	—
2017	Welcome to the World	6,505	59.95	Rev. Proof	70.	—
2018	Welcome to the World	20,000	59.95	Rev. Proof	60.	—

TEN DOLLARS, YEAR OF THE SNAKE, 2013.

Designers and Engravers:

Obv.:	Susanna Blunt, Susan Taylor
Rev.:	Aries Chung, Stan Witten
Composition:	99.99% Ag
Silver content:	15.87 g, 0.510 tr oz
Weight:	15.87 g
Diameter:	34.0 mm **Edge:** Reeded
Thickness:	2.1 mm **Die Axis:** ↑↑
Finish:	Specimen
Case of Issue:	Maroon leatherette clam style case, black flocked insert, encapsulated coin COA

DATE	DESCRIPTION	QUANTITY SOLD	ISSUE PRICE	FINISH	SP-68	SP-69
2013	Year of the Snake	22,986	39.95	Specimen	30.	—

TEN DOLLARS, WINTER SCENE, 2013.

Designers and Engravers:

Obv.:	Susanna Blunt, Susan Taylor
Rev.:	Rémi Clark, José Osio
Composition:	99.99% Ag, Coloured
Silver content:	15.87 g, 0.510 tr oz
Weight:	15.87 g
Diameter:	34.0 mm **Edge:** Reeded
Thickness:	2.1 mm **Die Axis:** ↑↑
Finish:	Proof
Case of Issue:	Maroon leatherette clam style case, black flocked insert, encapsulated coin COA

DATE	DESCRIPTION	QUANTITY SOLD	ISSUE PRICE	FINISH	PR-69	PR-70
2013	Winter Scene	8,001	69.95	Proof	60.	—

TEN DOLLARS, YEAR OF THE SNAKE (CHINESE CHARACTER), 2013.

The Snake personality is graceful and soft-spoken. It has a hypnotic beauty and never gives itself totally away. The mysterious Snake is a strate[g]ic planner that has everyone guessing its next move. The Snake is a strong individual and is usually destined for great success. This is a special editi[on] Year of the Snake.

Designers and Engravers:

Obv.:	Susanna Blunt, Susan Taylor
Rev.:	Simon Ng, Konrad Wachelko
Composition:	99.99% Ag
Silver content:	15.87 g, 0.510 tr oz
Weight:	15.87 g
Diameter:	34.0 mm **Edge:** Reeded
Thickness:	2.1 mm **Die Axis:** ↑↑
Finish:	Specimen
Case of Issue:	Maroon leatherette clam style case, black flocked insert, encapsulated coin COA

DATE	DESCRIPTION	QUANTITY SOLD	ISSUE PRICE	FINISH	SP-68	SP-69
2013	Year of the Snake	5,647	43.88	Specimen	35.	—

O CANADA SET ONE

TEN DOLLARS, O CANADA SET ONE, 2013.

Designers and Engravers:

Obv.:	Susanna Blunt, Susan Taylor
Rev.:	See reverse illustrations

Composition: 99.99% Ag
Silver content: 15.87 g, 0.51 tr oz

Weight:	15.87 g	**Edge:**	Reeded
Diameter:	34.0 mm	**Die Axis:**	↑↑
Thickness:	2.2 mm	**Finish:**	Matte Proof

Case of Issue:

Single: Maroon leatherette clam style case, black flocked insert, encapsulated coin, COA, custom coloured box

Subscription: 12-hole wooden case, red flocked top insert, black flocked bottom insert, encapsulated coins, COA, custom box

Common Obverse

The Inukshuk
Designer: Tony Bianco
Engraver: Samantha Strath

The Beaver
Designer: Pierre Leduc
Engraver: Stan Witten

The Royal Canadian Mounted Police
Designer: Tony Bianco
Engraver: Konrad Wachelko

The Polar Bear
Designer: Pierre Leduc
Engraver: Steven Stewart

Summer Fun
Designer: Claudio D'Angelo
Engraver: Christie Paquet

The Wolf
Designer: Pierre Leduc
Engraver: Eric Boyer

Niagara Falls
Designer: Emily Damstra
Engraver: Konrad Wachelko

The Caribou
Designer: Pierre Leduc
Engraver: Stan Witten

Hockey
Designer: Tony Bianco
Engraver: Cecily Mok

The Orca
Designer: Pierre Leduc
Engraver: Alex Tirabasso

The Maple Leaf (with colour)
Designer: Emily Damstra
Engraver: Steven Stewart

Canadian Holiday Season
Designer: Doug Geldart
Engraver: Eric Boyer

TEN DOLLARS, O CANADA SET ONE, 2013, PRICING TABLE.

DATE	DESCRIPTION	QUANTITY SOLD	ISSUE PRICE	FINISH	PR-69	PR-70
2013	The Inukshuk	38,843	39.95	Proof	30.	—
2013	The Beaver	38,560	39.95	Proof	30.	—
2013	The Royal Canadian Mounted Police	36,914	39.95	Proof	30.	—
2013	The Polar Bear	38,555	39.95	Proof	30.	—
2013	Summer Fun	34,867	39.95	Proof	30.	—
2013	The Wolf	34,899	39.95	Proof	30.	—
2013	Niagara Falls	33,544	39.95	Proof	30.	—
2013	The Caribou	33,522	39.95	Proof	30.	—
2013	Hockey	33,325	39.95	Proof	30.	—
2013	The Orca	30,834	39.95	Proof	30.	—
2013	The Maple Leaf (with colour)	42,551	54.95	Proof	40.	—
2013	Canadian Holiday Season	31,022	39.95	Proof	30.	—
2013	Set of 12 Coins	—	479.40	Proof	300.	*

TEN DOLLARS, O CANADA SET ONE, SELECTIVELY GOLD PLATED, 2013.

The coins in this set are the same as the O Canada Set issued in 2013, however each coin is framed by a ring of gold plating. Single coins were available from the Mint, and can only be obtained from the break up of sets.

Designers and Engravers: See O Canada Set

Specifications: As O Canada Set except the coins are selectively gold plated

Case of Issue: Wooden case, red flocked insert at top, black flocked insert at bottom, encapsulated coins, COA, custom beauty box

DATE	DESCRIPTION	QUANTITY SOLD	ISSUE PRICE	FINISH	PR-69	PR-70
2013	The Inukshuk, Selectively gold plated	—	N.I.I.	Proof	60.	—
2013	The Beaver, Selectively gold plated	—	N.I.I.	Proof	60.	—
2013	The Royal Canadian Mounted Police, Selectively gold plated	—	N.I.I.	Proof	60.	—
2013	The Polar Bear, Selectively gold plated	—	N.I.I.	Proof	60.	—
2013	Summer Fun, Selectively gold plated	—	N.I.I.	Proof	60.	—
2013	The Wolf, Selectively gold plated	—	N.I.I.	Proof	60.	—
2013	Niagara Falls, Selectively gold plated	—	N.I.I.	Proof	60.	—
2013	The Caribou, Selectively gold plated	—	N.I.I.	Proof	60.	—
2013	Hockey, Selectively gold plated	—	N.I.I.	Proof	60.	—
2013	The Orca, Selectively gold plated	—	N.I.I.	Proof	60.	—
2013	Maple Leaf (with colour), Selectively gold plated	—	N.I.I.	Proof	60.	—
2013	Canadian Holiday Season, Selectively gold plated	—	N.I.I.	Proof	60.	—
2013	Set of 12 coins	637	899.95	Proof	650.	*

Note: For other coins in the O Canada, Series One, see pages 324 and 428.

DUCKS OF CANADA SERIES

N DOLLARS, DUCKS OF CANADA SERIES, 2013-2016.

Common Obverse

Mallard
Des.: Trevor Tennant

Wood Duck
Des.: Trevor Tennant

Northern Pintail
Des.: Samantha Strath

Harlequin Duck
Des.: Trevor Tennant

Cinnamon Teal
Des.: Denis Mayer Jr.

Canvasback
Des.: Glen Scrimshaw

signers:		Engravers:	
Obv.:	Susanna Blunt	Obv.:	Susan Taylor
Rev.:	See reverse illustrations	Rev.:	RCM Staff
mposition:	99.99% Ag, Coloured		
ver content:	15.87 g, 0.510 tr oz		
ight:	15.87 g	Edge:	Reeded
ameter:	34.0 mm	Die Axis:	↑↑
ickness:	2.1 mm	Finish:	Proof
se of Issue:	Maroon leatherette clam style case, black flocked insert, encapsulated coin, COA		

DATE	DESCRIPTION	QUANTITY SOLD	ISSUE PRICE	FINISH	PR-69	PR-70
2013	Mallard	8,998	69.95	Proof	60.	—
2013	Wood Duck	9,866	69.95	Proof	60.	—
2014	Northern Pintail	9,919	69.95	Proof	60.	—
2014	Harlequin Duck	5,837	69.95	Proof	60.	—
2015	Cinnamon Teal	2,944	69.95	Proof	60.	—
2016	Canvasback	3,017	69.95	Proof	60.	—

N DOLLARS, 75TH ANNIVERSARY OF SUPERMAN™: VINTAGE, 2013.

Designers and Engravers:	
Obv.:	Susanna Blunt, Susan Taylor
Rev.:	DC Comics/Warner Brothers, Konrad Wachelko
Composition:	99.99% Ag
Silver content:	7.96 g, 0.25 tr oz
Weight:	7.96 g
Diameter:	27.0 mm
Thickness:	1.8 mm
Edge:	Reeded
Die Axis:	↑↑
Finish:	Proof

se of Issue: Clear plastic cover, black plastic coin display, encapsulated coin, COA, custom box

DATE	DESCRIPTION	QUANTITY SOLD	ISSUE PRICE	FINISH	PR-69	PR-70
2013	75th Anniversary of Superman™: Vintage	14,972	44.75	Proof	45.	—

DRAGONFLY SERIES

TEN DOLLARS, DRAGONFLY SERIES, 2013-2015.

These coins were issued to commemorate Canada's dragonfly species and their habitats.

Common Obverse	Twelve-Spotted Skimmer Green	Darner	Pygmy Snaketail

Designers:
Obv.:   Susanna Blunt
Rev.:   Celia Godkin
Composition: 99.99% Ag, Hologram with colour
Silver content: 15.87 g, 0.510 tr oz
Weight: 15.87 g
Diameter: 34.0 mm
Thickness: 2.1 mm
Case of Issue: Maroon leatherette clam style case, black flocked insert, encapsulated coin, COA

Engravers:
Obv.:   Susan Taylor
Rev.:   Samantha Strath

Edge: Reeded
Die Axis: ↑↑
Finish: Proof

DATE	DESCRIPTION	QUANTITY SOLD	ISSUE PRICE	FINISH	PR-69	PR-70
2013	Twelve-Spotted Skimmer Dragonfly	9,923	79.95	Proof	50.	—
2014	Green Darner Dragonfly	7,471	79.95	Proof	50.	—
2015	Pygmy Snaketail	3,159	79.95	Proof	50.	—

TEN DOLLARS, DREAMCATCHER, 2013.

Many variations exist across the First Nations cultures, but they all exercise the same tradition of stopping bad dreams, and letting good dr
through to the mind of the dreamer.

Designers and Engravers:
Obv.:   Susanna Blunt, Susan Taylor
Rev.:   Darlene Gait, Samantha Strath
Composition: 99.99% Ag, Hologram, with colour
Silver content: 15.87 g, 0.510 tr oz
Weight: 15.87 g
Diameter: 34.0 mm   **Edge:** Reeded
Thickness: 2.1 mm   **Die Axis:** ↑↑
Finish: Proof
Case of Issue: Maroon leatherette clam style case, black flocked insert, encapsulated coin, COA

DATE	DESCRIPTION	QUANTITY SOLD	ISSUE PRICE	FINISH	PR-69	PR-70
2013	Dreamcatcher	9,957	74.95	Proof	70.	—

N DOLLARS, A PARTRIDGE IN A PEAR TREE, 2013.

Designers and Engravers:

Obv.:	Susanna Blunt, Susan Taylor
Rev.:	Risto Turlinen, José Osio
Silver content:	99.99% Ag, Coloured
Silver content:	15.87 g, 0.510 tr oz
Weight:	15.87 g
Diameter:	34.0 mm
Thickness:	2.1 mm
Finish:	Proof
Case of Issue:	Maroon leatherette clam style case, black flocked insert, encapsulated coin, COA

Edge: Reeded
Die Axis: ↑↑

DATE	DESCRIPTION	QUANTITY SOLD	ISSUE PRICE	FINISH	PR-69	PR-70
2013	A Partridge in a Pear Tree	4,475	64.95	Proof	50.	—

N DOLLARS, HOLIDAY CANDLES, 2013.

Designers and Engravers:

Obv.:	Susanna Blunt, Susan Taylor
Rev.:	Claudio D'Angelo, RCM Staff
Composition:	99.99% Ag, Coloured
Silver content:	15.87 g, 0.510 tr oz
Weight:	15.87 g
Diameter:	34.0 mm
Thickness:	2.0 mm
Finish:	Proof
Case of Issue:	Maroon leatherette clam style case, black flocked insert, encapsulated coin, COA

Edge: Reeded
Die Axis: ↑↑

DATE	DESCRIPTION	QUANTITY SOLD	ISSUE PRICE	FINISH	PR-69	PR-70
2013	Holiday Candles	3,188	74.95	Proof	60.	—

N DOLLARS, YEAR OF THE HORSE, 2014.

Designers and Engravers:

Obv.:	Susanna Blunt, Susan Taylor
Rev.:	Simon Ng, Samantha Strath
Composition:	99.99% Ag
Silver content:	15.87 g, 0.510 tr oz
Weight:	15.87 g
Diameter:	34.0 mm
Thickness:	2.0 mm
Finish:	Specimen
Case of Issue:	Maroon leatherette clam style case, black flocked insert, encapsulated coin, COA

Edge: Reeded
Die Axis: ↑↑

DATE	DESCRIPTION	QUANTITY SOLD	ISSUE PRICE	FINISH	SP-68	SP-69
2014	Year of the Horse	25,436	39.95	Specimen	40.	—

N DOLLARS, 2014 FIFA™ WORLD CUP, 2014.

Designers and Engravers:

Obv.:	Susanna Blunt, Susan Taylor
Rev.:	Greg Banning, José Osio
Composition:	99.99% Ag
Silver content:	15.87 g, 0.510 tr oz
Weight:	15.87 g
Diameter:	33.9 mm
Thickness:	2.0 mm
Finish:	Proof
Case of Issue:	Black and white clam style case, black flocked insert, encapsulated coin, COA, full colour sleeve

Edge: Reeded
Die Axis: ↑↑

DATE	DESCRIPTION	QUANTITY SOLD	ISSUE PRICE	FINISH	PR-69	PR-70
2014	2014 FIFA™ World Cup	7,674	54.95	Proof	50.	—

TEN DOLLARS, SKATING IN CANADA, 2014.

Designers and Engravers:

Obv.:	Susanna Blunt, Susan Taylor
Rev.:	Tony Harris, Matt Bowen
Composition:	99.99% Ag, Coloured
Silver content:	15.87 g, 0.510 tr oz
Weight:	15.87 g
Diameter:	34.0 mm
Thickness:	2.2 mm
Finish:	Proof
Case of Issue:	Maroon clam style case, black flocked insert, encapsulated coin, COA

Edge: Reeded
Die Axis: ↑↑

DATE	DESCRIPTION	QUANTITY SOLD	ISSUE PRICE	FINISH	PR-69	PR-70
2014	Skating in Canada	4,653	64.95	Proof	60.	—

TEN DOLLARS, THE MOBILISATION OF OUR NATION, 2014.
This coin was issued to commemorate the 100th anniversary of the declaration of World War One.

Designers and Engravers:

Obv.:	Susanna Blunt, Susan Taylor
Rev.:	Maskull Lasserre, Matt Bowen
Composition:	99.99% Ag
Silver content:	15.87 g, 0.510 tr oz
Weight:	15.87 g
Diameter:	34.0 mm
Thickness:	2.0 mm
Finish:	Matte proof
Case of Issue:	Maroon clam style case, black flocked insert, encapsulated coin, COA

Edge: Reeded
Die Axis: ↑↑

DATE	DESCRIPTION	QUANTITY SOLD	ISSUE PRICE	FINISH	PR-69	PR-70
2014	The Mobilisation of our Nation	7,313	44.95	Proof	45.	—

TEN DOLLARS, POPE JOHN PAUL II, 2014.
This coin celebrates the canonization of Pope John Paul II on April 27, 2014.

Designers and Engravers:

Obv.:	Susanna Blunt, Susan Taylor
Rev.:	RCM Staff, Christie Paquet
Composition:	99.99% Ag
Silver content:	15.87 g, 0.510 tr oz
Weight:	15.87 g
Diameter:	34.0 mm
Thickness:	2.0 mm
Finish:	Matte proof
Case of Issue:	Maroon clam style case, black flocked insert, encapsulated coin, COA

Edge: Reeded
Die Axis: ↑↑

DATE	DESCRIPTION	QUANTITY SOLD	ISSUE PRICE	FINISH	PR-69	PR-70
2014	Pope John Paul II	8,499	69.95	Proof	70.	—

O CANADA SET TWO

TEN DOLLARS, O CANADA SET TWO, 2014.

Common Obverse

Designers and Engravers:

Obv.:	Susanna Blunt, Susan Taylor
Rev.:	See reverse illustrations

Composition: 99.99% Ag
Silver content: 15.87 g, 0.51 tr oz
Weight: 15.87 g
Diameter: 34.0 mm
Thickness: 2.1 mm

Edge: Reeded
Die Axis: ↑↑
Finish: Matte Proof

Case of Issue:

Singly: Maroon leatherette clam style case, black flocked insert, encapsulated coin, COA, custom coloured box

Subscription: 10-hole wooden case, red flocked top insert, black flocked bottom insert, encapsulated coins, COA, custom box

The Igloo
Designer: Yves Bérubé
Engraver: Cecily Mok

Grizzly Bear
Designer: Glen Loates
Engraver: José Osio

Skiing Canada's Slopes
Designer: Kendra Dixon
Engraver: RCM Staff

Moose
Designer: Claudio D'Angelo
Engraver: Stan Witten

Down by the Old Maple Tree
Designer: Claudio D'Angelo
Engraver: RCM Staff

Canada Goose
Des.: Jean Charles Daumas
Engraver: Matt Bowen

Canadian Cowboy
Designer: Bernie Brown
Engraver: Cecily Mok

Bison
Designer: Trevor Tennant
Engraver: RCM Staff

The Northern Lights
Designer: Julius Csotonyi
Engraver: RCM Staff

Canadian Holiday Scene
Designer: Doug Geldart
Engraver: Cecily Mok

TEN DOLLARS, O CANADA SET TWO, 2014, PRICING TABLE.

DATE	DESCRIPTION	QUANTITY SOLD	ISSUE PRICE	FINISH	PR-69	PR-70
2014	The Igloo	20,736	39.95	Proof	30.	—
2014	Grizzly Bear	20,933	39.95	Proof	30.	—
2014	Skiing Canada's Slopes	17,384	39.95	Proof	30.	—
2014	Moose	19,791	39.95	Proof	30.	—
2014	Down by the Old Maple Tree	17,122	39.95	Proof	30.	—
2014	Canada Goose	16,840	39.95	Proof	30.	—
2014	Canadian Cowboy	16,521	39.95	Proof	30.	—
2014	Bison	16,614	39.95	Proof	30.	—
2014	The Northern Lights (with colour)	19,058	54.95	Proof	45.	—
2014	Canadian Holiday Scene	17,178	39.95	Proof	30.	—

TEN DOLLARS, O CANADA SET TWO, SELECTIVELY GOLD PLATED SET, 2014.

The coins in this set are the same as the O Canada Series issued in 2014, however each coin is framed by a ring of gold plating. Single coins were not available from the Mint, and can only be obtained from the break up of sets.

Common Obverse

Reverse
Moose

Designers and Engravers: See O Canada Set
Specifications: As O Canada Set except the coins are selectively gold plated
Case of Issue: Red wooden case, black flocked insert,encapsulated coins, COA, custom box

DATE	DESCRIPTION	QUANTITY SOLD	ISSUE PRICE	FINISH	PR-69	PR-70
2014	The Igloo, Selectively gold plated	—	N.I.I.	Matte Proof	90.	—
2014	Grizzly Bear, Selectively gold plated	—	N.I.I.	Matte Proof	90.	—
2014	Skiing Canada's Slopes, Selectively gold plated	—	N.I.I.	Matte Proof	90.	—
2014	Moose, Selectively gold plated	—	N.I.I.	Matte Proof	90.	—
2014	Down by the Old Maple Tree, Selectively gold plated	—	N.I.I.	Matte Proof	90.	—
2014	Canada Goose, Selectively gold plated	—	N.I.I.	Matte Proof	90.	—
2014	Canadian Cowboy, Selectively gold plated	—	N.I.I.	Matte Proof	90.	—
2014	Bison, Selectively gold plated	—	N.I.I.	Matte Proof	90.	—
2014	The Northern Lights (with colour), Selectively gold plated	—	N.I.I.	Matte Proof	90.	—
2014	Canadian Holiday Scene, Selectively gold plated	—	N.I.I.	Matte Proof	90.	—
2014	Set of 10 coins	637	849.95	Matte Proof	750.	*

N DOLLARS, 70TH ANNIVERSARY OF D-DAY, 1944-2014.

Designed by Canadian artist Maskull Lasserre, this coin's reverse depicts Canadian infantry soldiers in battle gear as they disembark to make their
 to Juno Beach.

Designers and Engravers:

Obv.:	Susanna Blunt, Susan Taylor		
Rev.:	Maskull Lasserre, RCM Staff		
Composition:	99.99% Ag		
Silver content:	15.87 g, 0.510 tr oz		
Weight:	15.87 g		
Diameter:	34.0 mm	**Edge:**	Reeded
Thickness:	2.0 mm	**Die Axis:**	↑↑
Finish:	Proof		
Case of Issue:	Maroon clam style case, black flocked insert, encapsulated coin, COA		

DATE	DESCRIPTION	QUANTITY SOLD	ISSUE PRICE	FINISH	PR-69	PR-70
2014 (1944-)	70th Anniversary of D-Day	8,003	49.95	Proof	55.	—

N DOLLARS, "WAIT FOR ME, DADDY", 2014.

Based on the iconic 1940 photograph taken in British Columbia by photographer Claude Dettloff, this coin commemorates the 75th anniversary of
 declaration of the Second World War.

Designers and Engravers:

Obv.:	Susanna Blunt, Susan Taylor		
Rev.:	Claude Dettloff, RCM Staff		
Composition:	99.99% Ag, Selectively gold plated		
Silver content:	15.87 g, 0.510 tr oz		
Weight:	15.87 g		
Diameter:	34.0 mm	**Edge:**	Reeded
Thickness:	N/A	**Die Axis:**	↑↑
Finish:	Proof		
Case of Issue:	Maroon clam style case, black flocked insert, encapsulated coin, COA		

DATE	DESCRIPTION	QUANTITY SOLD	ISSUE PRICE	FINISH	PR-69	PR-70
2014	"Wait For Me, Daddy"	10,000	59.95	Proof	55.	—

N DOLLARS, ICONIC SUPERMAN™ COMIC BOOK COVERS #1 (1938), 2014.

This coin pays homage to the 1938 debut of Superman™ as seen on the cover of Action Comics.

Designers and Engravers:

Obv.:	Susanna Blunt, Susan Taylor		
Rev.:	DC Comics, RCM Staff		
Composition:	99.99% Ag		
Silver content:	15.87 g, 0.510 tr oz		
Weight:	15.87 g		
Diameter:	34.0 mm	**Edge:**	Reeded
Thickness:	N/A	**Die Axis:**	↑↑
Finish:	Proof		
Case of Issue:	Coloured custom case, black flocked insert, encapsulated coin, COA		

DATE	DESCRIPTION	QUANTITY SOLD	ISSUE PRICE	FINISH	PR-69	PR-70
2014	Iconic Superman™ Comic Book Covers #1 (1938)	9,999	69.95	Proof	70.	—

FIRST NATIONS ART SERIES

TEN DOLLARS, FIRST NATIONS ART SERIES, 2014-2015.
This series celebrates the artwork of Kwaguilth artist Richard Hunt and Coast Salish artist Darlene Gait.

Common Obverse

Salmon
Des.: Darlene Gait

Mother Feeding Baby
Des.: Richard Hunt

Designers:		**Engravers:**	
Obv.:	Susanna Blunt	Obv.:	Susan Taylor
Rev.:	See reverse illustrations	Rev.:	RCM Staff
Composition:	99.99% Ag, Hologram		
Silver content:	15.87 g, 0.510 tr oz		
Weight:	15.87 g	**Edge:**	Reeded
Diameter:	34.0 mm	**Die Axis:**	↑↑
Thickness:	N/A	**Finish:**	Proof
Case of Issue:	Maroon leatherette clam style case, black flocked insert, encapsulated coin, COA		

DATE	DESCRIPTION	QUANTITY SOLD	ISSUE PRICE	FINISH	PR-69	PR-7(
2014	Salmon	8,406	74.95	Proof	75.	—
2015	Mother Feeding Baby	2,054	79.95	Proof	75.	—

TEN DOLLARS, YEAR OF THE SHEEP, 2015.
An artistic rendering of bamboo fills the coin's field while the Chinese character for sheep or ram is seen in the sheep's shoulder.

Designers and Engravers:			
Obv.:	Susanna Blunt, Susan Taylor		
Rev.:	Simon Ng, RCM Staff		
Composition:	99.99% Ag, Hologram, with colour		
Silver content:	15.87 g, 0.510 tr oz		
Weight:	15.87 g		
Diameter:	34.0 mm	**Edge:**	Reeded
Thickness:	N/A	**Die Axis:**	↑↑
Finish:	Specimen		
Case of Issue:	Maroon leatherette clam style case, black flocked insert, encapsulated coin, COA		

DATE	DESCRIPTION	QUANTITY SOLD	ISSUE PRICE	FINISH	SP-68	SP-6(
2015	Year of the Sheep	15,223	39.88	Specimen	40.	—

CANADIAN NHL SET

N DOLLARS, CANADIAN NHL SET, 2015.
This set of seven coins is comprised of the Canadian hockey teams of The National Hockey League (NHL).

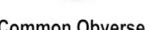

Common Obverse

Calgary Flames

Edmonton Oilers

Montreal Canadiens

Ottawa Senators

Toronto Maple Leafs

Vancouver Canucks

Winnipeg Jets

signers:		Engravers:	
Obv.:	Susanna Blunt	Obv.: Susan Taylor	
Rev.:	RCM Staff	Rev.: RCM Staff	
mposition:	99.99% Ag, Hologram with colour		
er content:	15.87 g, 0.510 tr oz		
ight:	15.87 g	Edge:	Reeded
meter:	34.0 mm	Die Axis:	↑↑
ckness:	N/A	Finish:	Reverse Proof
se of Issue:	Maroon leatherette clam style case, black flocked insert, encapsulated coin, COA		

DATE	DESCRIPTION	QUANTITY SOLD	ISSUE PRICE	FINISH	PR-69	PR-70
2015	Calgary Flames	4,510	74.95	Proof	50.	—
2015	Edmonton Oilers	4,337	74.95	Proof	50.	—
2015	Montreal Canadiens	5,997	74.95	Proof	60.	—
2015	Ottawa Senators	4,874	74.95	Proof	50.	—
2015	Toronto Maple Leafs	5,997	74.95	Proof	50.	—
2015	Vancouver Canucks	5,901	74.95	Proof	50.	—
2015	Winnipeg Jets	4,553	74.95	Proof	50.	—

TEN DOLLARS, CELEBRATING CANADA, 2015.

A symbolic map-like representation designed by Kwame Delfish depicts the Canadian Rocky Mountains, a white-tailed deer, the wheat grow
provinces of Canada, the fishing industry, the Tower of Peace in Ottawa, a partial map of Nunavut, and the lighthouse at Peggy's Cove, Nova Sco

Designers and Engravers:

Obv.:	Susanna Blunt, Susan Taylor
Rev.:	Kwame Delfish, RCM Staff
Composition:	99.99% Ag, Selectively gold plated
Silver content:	15.87 g, 0.510 tr oz
Weight:	15.87 g
Diameter:	34.0 mm
Thickness:	N/A
Finish:	Proof
Case of Issue:	Maroon leatherette clam style case, black flocked insert, encapsulated coin, COA

Edge: Reeded
Die Axis: ↑↑

DATE	DESCRIPTION	QUANTITY SOLD	ISSUE PRICE	FINISH	PR-69	PR-70
2015	Celebrating Canada	2,469	69.95	Proof	75.	—

TEN DOLLARS, WINTER SCENE, 2015.

Designed by artist Remi Clark, this coin's reverse captures the iconic rolling hills and winter snowfall of Canada.

Designers and Engravers:

Obv.:	Susanna Blunt, Susan Taylor
Rev.:	Louise Martineau, RCM Staff
Composition:	99.99% Ag, Coloured
Silver content:	15.87 g, 0.510 tr oz
Weight:	15.87 g
Diameter:	34.0 mm
Thickness:	N/A
Finish:	Proof
Case of Issue:	Maroon leatherette clam style case, black flocked insert, encapsulated coin, COA

Edge: Reeded
Die Axis: ↑↑

DATE	DESCRIPTION	QUANTITY SOLD	ISSUE PRICE	FINISH	PR-69	PR-7
2015	Winter Scene	2,159	64.95	Proof	60.	—

TEN DOLLARS, 200TH ANNIVERSARY OF THE BIRTH OF SIR JOHN A. MACDONALD, 2015.

Designed by Joel Kimmel, this ten dollar coin celebrates the 200th anniversary of the birth of Canada's first Prime Minister.

Designers and Engravers:

Obv.:	Susanna Blunt, Susan Taylor
Rev.:	Joel Kimmel, RCM Staff
Composition:	99.99% Ag, Selectively gold plated
Silver content:	15.87 g, 0.510 tr oz
Weight:	15.87 g
Diameter:	34.0 mm
Thickness:	N/A
Finish:	Proof
Case of Issue:	Maroon leatherette clam style case, black flocked insert, encapsulated coin, COA

Edge: Reeded
Die Axis: ↑↑

DATE	DESCRIPTION	QUANTITY SOLD	ISSUE PRICE	FINISH	PR-69	PR-7
2015	200th Anniv. Birth Sir John A. MacDonald	2,886	69.95	Proof	65.	—

CANOE ACROSS CANADA SET

N DOLLARS, CANOE ACROSS CANADA SET, 2015.

Designed by Greg Banning, this set of six coins depicts some of Canada's most scenic spots to canoe, from canoeing down a river (coin one), to Yukon River (coin two), the Bow River in Alberta (coin three), Ontario's Georgian Bay Islands National Park (coin four), and to a lake near Quebec's urentian Mountains (coin five).

Common Obverse

Splendid Surroundings

Wondrous West

Magnificent Mountains

Serene Scene

Mirror, Mirror

Exquisite Ending

signers:		Engravers:	
Obv.:	Susanna Blunt	Obv.:	Susan Taylor
Rev.:	Greg Banning	Rev.:	RCM Staff

mposition:	99.99% Ag		
ver content:	15.87 g, 0.510 tr oz		
ight:	15.87 g	Edge:	Reeded
meter:	34.0 mm	Die Axis:	↑↑
ckness:	N/A	Finish:	Proof

se of Issue: Singly: Maroon leatherette clam style case, black flocked insert, encapsulated coin, COA
Subscription: Six-hole wooden canoe-shaped case, painted red exterior, black mount, encapsulated coins, COA

DATE	DESCRIPTION	QUANTITY SOLD	ISSUE PRICE	FINISH	PR-69	PR-70
2015	Splendid Surroundings	7,929	44.95	Proof	40.	—
2015	Wondrous West	8,490	44.95	Proof	40.	—
2015	Magnificent Mountains	7,847	44.95	Proof	40.	—
2015	Serene Scene	7,466	44.95	Proof	40.	—
2015	Mirror, Mirror	7,298	44.95	Proof	40.	—
2015	Exquisite Ending	7,311	44.95	Proof	40.	—

FIFA WOMEN'S WORLD CUP™ SET

TEN DOLLARS, FIFA WOMEN'S WORLD CUP™ SET, 2015.

Celebrating the FIFA Women's World Cup hosted in Moncton, Montreal, Ottawa, Winnipeg, Edmonton and Vancouver, this set reflects the excitem of women's soccer. A set of three $75 gold coins was also issued for the FIFA Women's World Cup™ in 2015 (see page 439).

Common Obverse

Canada Welcomes The World

"Go Canada Go!"

The Goalie

Heading The Ball

The Kicker

Celebration

Designers:			**Engravers:**	
Obv.:	Susanna Blunt		Obv.:	Susan Taylor
Rev.:	Greg Banning		Rev.:	RCM Staff
Composition:	99.99% Ag			
Silver content:	15.87 g, 0.510 tr oz			
Weight:	15.87 g		**Edge:**	Reeded
Diameter:	34.0 mm		**Die Axis:**	↑↑
Thickness:	N/A		**Finish:**	Proof
Case of Issue:	Singly: Maroon leatherette clam style case, black flocked insert, encapsulated coin, COA, custom box			
	Subscription: Six-hole wooden case, black flocked insert, encapsulated coins, COA			

DATE	DESCRIPTION	QUANTITY SOLD	ISSUE PRICE	FINISH	PR-69	PR-7(
2015	Canada Welcomes The World, Coloured	5,104	59.95	Proof	50.	—
2015	"Go Canada GO!", Coloured	4,363	59.95	Proof	50.	—
2015	The Goalie	5,103	54.95	Proof	50.	—
2015	Heading The Ball	5,358	54.95	Proof	50.	—
2015	The Kicker	5,498	54.95	Proof	50.	—
2015	Celebration	5,038	54.95	Proof	50.	—

COLOURFUL SONGBIRDS OF CANADA SET

N DOLLARS, COLOURFUL SONGBIRDS OF CANADA SET, 2015.
This five-coin set captures the colourful beauty of some of Canada's songbirds.

Common Obverse

The Northern Cardinal
Des.: Derek C. Wicks
Engr.: RCM Staff

The Magnolia Warbler
Des.: Hélène Girard
Engr.: RCM Staff

The Blue Jay
Designer and Engraver:
RCM Staff

The Baltimore Oriole
Designer and Engraver:
RCM Staff

The Violet-Green Swallow
Designer and Engraver:
RCM Staff

signers:		Engravers:	
Obv.:	Susanna Blunt	Obv.:	Susan Taylor
Rev.:	See reverse illustrations	Rev.:	See reverse illustrations

mposition: 99.99% Ag
ver content: 15.87 g, 0.510 tr oz
ight: 15.87 g
meter: 34.0 mm
ckness: N/A
se of Issue: Singly: Maroon leatherette clam style case, black flocked insert, encapsulated coin, COA
Subscription: Five-hole musical paperboard case, white flocked insert, custom case, encapsulated coins, COA

Edge: Reeded
Die Axis: ↑↑
Finish: Proof

DATE	DESCRIPTION	QUANTITY SOLD	ISSUE PRICE	FINISH	PR-69	PR-70
2015	The Northern Cardinal	13,063	64.95	Proof	65.	—
2015	The Magnolia Warbler	10,255	64.95	Proof	65.	—
2015	The Blue Jay	12,109	64.95	Proof	65.	—
2015	The Baltimore Oriole	9,469	64.95	Proof	65.	—
2015	The Violet-Green Swallow	9,806	64.95	Proof	65.	—

ADVENTURE CANADA SERIES

TEN DOLLARS, ADVENTURE CANADA, 2015.

There's an endless variety of adventures to be found across Canada. Every season and every geographical region has something new and excit
to offer.

Common Obverse

Windsurfing

Whitewater Rafting

Mountain Bking

Ice Climbing

Dog Sledding

Designers:		**Engravers:**	
Obv.:	Susanna Blunt	Obv.:	Susan Taylor
Rev.:	Ken Ryan	Rev.:	Ken Ryan
Composition:	99.99% Ag		
Silver content:	15.87 g, 0.510 tr oz		
Weight:	15.87 g	**Edge:**	Reeded
Diameter:	34.0 mm	**Die Axis:**	↑↑
Thickness:	N/A	**Finish:**	Matte Proof
Case of Issue:	Maroon leatherette clam style case, black flocked insert, encapsulated coin, COA		

DATE	DESCRIPTION	QUANTITY SOLD	ISSUE PRICE	FINISH	PR-69	PR-7(
2015	Adventures Canada: Windsurfing	1,449	44.95	Matte Proof	45.	—
2015	Adventures Canada: Whitewater Rafting	1,104	44.95	Matte Proof	45.	—
2015	Adventures Canada: Mountain Biking	2,248	44.95	Matte Proof	45.	—
2015	Adventures Canada: Ice Climbing	1,162	44.95	Matte Proof	45.	—
2015	Adverntures Canada: Dog Sledding	1,109	44.95	Matte Proof	45.	—

LOONEY TUNES™ SET

EN DOLLARS, LOONEY TUNES™, 2015.

Common Obverse

Bugs. Daffy. Tweety. Sylvester. For many Canadians, the mere mention of these names evoke fond childhood memories of spending Saturday mornings in front of a television, transfixed and spellbound as these characters—and many more—outsmarted each other in situations that could only exist in our imaginations.

"I Tawt I Taw A Putty Tat!"

"Suffering Succotash!"

"Where's The Kaboom?"

"Beep! Beep!"

"Wile E. Coyote – Super Genius"

"You're Despicable"

"What's Up, Doc?"

"That's All Folks!"

signers:			**Engravers:**	
Obv.:	Susanna Blunt		Obv.:	Susan Taylor
Rev.:	Warner Bros.		Rev.:	Warner Bros.
mposition:	99.99% Ag			
ver content:	15.87 g, 0.510 tr oz			
eight:	15.87 g		**Edge:**	Reeded
ameter:	34.0 mm		**Die Axis:**	↑↑
ickness:	N/A		**Finish:**	Matte Proof
se of Issue:	Graphic paperboard box.			

DATE	DESCRIPTION	QUANTITY SOLD	ISSUE PRICE	FINISH	PR-69	PR-70
2015	"I Tawt I Taw A Putty Tat!"	11,519	49.95	Matte Proof	40.	—
2015	"Suffering Succotash!"	9,528	49.95	Matte Proof	40.	—
2015	"Where's The Kaboom?"	9,710	49.95	Matte Proof	40.	—
2015	"Beep! Beep!"	8,941	49.95	Matte Proof	40.	—
2015	"Wile E. Coyote – Super Genius"	8,795	49.95	Matte Proof	40.	—
2015	"You're Despicable"	8,849	49.95	Matte Proof	40.	—
2015	"What's Up, Doc?"	8,891	49.95	Matte Proof	40.	—
2015	"That's All Folks!"	8,899	49.95	Matte Proof	40.	—

DC COMICS™ ORIGINALS SET

TEN DOLLARS, *DC COMICS™ ORIGINALS*, 2015.

The *DC Comics Original*s series has a classic, slightly retro style, recalling the look most comic book fans grew up with and remember fondly. Bas itself on the DC Comics style of the 1980s, this series celebrates one of the most established looks for the DC Comics pantheon of Super Heroes, a a few of its villains too.

Common Obverse

Gauntlet

Strength

Unity

Legacy

Designers:		Engravers:	
Obv.:	Susanna Blunt	Obv.:	Susan Taylor
Rev.:	DC Comics	Rev.:	DC Comics
Composition:	99.99% Ag		
Silver content:	15.87 g, 0.510 tr oz		
Weight:	15.87 g	Edge:	Reeded
Diameter:	34.0 mm	Die Axis:	↑↑
Thickness:	N/A	Finish:	Matte Proof
Case of Issue:	Premium graphic case.		

DATE	DESCRIPTION	QUANTITY SOLD	ISSUE PRICE	FINISH	PR-69	PR-70
2015	DC Comics™ Originals: Gauntlet	10,763	54.95	Matte Proof	50.	—
2015	DC Comics™ Originals: Strength	9,638	54.95	Matte Proof	50.	—
2015	DC Comics™ Originals: Unity	9,459	54.95	Matte Proof	50.	—
2015	DC Comics™ Originals: Legacy	11,158	54.95	Matte Proof	50.	—

GOALIES SET

EN DOLLARS, GOALIES, 2015.

NHL® history comes alive! Relive the excitement of the Original Six™ era with this commemorative series of coins that celebrates legendary altenders from each team.

Common Obverse

Eddie Giacomin

Gerry Cheevers

Glenn Hall

Jaques Plante

Johnny Bower

Terry Sawchuk

signers:
  Obv.:   Susanna Blunt
  Rev.:   Steven Rosati
mposition: 99.99% Ag
ver content: 15.87 g, 0.510 tr oz
ight: 15.87 g
ameter: 34.0 mm
ickness: N/A
se of Issue: Brown clamshell with graphic beauty box.

Engravers:
  Obv.:   Susan Taylor
  Rev.:   Steven Rosati

Edge: Reeded
Die Axis: ↑↑
Finish: Proof

DATE	DESCRIPTION	QUANTITY SOLD	ISSUE PRICE	FINISH	PR-69	PR-70
2015	Goalies: Eddie Giacomin	6,232	74.95	Proof	75.	—
2015	Goalies: Gerry Cheevers	6,417	74.95	Proof	75.	—
2015	Goalies: Glenn Hall	5,416	74.95	Proof	75.	—
2015	Goalies: Jacques Plante	7,417	74.95	Proof	75.	—
2015	Goalies: Johnny Bower	7,232	74.95	Proof	75.	—
2015	Goalies: Terry Sawchuk	6,279	74.95	Proof	75.	—

EN DOLLARS, WINTER FUN, 2016.

Designers and Engravers:
  Obv.:   Susanna Blunt
  Rev.:   Maurade Baynton
Composition: 99.99% Ag, Coloured
Silver content: 15.87 g, 0.510 tr oz
Weight: 15.87 g
Diameter: 34.0 mm   **Edge:** Reeded
Thickness: N/A   **Die Axis:** ↑↑
Finish: Proof
Case of Issue: Maroon clamshell with black beauty box.

DATE	DESCRIPTION	QUANTITY SOLD	ISSUE PRICE	FINISH	PR-69	PR-70
2016	Winter Fun	2,986	64.95	Proof	65.	—

TEN DOLLARS, CELEBRATION OF LOVE, 2016.

Designers and Engravers:
Obv.:	Susanna Blunt		
Rev.:	Anna Bucciarelli		
Composition:	99.99% Ag, Coloured		
Silver content:	7.96 g, 0.25 tr oz		
Weight:	7.96 g	Edge:	Reeded
Diameter:	27 mm	Die Axis:	↑↑
Thickness:	N/A	Finish:	Proof
Case of Issue:	Premium graphic box.		

DATE	DESCRIPTION	QUANTITY SOLD	ISSUE PRICE	FINISH	PR-69	PR-70
2016	Celebration of Love	14,888	49.95	Proof	55.	—

BATMAN V SUPERMAN: DAWN OF JUSTICE™ SERIES

TEN DOLLARS, *BATMAN V SUPERMAN: DAWN OF JUSTICE™*, 2016.

With the release of the highly anticipated movie *Batman v Superman: Dawn of Justice*, the Royal Canadian Mint is excited to introduce unforgettable series of coins!

Common Obverse

Designers and Engravers:
Obv.:	Susanna Blunt, Susan Taylor		
Rev.:	DC Comics		
Composition:	99.99% Ag		
Silver content:	15.87 g, 0.510 tr oz		
Weight:	15.87 g	Edge:	Reeded
Diameter:	34.0 mm	Die Axis:	↑↑
Thickness:	N/A	Finish:	Matte Proof
Case of Issue:	Premium graphic case.		

Logo	**Superman™**	**Batman™**	**Wonder Woman™**

DATE	DESCRIPTION	QUANTITY SOLD	ISSUE PRICE	FINISH	PR-69	PR-70
2016	Batman v Superman: Dawn of Justice™ – Logo	14,953	49.95	Matte Proof	50.	—
2016	Batman v Superman: Dawn of Justice™ – Superman	13,638	49.95	Matte Proof	50.	—
2016	Batman v Superman Dawn of Justice™ – Batman	14,594	49.95	Matte Proof	50.	—
2016	Batman v Superman: Dawn of Justice™ – Wonder Woman	12,087	49.95	Matte Proof	50.	—

REFLECTIONS OF WILDLIFE SET

EN DOLLARS, REFLECTIONS OF WILDLIFE, 2016.

The three-coin Reflections of Wildlife series continues its celebration of this natural beauty through depictions of a quiet, contemplative moment in the wild.

| Common Obverse | Grizzly Bear | Otter | Arctic Fox |

signers:		**Engravers:**	
Obv.:	Susanna Blunt	Obv.:	Susan Taylor
Rev.:	Maurade Baynton	Rev.:	Maurade Baynton
mposition:	99.99% Ag		
ver content:	15.87 g, 0.510 tr oz		
eight:	15.87 g	**Edge:**	Reeded
ameter:	34.0 mm	**Die Axis:**	↑↑
ickness:	N/A	**Finish:**	Proof
se of Issue:	Maroon clamshell with black beauty box.		

DATE	DESCRIPTION	QUANTITY SOLD	ISSUE PRICE	FINISH	PR-69	PR-70
2016	Reflections of Wildlife – Grizzly Bear	11,078	39.95	Proof	40.	—
2016	Reflections of Wildlife – Otter	8,219	39.95	Proof	40.	—
2016	Reflections of Wildlife – Arctic Fox	7,556	39.95	Proof	40.	—

DAY OF THE DINOSAURS SET

EN DOLLARS, DAY OF THE DINOSAURS, 2016.

The prehistoric creatures that roamed the land before us inspire a mix of awe, curiosity and even fear.

| Common Obverse | The Spiked Lizard
Designer: RCM Staff | Terror of the Sky
Designer: Dino Pulera | The Armoured Tank
Designer: Julius Csotonyi |

signers:		**Engravers:**	
Obv.:	Susanna Blunt	Obv.:	Susan Taylor
Rev.:	See reverse illustrations	Rev.:	See reverse illustrations
mposition:	99.99% Ag, selective colour		
ver content:	15.87 g, 0.510 tr oz		
eight:	15.87 g	**Edge:**	Reeded
ameter:	34.0 mm	**Die Axis:**	↑↑
ickness:	N/A	**Finish:**	Proof
se of Issue:	Maroon clamshell with black beauty box.		

DATE	DESCRIPTION	QUANTITY SOLD	ISSUE PRICE	FINISH	PR-69	PR-70
2016	The Spiked Lizard	7,297	44.95	Proof	45.	—
2016	Terror of the Sky	7,333	44.95	Proof	45.	—
2016	The Armoured Tank	7,217	44.95	Proof	45.	—

TEN DOLLARS, YEAR OF THE MONKEY, 2016.

Designers and Engravers:
Obv.:	Susanna Blunt
Rev.:	Simon Ng

Composition: 99.99% Ag
Silver content: 15.87 g, 0.510 tr oz
Weight: 15.87 g   **Edge:** Reeded
Diameter: 34.0 mm   **Die Axis:** ↑↑
Thickness: N/A   **Finish:** Specimen
Case of Issue: Maroon clamshell with black beauty box.

DATE	DESCRIPTION	QUANTITY SOLD	ISSUE PRICE	FINISH	SP-68	SP-69
2016	Year of the Monkey	15,878	39.88	Specimen	40.	—

TEN DOLLARS, STAR TREK™ SERIES, 2016.

From warp drives to teleporters, *U.S.S. Enterprise* (NCC-1701) has offered us an exciting vision of what space travel could entail in the 23rd centu Her five-year mission under the command of Captain James Tiberius Kirk (played by Canadian actor William Shatner) made legends of both the sl and her captain, as featured together on this fine silver coin that celebrates the 50th anniversary of *Star Trek™*.

**Common
Obverse**

Designers and Engravers:
Obv.:	Susanna Blunt and Susan Taylor
Rev.:	RCM Staff

Composition: 99.99% Ag, selective colour
Silver content: 15.87 g, 0.510 tr oz
Weight: 15.87 g   **Edge:** Reeded
Diameter: 34.0 mm   **Die Axis:** ↑↑
Thickness: N/A   **Finish:** Proof
Case of Issue: Colorful custom graphic box.

 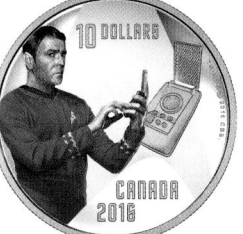  

Captain Kirk	Scotty	Spock	Uhura

DATE	DESCRIPTION	QUANTITY SOLD	ISSUE PRICE	FINISH	PR-69	PR-70
2016	Star Trek™: Captain Kirk	12,498	54.95	Proof	75.	—
2016	Star Trek™: Scotty	12,080	54.95	Proof	50.	—
2016	Star Trek™: Spock	11,460	54.95	Proof	60.	—
2016	Star Trek™: Uhura	10,115	54.95	Proof	50.	—

TEN DOLLARS, ICONIC CANADA: INUKSHUK, 2016.

Designers and Engravers:
Obv.:	Susanna Blunt
Rev.:	Tony Bianco

Composition: 99.99% Ag, Reverse gold plating
Silver content: 15.87 g, 0.510 tr oz
Weight: 15.87 g   **Edge:** Reeded
Diameter: 34.0 mm   **Die Axis:** ↑↑
Thickness: N/A   **Finish:** Proof
Case of Issue: Maroon clamshell with black beauty box.

DATE	DESCRIPTION	QUANTITY SOLD	ISSUE PRICE	FINISH	PR-69	PR-70
2016	Iconic Canada: Inukshuk	5,983	59.95	Proof	80.	—

EN DOLLARS, MAPLE LEAF SILHOUETTE: CANADA GEESE (SHAPED), 2016.

Designers and Engravers:

Obv.:	Susanna Blunt, Susan Taylor
Rev.:	Trevor Tennant

Composition:	99.99% Ag		
Silver content:	15.67 g, 0.504 tr oz		
Weight:	15.67 g	Edge:	Plain
Diameter:	39.6 x 38 mm	Die Axis:	↑↑
Thickness:	N/A	Finish:	Proof
Case of Issue:	Maroon clamshell with black beauty box.		

DATE	DESCRIPTION	QUANTITY SOLD	ISSUE PRICE	FINISH	PR-69	PR-70
2016	Maple Leaf Silhouette: Canada Geese	11.704	84.95	Proof	80.	—

PASSION TO PLAY SET

EN DOLLARS, PASSION TO PLAY, 2017.

On the ice or in the streets, youth hockey is a timeless tradition that plays out year-round from coast to coast, and embodies the purest spirit of the sport! This e silver coin set pays tribute to this nationwide passion to play that has endured for over 100 years, and celebrates fan loyalties to Canada's beloved NHL® teams.

Common Obverse	Edmonton Oilers	Ottawa Senators	Winnipeg Jets

Toronto Maple Leafs	Calgary Flames	Vancouver Canucks	Montreal Canadiens

·signers:

Obv.:	Susanna Blunt
Rev.:	Silvia Pecota

Engravers:

Obv.:	Susan Taylor
Rev.:	Silvia Pecota

·mposition:	99.99% Ag
·lver content:	15.87 g, 0.510 tr oz
·eight:	15.87 g
·ameter:	34.0 mm
·ickness:	N/A
·se of Issue:	Maroon clamshell with custom graphic box.

Edge:	Reeded
Die Axis:	↑↑
Finish:	Matte Proof

DATE	DESCRIPTION	QUANTITY SOLD	ISSUE PRICE	FINISH	PR-69	PR-70
2017	Passion to Play: Edmonton Oilers	3,676	74.95	Matte Proof	75.	—
2017	Passion to Play: Ottawa Senators	3,547	74.95	Matte Proof	75.	—
2017	Passion to Play: Winnipeg Jets	3,674	74.95	Matte Proof	75.	—
2017	Passion to Play: Toronto Maple Leafs	5,696	74.95	Matte Proof	75.	—
2017	Passion to Play: Calgary Flames	3,592	74.95	Matte Proof	75.	—
2017	Passion to Play: Vancouver Canucks	4,280	74.95	Matte Proof	75.	—
2017	Passion to Play: Montreal Canadiens	5,568	74.95	Matte Proof	75.	—

CELBRATING CANADA'S 150TH SET

TEN DOLLARS, CELBRATING CANADA'S 150TH, 2017.

From colourful flora to iconic fauna and landmarks, breathtaking images of Canada's landscapes reflect the diversity of the Canadian experience.

Common Obverse

Common Loon
Des.: Jim Cumming

Designers and Engravers:

Obv.:	Susanna Blunt, Susan Taylor
Rev.:	See reverse illustrations
Composition:	99.99% Ag
Silver content:	15.87 g, 0.510 tr oz
Weight:	15.87 g
Diameter:	34.0 mm
Thickness:	N/A
Case of Issue:	Maroon clamshell with black beauty box.

Edge:	Reeded
Die Axis:	↑↑
Finish:	Matte Proof

Kayaking on the River
Des.: Daniel Dagenais

Lighthouse at Peggy's Cove
Des.: Dale Wilson

Great Blue Heron
Des.: Claude Belanger

Canola Field
Des.: John Sylvester

**Float Planes
on the Mackenzie River**
Des.: Adam Hill

Grizzly Bear
Des.: "Jenny" Janet Stevens

Panmure Island
Des.: Robert Hamilton

**Aurora Borealis
at McIntyre Creek**
Des.: Peter Mather

Wild Swift Fox and Pups
Des.: John E. Marriott

Peyto Lake
Des.: Missy Mandel

Iceberg at Dawn
Des.: Dale Wilson

Drum Dancing
Des.: Michelle Valberg

TEN DOLLARS, CELBRATING CANADA'S 150TH, 2017 PRICING TABLE.

DATE	DESCRIPTION	QUANTITY SOLD	ISSUE PRICE	FINISH	PR-69	PR-70
2017	Common Loon	10,967	44.95	Matte Proof	45.	—
2017	Kayaking on the River	9,710	44.95	Matte Proof	45.	—
2017	Lighthouse at Peggy's Cove	10,177	44.95	Matte Proof	45.	—
2017	Great Blue Heron	8,781	44.95	Matte Proof	45.	—
2017	Canola Field	8,369	44.95	Matte Proof	45.	—
2017	Float Planes on the Mackenzie River	7,214	44.95	Matte Proof	45.	—
2017	Grizzly Bear	1,005	51.95	Matte Proof	52.	—
2017	Panmure Island	25,000	51.95	Matte Proof	52.	—
2017	Aurora Borealis at McIntyre Creek	25,000	51.95	Matte Proof	52.	—
2017	Wild Swift Fox and Pups	25,000	51.95	Matte Proof	52.	—
2017	Peyto Lake	25,000	51.95	Matte Proof	52.	—
2017	Iceberg at Dawn	25,000	51.95	Matte Proof	52.	—
2017	Drum Dancing	25,000	51.95	Matte Proof	52.	—

ICONIC CANADA SERIES, 2017

TEN DOLLARS, ICONIC CANADA SERIES, 2017.

Each coin in this five-coin subscription is a visual celebration of a nation and its spirit, through the richly varied images that have come to represent the Canadian experience.

Common Obverse

Dog Sledding Under The Northern Lights
Dss.: Claudio D'Angelo

The Sugar Shack
Des.: Tony Bianco

Spring Sightings
Des.: Silvia Pecota

The Beaver
Des.: Glen Loates

Autumn's Palette
Des.: Tony Bianco

Designers:
  Obv.: Susanna Blunt
  Rev.: See reverse illustrations
Composition: 99.99% Ag, Coloured
Weight: 15.87 g
Diameter: 34 mm
Thickness: N/A
Case of Issue: Maroon clamshell with black beauty box.

Engravers:
  Obv.: Susan Taylor

Silver content: 15.87 g, 0.510 tr oz
Edge: Reeded
Die Axis: ↑↑
Finish: Matte Proof

DATE	DESCRIPTION	MINTAGE	ISSUE PRICE	FINISH	PR-69	PR-70
2017	Dog Sledding Under The Northern Lights	15,000	51.95	Matte Proof	52.	—
2017	The Sugar Shack	15,000	51.95	Matte Proof	52.	—
2017	Spring Sightings	15,000	51.95	Matte Proof	52.	—
2017	The Beaver	15,000	51.95	Matte Proof	52.	—
2017	Autumn's Palette	15,000	51.95	Matte Proof	52.	—

TEN DOLLARS, YEAR OF THE ROOSTER, 2017.

Designers and Engravers:

Obv.:	Susanna Blunt
Rev.:	Three Degrees Creative Group

Composition: 99.99% Ag
Silver content: 15.87 g, 0.510 tr oz
Weight: 15.87 g
Diameter: 34 mm   **Edge:** Reeded
Thickness: N/A   **Die Axis:** ↑↑
Finish: Specimen
Case of Issue: Maroon clamshell with black beauty box.

DATE	DESCRIPTION	QUANTITY SOLD	ISSUE PRICE	FINISH	SP-68	SP-69
2017	Year of the Rooster	11,898	41.88	Specimen	42.	—

BIRDS AMONG NATURE'S COLOURS SERIES

TEN DOLLARS, BIRDS AMONG NATURE'S COLOURS, 2017.

Among the many species of birds that breed in Canada, where their interactions with the environment leaves us with a greater appreciation for the beau
that surrounds us – as beautifully showcased in this unique five-coin set.

Designers and Engravers:

Obv.:	Susanna Blunt, Susan Taylor
Rev.:	See reverse illustrations

Composition: 99.99% Ag, Coloured
Silver content: 15.87 g, 0.510 tr oz
Weight: 15.87 g   **Edge:** Reeded
Diameter: 34.0 mm   **Die Axis:** ↑↑
Thickness: N/A   **Finish:** Proof
Case of Issue: Maroon clamshell with black beauty box, COA.

Common Obverse

Chickadee
Des.: Jean-Charles Daumas

Northern Flicker
Des.: Jean-Chares Daumas

Tufted Titmouse
Des.: Derek C. Wicks

Purple Martin
Des.: Derek C. Wicks

Nuthatch
Des.: Derek C. Wicks

DATE	DESCRIPTION	MINTAGE	ISSUE PRICE	FINISH	PR-69	PR-70
2017	Chickadee	15,000	64.95	Proof	65.	—
2017	Northern Flicker	15,000	64.95	Proof	65.	—
2017	Tufted Titmouse	15,000	64.95	Proof	65.	—
2017	Purple Martin	15,000	64.95	Proof	65.	—
2017	Nuthatch	15,000	64.95	Proof	65.	—

LEARNING TO PLAY SERIES

EN DOLLARS, LEARNING TO PLAY SERIES, 2018.
Celebrate Canadian hockey and family togetherness with this series of seven exclusive coins that feature the Canadian NHL teams, and celebrate ildren learning to play.

Common Obverse

Calgary Flames

Edmonton Oilers

Montreal Canadiens

Ottawa Senators

Toronto Maple Leafs

Vancouver Canucks

Winnipeg Jets

esigners:
Obv.:   Susanna Blunt
Rev.:   John Mantha
omposition: 99.99% Ag, with colour
lver content: 15.87 g, 0.510 tr oz
eight: 15.87 g
ameter: 34.0 mm
ickness: N/A
se of Issue: Maroon clamshell with black beauty box, COA

Engravers:
Obv.:   Susan Taylor
Rev.:   RCM Staff

Edge: Reeded
Die Axis: ↑↑
Finish: Matte Proof

DATE	DESCRIPTION	MINTAGE	ISSUE PRICE	FINISH	PR-69	PR-70
2018	Calgary Flames	7,000	74.95	Matte Proof	75.	—
2018	Edmonton Oilers	7,000	74.95	Matte Proof	75.	—
2018	Montreal Canadiens	7,000	74.95	Matte Proof	75.	—
2018	Ottawa Senators	7,000	74.95	Matte Proof	75.	—
2018	Toronto Maple Leafs	7,000	74.95	Matte Proof	75.	—
2018	Vancouver Canucks	7,000	74.95	Matte Proof	75.	—
2018	Winnipeg Jets	7,000	74.95	Matte Proof	75.	—

TEN DOLLARS, YEAR OF THE DOG, 2018.

Designers and Engravers:

Obv.:	Susanna Blunt
Rev.:	Simon Ng

Composition:	99.99% Ag		
Silver content:	15.87 g, 0.510 tr oz		
Weight:	15.87 g	**Edge:**	Reeded
Diameter:	34.0 mm	**Die Axis:**	↑↑
Thickness:	N/A	**Finish:**	Specimen
Case of Issue:	Maroon clamshell with black beauty box, COA.		

DATE	DESCRIPTION	MINTAGE	ISSUE PRICE	FINISH	SP-68	SP-69
2018	Year of the Dog	15,888	41.88	Specimen	42.	—

TEN DOLLARS, *YIN* AND *YANG* - TIGER AND DRAGON, 2018.

These amazing *yin* and *yang*-shaped coins feature two heroes of Chinese tradition — the Tiger and the Dragon — fit together to form a perfe whole. The theme of balance is fully realized in their stunning imagery, rich colour, and singular design.

Designers and Engravers:

Obv.:	Susanna Blunt
Rev.:	Three Degrees Creative Group

Composition:	99.99% Ag		
Silver content:	15.87 g, 0.510 tr oz		
Weight:	15.87 g (per coin)	**Edge:**	Plain
Diameter:	39 mm (combined)	**Die Axis:**	↑↑
Thickness:	N/A	**Finish:**	Proof
Case of Issue:	Maroon clamshell with black beauty box, COA.		

TEN DOLLARS, BLACK AND WHITE *YIN* AND *YANG* - TIGER AND DRAGON, 2018.

Designers and Engravers:

Obv.:	Susanna Blunt
Rev.:	Simon Ng

Composition:	99.99% Ag		
Silver content:	15.87 g, 0.510 tr oz		
Weight:	15.87 g (per coin)	**Edge:**	Plain
Diameter:	39 mm (combined)	**Die Axis:**	↑↑
Thickness:	N/A	**Finish:**	Proof
Case of Issue:	Maroon clamshell with black beauty box, COA.		

DATE	DESCRIPTION	MINTAGE	ISSUE PRICE	FINISH	PR-69	PR-70
2018	*Yin* and *Yang* — Tiger and Dragon	6,000	164.95	Proof	165.	—
2018	Black and White *Yin* and *Yang* — Tiger and Dragon	6,000	164.95	Proof	165.	—

EN DOLLARS, THE COMMON LOON: BEAUTY AND GRACE, 2018.

For many Canadians, the common loon (*Gavia immer*) is synonymous with summer evenings spent by the lake, where its wavering call embodies the dependent spirt of the Canadian wilderness.

Designers and Engravers:
Obv.:	Susanna Blunt
Rev.:	Arnold Nogy
Composition:	99.99% Ag
Silver content:	23.17 g, 0.75 tr oz
Weight:	23.17 g
Diameter:	36.07 mm
Thickness:	N/A
Case of Issue:	Maroon clamshell with black beauty box, COA.

	Edge:	Reeded
	Die Axis:	↑↑
	Finish:	Proof

DATE	DESCRIPTION	MINTAGE	ISSUE PRICE	FINISH	PR-69	PR-70
2018	The Common Loon: Beauty and Grace	7,500	69.95	Proof	70.	—

STAR TREK™ STARSHIPS SERIES

EN DOLLARS, STAR TREK™ STARSHIPS, 2018.

Collect all three coins of the most famous starships in the Star Trek universe.

Common Obverse

Enterprise-D
(Star Trek - The Next Generation)

Voyager
(Star Trek - Voyager)

Enterprse NX-01
(Star Trek - Enterprise)

signers:
Obv.:	Susanna Blunt
Rev.:	RCM Staff
mposition:	99.99% Ag
ver content:	15.87 g, 0.510 tr oz
eight:	15.87 g
ameter:	34.0 mm
ickness:	N/A
se of Issue:	Graphic beauty box, COA.

Engravers:
Obv.:	Susan Taylor
Rev.:	RCM Staff

Edge:	Reeded
Die Axis:	↑↑
Finish:	Proof

DATE	DESCRIPTION	MINTAGE	ISSUE PRICE	FINISH	PR-69	PR-70
2018	*Enterprise-D*	10,000	64.95	Proof	65.	—
2018	*Voyager*	10,000	64.95	Proof	65.	—
2018	*Enterprise NX-01*	10,000	64.95	Proof	65.	—

TEN DOLLAR DERIVATIVES

DATE	DESCRIPTION	MINTAGE	ISSUE PRICE	ISSUER	FINISH	MARKET PRICE
2010	**Ten Dollar Blue Whale;** Souvenir sheet of two $10 Blue Whale postage stamps; Booklet; Maple wood case	9,719	79.95	RCM, CP	Proof	75.

FIFTEEN DOLLARS

FIFTEEN DOLLARS, 100TH ANNIVERSARY OF THE OLYMPIC MOVEMENT, 1992-1996.

The International Olympic Committee initiated a commemorative coin programme to mark the centennial of the modern Olympic movement in 199 Five mints, those of Canada, Australia, France, Austria and Greece, participated by each issuing one gold and two silver coins over a five year peric The total collection comprises five gold and ten silver coins.

The Royal Canadian Mint issued the first three coins in 1992. The silver fifteen dollar coins are listed here, the 1992 $175 gold coin on page 451 The Standard Catalogue lists only the coins issued by the Royal Canadian Mint.

Common Obverse
Designer and Engraver:
Dora de Pédery-Hunt

Coin No. 1
Speed Skater,
Pole Vaulter, Gymnast
Designer: David Craig
Engraver: Sheldon Beveridge

Coin No. 2
The Spirit Of the Generations
Designer: Stewart Sherwood
Engraver: Terry Smith

Composition:	92.5% Ag, 7.5% Cu	
Silver content:	31.108 g, 1.00 tr oz	
Weight:	33.63 g	
Diameter:	40.0 mm	**Edge: Lettering:** Citius, Altius, Fortius
Thickness:	3.1 mm	**Die Axis:** ↑↑
Case of Issue:	Singly: Burgundy leatherette case	**Finish:** Proof
	Set: Wooden display case	

DATE	DESCRIPTION	QUANTITY SOLD	ISSUE PRICE	FINISH	PR-68	PR-69
1992	Speed Skater, with edge lettering	105,645	46.95	Proof	50.	—
1992	Speed Skater, without edge lettering	Included	46.95	Proof	375.	—
1992	Spirit of the Generations, with edge lettering	Included	46.95	Proof	50.	—
1992	Spirit of the Generations, without edge lettering	Included	46.95	Proof	375.	—

NOTE TO COLLECTORS

When the initials N.I.I. appear in the pricing table it indicates the coin was part of a set issued by the Royal Canadian Mint, and not issued individual Coin designs that are found only in sets offered by the Royal Canadian Mint are listed individually by denomination, and date in Volume Two.

SP-68 / PR-69	This price is based on the item still being in the original package as sold by the Mint.
SP-69 / PR-70	This price is based on the item being graded by a reputable third-party grading company.
	Prices are generally not listed due to the low number of sales of certified products in these grades.
	Price should be based on population reports and market demand.

CHINESE LUNAR CALENDAR SERIES

FTEEN DOLLARS, CHINESE LUNAR CALENDAR STERLING SILVER COIN SERIES, 1998-2009.

Common Obverse except for date

Starting in 1998 with the year of the Tiger, the Royal Canadian Mint embarked on a twelve-year series of Chinese Lunar calendar coins which ended in 2009. The twelve sterling silver coins were issued one per year to commemorate the start of each new year of the twelve-year cycle. The coins were available singly or by subscription. The subscription was for a five-year period beginning in 1999 and ending in 2003. The five coins, shipped one per year, were offered at a fixed price of $428.28 including a sterling silver medallion housed in a 13-hole presentation box made of embossed red velvet and gold moiré. The single presentation box is a smaller version of the larger one, red and gold moiré.

Note: Coins illustrated smaller than actual size.

Year of the Tiger 1998
Designer: Harvey Chan
Engraver: Stan Witten

Year of the Rabbit 1999
Designer: Harvey Chan
Engraver: José Osio

Year of the Dragon 2000
Designer: Harvey Chan
Engraver: José Osio

Year of the Snake 2001
Designer: Harvey Chan
Engraver: José Osio

Year of the Horse 2002
Designer: Harvey Chan
Engraver: José Osio

Year of the Ram 2003
Designer: Harvey Chan
Engraver: José Osio

Year of the Monkey 2004
Designer: Harvey Chan
Engraver: Stan Witten

Year of the Rooster 2005
Designer: Harvey Chan
Engraver: José Osio

Year of the Dog 2006
Designer: Harvey Chan
Engraver: José Osio

Year of the Pig 2007
Designer: Harvey Chan
Engraver: José Osio

Year of the Rat 2008
Designer: Harvey Chan
Engraver: José Osio

Year of the Ox 2009
Designer: Harvey Chan
Engraver: José Osio

FIFTEEN DOLLARS, CHINESE LUNAR CALENDAR STERLING SILVER COIN SERIES, 1998-2009 (cont.).

Designers:
Obv.: Dora de Pédery-Hunt
Rev.: See reverse illustrations
Composition: 92.5% Ag, 7.5% Cu,
24-karat gold plated cameo
Silver content: 30.71 to 31.45 g, 0.987 to 1.011 tr oz
Weight: 33.2 to 34.0 g
Diameter: 40.0 mm
Thickness: 3.0 to 3.35 mm
Case of Issue:

Engravers:
Obv.: Dora de Pédery-Hunt
Rev.: See reverse illustrations

Edge: Reeded
Die Axis: ↑↑
Finish: Proof

Set: A thirteen-hole embossed red velvet presentation box with goldmoiré sides. Included is a sterling silver medallion carrying the twelve signs of the zodiac.
Singly: Embossed red velvet presentation box as above, encapsulated, COA

DATE	DESCRIPTION	QUANTITY SOLD	ISSUE PRICE	FINISH	PR-69	PR-70
1998	Empty case to hold 12 sterling silver coins and a sterling silver medallion	—	—	—	125.	*
1998	Year of the Tiger	68,888	68.88	Proof	200.	—
1999	Year of the Rabbit	77,791	72.88	Proof	75.	—
2000	Year of the Dragon	88,634	72.88	Proof	100.	—
2001	Year of the Snake	60,754	94.88	Proof	60.	—
2002	Year of the Horse	59,395	94.88	Proof	60.	—
2003	Year of the Ram	53,714	94.88	Proof	60.	—
2004	Year of the Monkey	46,175	105.88	Proof	80.	—
2005	Year of the Rooster	44,690	105.88	Proof	60.	—
2006	Year of the Dog	41,634	112.88	Proof	60.	—
2007	Year of the Pig	10,752	88.88	Proof	60.	—
2008	Year of the Rat	9,209	88.88	Proof	60.	—
2009	Year of the Ox	7,096	88.88	Proof	60.	—

FIFTEEN DOLLARS, CHINESE LUNAR CALENDAR DERIVATIVES

DATE	DESCRIPTION	MINTAGE	ISSUE PRICE	ISSUER	FINISH	MARKET PRICE
1998	**Year of the Tiger**, Fifteen dollar coin; Souvenir stamp sheet; Presentation album	8,000	88.88	RCM, CP	Proof	200.
1999	**Year of the Rabbit**, as 1998	8,000	88.88	RCM, CP	Proof	75.
2000	**Year of the Dragon**, as 1998	10,000	88.88	RCM, CP	Proof	100.
2000	**Year of the Dragon**, 18kt gold stamp, Mint stamp, Presentation case	N/A	N/A	RCM, CP	Proof	550.
2001	**Year of the Snake**, as 1998	8,000	94.88	RCM, CP	Proof	60.
2002	**Year of the Horse**, as 1998	8,000	98.88	RCM, CP	Proof	60.
2003	**Year of the Ram**, as 1998	8,000	98.88	RCM, CP	Proof	60.
2004	**Year of the Monkey**, as 1998	8,000	105.88	RCM, CP	Proof	80.
2005	**Year of the Rooster**, as 1998	8,000	105.88	RCM, CP	Proof	60.
2006	**Year of the Dog**, as 1998	8,000	112.88	RCM, CP	Proof	60.
2007	**Year of the Pig**, as 1998	8,000	112.88	RCM, CP	Proof	60.
2008	**Year of the Rat**, as 1998	8,000	112.88	RCM, CP	Proof	60.
2009	**Year of the Ox**, as 1998	8,000	112.88	RCM, CP	Proof	60.

VIGNETTES OF ROYALTY SERIES

FTEEN DOLLARS, VIGNETTES OF ROYALTY SERIES, 2008-2009.

Common Obverse

Victoria
Designer: Leonard C. Wyon
Engraver: RCM Staff

Edward VII
Designer: G. W. De Saulles
Engraver: RCM Staff

George V
Designer: E. B. MacKennal
Engraver: RCM Staff

George VI
Designer: T. H. Paget
Engraver: RCM Staff

Elizabeth II
Designer: Mary Gillick
Engraver: RCM Staff

signers:		Engravers:	
Obv.:	Susanna Blunt	Obv.:	Susan Taylor
Rev.:	See reverse illustrations	Rev.:	See reverse illustrations
mposition:	92.5% Ag, 7.5% Cu		
ver content:	27.75 g, 0.89 tr oz		
ight:	30.0 g	Edge:	Plain
ameter:	36.2 mm	Die Axis:	↑↑
ickness:	3.2 mm	Finish:	Proof-like
se of Issue:	Singly: Maroon leatherette clam style case, black flocked insert, encapsulated coin, COA		
	Set: Five-hole maroon clam style case to hold the series of coins.		

DATE	DESCRIPTION	ISSUE DATE	QUANTITY SOLD	ISSUE PRICE	FINISH	PL-68	PL-69
2008	Victoria	Oct. 31, 2007	3,442	99.95	Proof-like	75.	—
2008	Edward VII	July 23, 2008	6,261	99.95	Proof-like	75.	—
2008	George V	Oct. 1, 2008	—	99.95	Proof-like	75.	—
2009	George VI	Apr. 15, 2009	10,045	99.95	Proof-like	75.	—
2009	Elizabeth II	Oct. 1, 2009	2,643	99.95	Proof-like	75.	—
—	Vignettes of Royalty Set, 5 coins	—	N/A	499.95	Proof-like	325.	—

NOTES FOR COLLECTORS

1. The RCM Report of 2009 does not break down the "quantity sold" figures for the George V and George VI coins, but group all under George VI.
2. It is interesting to note that after 55 years the Royal Canadian Mint recognises a Proof-like finish. The vignettes are struck in ultra high relief on a Proof-like background.

PLAYING CARD MONEY SERIES

FIFTEEN DOLLARS, PLAYING CARD MONEY SERIES, 2008-2009.

This series was issued to commemorate the issue of playing cards used as money during times of chronic shortages in the 17th- and 18th- centur͏ in New France.

2008 Obverse

Jack of Hearts

Queen of Spades

2009 Obverse

King of Hearts

Ten of Spades

Designers:		Engravers:	
Obv.:	Susanna Blunt	Obv.:	Susan Taylor
Rev.:	Original artwork by Henry Beau	Rev.:	José Osio
	Public Archives of Canada		

Composition: 92.5% Ag, 7.5% Cu, Painted; Gold plate on edge
Silver content: 29.193 g, 0.938 tr oz
Weight: 31.56 g   **Edge:** Plain
Size: 49.8 x 28.6 mm   **Die Axis:** ↑↑
Thickness: 2.4 to 2.7 mm   **Finish:** Proof
Case of Issue: Singly: Maroon leatherette clam style case, black flocked insert, encapsulated coin, COA
Set: Four-hole maroon clam style case, black flocked insert, encapsulated coins

DATE	DESCRIPTION	ISSUE DATE	QUANTITY SOLD	ISSUE PRICE	FINISH	PR-69	PR-70
2008	Jack of Hearts	July 23, 2008	11,362	89.95	Proof	75.	—
2008	Queen of Spades	Oct. 1, 2008	8,714	89.95	Proof	75.	—
2009	King of Hearts	Apr. 15, 2009	5,798	89.95	Proof	75.	—
2009	Ten of Spades	July 22, 2009	5,921	89.95	Proof	75.	—
—	Playing Card Money Set	—	278	359.80	Proof	275.	*

Common Obverse
except for date

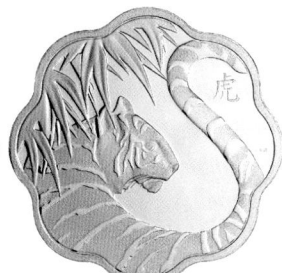

Year of the Tiger 2010
Engraver: José Osio

LUNAR LOTUS SERIES

FIFTEEN DOLLARS, SILVER LUNAR LOTUS SERIES, 2010-2018.

A new Lunar Calendar series was introduced in 2010. The new series, beginning with the 2010 Year of the Tiger, will run for twelve years. The scalloped coin is reminiscent of a lotus flower.

Note: Coins illustrated smaller than actual size.

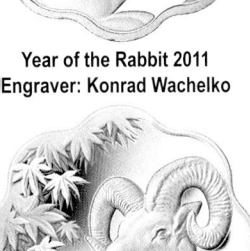

Year of the Rabbit 2011
Engraver: Konrad Wachelko

Year of the Dragon 2012
Engraver: Cecily Mok

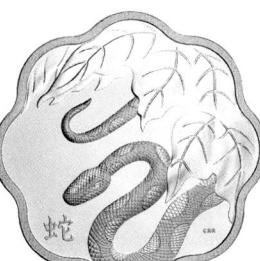

Year of the Snake 2013
Engraver: Christie Paquet

Year of the Horse 2014
Engraver: Eric Boyer

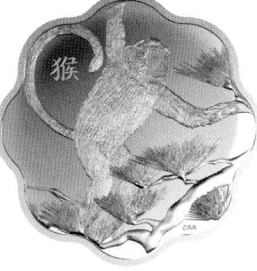

Year of the Sheep, 2015
Engraver: RCM Staff

Year of the Monkey, 2016
Engraver: RCM Staff

Year of the Rooster, 2017
Engraver: RCM Staff

Year of the Dog, 2018
Engraver: RCM Staff

Designers:		Engravers:	
Obv.:	Susanna Blunt	Obv.:	Susan Taylor
Rev.:	Three Degrees Creative Group Inc.	Rev.:	See reverse illustrations
Composition:	2010-2012: 92.5% Ag, 7.5% Cu	Silver content:	2010-2012: 24.327 g, 0.782 tr oz
	2013-2018: 99.99% Ag		2013-2017: 26.7 g, 0.858 tr oz
			2018: 26.51 g, 0.85 tr oz
Weight:	26.3 to 26.51 g	Edge:	Plain
Diameter (scalloped):	38.0 mm	Die Axis:	↑↑
Thickness:	2.9 mm	Finish:	Proof
Case of Issue:	Singly: Silver satin-like covered case, black flocked insert, encapsulated coin, COA		
	Set: Hardwood exterior with high-gloss finish and silk-screened paper. Interior has high-gloss finish in Chinese red with a silver design. Wooden insert accommodates 12 coins.		

DATE	DESCRIPTION	QUANTITY SOLD	ISSUE PRICE	FINISH	PR-69	PR-70
2010	Year of the Tiger	10,268	88.88	Proof	130.	—
2011	Year of the Rabbit	19,888	88.88	Proof	150.	—
2012	Year of the Dragon	25,216	98.88	Proof	100.	—
2013	Year of the Snake	21,906	98.88	Proof	100.	—
2014	Year of the Horse	20,575	98.88	Proof	100.	—
2015	Year of the Sheep	16,056	98.88	Proof	100.	—
2016	Year of the Monkey	13,391	98.88	Proof	100.	—
2017	Year of the Rooster	11,668	101.88	Proof	100.	—
2018	Year of the Dog	18,888	101.88	Proof	100.	—

CLASSIC CHINESE ZODIAC SERIES

FIFTEEN DOLLARS, CLASSIC CHINESE ZODIAC SERIES, 2010-2018.

A second Lunar Calendar series was introduced in 2010. T[ ]
new series is distributed by the Asian Business Centre and the Ro[ ]
Canadian Mint. The proposed quantity was 9,999 units.

Note: Coins illustrated smaller than actual siz[ ]

Common Obverse

Year of the Tiger, 2010
Engraver: Konrad Wachelko

Year of the Rabbit, 2011
Engraver: William Woodruff

Year of the Dragon, 2012
Engraver: Stan Witten

Year of the Snake, 2013
Engraver: Stan Witten

Year of the Horse, 2014
Engraver: Konrad Wachelko

Year of the Sheep, 2015
Engraver: RCM Staff

Year of the Monkey, 2016
Engraver: RCM Staff

Year of the Rooster, 2017
Engraver: RCM Staff

Year of the Dog, 2018
Engraver: RCM Staff

Designers:
Obv.:   Susanna Blunt
Rev.:   Aries Cheung
Composition: 99.99% Ag
Weight: 31.39 g
Diameter: 38.0 mm
Thickness: 3.2 mm
Case of Issue: Singly: Silver satin-like covered case, black flocked insert, encapsulated coin, COA
                   Set: Hardwood exterior with high-gloss finish and silk-screened paper. Interior has high-gloss finish in Chinese red with a silver design. Wooden insert accommodates 12 coins.

Engravers:
Obv.:   Susan Taylor
Rev.:   See reverse illustrations
Silver content: 31.39 g, 1.01 tr oz
Edge: Reeded
Die Axis: ↑↑
Finish: Proof

DATE	DESCRIPTION	QUANTITY SOLD	ISSUE PRICE	FINISH	PR-69	PR-7C
2010	Year of the Tiger	N/A	88.88	Proof	150.	—
2011	Year of the Rabbit	9,999	98.88	Proof	170.	—
2012	Year of the Dragon	19,644	98.88	Proof	100.	—
2013	Year of the Snake	14,213	98.88	Proof	100.	—
2014	Year of the Horse	15,738	98.88	Proof	100.	—
2015	Year of the Sheep	9,256	98.88	Proof	100.	—
2016	Year of the Monkey	9,817	98.88	Proof	100.	—
2017	Year of the Rooster	8,256	101.88	Proof	100.	—
2018	Year of the Dog	10,888	101.88	Proof	100.	

CONTINUITY OF THE CROWN SET

FTEEN DOLLARS, CONTINUITY OF THE CROWN SET, 2011.

| Common Obverse | HRH Prince Henry of Wales
Engraver: Stan Witten | HRH Prince William of Wales
Engraver: Konrad Wachelko | The Prince of Wales
Engraver: William Woodruff |

signers:
Obv.: Susanna Blunt
Rev.: Laurie McGaw
mposition: 92.5% Ag, 7.5% Cu
ver content: 23.29 g, 0.75 tr oz
ight: 25.175 g
meter: 36.2 mm
ickness: 3.0 mm
se of Issue: Singly: Maroon clam style case, black flocked insert, encapsulated coin, COA
Set: Three-hole maroon clam style case to hold the coins.

Engravers:
Obv.: Susan Taylor
Rev.: See reverse illustrations

Edge: Plain
Die Axis: ↑↑
Finish: Proof-like

DATE	DESCRIPTION	QUANTITY SOLD	ISSUE PRICE	FINISH	PR-69	PR-70
2011	HRH Prince Henry of Wales	5,751	109.95	Proof-like	60.	—
2011	HRH Prince William of Wales	6,217	109.95	Proof-like	60.	—
2011	The Prince of Wales	4,788	109.95	Proof-like	60.	—
2011	Set of 3 coins	—	329.85	Proof-like	150.	—

CHINESE HISTORY AND TRADITIONS SERIES

FIFTEEN DOLLARS, CHINESE HISTORY AND TRADITIONS SERIES, 2011-2015.
Featuring a hologram on the coins' reverses, this series celebrates the history and traditions of Chinese culture with depictions of a magpie and lo▮ flower (Maple of Happiness), two deer (Maple of Good Fortune), an elephant decorated with a chrysanthemum (Maple of Peace), two cranes (Ma▮ of Longevity), and three fish (Maple of Prosperity).

Common Obverse

Maple of Happiness
Designer: Simon Ng
Engraver: Stan Witten

Maple of Good Fortune
Designer: Three Degree
Creative Group
Engraver: Cecily Mok

Maple of Peace
Designer: Simon Ng
Engraver: Steven Stewart

Maple of Longevity
Designer: Simon Ng
Engraver: RCM Staff

Maple of Prosperity
Designer: Albert Ng
Engraver: RCM Staff

Designers:
    Obv.:   Susanna Blunt
    Rev.:   See reverse illustrations
Composition: 99.99% Ag, Hologram
Silver content: 31.1 g, 1.0 tr oz
Weight: 31.1 g
Diameter: 38.0 mm
Thickness: 3.1 mm

Engravers:
    Obv.:   Susan Taylor
    Rev.:   See reverse illustrations

Edge: Reeded
Die Axis: ↑↑
Finish: Proof

Case of Issue: Maroon leatherette clam style case, black flocked insert, encapsulated coin, COA

DATE	DESCRIPTION	QUANTITY SOLD	ISSUE PRICE	FINISH	PR-69	PR-7(
2011	Maple of Happiness	8,209	98.88	Proof	80.	—
2012	Maple of Good Fortune	8,866	98.88	Proof	80.	—
2013	Maple of Peace	8,510	98.88	Proof	90.	—
2014	Maple of Longevity	9,821	98.88	Proof	90.	—
2015	Maple of Prosperity	3,483	98.88	Proof	90.	—

Note: For the other coins in the Chinese History and Traditions Series see page 190-191.

SUPERMAN™ SERIES

FTEEN DOLLARS, 75TH ANNIVERSARY OF SUPERMAN™: MODERN DAY, 2013.

Depicting a modern rendering of Superman™, Superman's™ native Kryptonian language encircles the outside rim and reads "75 Years of >erman".

Designers and Engravers:

Obv.:	Susanna Blunt, Susan Taylor
Rev.:	DC Comics/Warner Brothers, Samantha Strath
Composition:	99.99% Ag, Painted
Silver content:	15.87 g, 0.510 tr oz
Weight:	15.87 g
Diameter:	34.0 mm
Thickness:	2.1 mm
Finish:	Matte Proof
Case of Issue:	Clear plastic cover, black plastic coin display, encapsulated coin, COA, custom beauty box

Edge: Reeded
Die Axis: ↑↑

DATE	DESCRIPTION	QUANTITY SOLD	ISSUE PRICE	FINISH	PR-69	PR-70
2013	75th Anniv. of Superman™: Modern Day	14,962	69.75	Proof	75.	—

FTEEN DOLLARS, ICONIC SUPERMAN™ COMIC BOOK COVERS: ACTION COMICS #419 (1972), 2014.

Based on the 1972 iconic comic book cover, this coin commemorates Superman's strength as he fights the evils that lurk within Metropolis.

Designers and Engravers:

Obv.:	Susanna Blunt, Susan Taylor
Rev.:	DC Comics/Warner Brothers, RCM Staff
Composition:	99.99% Ag, Painted
Silver content:	23.17 g, 0.75 tr oz
Weight:	23.17 g
Diameter:	36.07 mm
Thickness:	2.1 mm
Finish:	Proof
Case of Issue:	Custom case, black flocked insert, encapsulated coin, COA

Edge: Reeded
Die Axis: ↑↑

DATE	DESCRIPTION	QUANTITY SOLD	ISSUE PRICE	FINISH	PR-69	PR-70
2014	Action Comics #419 (1972)	10,000	89.95	Proof	75.	—

EXPLORING CANADA SERIES

FIFTEEN DOLLARS, EXPLORING CANADA SERIES, 2014-2015.
This set celebrates the adventurous and courageous spirit of Canada's pioneering explorers.

Common Obverse	The Voyageurs	The Gold Rush	The Arctic Expedition
The Vikings	The West Coast Exploration	The Pioneering Mapmakers	The Wild Rivers Exploration

Building the
Canadian Pacific Railway

Scientific Exploration

Space Exploration

Designers:		**Engravers:**	
Obv.:	Susanna Blunt	Obv.:	Susan Taylor
Rev.:	John Mantha	Rev.:	RCM Staff
Composition:	99.99% Ag		
Silver content:	23.17 g, 0.75 tr oz		
Weight:	23.17 g	**Edge:**	Reeded
Diameter:	36.07 mm	**Die Axis:**	↑↑
Thickness:	N/A	**Finish:**	Matte Proof
Case of Issue:	Singly: Maroon leatherette clam style case, black flocked insert, encapsulated coin, COA, custom case		
	Subscription: 10-hole graphic paperboard case, encapsulated coins, COA		

Note: Coins illustrated smaller than actual size.

TEEN DOLLARS, EXPLORING CANADA SERIES, 2014-2015, PRICING TABLE

DATE	DESCRIPTION	QUANTITY SOLD	ISSUE PRICE	FINISH	PR-69	PR-70
2014	The Voyageurs	7,907	54.95	Proof	50.	—
2014	The Gold Rush	8,001	54.95	Proof	50.	—
2014	The Arctic Expedition	3,103	54.95	Proof	50.	—
2014	The Vikings	6,601	54.95	Proof	50.	—
2014	The West Coast Exploration	6,202	54.95	Proof	50.	—
2014	The Pioneering Mapmakers	5,775	54.95	Proof	50.	—
2015	The Wild Rivers Exploration	5,625	54.95	Proof	50.	—
2015	Building the Canadian Pacific Railway	6,144	54.95	Proof	50.	—
2015	Scientific Exploration	5,574	54.95	Proof	50.	—
2015	Space Exploration	5,529	54.95	Proof	50.	—

ARTWORK BY FRANKLIN CARMICHAEL

TEEN DOLLARS, ARTWORK BY FRANKLIN CARMICHAEL, 2015.

Celebrating the artwork of Canada's youngest member of the Group of Seven on the 125th anniversary of Franklin Carmichael's birth, this set of
ns features three of Carmichael's most famous works.

| Common Obverse | The Upper Ottawa, Near Mattawa (c. 1924) | Cranberry Lake (c. 1934) | Landscape |

signers:
Obv.:   Susanna Blunt
Rev.:   Franklin Carmichael
mposition: 99.99% Ag, Hologram
ver content: 23.17 g, 0.75 tr oz
ight: 23.17 g
meter: 36.07 mm
ckness: N/A
se of Issue: Maroon leatherette clam style case to hold three coins, black flocked insert, encapsulated coin, COA

Engravers:
Obv.:   Susan Taylor
Rev.:   RCM Staff

Edge: Reeded
Die Axis: ↑↑
Finish: Proof

DATE	DESCRIPTION	QUANTITY SOLD	ISSUE PRICE	FINISH	PR-69	PR-70
2015	*The Upper Ottawa, Near Mattawa (c. 1924)*	385	N.I.I.	Proof	70.	—
2015	*Cranberry Lake (c. 1934)*	381	N.I.I.	Proof	70.	—
2015	*Landscape*	—	N.I.I.	Proof	70.	—
2015	Set of 3 coins	2,601	199.95	Proof	180.	*

CELEBRATION OF SPRING SERIES

FIFTEEN DOLLARS, CELEBRATION OF SPRING, 2016-2017.

Designers and Engravers:
Obv.:	Susanna Blunt, Susan Taylor
Rev.:	Jan Poynter
Composition:	99.99% Ag, Painted
Silver content:	23.17 g, 0.75 tr oz
Weight:	23.17 g
Diameter:	36.07 mm
Thickness:	N/A
Edge:	Reeded
Die Axis:	↑↑
Finish:	Proof
Case of Issue:	Maroon clamshell with graphic beauty box, COA.

Common Obverse   Cherry Blossoms   Lilac Blossoms

DATE	DESCRIPTION	QUANTITY SOLD	ISSUE PRICE	FINISH	PR-69	PR-70
2016	Celebration of Spring: Cherry Blossoms	6,499	64.95	Proof	100.	—
2017	Celebration of Spring: Lilac Blossoms	10,000	69.95	Proof	70.	—

NATIONAL HEROES SERIES

FIFTEEN DOLLARS, NATIONAL HEROES, 2016.

Bravery in its purest form is the willingness to save another's life despite personal risk. The Royal Canadian Mint proudly honours everyday hero

Common Obverse

Designers and Engravers:
Obv.:	Susanna Blunt, Susan Taylor		
Rev.:	Ken Ryan		
Composition:	99.99% Ag, Painted		
Silver content:	23.17 g, 0.75 tr oz		
Weight:	23.17 g	**Edge:**	Reeded
Diameter:	36.07 mm	**Die Axis:**	↑↑
Thickness:	N/A	**Finish:**	Proof
Case of Issue:	Maroon leatherette clam style case, black flocked insert, encapsulated coin, COA, custom case		

Firefighters   Paramedics   Police   Military

DATE	DESCRIPTION	QUANTITY SOLD	ISSUE PRICE	FINISH	PR-69	PR-70
2016	National Heroes: Firefighters	9,997	69.95	Proof	120.	—
2016	National Heroes: Paramedics	8,435	69.95	Proof	60.	—
2016	National Heroes: Police	8,132	69.95	Proof	60.	—
2016	National Heroes: Military	8,163	69.95	Proof	60.	—

Note: Coins illustrated smaller than actual size.

GREAT CANADIAN OUTDOORS SERIES

TEEN DOLLARS, GREAT CANADIAN OUTDOORS, 2017.

Canadians have a deep, enduring connection with nature that is evidenced by the many activities we enjoy outside thoroughout the year — summer, ter, rain or sun! This four-coin series explores a nation at play in our favourite playground, the Canadian landscape. The reverse design is made sible by combining photo-luminescent (glow-in-the-dark) technology, a full colour application, *and* traditional engraving.

Common Obverse

Designers and Engravers:
Obv.:	Susanna Blunt, Susan Taylor
Rev.:	Joel Kimmel

Composition:	99.99% Ag, Painted		
Silver content:	23.17 g, 0.75 tr oz		
Weight:	23.17 g	**Edge:**	Reeded
Diameter:	36.07 mm	**Die Axis:**	↑↑
Thickness:	N/A	**Finish:**	Proof
Case of Issue:	Maroon clamshell with black beauty box, COA		

Night Skiing	Sunset Canoeing	Around the Campfire	Nature Walk at Sunrise

signers :
Obv.:	Susanna Blunt
Rev.:	Joel Kimmel

Engravers:
Obv.:	Susan Taylor

mposition:	99.99% Ag, Painted
ver content:	23.17 g, 0.75 tr oz
ight:	23.17 g
meter:	36.07 mm
ckness:	N/A
se of Issue:	Maroon clamshell with black beauty box. COA

Edge:	Reeded
Die Axis:	↑↑
Finish:	Proof

DATE	DESCRIPTION	MINTAGE	ISSUE PRICE	FINISH	PR-69	PR-70
2017	Great Canadian Outdoors: Night Skiing	15,000	69.95	Proof	70.	—
2017	Great Canadian Outdoors: Sunset Canoeing	15,000	69.95	Proof	70.	—
2017	Great Canadian Outdoors: Around the Campfire	15,000	69.95	Proof	70.	—
2017	Great Canadian Outdoors: Nature Walk at Sunrise	15,000	69.95	Proof	70.	—

IN THE EYES OF... SERIES

FIFTEEN DOLLARS, IN THE EYES OF..., 2017.

The eyes are the focus of this new series in which an innovative enamel effect provides like-like colour, while glow-in-the-dark allows the ani
eyes to peer out from the dark.

| Common Obverse | In The Eyes of the Great Horned Owl | In The Eyes of the Lynx | In The Eyes of the Wolf |

Designers:

| Obv.: | Susanna Blunt |
| Rev.: | Curtis Atwater |

Composition: 99.99% Ag
Silver content: 23.17 g, 0.75 tr oz
Weight: 23.17 g
Diameter: 36 mm
Thickness: N/A
Case of Issue: Maroon clamshell with black beauty box, encapsulated coin, COA

Engravers:

| Obv.: | Susan Taylor |
| Rev.: | RCM Staff |

Edge: Reeded
Die Axis: ↑↑
Finish: Proof

DATE	DESCRIPTION	MINTAGE	ISSUE PRICE	FINISH	PR-69	PR-7(
2017	In The Eyes of the Great Horned Owl	6,500	79.95	Proof	80.	—
2017	In The Eyes of the Lynx	6,500	79.95	Proof	80.	—
2017	In The Eyes of the Wolf	6,500	79.95	Proof	80.	—

FIFTEEN DOLLARS, MAGNIFICENT BALD EAGLES, 2018.

Designers and Engravers:

| Obv.: | Susanna Blunt, Susan Taylor |
| Rev.: | Tony Bianco |

Composition: 99.99% Ag
Silver content: 31.39 g, 1.01 tr oz
Weight: 31.39 g
Diameter: 38 mm
Thickness: N/A
Finish: Proof

Edge: Reeded
Die Axis: ↑↑

Case of Issue: Maroon clamshell with black beauty box, COA

DATE	DESCRIPTION	MINTAGE	ISSUE PRICE	FINISH	PR-69	PR-7(
2018	Magnificent Bald Eagles	5,500	94.95	Proof	95.	—

TWENTY DOLLARS

CALGARY OLYMPIC WINTER GAMES

WENTY DOLLARS, CALGARY OLYMPIC WINTER GAMES, 1985-1988.

In 1988, Calgary, Alberta, hosted the XV Olympic Winter Games. To commemorate the event, and assist in the financing, the Federal Government, through Royal Canadian Mint, agreed to produce a series of ten sterling silver coins and one gold coin. The silver coins were issued in sets of two $20.00 coins r the period September 1985 through September 1987. Unlike the 1976 Olympic coins, the Calgary Winter Olympic coins were issued in proof quality only. The date on the coins (obverse) is the year of minting while the reverse carries the date 1988, the year of the games. Mintage was limited to a total 5,000,000 coins, resulting if minted in equal numbers, in 500,000 complete sets of the ten coins. The first offering of the coins for sale by the Royal nadian Mint was based on 350,000 complete sets at $370.00 per set. By the fifth series the complete set was being offered at $420.00.

Edge lettering was used for the first time on Canadian silver coins. "XV OLYMPIC WINTER GAMES - JEUX OLYMPIQUES D'HIVER" appeared on ten silver coins. There are existing varieties that have missed the edge lettering process.

signers:	See each coin	Engravers:	See each coin
mposition:	92.5% Ag, 7.5% Cu	Thickness:	3.0 mm
ver content:	31.51 g, 1.01 tr oz	Edge:	Lettered
ight:	34.07 g	Die Axis:	↑↑
meter:	40.0 mm	Finish:	Proof
se of Issue:	Green velvet, Olympic Logo, one or two coin display.		

RIES ONE

1985 Reverse Arnold Machin	**Coin No. 1 Downhill Skiing** Ian Stewart, Terrence Smith	**Coin No. 2 Speed Skating** Friedrich Peter, Ago Aarand

RIES TWO

1986 Obverse Arnold Machin	**Coin No. 3 Hockey** Ian Stewart, Victor Coté	**Coin No. 4 Biathlon** John Mardon, Sheldon Beveridge

DATE	DESCRIPTION	ISSUE DATE	QUANTITY SOLD	ISSUE PRICE	FINISH	PR-68	PR-69
1985	Downhill Skiing	Sept. 15, 1985	406,360	37.00	Proof	30.	—
1985	Speed Skating	Sept. 15, 1985	354,222	37.00	Proof	30.	—
1985	Speed Skating, no edge lettering	Sept. 15, 1985	Included	37.00	Proof	200.	—
1985	Set of 2 Series One coins	Sept. 15, 1985	Included	74.00	Proof	60.	*
1986	Hockey	Feb. 25, 1986	396,602	37.00	Proof	30.	—
1986	Hockey, no edge lettering	Feb. 25, 1986	Included	37.00	Proof	200.	—
1986	Biathlon	Feb. 25, 1986	308,086	37.00	Proof	30.	—
1986	Biathlon, no edge lettering	Feb. 25, 1986	Included	37.00	Proof	200.	—
1986	Set of 2 Series Two coins		Included	79.00	Proof	60.	*

CALGARY OLYMPIC WINTER GAMES (cont.).

SERIES THREE

| 1986 Obverse | Coin No. 5 Cross-Country Skiing | Coin No. 6 Free-Style Skiing |
| Arnold Machin | Ian Stewart, Terrence Smith | Walter Ott, Walter Ott |

SERIES FOUR

| 1987 Obverse | Coin No. 7 Figure Skating | Coin No. 8 Curling |
| Arnold Machin | Raymond Taylor, Walter Ott | Walter Ott, Sheldon Beveridge |

SERIES FIVE

| 1987 Obverse | Coin No. 9 Ski-Jumping | Coin No. 10 Bobsleigh |
| Arnold Machin | Raymond Taylor, David Kierans | John Mardon, Victor Coté |

DATE	DESCRIPTION	ISSUE DATE	QUANTITY SOLD	ISSUE PRICE	FINISH	PR-68	PR-69
1986	Cross-Country Skiing	Aug. 18, 1986	303,199	39.50	Proof	30.	—
1986	Free-Style Skiing	Aug. 18, 1986	294,322	39.50	Proof	30.	—
1986	Free-Style Skiing, no edge lettering	Aug. 18, 1986	Included	39.50	Proof	200.	—
1986	Set of 2 Series Three coins	Aug. 18, 1986	Included	79.00	Proof	60.	*
1987	Figure Skating	Mar. 14, 1987	334,875	39.50	Proof	30.	—
1987	Figure Skating, no edge lettering	Mar. 14, 1987	Included	39.50	Proof	200.	—
1987	Curling	Mar. 14, 1987	286,457	39.50	Proof	30.	—
1987	Set of 2 Series Four coins	Mar. 14, 1987	Included	79.00	Proof	60.	*
1987	Ski-Jumping	Aug. 11, 1987	290,954	42.00	Proof	30.	—
1987	Bobsleigh	Aug. 11, 1987	274,326	42.00	Proof	30.	—
1987	Set of 2 Series Five coins	Aug. 11, 1987	Included	84.00	Proof	60.	*

AVIATION COMMEMORATIVES

WENTY DOLLARS, AVIATION COMMEMORATIVES, SERIES ONE, 1990-1994.

Canada's aviation heroes and achievements are commemorated on this series of twenty dollar sterling silver coins. The series consists of ten ns issued two per year over five years. For the first time each coin design contains a 24-karat gold covered oval cameo portrait of the aviation hero nmemorated. All coins were issued in proof quality and a maximum of 50,000 of each coin was offered for sale during the program. The issue price he ten-coin case was $37.00.

signers:		Engravers:	
Obv. and Rev.:	See each coin	Obv. and Rev.:	See each coin
mposition:	92.5% Ag, 7.5% Cu, 24-karat gold-covered cameo		
ver content:	28.77 g, 0.925 tr oz	Edge:	Interrupted serrations
ight:	31.103 g	Die Axis:	↑↑
meter:	38.0 mm	Finish:	Proof
ickness:	3.5 mm		
se of Issue:	Aluminum case in the shape of a wing. Single and ten coin display cases made from recycled Canadian airplanes.		

1990 Obverse
Designer and Engraver:
Dora de Pédery-Hunt

Coin No. 1
Avro Anson and the North
American Harvard
Robert Leckie
Rev. Designer: Geoff Bennett
Rev. Engraver: S. Beveridge
Portrait Engr.: Terrence Smith

Coin No. 2
Avro Lancaster
J. E. Fauquier
Rev. Designer: R.R. Carmichael
Rev. Engraver: Ago Aarand
Portrait Engr.: S. Beveridge

1991 Obverse
Designer and Engraver:
Dora de Pédery-Hunt

Coin No. 3
A.E.A. Silver Dart
F.W. Baldwin / J.A.D. McCurdy
Rev. Designer: George Velinger
Rev. Engraver: S. Beveridge
Portrait Engr.: Terrence Smith

Coin No. 4
de Havilland Beaver
Phillip C. Garratt
Rev. Designer: Peter Mossman
Rev. Engraver: Ago Aarand
Portrait Engr.: William Woodruff

DATE	DESCRIPTION	SERIES	ISSUE DATE	QUANTITY SOLD	ISSUE PRICE	FINISH	PR-68	PR-69
1990	Avro Anson/N.A. Harvard	One	Sept. 15/90	41,844	55.50	Proof	50.	—
1990	Avro Lancaster	One	Sept. 15/90	43,596	55.50	Proof	120.	—
1991	A.E.A. Silver Dart	One	May 16/91	35,202	55.50	Proof	50.	—
1991	de Havilland Beaver	One	May 16/91	36,197	55.50	Proof	50.	—

TWENTY DOLLARS, AVIATION COMMEMORATIVES, SERIES ONE, 1990-1994 (cont.).

1992 Obverse
Designer and Engraver:
Dora de Pédery-Hunt

Coin No. 5
Curtiss JN-4 (Canuck)
Sir Frank Wilton Baillie
Rev. Designer: George Velinger
Rev. Engr.: Sheldon Beveridge
Portrait Engr.: Terrence Smith

Coin No. 6
de Havilland Gipsy Moth
Murton A. Seymour
Rev. Designer: John Mardon
Rev. Engraver: Ago Aarand
Portrait Engr.: Susan Taylor

1993 Obverse
Designer and Engraver:
Dora de Pédery-Hunt

Coin No. 7
Fairchild 71c
James A. Richardson
Rev. Designer: R. R. Carmichael
Rev. Engraver: Susan Taylor
Portrait Engr.: Susan Taylor

Coin No. 8
Lockheed 14 Super Electra
Zebulon Lewis Leigh
Rev. Designer: R. R. Carmichael
Rev. Engraver: S. Beveridge
Portrait Engr.: S. Beveridge

1994 Obverse
Designer and Engraver:
Dora de Pédery-Hunt

Coin No. 9
Curtiss HS-2L
Stuart Graham
Rev. Designer: John Mardon
Rev. Engraver: S. Beveridge
Portrait Engr.: Susan Taylor

Coin No. 10
Canadian Vickers Vedette
Wilfred T. Reid
Rev. Designer: R. R. Carmichael
Rev. Engraver: S. Beveridge
Portrait Engr.: S. Beveridge

DATE	DESCRIPTION	SERIES	ISSUE DATE	QUANTITY SOLD	ISSUE PRICE	FINISH	PR-68	PR-69
1992	Curtiss JN-4 (Canuck)	One	Aug. 13/92	33,105	55.50	Proof	50.	—
1992	de Havilland Gipsy Moth	One	Aug. 13/92	32,537	55.50	Proof	50.	—
1993	Fairchild 71c	One	May 3/93	32,199	55.50	Proof	50.	—
1993	Lockheed 14 Super Electra	One	May 3/93	32,550	55.50	Proof	50.	—
1994	Curtiss HS-2L	One	Mar. 24/94	31,242	55.50	Proof	50.	—
1994	Canadian Vickers Vedette	One	Mar. 24/94	30,880	55.50	Proof	50.	—
1990-94	Set of 10 Series One coins	One	—	—	—	Proof	425.	*

TWENTY DOLLARS, AVIATION COMMEMORATIVES, SERIES TWO, 1995-1999.

This is the second series of the aviation cameo coins of Canada. The theme of this series is "Powered Flight in Canada — Beyond World War II." The reverses, physical and chemical specifications are the same as the first series.

SERIES TWO

1995 Obverse
Designer and Engraver:
Dora de Pédery-Hunt

Coin No. 1
Fleet 80 Canuck
J. Omer (Bob) Noury
Rev. Designer: Robert Bradford
Rev. Engraver: Cosme Saffioti
Portrait Engr.: Cosme Saffioti

Coin No. 2
DHC-1 Chipmunk
W. C. Russell Bannock
Rev. Designer: Robert Bradford
Rev. Engraver: William Woodruff
Portrait Engr.: Ago Aarand

1996 Obverse
Designer and Engraver:
Dora de Pédery-Hunt

Coin No. 3
Avro Canada CF-100 Canuck
Janus Zurakowski
Rev. Designer: Jim Bruce
Rev. Engraver: Stan Witten
Portrait Engr.: Cosme Saffioti

Coin No. 4
Avro Canada CF-105 Arrow
James A. Chamberlin
Rev. Designer: Jim Bruce
Rev. Engraver: William Woodruff
Portrait Engr.: S. Beveridge

1997 Obverse
Designer and Engraver:
Dora de Pédery-Hunt

Coin No. 5
Canadair F-86 Sabre
Fern Villeneuve
Rev. Designer: Ross Buckland
Rev. Engraver: William Woodruff
Portrait Engr.: Cosme Saffioti

Coin No. 6
Canadair CT-114 Tutor Jet
Edward Higgins
Rev. Designer: Ross Buckland
Rev. Engraver: Stan Witten
Portrait Engr.: Ago Aarand

TWENTY DOLLARS, AVIATION COMMEMORATIVES, SERIES TWO, 1995-1999 (cont.).

1998 Obverse
Designer and Engraver:
Dora de Pédery-Hunt

Coin No. 7
Canadair CP-107 Argus
William S. Longhurst
Rev. Designer: Peter Mossman
Rev. Engraver: Sheldon
Beveridge

Coin No. 8
Canadair CL-215 Waterbomber
Paul Gagnon
Rev. Designer: Peter Mossman
Rev. Engraver: Stan Witten
Portrait Engr.: William Woodruff

1999 Obverse
Designer and Engraver:
Dora de Pédery-Hunt

Coin No. 9
de Havilland DHC-6 Twin Otter
George A. Neal
Rev. Designer: Neil Aird
Rev. Engraver: Cosme Saffioti
Portrait Engr.: Cosme Saffioti

Coin No. 10
de Havilland DHC-8 Dash 8
Robert H. (Bob) Fowler
Rev. Designer: Neil Aird
Rev. Engraver: William Woodruff
Portrait Engr.: Cosme Saffioti

DATE	DESCRIPTION	SERIES	ISSUE DATE	QUANTITY SOLD	ISSUE PRICE	FINISH	PR-68	PR-69
1995	Fleet 80 Canuck	Two	Sept. 16/95	17,438	57.95	Proof	50.	—
1995	DHC-1 Chipmunk	Two	Sept. 16/95	17,722	57.95	Proof	60.	—
1996	CF-100 Canuck	Two	July 25/96	18,508	57.95	Proof	50.	—
1996	CF-105 Arrow	Two	July 25/96	27,163	57.95	Proof	120.	—
1997	F86 Sabre	Two	Aug. 15/97	16,440	57.95	Proof	50.	—
1997	Tutor Jet	Two	Aug. 15/97	18,414	57.95	Proof	50.	—
1998	Argus	Two	June 5/98	14,711	57.95	Proof	50.	—
1998	Waterbomber	Two	June 5/98	15,237	57.95	Proof	50.	—
1999	Twin Otter	Two	April 15/99	14,173	57.95	Proof	75.	—
1999	Dash 8	Two	April 15/99	14,138	57.95	Proof	75.	—
1995-99	Set of 10 Series Two coins	Two	—	—	—	Proof	425.	*

Note: In 1998 a special issue two-coin set (coins 7 and 8) boxed with a cardboard model was offered to collectors.
See Derivatives, page 349.

TRANSPORTATION ON LAND, SEA AND RAIL SERIES

TWENTY DOLLARS, TRANSPORTATION ON LAND, SEA AND RAIL, 2000-2003.

Canada's first sterling silver hologram cameo twenty dollar coins were issued in 2000. This series of twelve coins commemorates Canadian achievements in transportation. Each coin bears a holographic cameo of famous Canadian methods of transportation.

Designers:	
Obv. and Rev.: See each coin	**Engravers:**
Composition: 92.5% Ag, 7.5% Cu, Holographic cameo; 2003 Selectively gold plated	Obv. and Rev.: See each coin
Silver content: 28.77 g, 0.925 tr oz	
Weight: 31.103 g	**Edge:** Interrupted serrations
Diameter: 38.0 mm	**Die Axis:** ↑↑
Thickness: 3.5 mm	**Finish:** Proof
Case of Issue: Charcoal coloured anodized aluminum case with RCM logo, black flocked insert, COA	

TRANSPORTATION ON LAND, SEA AND RAIL, 2000.

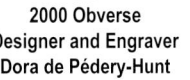

2000 Obverse	Coin No. 1	Coin No. 2	Coin No. 3
Designer and Engraver	H.S. Taylor Steam Buggy	The Bluenose	The Toronto
Dora de Pédery-Hunt	John Mardon	J. Franklin Wright	J. Mardon, Stan Witten
	Cosme Saffioti	Stan Witten	Cosme Saffioti

DATE	DESCRIPTION	ISSUE DATE	QUANTITY SOLD	ISSUE PRICE	FINISH	PR-69	PR-70
2000	H.S. Taylor Steam Buggy	Apr.18/2000	Total	59.95	Proof	55.	—
2000	The Bluenose	Apr.18/2000	mintage	59.95	Proof	120.	—
2000	The Toronto	Apr.18/2000	all coins	59.95	Proof	55.	—
2000	Set of 3 coins	—	44,367	179.85	Proof	200.	*

TRANSPORTATION ON LAND, SEA AND RAIL, 2001.

2001 Obverse	Coin No. 4	Coin No. 5	Coin No. 6
Designer and Engraver	The Russell "Light Four"	The Marco Polo	The Scotia
Dora de Pédery-Hunt	Model L Touring Car	J. Franklin Wright	Don Curley
	John Mardon, José Osio	Stan Witten	William Woodruff

DATE	DESCRIPTION	ISSUE DATE	QUANTITY SOLD	ISSUE PRICE	FINISH	PR-69	PR-70
2001	The Russell "Light Four"	Apr.17/2001	Total	59.95	Proof	50.	—
2001	The Marco Polo	Apr.17/2001	mintage	59.95	Proof	50.	—
2001	The Scotia	Apr.17/2001	all coins	59.95	Proof	50.	—
2001	Set of 3 coins	—	41,828	179.85	Proof	130.	*

TRANSPORTATION ON LAND, SEA AND RAIL SERIES (cont.).

TWENTY DOLLARS, TRANSPORTATION ON LAND, SEA AND RAIL, 2002.

2002 Obverse	Coin No. 7	Coin No. 8	Coin No. 9
Designer and Engraver	The Gray-Dort	The William Lawrence	D-10 Locomotive
Dora de Pédery-Hunt	John Mardon	Bonnie Ross	Dan Fell
	Cosme Saffioti	William Woodruff	William Woodruff

DATE	DESCRIPTION	ISSUE DATE	QUANTITY SOLD	ISSUE PRICE	FINISH	PR-69	PR-70
2002	The Gray-Dort	Apr.17/2002	Total	59.95	Proof	50.	—
2002	The William Lawrence	Apr.17/2002	mintage	59.95	Proof	50.	—
2002	D-10 Locomotive	Apr.17/2002	all coins	59.95	Proof	50.	—
2002	Set of 3 coins	—	35,944	195.00	Proof	130.	*

TWENTY DOLLARS, TRANSPORTATION ON LAND, SEA AND RAIL, 2003.

2003 Obverse	Coin No. 10	Coin No. 11	Coin No. 12
Designer and Engraver	HMCS Bras d'Or	C.N.R. FA-1 Diesel Electric	Bricklin SV-1 (Land)
Dora de Pédery-Hunt	Hydrofoil designed by	Locomotive - No. 9400	designed by Malcolm in 1974
	DeHavilland in 1967	John Mardon	Brian Hughes
	Donald Curley, Stan Witten	William Woodruff	José Osio

DATE	DESCRIPTION	ISSUE DATE	QUANTITY SOLD	ISSUE PRICE	FINISH	PR-69	PR-70
2003	HMCS Bras d'Or	Apr.7/2003	Total	59.95	Proof	65.	—
2003	C.N.R. FA-1 Diesel Electric Locomotive	Apr.7/2003	mintage	59.95	Proof	65.	—
2003	Bricklin SV-1	Apr.7/2003	all coins	59.95	Proof	65.	—
2003	Set of 3 coins	—	31,997	195.00	Proof	100.	*

Note: 1. The 2002 Land, Sea and Rail collection was offered with matching COA in a limited edition of 2,500.
2. Coins illustrated smaller than actual size.

NATURAL WONDERS SERIES

TWENTY DOLLARS, NATURAL WONDERS SERIES, 2003-2005.
The Royal Canadian Mint, in 2003, introduced a new series of twenty dollar commemorative coins. Each coin carries a holographic, decal, or a ectively gold plated image of one of Canada's natural wonders.

Designers and Engravers: See illustrations
Composition: 99.99% Ag
Silver content: 31.39 g, 1.01 tr oz
Weight: 31.39 g   **Edge:** Reeded
Diameter: 38.0 mm   **Die Axis:** ↑↑
Thickness: 3.5 mm
Finish: Proof
Case of Issue:
(A) Veneer, wooden clam style case, light brown flocked interior, encapsulated coin, COA
(B) Red leatherette clam style case, flocked black insert, encapsulated coin, COA

2003 Obverse
Designer and Engraver:
Dora de Pédery-Hunt

2004-2005 Obverse
Designer: Susanna Blunt
Engraver: Susan Taylor

Niagara Falls
Designer and Engraver:
Gary Corcoran

Rocky Mountains
Designer and Engraver:
José Osio

Icebergs
Designer and Engraver:
RCM Staff

Northern Lights
Designer: Gary Corcoran
Engraver: Stan Witten

Hopewell Rocks
Designer and Engraver:
Stan Witten

Diamonds
Designer and Engraver:
José Osio

DATE	DESCRIPTION	QUANTITY SOLD	ISSUE PRICE	FINISH	PR-69	PR-70
2003	Niagara Falls, Hologram	29,967	79.95	Proof	70.	—
2003	Rocky Mountains, Decal	28,793	69.95	Proof	50.	—
2004	Icebergs, Hologram	24,879	69.95	Proof	50.	—
2004	Northern Lights, Double Image Hologram	34,135	79.95	Proof	50.	—
2004	Hopewell Rocks, Selectively gold plated	16,918	69.95	Proof	50.	—
2005	Diamonds, Double Image Hologram	35,000	69.95	Proof	50.	—

CANADIAN LIGHTHOUSE SERIES

TWENTY DOLLARS (1 ounce), CANADIAN LIGHTHOUSE SERIES, 2004-2005.

Designers:		**Engravers:**	
Obv.:	Susanna Blunt	Obv.:	Susan Taylor
Rev.:	See reverse illustrations	Rev.:	See reverse illustraitons
Composition:	99.99% Ag		
Weight:	31.1035 g, 1 oz	**Edge:**	Reeded
Diameter:	38.0 mm	**Die Axis:**	↑↑
Thickness:	3.2 mm		
Finish:	Proof, Frosted relief against a mirror background		
Case of Issue:	Maroon leatherette clam style case, black insert, encapsulated coin, COA		

Sambro Island Lighthouse
Designer: Hedley Doty
Engraver: William Woodruff

Toronto Island Lighthouse
Designer: Brian Hughes
Engraver: William Woodruff

DATE	DESCRIPTION	QUANTITY SOLD	ISSUE PRICE	FINISH	PR-69	PR-70
2004	Sambro Island Lighthouse	18,476	69.95	Proof	40.	—
2005	Toronto Island Lighthouse	14,006	69.95	Proof	55.	—

Note: See page 629 for Sambro Island Lighthouse derivative.

TALL SHIPS SERIES

TWENTY DOLLARS, TALL SHIPS SERIES, 2005-2007.

2005 Obverse

2006 Obverse

2007 Obverse

Three-Masted Ship
Designer: Bonnie Ross
Engraver: William Woodruff

Ketch
Designer: John M. Horton
Engraver: Susan Taylor

Brigantine
Designer: Bonnie Ross
Engraver: William Woodruff

Designers:
Obv.:	Susanna Blunt
Rev.:	See reverse illustrations

Composition: 99.99% Ag, Hologram
Silver content: 31.39 g, 1.01 tr oz
Weight: 31.39 g
Diameter: 38.0 mm
Thickness: 3.0 mm
Case of Issue: Maroon plastic slide case, black plastic insert, encapsulated coin, COA

Engravers:
Obv.:	Susan Taylor
Rev.:	See reverse illustrations

Edge: Reeded
Die Axis: ↑↑
Finish: Proof

DATE	DESCRIPTION	QUANTITY SOLD	ISSUE PRICE	FINISH	PR-69	PR-70
2005	Three-Masted Ship, Hologram	18,276	69.95	Proof	60.	—
2006	Ketch, Hologram	10,299	69.95	Proof	70.	—
2007	Brigantine, Hologram	7,935	74.95	Proof	70.	—

NATIONAL PARKS SERIES

TWENTY DOLLARS, NATIONAL PARKS SERIES, 2005-2006.

| 2005 Obverse
Designer: Susanna Blunt
Engraver: Susan Taylor | North Pacific Rim National
Park Reserve of Canada (QC)
Designer: Susanna Blunt
Engraver: Stan Witten | Mingan Archipelago National
Park Reserve of Canada (QC)
Designer: Pierre Leduc
Engraver: José Osio |

2006 Obverse
Designer: Susanna Blunt
Engraver: Susan Taylor

Georgian Bay Islands
National Park (ON)
Designer: Tony Bianco
Engraver: William Woodruff

Nahanni National Park
Reserve of Canada (NWT)
Designer: Virginia Boulay
Engraver: William Woodruff

Jasper National Park of
Canada (AL)
Designer: Michelle Grant
Engraver: William Woodruff

Designers:	See illustrations	**Engravers:**	See illustrations
Composition:	99.99% Ag		
Silver content:	31.39 g, 1.01 tr oz		
Weight:	31.39 g	**Edge:**	Reeded
Diameter:	38.0 mm	**Die Axis:**	↑↑
Thickness:	3.0 mm	**Finish:**	Proof
Case of Issue:	Maroon plastic slide case, black plastic insert, encapsulated coin, COA		

DATE	DESCRIPTION	QUANTITY SOLD	ISSUE PRICE	FINISH	PR-69	PR-70
2005	North Pacific Rim National Park Reserve of Canada (QC)	21,695	69.95	Proof	50.	—
2005	Mingan Archipelago National Park Reserve of Canada (QC)	Included	69.95	Proof	50.	—
2006	Georgian Bay Islands National Park (ON)	20,218	69.95	Proof	50.	—
2006	Nahanni National Park Reserve of Canada (NWT)	Included	69.95	Proof	75.	—
2006	Jasper National Park of Canada (AL)	Included	69.95	Proof	70.	—

Note:
1. National Parks single quantities were not recorded in the RCM Reports of 2005 and 2006 as individual entries, but only as totals sold for those years. There will be a difference between the projected issue as noted on the certificate of authenticity and the actual number sold.
2. Coins illustrated smaller than actual size.

CANADIAN ARCHITECTURAL SET

TWENTY DOLLARS, CANADIAN ARCHITECTURAL SET, 2006.

| Common Obverse | Notre Dame Basilica | 30th Anniversary CN Tower | Pengrowth Saddledome |

Designers:
  Obv.: Susanna Blunt
  Rev.: Jianping Yan
Composition: 99.99% Ag, Photographic hologram
Silver content: 31.1 g, 1.0 tr oz
Weight: 31.1 g
Diameter: 38.0 mm
Thickness: 3.0 mm
Case of Issue: Maroon plastic slide case, black plastic insert, encapsulated coin, COA

Engravers:
  Obv.: Susan Taylor
  Rev.: RCM Staff

Edge: Reeded
Die Axis: ↑↑
Finish: Proof

DATE	DESCRIPTION	QUANTITY SOLD	ISSUE PRICE	FINISH	PR-69	PR-70
2006	Notre Dame Basilica, Photographic Hologram	30,906	69.95	Proof	60.	—
2006	30th Anniv. CN Tower, Photographic Hologram	Included	69.95	Proof	65.	—
2006	Pengrowth Saddledome, Photographic Hologram	Included	69.95	Proof	60.	—

TWENTY DOLLARS, 125TH ANNIVERSARY OF THE FIRST INTERNATIONAL POLAR YEAR, 2007.

| Common Obverse | Silver | Blue Plasma |

Designers:
  Obv.: Susanna Blunt
  Rev.: Laurie McGaw
Composition: 92.5% Ag, 7.5% Cu
Silver content: 25.70 g, 0.826 tr oz
Weight: 27.78 g
Diameter: 40.0 mm
Thickness: 2.5 mm
Case of Issue: Maroon clam style case, black flocked insert, encapsulated coin, COA

Engravers:
  Obv.: Susan Taylor
  Rev.: Susan Taylor

Edge: Reeded
Die Axis: ↑↑
Finish: Proof and Proof Plasma

DATE	DESCRIPTION	QUANTITY SOLD	ISSUE PRICE	FINISH	PR-69	PR-70
2007	125th Anniv. First Int'l Polar Year, Silver	9,164	64.95	Proof	50.	—
2007	125th Anniv. First Int'l Polar Year, Blue Plasma	3,005	249.95	Proof	175.	—

Note: Coins illustrated smaller than actual size.

CRYSTAL SNOWFLAKE SERIES

TWENTY DOLLARS, CRYSTAL SNOWFLAKE SERIES, 2007-2013.

Designers:		**Engravers:**	
Obv.:	Susanna Blunt	Obv.:	Susan Taylor
Rev.:	Konrad Wachelko	Rev.:	Konrad Wachelko
Composition:	2007: 92.5% Ag, 7.5% Cu	**Silver content:**	2007: 46.34 g, 1.490 tr oz
	2008-2013: 99.99% Ag,		2008-2011: 31.39 g, 1.01 tr oz
	with crystallised Swarovski elements		2012-2013: 31.0 g, 1.0 tr oz
Weight:	2007: 50.0 g		
	2008-2013: 31.0 to 31.39 g	**Edge:**	Reeded
Diameter:	38.0 mm	**Die Axis:**	↑↑
Thickness:	2007: 4.8 mm	**Finish:**	Proof
	2008-2013: 3.0 to 3.2 mm		
Case of Issue:	Maroon clam style case, black flocked insert, encapsulated coin, COA		

2007-2008
Obverse with RCM Logo

2010-2012
Obverse without RCM Logo

2007 Aquamarine Snowflake

2008 Amethyst Snowflake

2008 Sapphire Snowflake

2009 Blue Snowflake

2009 Rose Snowflake

2010 Blue Snowflake

2010 Tanzanite Snowflake

TWENTY DOLLARS, CRYSTAL SNOWFLAKE SERIES, 2007-2013 (cont.).

2011 Emerald Snowflake

2011 Topaz Snowflake

2011 Hyacinth Snowflake

2011 Montana Snowflake

2012 Holiday Snowstorm

2012 Crystal Snowflake

2013 Winter Snowflake

DATE	DESCRIPTION	QUANTITY SOLD	ISSUE PRICE	FINISH	PR-69	PR-70
2007	Crystal Snowflake, Aquamarine	4,989	94.95	Proof	325.	—
2007	Crystal Snowflake, Iridescent	4,980	94.95	Proof	225.	—
2008	Crystal Snowflake, Amethyst	7,172	94.95	Proof	125.	—
2008	Crystal Snowflake, Sapphire	7,765	94.95	Proof	125.	—
2009	Crystal Snowflake, Blue	7,477	94.95	Proof	90.	—
2009	Crystal Snowflake, Rose	7,004	94.95	Proof	90.	—
2010	Crystal Snowflake, Blue	7,390	94.95	Proof	90.	—
2010	Crystal Snowflake, Tanzanite	7,241	94.95	Proof	90.	—
2011	Crystal Snowflake, Emerald	6,586	114.95	Proof	90.	—
2011	Crystal Snowflake, Topaz	6,041	114.95	Proof	90.	—
2011	Small Crystal Snowflakes, Hyacinth	5,660	114.95	Proof	90.	—
2011	Small Crystal Snowflakes, Montana	5,822	114.95	Proof	90.	—
2012	Holiday Snowstorm	4,886	114.95	Proof	90.	—
2012	Crystal Snowflake	4,896	114.95	Proof	90.	—
2013	Winter Snowflake	4,166	114.95	Proof	90.	—

HOLIDAY SERIES

TWENTY DOLLARS, HOLIDAY SERIES, 2007-2011.

**Obverse
2007-2008
With RCM Logo**

**Obverse
2010-2011
Without RCM Logo**

Designers and Engravers:

Obv.:	Susanna Blunt, Susan Taylor
Rev.:	See reverse illustrations
Composition:	99.99% Ag
Silver content:	31.39 g, 1.01 tr oz
Weight:	31.39 g
Diameter:	38.0 mm
Thickness:	3.1 to 3.3 mm
Edge:	Reeded
Die Axis:	↑↑
Finish:	2007-2008: Proof; 2010-2011: Proof, with crystallised Swarovski elements
Case of Issue:	Maroon clam style case, black flocked insert, encapsulated coin, COA

**2007
Holiday Sleigh Ride
Designer: Tony Bianco
Engraver: RCM Staff**

**2008
Holiday Carols
Designer: Tony Bianco
Engravers: C. Mok, K. Wachelko**

**2010
Holiday Pine Cones, Moonlight
Designer: Susan Taylor
Engraver: RCM Staff**

**2010
Holiday Pine Cones, Ruby
Designer: Susan Taylor
Engraver: RCM Staff**

**2011
Christmas Tree
Designer: Tony Bianco
Engraver: José Osio**

DATE	DESCRIPTION	QUANTITY SOLD	ISSUE PRICE	FINISH	PR-69	PR-70
2007	Holiday Sleigh Ride	6,804	69.95	Proof	65.	—
2008	Holiday Carols	5,224	69.95	Proof	55.	—
2010	Holiday Pine Cones, Moonlight	4,754	99.95	Proof	90.	—
2010	Holiday Pine Cones, Ruby	4,907	99.95	Proof	90.	—

CRYSTAL RAINDROP SERIES

TWENTY DOLLARS, CRYSTAL RAINDROP SERIES, 2008-2012.

2008
Obverse
With RCM Logo

2009-2012
Obverse
Without RCM Logo

Designers and Engravers:

Obv.:	Susanna Blunt, Susan Taylor
Rev.:	See reverse illustrations
Composition:	99.99% Ag, Colourised, Crystallised Swarovski element
Silver content:	31.39 g, 1.01 tr oz
Weight:	31.39 g
Diameter:	38.0 mm
Thickness:	3.1 mm
Edge:	Reeded
Die Axis:	↑↑
Finish:	Proof
Case of Issue:	Maroon clam style case, black flocked insert, encapsulated coin, COA

2008
Crystal Raindrop
Designer: Celia Godkin
Engraver: Cecily Mok

2009
Autumn Crystal Raindrop
Designer: Celia Godkin
Engraver: RCM Staff

2010
Maple Leaf with Crystal Raindrop
Designer: Celia Godkin
Engraver: Susan Taylor

2011
Crystal Raindrop and Maple Leaf
Designer: Celia Godkin
Engraver: Cecily Mok

2012
The Sugar Maple
Designer: Celia Godkin
Engraver: RCM Staff

DATE	DESCRIPTION	QUANTITY SOLD	ISSUE PRICE	FINISH	PR-69	PR-70
2008	Crystal Raindrop	13,122	89.95	Proof	130.	—
2009	Autumn Crystal Raindrop	9,998	94.95	Proof	150.	—
2010	Maple Leaf with Crystal Raindrop	9,659	104.95	Proof	110.	—
2011	Crystal Raindrop and Maple Leaf	9,594	109.95	Proof	110.	—
2012	The Sugar Maple	9,933	119.95	Proof	110.	—

GREAT CANADIAN LOCOMOTIVES SERIES

TWENTY DOLLARS, GREAT CANADIAN LOCOMOTIVES SERIES, 2008-2011

The Hudson, Locomotive 2850 was chosen to transport King George VI and Queen Elizabeth from Quebec City to Vancouver, during their royal v of 1939. The royal crest was mounted on the engine and tender, and remained after the visit, thus The Royal Hudson.

The Jubilee was introduced in 1936 for the CPR's 50th anniversary of the completion of the Transcontinental Railway in 1886. Classed as a 2-1 engine, The Selkirk engines were built by Montreal Locomotive Works for Canadian Pacific Railway to handle the steep grades of the Selkirk Mounta in British Columbia.

The D-10-class ten wheeler type 4-6-0 locomotive was a typical Canadian Pacific Railway steam locomotive. Five hundred and eight locomotiv were built between 1905 and 1913 and formed the backbone of CPR's freight locomotive fleet. Most burned coal, but 28 were converted to oil.

2008	2008
Obverse	The Royal Hudson
With RCM Logo	Konrad Wachelko

2009-2011	2009	2010	2011
Obverse	The Jubilee	The Selkirk	D-10
Without RCM Logo	William Woodruff	William Woodruff	Marcos Hallam

Designers:
   Obv.:   Susanna Blunt
   Rev.:   RCM Engravers (from Canadian
           Canadian Pacific Railway Archives)

Engravers:
   Obv.:   Susan Taylor
   Rev.:   See reverse illustrations

Composition: 99.99% Ag
Silver content: 31.39 g, 1.01 tr oz
Weight: 31.39 g
Diameter: 38.0 mm
Thickness: 3.2 mm
Case of Issue: Maroon leatherette clam style case, black flocked insert, encapsulated coin, COA

Edge: Plain, edge lettering "ROYAL HUDSON", "JUBILEE", "SELKIRK" or "D-10"
Die Axis: ↑↑
Finish: Proof

DATE	DESCRIPTION	QUANTITY SOLD	ISSUE PRICE	FINISH	PR-69	PR-70
2008	The Royal Hudson	8,345	69.95	Proof	75.	—
2009	The Jubilee	6,036	69.95	Proof	75.	—
2010	The Selkirk	5,874	79.95	Proof	75.	—
2011	D-10	8,662	79.95	Proof	75.	—

Note: Coins illustrated smaller than actual size.

CANADIAN INDUSTRY SERIES

TWENTY DOLLARS, CANADIAN INDUSTRY SERIES, 2008-2009.

Common Obverse

Agriculture Trade
Engraver: José Osio

Coal Mining Trade
Engraver: Christie Paquet

Designers:		Engravers:		
Obv.:	Susanna Blunt	Obv.:	Susan Taylor	
Rev.:	John Mardon	Rev.:	See reverse illustrations	
Composition:	99.99% Ag			
Silver content:	31.39 g, 1.01 tr oz			
Weight:	31.39 g	Edge:	Reeded	
Diameter:	38.0 mm	Die Axis:	↑↑	
Thickness:	3.1 mm	Finish:	Proof	
Case of Issue:	Maroon clam style case, black flocked insert, encapsulated coin, COA			

DATE	DESCRIPTION	QUANTITY SOLD	ISSUE PRICE	FINISH	PR-69	PR-70
2008	Agriculture Trade	5,802	69.95	Proof	70.	—
2009	Coal Mining Trade	3,349	74.95	Proof	70.	—

TWENTY DOLLARS, SUMMER MOON MASK, 2009.

Designers and Engravers:			
Obv.:	Susanna Blunt, Susan Taylor		
Rev.:	Jody Broomfield, Susan Taylor		
Composition:	99.99% Ag		
Silver content:	31.39 g, 1.01 tr oz		
Weight:	31.39 g	Edge:	Reeded
Diameter:	38.0 mm	Die Axis:	↑↑
Thickness:	3.2 mm	Finish:	Proof
Case of Issue:	Maroon leatherette clam style case, black flocked insert, encapsulated coin, COA		

DATE	DESCRIPTION	QUANTITY SOLD	ISSUE PRICE	FINISH	PR-69	PR-70
2009	Summer Moon Mask	2,834	69.95	Proof	170.	—

TWENTY DOLLARS, 475TH ANNIVERSARY JACQUES CARTIER'S ARRIVAL AT GASPÉ, 1534-2009.

Designers and Engravers:			
Obv.:	Susanna Blunt, Susan Taylor		
Rev.:	John Mardon, Stan Witten		
Composition:	99.99% Ag		
Silver content:	31.39 g, 1.01 tr oz		
Weight:	31.39 g	Edge:	Reeded
Diameter:	38.0 m	Die Axis:	↑↑
Thickness:	3.2 mm	Finish:	Proof
Case of Issue:	Maroon leatherette clam style case, black flocked insert, encapsulated coin, COA		

DATE	DESCRIPTION	QUANTITY SOLD	ISSUE PRICE	FINISH	PR-69	PR-70
2009 (1534-)	475th Anniversary of Jacques Cartier's Arrival at Gaspé	1,516	169.95	Proof	225.	—

2008-2009 CANADIAN NHL TEAM GOALIE MASKS SET

TWENTY DOLLARS, 2008-2009 CANADIAN NHL TEAM GOALIE MASKS SET, 2009.

The goalie mask, first introduced by all-star Montreal goalie Jacques Plante on November 1st, 1959, has become a necessary part of goaltender's equipment.

Common Obverse

Designers and Engravers:

Obv.:	Susanna Blunt, Susan Taylor
Rev.:	Marcos Hallam
Composition:	92.5% Ag, 7.5% Cu, Painted
Silver content:	25.70 g, 0.826 tr oz
Weight:	27.78 g
Diameter:	40.0 mm
Thickness:	2.6 mm
Edge:	Reeded
Die Axis:	↑↑
Finish:	Proof
Case of Issue:	Lucite stand, encapsulated coin, COA, cardboard outer box

Calgary Flames

Edmonton Oilers

Montreal Canadiens

Ottawa Senators

Toronto Maple Leafs

Vancouver Canucks

DATE	DESCRIPTION	QUANTITY SOLD	ISSUE PRICE	FINISH	PR-69	PR-70
2009	Calgary Flames	125	74.95	Proof	90.	—
2009	Edmonton Oilers	147	74.95	Proof	90.	—
2009	Montreal Canadiens	748	74.95	Proof	100.	—
2009	Ottawa Senators	95	74.95	Proof	90.	—
2009	Toronto Maple Leafs	244	74.95	Proof	90.	—
2009	Vancouver Canucks	129	74.95	Proof	90.	—

Note: Quantity Sold numbers are those for 2009. The Royal Mint Annual Report for 2010 did not report additional units sold.

PAINTED WILDFLOWER SERIES

TWENTY DOLLARS, PAINTED WILDFLOWER SERIES, 2010-2015.

Common Obverse

2010
Water Lily
Designer: Claudio D'Angelo
Engraver: Cecily Mok

2011
Crystal Dewdrop and Wild Rose
Designer: Margaret Dest
Engraver: José Osio

2012
Rhododendron
Designer: Claudio D'Angelo
Engraver: RCM Staff

2013
Blue Flag Iris
Designer: Celia Godkin
Engraver: RCM Staff

2014
Red Trillium
Designer: Margaret Best
Engraver: RCM Staff

2015
Black-Eyed Susan
Designer: Laurie Koss
Engraver: RCM Staff

Designers:		Engravers:	
Obv.:	Susanna Blunt	Obv.:	Susan Taylor
Rev.:	See reverse illustrations	Rev.:	See reverse illustrations
Composition:	99.99% Ag, Painted, crystallised Swarovski elements		
Silver content:	31.39 g, 1.01 tr oz		
Weight:	31.39 g	Edge:	Reeded
Diameter:	38.0 mm	Die Axis:	↑↑
Thickness:	3.1 mm	Finish:	Proof
Case of Issue:	Maroon leatherette clam style case, black flocked insert, encapsulated coin, COA		

DATE	DESCRIPTION	QUANTITY SOLD	ISSUE PRICE	FINISH	PR-69	PR-70
2010	Water Lily	9,990	104.95	Proof	110.	—
2011	Crystal Dewdrop and Wild Rose	9,989	109.95	Proof	110.	—
2012	Rhododendron	9,991	119.95	Proof	110.	—
2013	Blue Flag Iris	9,953	119.95	Proof	110.	—
2014	Red Trillium	7,453	119.95	Proof	110.	—
2015	Black-Eyed Susan	3,768	119.95	Proof	110.	—

Note: Coins illustrated smaller than actual size.

TWENTY DOLLARS, 75TH ANNIVERSARY OF THE FIRST BANK NOTES ISSUED BY BANK OF CANADA, 1935-2010.

The reverse design on this coin is a reproduction of the allegory that appeared on the original 1935 $20 bank note; a woman symbolising agricult▪ admiring fruits of the field presented to her by a kneeling man.

Designers and Engravers:

Obv.:	Susanna Blunt, Susan Taylor
Rev.:	Konrad Wachelko
Composition:	99.99% Ag
Silver content:	31.39 g, 1.01 tr oz
Weight:	31.39 g
Diameter:	38.0 mm
Thickness:	3.2 mm
Edge:	Reeded
Die Axis:	↑↑ **Finish:** Proof
Case of Issue:	Maroon clam style case, black flocked insert, encapsulated coin, COA

DATE	DESCRIPTION	QUANTITY SOLD	ISSUE PRICE	FINISH	PR-69	PR-70
2010 (1935-)	75th Anniversary of First Notes Issued by Bank of Canada	6,720	79.95	Proof	70.	—

TWENTY DOLLARS, HRH PRINCE WILLIAM OF WALES AND MISS CATHERINE MIDDLETON, 2011.

This coin is embedded with a sapphire colour Swarovski element.

Designers and Engravers:

Obv.:	Susanna Blunt, Susan Taylor
Rev.:	Laurie McGaw, José Osio
Composition:	99.99% Ag, Swarovski element
Silver content:	31.39 g, 1.01 tr oz
Weight:	31.39 g
Diameter:	38.0 mm
Thickness:	3.2 mm
Edge:	Plain (laser engraved HRH PRINCE WILLIAM MISS CATHERINE MIDDLETC SAR LE PRINCE WILLIAM ET MLLE CATHERINE MIDDLETON)
Die Axis:	↑↑
Finish:	Proof
Case of Issue:	Maroon clam style case, black flocked insert, encapsulated coin, COA

DATE	DESCRIPTION	QUANTITY SOLD	ISSUE PRICE	FINISH	PR-69	PR-70
2011	HRH Prince William of Wales / Miss Catherine Middleton	24,858	104.95	Proof	60.	—

TWENTY DOLLARS, WINTER SCENE, 2011.

Designers and Engravers:

Obv.:	Susanna Blunt, Susan Taylor
Rev.:	Rémi Clark, José Osio
Composition:	92.50% Ag, 0.75% Cu
Silver content:	25.70 g, 0.826 tr oz
Weight:	27.78 g
Diameter:	40.0 mm **Edge:** Reeded
Thickness:	2.5 mm **Die Axis:** ↑↑
Finish:	Proof
Case of Issue:	Maroon leatherette clam style case, black flocked insert, encapsulated coi COA

DATE	DESCRIPTION	QUANTITY SOLD	ISSUE PRICE	FINISH	PR-69	PR-70
2011	Winter Scene	5,287	69.95	Proof	60.	—

CANADIAN GARDEN FLORA AND FAUNA SERIES

WENTY DOLLARS, CANADIAN GARDEN FLORA AND FAUNA SERIES, 2011-2015.
This series of coins feature a hand-crafted Venetian glass detail by master glassmaker Giuliano Donaggio from Murano, Italy, atop a coloured background signed by Maurice Gervais. This series was also issued in a gold $250 set (see page 466 and a 25¢ series of coins (see page 48).

Common Obverse

2011
Tulip with Ladybug
Designer: Cosme Saffioti
Engraver: RCM Staff
Ladybug: Giuliano Donnagio

2012
Aster with Bumble Bee
Designer: Cosme Saffioti
Engraver: Cecily Mok
Bumble Bee: Giuliano Donnagio

2013
Purple Coneflower and
Eastern Tailed Blue Butterfly
Designer: Maurice Gervais
Engraver: Konrad Wachelko
Butterfly: Giuliano Donnagio

2014
Water-lily and Leopard Frog
Designer: Maurice Gervaiso
Engraver: Konrad Wachelko
Leopard Frog: Giuliano Donnagio

2015
Turtle with Broadleaf
Arrowhead Flower
Designer: Maurice Gervais
Engraver: RCM Staff
Turtle: Giuliano Donnagio

signers:		Engravers:	
Obv.:	Susanna Blunt	Obv.:	Susan Taylor
Rev.:	See reverse illustrations	Rev.:	See reverse illustrations
mposition:	99.99% Ag, Coloured, Murano glass insect		
ver content:	31.39 g, 1.01 tr oz		
ight:	31.39 g	Edge:	Reeded
ameter:	38.0 mm	Die Axis:	↑↑
ickness:	3.1 mm	Finish:	Proof
se of Issue:	Maroon clam style case, black flocked insert, encapsulated coin, COA		

DATE	DESCRIPTION	QUANTITY SOLD	ISSUE PRICE	FINISH	PR-69	PR-70
2011	Tulip with Ladybug	4,985	139.95	Proof	1,100.	—
2012	Aster with Bumble Bee	9,991	139.95	Proof	240.	—
2013	Purple Coneflower and Eastern Tailed Blue Butterfly	9,994	149.95	Proof	240.	—
2014	Water-lily and Leopard Frog	12,500	149.95	Proof	140.	—
2015	Turtle with Broadleaf Arrowhead Flower	12,500	149.95	Proof	140.	—

TWENTY FOR TWENTY SERIES

TWENTY DOLLARS (¼ OUNCE), FINE SILVER, TWENTY FOR TWENTY SERIES, 2011-2016.

Common Obverse
2011-2012

2011 - Five Maple Leaves
Des.: Cosme Saffioti
Engr.: RCM Staff

2011 - Canoe
Des.: Jason Bouwman
Engr.: William Woodruff

2012 - Polar Bear
Des.: Emily Damsta
Engr.: Stan Witten

2012 - Farewell to the Penny
Des.: Jesse Koreck
Engr.: José Osio

2012 - Magical Reindeer
Des.: Virginia Boulay
Engr.: José Osio

2012 - Obverse:
Queen's Diamond Jubilee
Des.: Mary Gilllick
Engr.: RCM Staff

2012 - Reverse:
Queen's Diamond Jubilee
Des.: Laurie McGaw
Engr.: RCM Staff

Common Obverse
2013-2015

2013 - Hockey
Des.: Greg Banning
Engr.: José Osio

2013 - Wolf
Des.: Glen Loates
Engr.: Eric Boyer

2013 - Iceberg
Des.: Emily Damstra
Engr.: Christie Paquet

Designers:		**Engravers:**	
Obv.:	Susanna Blunt	Obv.:	Susan Taylor
Rev.:	See reverse illustrations	Rev.:	See reverse illustrations
Composition:	99.99% Ag		
Weight:	7.96 g, 0.25 tr oz	**Edge:**	Reeded
Diameter:	27.0 mm	**Die Axis:**	↑↑
Thickness:	1.8 mm	**Finish:**	Specimen
Case of Issue:	2011 Five Maple leaves: Vinyl pouch		
	2011-2013: Vinyl pouch, encapsulated coin, coloured folder		

DATE	DESCRIPTION	QUANTITY SOLD	ISSUE PRICE	FINISH	SP-68	SP-69
2011	$20, Five Maple Leaves	198,000	20.00	Specimen	35.	—
2011	$20, Canoe	244,000	20.00	Specimen	25.	—
2012	$20, Polar Bear	174,474	20.00	Specimen	25.	—
2012 (1952-)	$20, Queen's Diamond Jubilee	180,020	20.00	Specimen	25.	—
2012	$20, Farewell to the Penny	192,010	20.00	Specimen	25.	—
2012	$20, Magical Reindeer	162,620	20.00	Specimen	25.	—
2013	$20, Hockey	245,325	20.00	Specimen	25.	—
2013	$20, Wolf	248,779	20.00	Specimen	25.	—
2013	$20, Iceberg	222,741	20.00	Specimen	25.	—

TWENTY DOLLARS (¼ ounce), FINE SILVER, TWENTY FOR TWENTY SERIES, 2011-2016 (cont.).

2013 - Santa
Des.: Jesse Koreck
Engr.: Eric Boyer

2014 - Canada Goose
Des.: Trevor Tennant
Engr.: Cecily Mok

2014 - Bobcat
Des.: Ken Ryan
Engr.: RCM Staff

2014 - Summertime
Des.: RCM Staff
Engr.: RCM Staff

2014 - Snowman
Des.: J. Koreck
Engr.: RCM Staff

**2015 - FIFA Women's
World Cup™**
Des.: Joel Kimmel
Engr.: RCM Staff

2015 - Gingerbread Man
Des.: Chris & Rosina Reid
Engr.: RCM Staff

2015 - Bugs Bunny©
Des.: Warner Bros.
Entertainment Inc.
Engr.: RCM Staff

2015
DC Comics Originals™:
Superman
Des.: DC Comics
Engr.: RCM Staff

2016
Tyrannosaurus Rex
Des.: Julius Cstonyi
Engr.: RCM Staff

2016
Star Trek: Enterprise
Des.: RCM Staff
Engr.: RCM Staff

2016
*Batman V Superman:
Dawn of Justice™*
Des.: DC Comics
Engr.: RCM Staff

Designers:		**Engravers:**	
Obv.:	Susanna Blunt	Obv.:	Susan Taylor
Rev.:	See reverse illustrations	Rev.:	See reverse illustrations
Composition:	99.99% Ag		
Weight:	7.96 g, 0.25 tr oz	**Edge:**	Reeded
Diameter:	26.9 mm	**Die Axis:**	↑↑
Thickness:	1.8 mm	**Finish:**	Specimen
Case of Issue:	Vinyl pouch, encapsulated coin, coloured folder		

DATE	DESCRIPTION	QUANTITY SOLD	ISSUE PRICE	FINISH	SP-68	SP-69
2013	$20, Santa	221,922	20.00	Specimen	25.	—
2014	$20, Canada Goose	223,706	20.00	Specimen	25.	—
2014	$20, Bobcat	223,496	20.00	Specimen	25.	—
2014	$20, Summertime	197,937	20.00	Specimen	25.	—
2014	$20, Snowman	208,333	20.00	Specimen	25.	—
2015	$20, FIFA Women's World Cup™	168,086	20.00	Specimen	25.	—
2015	$20, Bugs Bunny©	270,194	20.00	Specimen	25.	—
2015	$20, Gingerbread Man	174,978	20.00	Specimen	25.	—
2015	$20, DC Comics™ Originals: Superman™	257,315	20.00	Specimen	25.	—
2016	$20, *Tyrannosaurus Rex*	155,657	20.00	Specimen	25.	—
2016	$20, *Star Trek*: Enterprise	207,287	20.00	Specimen	25.	—
2016	$20, *Batman v Superman: Dawn of Justice*™	159,790	20.00	Specimen	25.	—

THE QUEEN'S DIAMOND JUBILEE SERIES

TWENTY DOLLARS, DIAMOND JUBILEE WITH CRYSTAL, 1952-2012.

Designers and Engravers:

Obv.:	Susanna Blunt, Susan Taylor
Rev.:	Laurie McGaw, Susan Taylor
Composition:	99.99% Ag, Swarovski element
Silver content:	31.39 g, 1.01 tr oz
Weight:	31.39 g
Diameter:	38.0 mm
Thickness:	3.1 mm
Edge:	Reeded
Die Axis:	↑↑
Finish:	Proof
Case of Issue:	Maroon clam style case, black flocked insert, encapsulated coin, COA

DATE	DESCRIPTION	QUANTITY SOLD	ISSUE PRICE	FINISH	PR-69	PR-70
2012 (1952-)	Diamond Jubilee With Crystal	10,780	104.95	Proof	90.	—

TWENTY DOLLARS, QUEEN ELIZABETH II AND PRINCE PHILIP, 1952-2012.

This twenty-dollar silver coin is also found in the Queen's Diamond Jubilee Royal Silver Set.

Designers and Engravers:

Obv.:	Susanna Blunt, Susan Taylor
Rev.:	Laurie McGaw, Susan Taylor
Composition:	99.99% Ag
Silver content:	31.39 g, 1.01 tr oz
Weight:	31.39 g
Diameter:	38.0 mm
Thickness:	3.1 mm
Edge:	Reeded
Die Axis:	↑↑
Finish:	Proof
Case of Issue:	Black clam style case, black flocked insert, encapsulated coin, COA

DATE	DESCRIPTION	QUANTITY SOLD	ISSUE PRICE	FINISH	PR-69	PR-70
2012 (1952-)	Queen Elizabeth II and Prince Philip	5,627	84.95	Proof	75.	—

TWENTY DOLLARS, ROYAL CYPHER, 60TH JUBILEE, 1952-2012.

Designers and Engravers:

Obv.:	Susanna Blunt, Susan Taylor
Rev.:	Christie Paquet
Composition:	99.99% Ag
Silver content:	31.39 g, 1.01 tr oz
Weight:	31.39 g
Diameter:	38.0 mm
Thickness:	3.1 mm
Edge:	Reeded
Die Axis:	↑↑
Finish:	Proof
Case of Issue:	Maroon clam style case, black flocked insert, encapsulated coin, COA

DATE	DESCRIPTION	QUANTITY SOLD	ISSUE PRICE	FINISH	PR-69	PR-70
2012 (1952-)	Royal Cypher, 60th Jubilee	3,568	84.95	Proof	75.	—

THE QUEEN'S DIAMOND JUBILEE SERIES (cont.).

TENTY DOLLARS, THE QUEEN'S PORTRAIT, 2012.

Designers and Engravers:
Obv.:	Susanna Blunt, Susan Taylor
Rev.:	Laurie McGaw, Christie Paquet
Composition:	99.99% Ag
Silver content:	30.75 g, 0.99 tr oz
Weight:	30.75 g
Diameter:	36.0 mm
Thickness:	3.0 mm
Edge:	Plain
Die Axis:	↑↑
Finish:	Proof
Case of Issue:	Maroon clam style case, black flocked insert, encapsulated coin, COA

DATE	DESCRIPTION	QUANTITY SOLD	ISSUE PRICE	FINISH	PR-69	PR-70
2012	The Queen's Portrait	7,473	129.95	Proof	90.	—

TENTY DOLLARS, THE QUEEN'S VISIT TO CANADA, 2012.

Queen Elizabeth II has been an Honourary Commissioner of the RCMP since 1953. During a visit to England in 1969 to participate in the Royal dsor Horse Show, the RCMP presented the Queen with one of their finest horses Burmese. The RCMP has presented a further five horses since n, each to commemorate an important milestone.

Designers and Engravers:
Obv.:	Susanna Blunt, Susan Taylor
Rev.:	Bonnie Ross, Cecily Mok
Composition:	99.99% Ag
Silver content:	31.39 g, 1.01 tr oz
Weight:	31.39 g
Diameter:	38.0 mm
Thickness:	3.1 mm
Edge:	Reeded
Die Axis:	↑↑
Finish:	Proof
Case of Issue:	Maroon clam style case, black flocked insert, encapsulated coin, COA

DATE	DESCRIPTION	QUANTITY SOLD	ISSUE PRICE	FINISH	PR-69	PR-70
2012	The Queen's Visit to Canada	11,113	89.95	Proof	75.	—

TWENTY DOLLARS, WINNIPEG JETS, 2011-2012.

The Winnipeg Jets is a professional (NHL) ice hockey team based in Winnipeg, Manitoba. The team plays its home games at the MTS Centre a takes their name after Winnipeg's original WHA/NHL team.

Designers and Engravers:

Obv.:	Susanna Blunt, Susan Taylor		
Rev.:	William Woodruff, RCM Staff		
Composition:	99.99% Ag		
Silver content:	31.39 g, 1.01 tr oz		
Weight:	31.39 g		
Diameter:	37.8 mm	**Edge:**	Reeded
Thickness:	3.1 mm	**Die Axis:**	↑↑
Finish:	Proof		
Case of Issue:	Maroon leatherette clam style case, bla flocked insert, encapsulated coin, COA		

DATE	DESCRIPTION	QUANTITY SOLD	ISSUE PRICE	FINISH	PR-69	PR-7(
2011-2012	Winnipeg Jets	5,536	94.95	Proof	75.	—

TWENTY DOLLARS, 50 YEARS OF THE CANADIAN COAST GUARD, 1962-2012.

During a 1994 science expedition the CCGS Louis S. St. Laurent navigated through 3,700 kilometres of Arctic Ice visiting the North Pole as it ma the first crossing of the Arctic Ocean from the Pacific to the Atlantic. It was a joint Canada-US expedition with the USCGC Polar Sea. On August 22 1994, the Louis S. St. Laurent was the first Canadian ship to reach the North Pole.

Designers and Engravers:

Obv.:	Susanna Blunt, Susan Taylor		
Rev.:	Yves Bérubé, Stan Witten		
Composition:	99.99% Ag		
Silver content:	31.39 g, 1.01 tr oz		
Weight:	31.39 g		
Diameter:	38.0 mm	**Edge:**	Reeded
Thickness:	3.0 mm	**Die Axis:**	↑↑
Finish:	Proof		
Case of Issue:	Canadian maple wood case, black flocked insert, encapsulated coin, CO		

DATE	DESCRIPTION	QUANTITY SOLD	ISSUE PRICE	FINISH	PR-69	PR-7(
2012 (1962-)	50 Years of the Canadian Coast Guard	6,696	129.95	Proof	90.	—

TWENTY DOLLARS, THE THREE WISE MEN, 2012.

Designers and Engravers:

Obv.:	Susanna Blunt, Susan Taylor
Rev.:	Jason Bouwman, Stan Witten
Composition:	99.99% Ag, Crystal element
Silver content:	28.1 g, 0.9 tr oz
Weight:	28.1 g
Diameter:	40.0 mm
Thickness:	2.6 mm
Edge:	Reeded
Die Axis:	↑↑
Finish:	Proof
Case of Issue:	Maroon clam style case, black flocked insert, encapsulated coin, COA

DATE	DESCRIPTION	QUANTITY SOLD	ISSUE PRICE	FINISH	PR-69	PR-7(
2012	The Three Wise Men	3,916	114.95	Proof	90.	—

THE GROUP OF SEVEN SERIES

ENTY DOLLARS, THE GROUP OF SEVEN SERIES, 2012-2013.

The Group of Seven were a group of Canadian landscape artists from the 1920-1933 period, who believed that a distinct Canadian art movement ld be developed through direct contact with nature.

Common Obverse

Stormy Weather, Georgian Bay
Designer: F. H. Varley
Engraver: Marcos Hallam

Designers and Engravers:

Obv.:	Susanna Blunt, Susan Taylor
Rev.:	See reverse illustrations
Composition:	99.99% Ag
Silver content:	31.39 g, 1.01 tr oz
Weight:	31.39 g
Diameter:	38.0 mm
Thickness:	3.1 mm

Edge: Reeded
Die Axis: ↑↑
Finish: Proof

Case of Issue:

Singly:	Maroon leatherette clam style case, black flocked insert, encapsulated coin, COA
Subscription:	Seven-hole wooden case, black flocked insert. encapsulated coins, COA

Nova Scotia Fishing Village
Designer: Arthur Lismer
Engraver: Stan Witten

Houses, Cobalt (1931-1932)
Designer: Franklin Carmichael
Engraver: Susan Taylor

Toronto Street Winter Morning (1920)
Designer: Lawren S. Harris
Engraver: Susan Taylor

The Guardian of the Gorge
Designer: Franz Johnston
Engraver: Cecily Mok

Sumacs
Designer: J. E. H. MacDonald
Engraver: Steven Stewart

Saint-Tite-des-Caps
Designer: A. Y. Jackson
Engraver: Christie Paquet

DATE	DESCRIPTION	QUANTITY SOLD	ISSUE PRICE	FINISH	PR-69	PR-70
2012	Stormy Weather, Georgian Bay, F. H. Varley	6,962	89.95	Proof	100.	—
2012	Nova Scotia Fishing Village, Arthur Lismer	6,985	89.95	Proof	70.	—
2012	Houses, Cobalt (1931-1932), Franklin Carmichael	6,946	89.95	Proof	70.	—
2013	Toronto Street, Winter Morning (1920), Lawren S. Harris	6,694	89.95	Proof	70.	—
2013	The Guardian of the Gorge, Franz Johnston	6,795	89.95	Proof	70.	—
2013	Sumacs, J. E. H. MacDonald	6,479	89.95	Proof	70.	—
2013	Saint-Tite-des-Caps, A. Y. Jackson	6,409	89.95	Proof	70.	—

TWENTY DOLLARS, BULL MOOSE FROM THE MOOSE FAMILY, ROBERT BATEMAN MOOSE COIN, 1962-2012.

The reverse design on this coin features a bull moose's head and antlers taken from Robert Bateman's painting The Moose Family. The coin was issued to commemorate the 50th anniversary of the Canadian Wildlife Federation.

Designers and Engravers:

Obv.:	Susanna Blunt, Susan Taylor
Rev.:	Robert Bateman, Stan Witten
Composition:	99.99% Ag
Silver content:	31.39 g, 1.01 tr oz
Weight:	31.39 g
Diameter:	38.0 mm
Thickness:	3.1 mm
Edge:	Reeded
Die Axis:	↑↑
Finish:	Proof
Case of Issue:	Maroon clam style case, black flocked insert, encapsulated coin, COA

DATE	DESCRIPTION	QUANTITY SOLD	ISSUE PRICE	FINISH	PR-69	PR-70
2012 (1962-)	Bull Moose	7,499	94.95	Proof	115.	—

Note: For other coins in the Robert Bateman Moose Coin Series see pages 407, 456, and 491.

TWENTY DOLLARS, THE BEAVER, 2013.

Designers and Engravers:

Obv.:	Susanna Blunt, Susan Taylor
Rev.:	Glen Loates, José Osio
Composition:	99.99% Ag
Silver content:	31.39 g, 1.01 tr oz
Weight:	31.39 g
Diameter:	38.0 mm
Thickness:	3.1 mm
Edge:	Reeded
Die Axis:	↑↑
Finish:	Proof
Case of Issue:	Maroon clam style case, black flocked insert, encapsulated coin, COA

DATE	DESCRIPTION	QUANTITY SOLD	ISSUE PRICE	FINISH	PR-69	PR-70
2013	The Beaver	8,498	99.95	Proof	80.	—

TWENTY DOLLARS, 300TH ANNIVERSARY OF LOUISBOURG, 1713-2013.

This coin celebrates the 300th anniversary of the founding of Louisbourg by French colonists and the contributions that the thriving community played in Nova Scotia.

Designers and Engravers:

Obv.:	Susanna Blunt, Susan Taylor
Rev.:	John Horton, Christie Paquet
Composition:	99.99% Ag
Silver content:	31.6 g, 1.01 tr oz
Weight:	31.6 g
Diameter:	40.0 mm
Thickness:	3.0 mm
Edge:	Plain, Edge lettering "LOUISBOURG 30
Die Axis:	↑↑
Finish:	Proof
Case of Issue:	Maroon clam style case, black flocked insert, encapsulated coin, COA

DATE	DESCRIPTION	QUANTITY SOLD	ISSUE PRICE	FINISH	PR-69	PR-70
2013 (1713-)	300th Anniversary of Louisbourg	4,976	89.95	Proof	80.	—

WORLD BASEBALL CLASSIC SET

TWENTY DOLLARS, WORLD BASEBALL CLASSIC SET, 2013.

These coins were issued to celebrate the World Baseball Classic Tournament held March 2nd to 19th, 2013. For other coins in this set see pages and 451.

Common Obverse

Designers and Engravers:

Obv.:	Susanna Blunt, Susan Taylor
Rev.:	Steve Hepburn, Christie Paquet

Composition: 99.99% Ag
Silver content: 31.1 g, 1.0 tr oz
Weight: 31.1 g
Diameter: 38.0 mm
Thickness: 3.2 mm
Edge: Reeded
Die Axis: ↑↑
Finish: Proof
Case of Issue: Maroon leatherette clam style case, black flocked insert, encapsulated coin, COA, custom sleeve

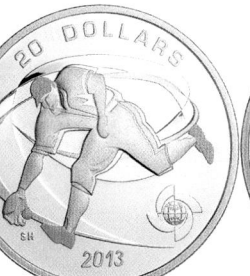

Fielder	Hitter	Pitcher	Runner

DATE	DESCRIPTION	QUANTITY SOLD	ISSUE PRICE	FINISH	PR-69	PR-70
2013	Fielder	866	114.95	Proof	90.	—
2013	Hitter	1,405	114.95	Proof	90.	—
2013	Pitcher	938	114.95	Proof	90.	—
2013	Runner	864	114.95	Proof	90.	—

TWENTY DOLLARS, CANADIAN CONTEMPORARY ART, 2013.

The coin's reverse features the artwork of Canadian artist Carlito Dalceggio and depicts the fusion of humanity and nature.

Designers and Engravers:

Obv.:	Susanna Blunt, Susan Taylor
Rev.:	Carlito Dalceggio, Alex Tirabasso

Composition: 99.99% Ag
Silver content: 31.39 g, 1.01 tr oz
Weight: 31.39 g
Diameter: 38.0 mm
Thickness: 3.1 mm   **Die Axis:** ↑↑
Edge: Reeded   **Finish:** Proof
Case of Issue: Maroon clam style case, black flocked insert, encapsulated coin, COA

DATE	DESCRIPTION	QUANTITY SOLD	ISSUE PRICE	FINISH	PR-69	PR-70
2013	Canadian Contemporary Art	3,814	89.95	Proof	90.	—

UNTAMED CANADA SERIES, 2013-2014

TWENTY DOLLARS, THE ARCTIC FOX, 2013.

This is the first coin in the Untamed Canada Series. The Arctic Fox also known as the white fox, polar fox or snow fox, is a small fox native to Arctic regions. It has fur on the bottom of its feet to protect it from the cold while digging. A $25 gold version of this series was issued in 2013-2⚫ (see page 433).

Designers and Engravers:

Obv.:	Susanna Blunt, Susan Taylor
Rev.:	Tivadar Bote, Steven Stewart
Composition:	99.99% Ag
Silver content:	28.02 g, 0.90 tr oz
Weight:	28.02 g
Diameter:	40.0 mm **Edge:** Reeded
Thickness:	2.5 mm **Die Axis:** ↑↑
Finish:	Proof
Case of Issue:	Maroon clam style case, black flocked insert, encapsulated coin, COA

TWENTY DOLLARS, PRONGHORN, 2013.

This is the second coin in the Untamed Canada Series. The Pronghorn is fleet-footed and one of the fastest animals in North America. They can more than 85 kilometres an hour, outrunning coyotes and bobcats.

Designers and Engravers:

Obv.:	Susanna Blunt, Susan Taylor
Rev.:	Tivadar Bote, Steven Stewart
Composition:	99.99% Ag
Silver content:	31.6 g, 1.01 tr oz
Weight:	31.60 g
Diameter:	40.0 mm **Edge:** Reeded
Thickness:	2.9 mm **Die Axis** ↑↑
Finish:	Proof
Case of Issue:	Maroon clam style case, black flocked insert, encapsulated coin, COA

TWENTY DOLLARS, WOLVERINE, 2014.

This is the third and final coin in the Untamed Canada Series. The wolverine is the largest member of the weasel family and resembles a small b⚫

Designers and Engravers:

Obv.:	Susanna Blunt, Susan Taylor
Rev.:	Tivadar Bote, Steven Stewart
Composition:	99.99% Ag
Silver content:	31.6 g, 1.01 tr oz
Weight:	31.60 g
Diameter:	40.0 mm **Edge:** Reeded
Thickness:	2.9 mm **Die Axis:** ↑↑
Finish:	Proof
Case of Issue:	Maroon clam style case, black flocked insert, encapsulated coin, COA

DATE	DESCRIPTION	QUANTITY SOLD	ISSUE PRICE	FINISH	PR-69	PR-7⚫
2013	The Arctic Fox	7,538	84.95	Proof	80.	—
2013	Pronghorn	4,181	89.95	Proof	80.	—
2014	Wolverine	3,905	89.95	Proof	80.	—

TENTY DOLLARS, HOLIDAY WREATH, 2013.

Designers and Engravers:
Obv.:	Susanna Blunt, Susan Taylor
Rev.:	Maurice Gervais, Samantha Strath

Composition: 99.99% Ag, Swarovski elements
Silver content: 31.2 g, 1.0 tr oz
Weight: 31.2 g
Diameter: 37.9 mm
Thickness: 3.0 mm
Edge: Reeded
Die Axis: ↑↑
Finish: Proof
Case of Issue: Maroon clam style case, black flocked insert, encapsulated coin, COA

DATE	DESCRIPTION	QUANTITY SOLD	ISSUE PRICE	FINISH	PR-69	PR-70
2013	Holiday Wreath	4,671	114.95	Proof	100.	—

CANADIAN MAPLE CANOPY SERIES

TENTY DOLLARS, CANADIAN MAPLE CANOPY SERIES, 2013-2014.
The Maple Canopy Series features the changing foliage of a Canadian maple tree as it passes through the seasons.

Designers and Engravers:
Obv.:	Susanna Blunt, Susan Taylor
Rev.:	See reverse illustrations

Composition: 99.99% Ag, Coloured
Silver content: 31.2 g, 1.0 tr oz

Weight:	31.2 g	**Edge:**	Reeded
Diameter:	38.0 mm	**Die Axis:**	↑↑
Thickness:	3.1 mm	**Finish:**	Proof

Case of Issue: Maroon clam style case, black flocked insert, encapsulated coin, COA

Common Obverse

Spring
Designer: Emily Damstra
Engraver: Matt Bowen

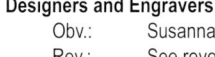

Autumn
Designer: Margaret Best
Engraver: Matt Bowen

Spring Splendour
Designer: Margaret Best
Engraver: Alex Tirabasso

Autumn Allure
Designer: Emily Damstra
Engraver: RCM Staff

DATE	DESCRIPTION	QUANTITY SOLD	ISSUE PRICE	FINISH	PR-69	PR-70
2013	Spring	7,494	99.95	Proof	90.	—
2013	Autumn	7,426	99.95	Proof	90.	—
2014	Spring Splendour	7,498	99.95	Proof	90.	—
2014	Autumn Allure	7,501	99.95	Proof	90.	—

TWENTY DOLLARS, CANDY CANE, 2013.

Designers: and Engravers:

Obv.:	Susanna Blunt, Susan Taylor
Rev.:	Steven Stewart, RCM Staff
Composition:	99.99% Ag, Coloured Murano glass
Silver content:	31.2 g, 1.0 tr oz
Weight:	31.2 g
Diameter:	37.9 mm
Thickness:	3.0 mm
Edge:	Reeded
Die Axis:	↑↑
Finish:	Proof
Case of Issue:	Maroon clam style case, black flocked insert, encapsulated coin, COA

DATE	DESCRIPTION	QUANTITY SOLD	ISSUE PRICE	FINISH	PR-69	PR-70
2013	Candy Cane	9,983	149.95	Proof	100.	—

BUTTERFLIES OF CANADA SERIES

TWENTY DOLLARS, BUTTERFLIES OF CANADA SERIES, 2013-2015.

Featuring a slight "shimmer effect", this series of coins depicts a few of Canada's butterflies.

Designers and Engravers:

Obv.:	Susanna Blunt, Susan Taylor
Rev.:	Celia Godkin, See reverse illustrations
Composition:	99.99% Ag, Coloured
Silver content:	28.02 g, 0.90 tr oz
Weight:	2013-2014: 28.02 g **Edge:** Reeded
	2015: 31.83 g
Diameter:	40.0 mm **Die Axis:** ↑↑
Thickness:	N/A. **Finish:** Proof
Case of Issue:	Maroon clam style case, black flocked insert, encapsulated coin, COA, custom box

2013	2014	2015
Canadian Tiger Swallowtail	Red-Spotted Purple	Giant Sulphur *(Colias Gigantea)*
Engraver: Samantha Strath	Engraver: RCM Staff	Designer: Celia Godkin
		Engraver: RCM Staff

DATE	DESCRIPTION	QUANTITY SOLD	ISSUE PRICE	FINISH	PR-69	PR-70
2013	Canadian Tiger Swallowtail	9,024	99.95	Proof	90.	—
2014	Red-Spotted Purple	6,018	99.95	Proof	90.	—
2015	Giant Sulphur *(Colias Gigantea)*	3,901	99.95	Proof	90.	—

THE BALD EAGLE SET

TWENTY DOLLARS, THE BALD EAGLE SET, 2013.

Common Obverse

Portrait of Power
Engraver: Eric Boyer

Designers and Engravers:

Obv.:	Susanna Blunt, Susan Taylor
Rev.:	Claudio D'Angelo, See illustrations
Composition:	99.99% Ag
Silver content:	31.39 g, 1.01 tr oz
Weight:	31.39 g
Diameter:	38.0 mm
Thickness:	3.1 mm
Edge:	Plain, Edge lettering "1oz FINE SILVER" "1 oz ARGENT PUR"
Die Axis:	↑↑
Finish:	Proof
Case of Issue:	Maroon clam style case, black flocked insert, encapsulated coin, COA, custom box

Returning From the Hunt
Engraver: RCM Staff

Lifelong Mates
Engraver: RCM Staff

Mother Protecting Her Eaglets
Engraver: Eric Boyer

DATE	DESCRIPTION	QUANTITY SOLD	ISSUE PRICE	FINISH	PR-69	PR-70
2013	Portrait of Power	7,500	99.95	Proof	80.	—
2013	Portrait of Power, No Edge Lettering	Incl. above	99.95	Proof	225.	—
2013	Lifelong Mates	7,499	99.95	Proof	80.	—
2013	Returning From the Hunt	7,498	99.95	Proof	80.	—
2013	Mother Protecting Her Eaglets	7,495	99.95	Proof	80.	—

TWENTY DOLLARS, YEAR OF THE SNAKE, 2013.

Designers: and Engravers:

Obv.:	Susanna Blunt, Susan Taylor
Rev.:	RCM Staff
Composition:	99.99% Ag,
Silver content:	7.96 g, 0.25 tr oz
Weight:	7.96 g
Diameter:	27 mm
Thickness:	N/A
Edge:	Reeded
Die Axis:	↑↑
Finish:	Proof
Case of Issue:	Maroon clam style case, black flocked insert, encapsulated coin, COA

DATE	DESCRIPTION	QUANTITY SOLD	ISSUE PRICE	FINISH	SP-68	SP-69
2013	Year of the Snake	56,798	31.95	Specimen	30.	—

TWENTY DOLLARS, BIRTH OF THE ROYAL INFANT SET, 2013.
This three-coin set commemorates the birth of Prince George of Cambridge on July 22nd, 2013.

Common Obverse	Baby Bears Des.: Laurie McGaw Engr.: Eric Boyer, Cecily Mok	Baby Crib Des.: Laurie McGaw Engr.: RCM Staff	Hands Des.: Laurie McGaw Engr.: Alex Tirabasso

Designers:
  Obv.:   Susanna Blunt
  Rev.:   See reverse illustrations
Composition: 99.99% Ag
Weight: 31.1 to 31.3 g
Diameter: 38.0 mm
Thickness: 3.2 mm
Case of Issue: Maroon clam style case, 3-hole black flocked insert, encapsulated coin, COA, custom box

Engravers:
  Obv.:   Susan Taylor

Silver content: 31.1 g, 1.0 tr oz
Edge: Reeded
Die Axis: ↑↑
Finish: Proof

DATE	DESCRIPTION	QUANTITY SOLD	ISSUE PRICE	FINISH	PR-69	PR-70
2013	Baby Bears	—	N.I.I.	Proof	75.	—
2013	Baby Crib	—	N.I.I.	Proof	75.	—
2013	Hands	—	N.I.I.	Proof	75.	—
—	Set of 3 coins	5,306	249.95	Proof	180.	*

TWENTY DOLLARS, MAPLE LEAF IMPRESSION, 2013-2014.

Common Obverse	Maple Leaf Impression - Red	Maple Leaf Impression - Green

Designers:
  Obv.:   Susanna Blunt
  Rev.:   José Osio
Composition: 99.99% Ag, Enamelled
Silver content: 31.39 g, 1.01 tr oz
Weight: 31.39 g
Diameter: 38.0 mm
Case of Issue: Maroon clam style case, black flocked insert, encapsulated coin, COA

Engravers:
  Obv.:   Susan Taylor
  Rev.:   José Osio
Thickness: 3.1 mm
Edge: Reeded
Die Axis: ↑↑
Finish: Proof

DATE	DESCRIPTION	QUANTITY SOLD	ISSUE PRICE	FINISH	PR-69	PR-70
2013	Maple Leaf Impression - Red	9,176	114.95	Proof	100.	—
2014	Maple Leaf Impression - Green	5,562	114.95	Proof	100.	—

CANADIAN AUTUMN SERIES

WENTY DOLLARS, CANADIAN AUTUMN, 2013-2016.

There's an enchanting, almost mystical glow to Canada's forests on a sunny autumn day, when the colourful foliage beckons to be admired up-
se. With these beautifully coloured fine silver coins, relive the magic of a journey outdoors on such a day, when nature provides countless sights,
:hanting wonders and new discoveries to be made along the way.

Common Obverse

Designers and Engravers:

Obv.:	Susanna Blunt, Susan Taylor
Rev.:	See reverse illustrations
Composition:	99.99% Ag, Coloured
Silver content:	31.39 g, 1.01 tr oz
Weight:	31.39 g
Diameter:	38.0 mm
Thickness:	3.1 mm **Die Axis:** ↑↑
Edge:	Reeded **Finish:** Proof
Case of Issue:	Maroon clam style case, black flocked insert, encapsulated coin, COA custom box

2013 - Autumn Bliss
Designer: Tony Bianco
Engraver: Matt Bowen

2014 - Autumn Falls
Designer: Tony Bianco
Engraver: RCM Staff

2015 - Autumn Allure
Designer: Emily Damstra
Engraver: RCM Staff

2016 - Autumn Tranquility
Designer: Tony Bianco
Engraver: RCM Staff

DATE	DESCRIPTION	QUANTITY SOLD	ISSUE PRICE	FINISH	PR-69	PR-70
2013	Autumn Bliss	7,498	99.95	Proof	100.	—
2014	Autumn Falls	7,469	99.95	Proof	90.	—
2015	Autumn Express	5,315	109.95	Proof	110.	—
2016	Autumn Tranquility	3,998	102.95	Proof	105.	*

SUPERMAN™ SERIES

TWENTY DOLLARS, 75TH ANNIVERSARY OF SUPERMAN™ SET, 2013.

| Common Obverse | Man of Steel
Engraver: Samantha Strath | Metropolis
Engraver: Samantha Strath | The Shield
Engraver: Susan Taylor |

Designers:
Obv.: Susanna Blunt
Rev.: DC Comics/Warner Brothers
Composition: 99.99% Ag
Weight: 31.0 to 31.2 g
Diameter: 38.0 mm
Thickness: 3.1 mm
Case of Issue: Clear plastic cover, black plastic coin display, encapsulated coin, COA, custom box

Engravers:
Obv.: Susan Taylor
Rev.: See reverse illustrations
Silver content: 31.0 g, 1.0 tr oz
Edge: Reeded
Die Axis: ↑↑
Finish: Proof

DATE	DESCRIPTION	QUANTITY SOLD	ISSUE PRICE	FINISH	PR-69	PR-7(
2013	Man of Steel™, Painted	9,984	109.75	Proof	130.	—
2013	Metropolis, Achromatic Hologram	9,994	129.75	Proof	130.	—
2013	The Shield, Dual Enamel	9,976	119.75	Proof	130.	—

DINOSAURS OF CANADA SERIES

TWENTY DOLLARS, DINOSAURS OF CANADA SERIES, 2013-2015.

This series, whose renderings have been verified by the Royal Tyrrell Museum of Palaeontology, features prehistoric dinosaurs discovered in Canada.

| Common Obverse | Bathygnathus Borealis |

Designers and Engravers:
Obv.: Susanna Blunt, Susan Taylor
Rev.: Julius Csotonyi, Steven Stewart
Composition: 99.99% Ag
Silver content: 31.39 g, 1.0 tr oz
Weight: 31.39 g
Diameter: 38.0 mm
Thickness: 3.1 mm
Edge: Reeded
Die Axis: ↑↑
Finish: Proof
Case of Issue: Maroon clam style case, black flocked insert, encapsulated coin, COA

| Scutellosaurus | Xenoceratops Foremostensis | Albertosaurus |

ᐧENTY DOLLARS, DINOSAURS OF CANADA SERIES, 2013-2015, PRICING TABLE.

DATE	DESCRIPTION	QUANTITY SOLD	ISSUE PRICE	FINISH	PR-69	PR-70
2013	Bathygnathus Borealis	7,973	89.95	Proof	80.	—
2014	Scutellosaurus	5,245	89.95	Proof	80.	—
2014	Xenoceratops Foremostensis	4,321	89.95	Proof	80.	—
2015	Albertosaurus	1,970	89.95	Proof	80.	—

A STORY OF THE NORTHERN LIGHTS SERIES

ᐧENTY DOLLARS, A STORY OF THE NORTHERN LIGHTS SERIES, 2013-2015.

Common Obverse

Designers and Engravers:
Obv.: Susanna Blunt, Susan Taylor
Rev.: Nathalie Bertin, See reverse illustrations
Composition: 99.99% Ag, Hologram
Thickness: 3.0 mm
Silver content: 30.4 g, 0.98 tr oz   **Edge:** Reeded
Weight: 2013-2014: 30.4 g   **Die Axis:** ↑↑
2015: 31.39 g
Diameter: 2013-2014: 37.8 mm   **Finish:** Proof
2015: 38 mm
Case of Issue: Maroon clam style case, black flocked insert, encapsulated coin, COA

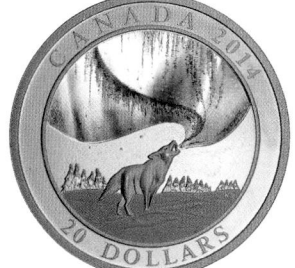

2013 - The Great Hare
Designer: Nathalie Bertin
Engraver: Samantha Strath

2014 - Howling Wolf
Designer: Nathalie Bertin
Engraver: RCM Staff

2015 - The Raven
Designer: Nathalie Bertin
Engraver: RCM Staff

DATE	DESCRIPTION	QUANTITY SOLD	ISSUE PRICE	FINISH	PR-69	PR-70
2013	The Great Hare	8,492	109.95	Proof	100.	—
2014	Howling Wolf	8,500	109.95	Proof	100.	—
2015	The Raven	6,886	109.95	Proof	100.	—

ᐧENTY DOLLARS, 50TH ANNIVERSARY OF CANADIAN PEACEKEEPING IN CYPRUS, 2014.

Designers and Engravers:
Obv.: Susanna Blunt, Susan Taylor
Rev.: Sylvia Pecota, Matt Bowen
Composition: 99.99% Ag, Blue enamel
Silver content: 31.39 g, 1.01 tr oz
Weight: 31.39 g
Diameter: 37.9 mm
Thickness: 3.0 mm
Edge: Reeded
Die Axis: ↑↑
Finish: Proof
Case of Issue: Maroon clam style case, black flocked insert, encapsulated coin, COA

DATE	DESCRIPTION	QUANTITY SOLD	ISSUE PRICE	FINISH	PR-69	PR-70
2014	50th Anniv. of Canadian Peacekeeping in Cyprus	3,511	114.95	Proof	90.	—

PREHISTORIC ANIMALS SERIES

TWENTY DOLLARS (1 OUNCE), PREHISTORIC ANIMALS, 2014-2015.

This $20 Woolly Mammoth was also issued in a set of two coins (see page 560), the second coin being the 1/10 ounce $5 gold maple (see page 42)

| Common Obverse | The Woolly Mammoth
Designer: M. Skrepnick | American Scimitar Sabre-Tooth Cat
Designer: Julius Csotonyi |

Designers:
Obv.:   Susanna Blunt
Rev.:   See reverse illustrations
Rev.:   M. Skrepnick, RCM Staff
Composition: 99.99% Ag
Silver content: 31.39 g, 1.0 tr oz
Weight: 31.39 g
Diameter: 38.0 mm
Thickness: N/A
Case of Issue: Maroon leatherette clam style case, black flocked insert, encapsulated coin, COA

Engravers:
Obv.:   Susan Taylor

Edge: Reeded
Die Axis: ↑↑
Finish: Proof

DATE	DESCRIPTION	QUANTITY SOLD	ISSUE PRICE	FINISH	PR-69	PR-70
2014	The Woolly Mammoth (1 oz)	7,502	89.95	Proof	80.	—
2015	Prehistoric Animals: American Scimitar Sabre-Tooth Cat	4,086	89.95	Proof	80.	—

TWENTY DOLLARS, POND HOCKEY, 2014.

Designers and Engravers:
Obv.:   Susanna Blunt, Susan Taylor
Rev.:   Richard DeWolfe, Matt Bowen
Composition: 99.99% Ag, Coloured
Silver content: 31.2 g, 1.0 tr oz
Weight: 31.2 g
Diameter: 37.9 mm
Thickness: 3.1 mm
Edge: Reeded
Die Axis: ↑↑
Finish: Proof
Case of Issue: Maroon clam style case, black flocked insert, encapsulated coin, COA

DATE	DESCRIPTION	QUANTITY SOLD	ISSUE PRICE	FINISH	PR-69	PR-70
2014	Pond Hockey	8,488	99.95	Proof	90.	—

ICONIC SUPERMAN™ COMIC BOOK COVERS

TWENTY DOLLARS, *ICONIC SUPERMAN*™ COMIC BOOK COVERS, 2014-2015.

Common Obverse:

Designers and Engravers:

Obv.:	Susanna Blunt, Susan Taylor
Rev.:	DC Comics/Warner Bros., RCM Staff
Composition:	99.99% Ag, Coloured
Silver content:	31.39 g, 1.0 tr oz
Weight:	31.39 g
Diameter:	38.0 mm
Thickness:	N/A
Edge:	Reeded
Die Axis:	↑↑
Finish:	Proof
Case of Issue:	Custom case, black flocked insert, encapsulated coin, COA

Superman Annual #1 (2012) · *Action Comics #1 (2011)* · *Superman Unchained #2 (2013)* · *Superman #28 (2014)*

DATE	DESCRIPTION	QUANTITY SOLD	ISSUE PRICE	FINISH	PR-69	PR-70
2014	Iconic Superman™ Comic Book Covers: Superman Annual #1 (2012)	9,999	109.95	Proof	100.	—
2015	Iconic Superman™ Comic Book Covers: Action Comics #1 (2011)	10,000	109.95	Proof	100.	—
2015	Iconic Superman™ Comic Book Covers: Superman Unchained #2 (2013)	9,988	109.95	Proof	100.	—
2015	Iconic Superman™ Comic Book Covers: Superman #28 (2014)	9,990	109.95	Proof	100.	—

TWENTY DOLLARS, VENETIAN GLASS SNOWMAN, 2014.

Designers and Engravers:

Obv.:	Susanna Blunt, Susan Taylor
Rev.:	Julius Csotonyi, RCM Staff
Composition:	99.99% Ag, Coloured Murano glass
Silver content:	31.2 g, 1.0 tr oz
Weight:	31.2 g
Diameter:	37.9 mm
Thickness:	3.0 mm
Edge:	Reeded
Die Axis:	↑↑
Finish:	Proof
Case of Issue:	Maroon clam style case, black flocked insert, encapsulated coin, COA

DATE	DESCRIPTION	QUANTITY SOLD	ISSUE PRICE	FINISH	PR-69	PR-70
2014	Venetian Glass Snowman	10,000	149.95	Proof	140.	—

THE GREAT LAKES SERIES

TWENTY DOLLARS, THE GREAT LAKES SERIES, 2014-2015.
Bathymetric maps of the five Great Lakes are detailed by a raised image on these twenty dollar silver coins.

Common Obverse

Lake Superior

Lake Ontario

Lake Erie

Lake Huron

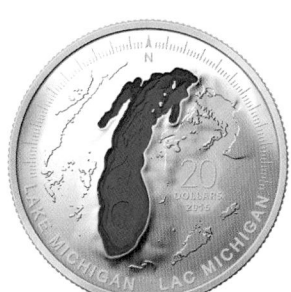

Lake Michigan

Designers:		**Engravers:**	
Obv.:	Susanna Blunt	Obv.:	Susan Taylor
Rev.:	RCM Staff	Rev.:	Eric Boyer
Composition:	99.99% Ag, Enamelled		
Silver content:	31.1 g, 1.0 tr oz		
Weight:	31.1 g	**Edge:**	Reeded
Diameter:	37.9 mm	**Die Axis:**	↑↑
Thickness:	3.1 mm	**Finish:**	Proof
Case of Issue:	Singly: Maroon clam style case, black flocked insert, encapsulated coin, COA		
	Subscription: Five-hole maple wood display case, black flocked insert, encapsulated coins, COA		

DATE	DESCRIPTION	QUANTITY SOLD	ISSUE PRICE	FINISH	PR-69	PR-70
2014	Lake Superior	9,992	114.95	Proof	100.	—
2014	Lake Ontario	9,680	114.95	Proof	115.	—
2014	Lake Erie	9,842	114.95	Proof	90.	—
2015	Lake Huron	8,071	114.95	Proof	100.	—
2015	Lake Michigan	8,284	114.95	Proof	100.	—

WENTY DOLLARS, THE WOODLAND CARIBOU, 2014.

Designers and Engravers:

Obv.:	Susanna Blunt, Susan Taylor
Rev.:	Trevor Tennant, Samantha Strath
Composition:	99.99% Ag, Coloured
Silver content:	31.2 g, 1.0 tr oz
Weight:	31.2 g
Diameter:	38.0 mm
Thickness:	3.1 mm
Edge:	Reeded
Die Axis:	↑↑
Finish:	Proof
Case of Issue:	Maroon clam style case, black flocked insert, encapsulated coin, COA

DATE	DESCRIPTION	QUANTITY SOLD	ISSUE PRICE	FINISH	PR-69	PR-70
2014	The Woodland Caribou	8,493	99.95	Proof	100.	—

WENTY DOLLARS, ICONIC POLAR BEAR, 2014.

Designers and Engravers:

Obv.:	Susanna Blunt, Susan Taylor
Rev.:	Glen Loates, Alex Tirabasso
Composition:	99.99% Ag, Coloured
Silver content:	31.2 g, 1.0 tr oz
Weight:	31.2 g
Diameter:	38.0 mm
Thickness:	3.1 mm
Edge:	Reeded
Die Axis:	↑↑
Finish:	Proof
Case of Issue:	Maroon clam style case, black flocked insert, encapsulated coin, COA

DATE	DESCRIPTION	QUANTITY SOLD	ISSUE PRICE	FINISH	PR-69	PR-70
2014	Iconic Polar Bear	8,500	99.95	Proof	100.	—

WENTY DOLLARS, 100TH ANNIVERSARY OF THE ROYAL ONTARIO MUSEUM, 2014.

Celebrating the centennial of the Royal Ontario Museum, this coin's reverse features the Statue of Cleopatra VII, purchased in the early 1900s by e museum's first director, with Michael-Lee Chin's crystalline shaped architectural design.

Designers and Engravers:

Obv.:	Susanna Blunt, Susan Taylor
Rev.:	Cecily Mok, Christie Paquet
Composition:	99.99% Ag, Sel.gold plated
Silver content:	31.39 g, 1.01 tr oz
Weight:	31.39 g
Diameter:	38.0 mm
Thickness:	3.0 mm
Edge:	Reeded
Die Axis:	↑↑
Finish:	Proof
Case of Issue:	Maroon clam style case, black flocked insert, encapsulated coin, COA

DATE	DESCRIPTION	QUANTITY SOLD	ISSUE PRICE	FINISH	PR-69	PR-70
2014	100th Anniv. of the Royal Ontario Museum	6,299	114.95	Proof	100.	—

TWENTY DOLLARS, RIVER RAPIDS, 2014.

This coin celebrates Canadian artist E. Robert Ross' painting depicting a set of rapids on the Madawaska River in Algonquin Provincial Park.

Designers and Engravers:

Obv.:	Susanna Blunt, Susan Taylor
Rev.:	E. Robert Ross, RCM Staff
Composition:	99.99% Ag, Painted, Engraved
Silver content:	31.39 g, 1.0 tr oz
Weight:	31.39 g
Diameter:	38.0 mm
Thickness:	3.1 mm **Die Axis:** ↑↑
Edge:	Reeded **Finish:** Proof
Case of Issue:	Maroon clam style case, black flocked insert, encapsulated coin, COA

DATE	DESCRIPTION	QUANTITY SOLD	ISSUE PRICE	FINISH	PR-69	PR-70
2014	River Rapids	14,086	99.95	Proof	90.	—

THE WOOD BISON SET

TWENTY DOLLARS, THE WOOD BISON SET, 2014.

Common Obverse

A Portrait
Designer: Doug Comeau
Engraver: Alex Tirabasso

Designers and Engravers:

Obv.:	Susanna Blunt, Susan Taylor
Rev.:	See reverse illustrations
Composition:	99.99% Ag
Silver content:	31.39 g, 1.01 tr oz
Weight:	31.39 g
Diameter:	38.0 mm
Thickness:	3.1 mm
Edge:	Plain, Edge lettering "1 OZ FINE SILVER 1 OZ ARGENT PUR"
Die Axis:	↑↑
Finish:	Proof
Case of Issue:	Maroon clam style case, black flocked insert, encapsulated coin, COA

The Bull and His Mate
Designer: Doug Comeau
Engraver: Matt Bowen

The Fight
Designer: Claudio D'Angelo
Engraver: Samantha Strath

A Family at Rest
Designer: Claudio D'Angelo
Engraver: RCM Staff

DATE	DESCRIPTION	QUANTITY SOLD	ISSUE PRICE	FINISH	PR-69	PR-70
2014	A Portrait	7,480	99.95	Proof	90.	—
2014	The Bull and his Mate	7,500	99.95	Proof	90.	—
2014	The Fight	7,501	99.95	Proof	90.	—
2014	A Family at Rest	7,498	99.95	Proof	90.	—

THE LEGEND OF NANABOOZHOO SET

WENTY DOLLARS, THE LEGEND OF NANABOOZHOO SET, 2014.

Nanaboozhoo is an important cultural character of the Anishinaase. He is a shape-shifting spirit that teaches right from wrong through his adventures.

| Common Obverse | Nanaboozhoo and the Thunderbird's Nest Engraver: José Osio | Nanaboozhoo and the Thunderbird Engraver: José Osio | Legend of Nanaboozhoo Engraver: Steven Stewart |

esigners:
  Obv.: Susanna Blunt
  Rev.: Cyril Assiniboine
omposition: 99.99% Ag
eight: 31.39 g
ameter: 38.0 mm
ickness: 3.1 mm
ase of Issue: Maroon clam style case, black flocked insert, encapsulated coin, COA

Engravers:
  Obv.: Susan Taylor
  Rev.: See reverse illustrations
Silver content: 31.39 g, 1.01 tr oz
Edge: Reeded
Die Axis: ↑↑
Finish: Proof

DATE	DESCRIPTION	QUANTITY SOLD	ISSUE PRICE	FINISH	PR-69	PR-70
2014	Nanaboozhoo and the Thunderbird's Nest	5,500	89.95	Proof	90.	—
2014	Nanaboozhoo and the Thunderbird, Selectively gold plated	5,500	114.95	Proof	90.	—
2014	Legend of Nanaboozhoo, Coloured	6,856	99.95	Proof	90.	—

LOST SHIPS IN CANADIAN WATERS SERIES

WENTY DOLLARS, LOST SHIPS IN CANADIAN WATERS, 2014-2015.

| Common Obverse | R.M.S. *Empress of Ireland* | Franklin's Lost Expedition | S.S. *Edmund Fitzgerald* |

esigners:
  Obv.: Susanna Blunt
  Rev.: John Horton
omposition: 99.99% Ag, Coloured
eight: 31.39 g
iameter: 38.0 mm
ickness: N/A
nish: Proof
ase of Issue: Maroon clam style case, black flocked insert, encapsulated coin, COA, custom box

Engravers:
  Obv.: Susan Taylor
  Rev.: RCM Staff
Silver content: 31.39 g, 1.01 tr oz
Edge: 2014: Plain with edge lettering
  2015: Plain with edge lettering
Die Axis: ↑↑

DATE	DESCRIPTION	QUANTITY SOLD	ISSUE PRICE	FINISH	PR-69	PR-70
2014	R.M.S. *Empress of Ireland*	7,003	109.95	Proof	90.	—
2015	Franklin's Lost Expedition	6,994	109.95	Proof	90.	—
2015	S.S. *Edmund Fitzgerald*	5,215	109.95	Proof	90.	—

THE BALD EAGLE SET

TWENTY DOLLARS, THE BALD EAGLE SET, 2014.

Common Obverse

Designers and Engravers:

Obv.:	Susanna Blunt, Susan Taylor
Rev.:	See reverse illustrations
Composition:	99.99% Ag
Silver content:	31.83 g, 1.01 tr oz
Weight:	31.83 g
Diameter:	38.0 mm
Thickness:	3.1 mm
Edge:	Reeded
Die Axis:	↑↑
Finish:	Proof
Case of Issue:	Maroon clam style case, black flocked insert, encapsulated coin, CO

Bald Eagle with Fish
Designer: Claudio D'Angelo
Engraver: Steven Stewart

Perched Bald Eagle
Selectively gold plated
Designer: Claudio D'Angelo
Engraver: Steven Stewart

Soaring Bald Eagle
Coloured
Designer: Claudio D'Angelo
Engraver: Eric Boyer

DATE	DESCRIPTION	QUANTITY SOLD	ISSUE PRICE	FINISH	PR-69	PR-70
2014	Bald Eagle with Fish, Proof	7,582	89.95	Proof	80.	—
2014	Perched Bald Eagle, Proof, Selectively gold plated	8,500	114.95	Proof	80.	—
2014	Soaring Bald Eagle, Proof with colour	8,498	99.95	Proof	80.	—

TWENTY DOLLARS, 75TH ANNIVERSARY OF THE FIRST ROYAL VISIT, 1939-2014.

Engraved from an archival photograph, the coin depicts King George VI and Queen Elizabeth standing on a train's platform.

Designers and Engravers:

Obv.:	Susanna Blunt, Susan Taylor
Rev.:	RCM Staff
Composition:	99.99% Ag
Silver content:	31.39 g, 1.01 tr oz
Weight:	31.39 g
Diameter:	38.0 mm
Thickness:	N/A
Edge:	Reeded
Die Axis:	↑↑
Finish:	Proof, Antique
Case of Issue:	Maroon clam style case, black flocked insert, encapsulated coin, COA, custom box

DATE	DESCRIPTION	QUANTITY SOLD	ISSUE PRICE	FINISH	PR-69	PR-70
2014 (1939-)	75th Anniversary of the First Royal Visit	4,995	139.95	Proof	110.	—

WENTY DOLLARS, ROYAL GENERATIONS, 2014.

Designed from an interpretation of a press photograph taken by Cathy Bursey-Sabourin, four generations of the Royal Family are depicted on the in's reverse: Queen Elizabeth II, Prince Charles, Prince William and Prince George.

Designers and Engravers:

Obv.:	Susanna Blunt, Susan Taylor
Rev.:	C. Bursey-Sabourin, RCM Staff
Composition:	99.99% Ag
Silver content:	31.39 g, 1.01 tr oz
Weight:	31.39 g
Diameter:	38.0 mm
Thickness:	N/A
Edge:	Reeded
Die Axis:	↑↑
Finish:	Proof
Case of Issue:	Maroon clam style case, black flocked insert, encapsulated coin, COA

DATE	DESCRIPTION	QUANTITY SOLD	ISSUE PRICE	FINISH	PR-69	PR-70
2014	Royal Generations	5,732	89.95	Proof	80.	—

STAINED GLASS SET

WENTY DOLLARS, STAINED GLASS SET, 2014.

Covered in translucent enamel, the Stained Glass set replicates memorable stained glass pieces in Canada from the windows of Craigdarroch astle in Victoria, British Columbia, to the McCausland stained glass dome in Casa Loma.

Common Obverse   **Craigdarroch Castle**   **Casa Loma**

esigners:		Engravers:	
Obv.:	Susanna Blunt	Obv.:	Susan Taylor
Rev.:	RCM Staff	Rev.:	RCM Staff
omposition:	99.99% Ag, Coloured		
lver content:	31.39 g, 1.01 tr oz		
eight:	31.39 g	Edge:	Reeded
ameter:	38.0 mm	Die Axis:	↑↑
hickness:	N/A	Finish:	Proof
ase of Issue:	Maroon clam style case, black flocked insert, encapsulated coin, COA		

DATE	DESCRIPTION	QUANTITY SOLD	ISSUE PRICE	FINISH	PR-69	PR-70
2014	Craigdarroch Castle	4,980	129.95	Proof	110.	—
2014	Casa Loma	3,238	129.95	Proof	110.	—

BABY ANIMALS SERIES

TWENTY DOLLARS, BABY ANIMALS SERIES, 2014-2016.

| Common Obverse | 2014 - The Beaver
Designer: Glen Loates | 2014 - Atlantic Puffin
Designer: Glen Loates | 2015 - Burrowing Owl
Designer: Arnold Nogy |

| 2015 - Black Bear
Designer: Clinton Jammer | 2015 - Mountain Goat
Designer: Glen Loates | 2015 - White-Tailed Deer
Designer: Glen Loates | 2015 - Porcupine
Designer: Trevor Tennant |

| 2016 - Raccoon
Designer: Trevor Tennant | 2016 - Common Loon
Designer: Glen Loates | 2016 - Caribou
Designer: Glen Loates | 2016 - Woodchuck
Designer: Michelle Grant |

Designers:		**Engravers:**	
Obv.:	Susanna Blunt	Obv.:	Susan Taylor
Rev.:	See reverse illustrations		
Composition:	99.99% Ag, Coloured	**Silver content:**	31.39 g, 1.01 tr oz
Weight:	31.39 g	**Edge:**	Reeded
Diameter:	38.0 mm	**Die Axis:**	↑↑
Thickness:	N/A	**Finish:**	Proof
Case of Issue:	Maroon clam style case, black flocked insert, encapsulated coin, COA		

TWENTY DOLLARS, BABY ANIMALS SERIES, 2014-2016, PRICING TABLE.

DATE	DESCRIPTION	QUANTITY SOLD	ISSUE PRICE	FINISH	PR-69	PR-70
2014	The Beaver	7,500	99.95	Proof	90.	—
2014	Atlantic Puffin	7,500	99.95	Proof	90.	—
2015	Burrowing Owl	7,716	99.95	Proof	90.	—
2015	Black Bear	7,502	99.95	Proof	90.	—
2015	Mountain Goat	7,482	99.95	Proof	90.	—
2015	White-Tailed Deer	7,448	99.95	Proof	90.	—
2015	Porcupine	6,961	99.95	Proof	90.	—
2016	Raccoon	4,004	99.95	Proof	100.	—
2016	Common Loon	3,908	99.95	Proof	100.	—
2016	Caribou	3,500	99.95	Proof	100.	—
2016	Woodchuck	3,383	99.95	Proof	100.	—

TWENTY DOLLARS, 75TH ANNIVERSARY OF THE ROYAL WINNIPEG BALLET, 2014.

Celebrating the 75th anniversary of the Royal Winnipeg ballet's inception, the coin comes in a music box that plays Tchaikovsky's Sleeping Beauty, a short period of time.

Designers and Engravers:

Obv.:	Susanna Blunt, Susan Taylor
Rev.:	David Cooper, RCM Staff
Composition:	99.99% Ag
Silver content:	31.6 g, 1.02 tr oz
Weight:	31.6 g
Diameter:	40.0 mm
Thickness:	N/A
Edge:	Reeded
Die Axis:	↑↑
Finish:	Proof
Case of Issue:	Grey and peach paperboard case, grey insert, encapsulated coin, COA

DATE	DESCRIPTION	QUANTITY SOLD	ISSUE PRICE	FINISH	PR-69	PR-70
2014	75th Anniversary of the Royal Winnipeg Ballet	7,499	99.95	Proof	90.	—

TWENTY DOLLARS, CELEBRATING EMILY CARR: TOTEM FOREST, 2014.

As one of Canada's most important artists, this coin features Emily Carr's iconic 1930 painting, Totem Forest. This coin was also issued in a three in set which includes a $200 gold (page 456) and a $300 platinum coin (page 504).

Designers and Engravers:

Obv.:	Susanna Blunt, Susan Taylor
Rev.:	Emily Carr, RCM Staff
Composition:	99.99% Ag
Silver content:	31.39 g, 1.01 tr oz
Weight:	31.39 g
Diameter:	38.0 mm
Thickness:	N/A	**Die Axis:**	↑↑
Edge:	Reeded	**Finish:**	Proof
Case of Issue:	Maroon clam style case, black flocked insert, encapsulated coin, COA, graphic, box

DATE	DESCRIPTION	QUANTITY SOLD	ISSUE PRICE	FINISH	PR-69	PR-70
2014	Celebrating Emily Carr: Totem Forest	4,459	89.95	Proof	90.	—

INTERCONNECTIONS SET

TWENTY DOLLARS, INTERCONNECTIONS SET, 2014.

Featuring the artwork of Andy Everson, the set celebrates the interconnectedness between landscape and nature.

Common Obverse

Designers and Engravers:

Obv.:	Susanna Blunt, Susan Taylor
Rev.:	Andy Everson, RCM Staff
Composition:	99.99% Ag, Hologram
Silver content:	31.39 g, 1.01 tr oz
Weight:	31.39 g
Diameter:	38.0 mm
Thickness:	N/A
Edge:	Reeded
Die Axis:	↑↑
Finish:	Proof
Case of Issue:	Maroon clam style case, black flocked insert, encapsulated coin, COA

Land - The Beaver

Air - The Thunderbird

Sea - The Orca

DATE	DESCRIPTION	QUANTITY SOLD	ISSUE PRICE	FINISH	PR-69	PR-70
2014	Land - The Beaver	4,415	114.95	Proof	115.	—
2014	Air - The Thunderbird	2,754	114.95	Proof	115.	—
2014	Sea - The Orca	2,343	114.95	Proof	115.	—

TWENTY DOLLARS, CHICKADEE WITH WINTER BERRIES, 2014.

Designers and Engravers:

Obv.:	Susanna Blunt, Susan Taylor
Rev.:	Steve Hepburn, RCM Staff
Composition:	99.99% Ag, Swarovski Crystals
Silver content:	31.39 g, 1.01 tr oz
Weight:	31.39 g
Diameter:	38.0 mm
Thickness:	N/A
Edge:	Reeded
Die Axis:	↑↑
Finish:	Proof
Case of Issue:	Maroon clam style case, black flocked insert, encapsulated coin, COA

DATE	DESCRIPTION	QUANTITY SOLD	ISSUE PRICE	FINISH	PR-69	PR-70
2014	Chickadee with Winter Berries	5,724	114.95	Proof	115.	—

WENTY DOLLARS, 25TH ANNIVERSARY OF THE CANADIAN SPACE AGENCY, 1989-2014.

This coin features an achromatic hologram showcasing a Canadian astronaut anchored to the Canadarm2.

Designers and Engravers:
Obv.:	Susanna Blunt, Susan Taylor
Rev.:	RCM Staff

Composition: 99.99% Ag, Hologram
Silver content: 31.39 g, 1.01 tr oz
Weight: 31.39 g
Diameter: 38.0 mm
Thickness: N/A   **Die Axis:** ↑↑
Edge: Reeded   **Finish:** Proof
Case of Issue: Maroon clam style case, black flocked insert, encapsulated coin, COA, custom box

DATE	DESCRIPTION	QUANTITY SOLD	ISSUE PRICE	FINISH	PR-69	PR-70
2014 (1989-)	25th Anniversary of the Canadian Space Agency	4,042	119.95	Proof	110.	—

MAJESTIC MAPLE LEAVES SERIES

WENTY DOLLARS, MAJESTIC MAPLE LEAVES, 2014-2017.

The 2014 Majestic Maple Leaves were also issued as part of a five-coin subscription. Please see the $5 Gold coin (page 426) and $5 Platinum coin (page 502).

2014 Common Obverse	**2014 Majestic Maple Leaves** Designer: Pierre Leduc	**2014 Majestic Maple Leaves, Coloured** Designer: Pierre Leduc	**2014 Majestic Maple Leaves, With Jade** Designer: Pierre Leduc

2016 Obverse	**2016 Majestic Maple Leaves, With Drusy Stone** Designer: Tony Bianco	**2017 Obverse**	**2017 Majestic Maple Leaves With Drusy Stone** Designer: Lisa Thomson-Khan

Designers:
Obv.:	Susanna Blunt
Rev.:	See reverse illustrations

Composition: 99.99% Ag
Weight: 31.39 g
Diameter: 38.0 mm
Thickness: N/A
Case of Issue: Singly: Maroon clam style case, black flocked insert, encapsulated coin, COA; 2014 Set: 3-hole wood case, black flocked insert

Engravers:
Obv.:	Susan Taylor

Silver content: 31.39 g, 1.01 tr oz
Edge: Reeded
Die Axis: ↑↑
Finish: Proof

TWENTY DOLLARS, MAJESTIC MAPLE LEAVES, 2014-2017, PRICING TABLE.

DATE	DESCRIPTION	QUANTITY SOLD	ISSUE PRICE	FINISH	PR-69	PR-70
2014	Majestic Maple Leaves	6,519	89.95	Proof	80.	—
2014	Majestic Maple Leaves, Coloured	6,021	99.95	Proof	90.	—
2014	Majestic Maple Leaves, With Jade	5,116	114.95	Proof	100.	—
2016	Majestic Maple Leaves, With Drusy Stone	3,999	159.95	Proof	150.	—
2017	Majestic Maple Leaves, With Drusy Stone	4,000	161.95	Proof	162.	—

THE WHITE-TAILED DEER SET

TWENTY DOLLARS, THE WHITE-TAILED DEER SET, 2014.

Common Obverse

Portrait
Designer: Desmond McCaffrey
Engraver: RCM Staff

Designers and Engravers:

Obv.:	Susanna Blunt, Susan Taylor
Rev.:	See reverse illustrations
Composition:	99.99% Ag
Silver content:	31.39 g, 1.01 tr oz
Weight:	31.39 g
Diameter:	38.0 mm
Thickness:	3.1 mm
Edge:	Plain Edge Lettering "1OZ FINE SILVER 9999 1OZ ARGENT PUR 9999"
Die Axis:	↑↑
Finish:	Proof
Case of Issue:	Maroon clam style case, black flocked insert, encapsulated coin, COA, custom box

A Challenge
Designer: Desmond McCaffrey
Engraver: RCM Staff

Mates
Designer: Claudio D'Angelo
Engraver: RCM Staff

A Doe and Her Fawns
Designer: Trevor Tennant
Engraver: RCM Staff

DATE	DESCRIPTION	QUANTITY SOLD	ISSUE PRICE	FINISH	PR-69	PR-70
2014	Portrait	6,503	99.95	Proof	90.	—
2014	A Challenge	6,682	99.95	Proof	90.	—
2014	Mates	5,212	99.95	Proof	90.	—
2014	A Doe and Her Fawns	4,960	99.95	Proof	90.	—

TWENTY DOLLARS, 100TH ANNIVERSARY OF HOCKEY CANADA, 2014.

Featuring a red and black enamel application, this coin celebrates the 100th anniversary of the founding of the Canadian Amateur Hockey Association (CAHA), a precursor to Hockey Canada.

Designers and Engravers:

Obv.:	Susanna Blunt, Susan Taylor
Rev.:	Team Canada Logo™, RCM Staff
Composition:	99.99% Ag, Enamelled
Silver content:	31.39 g, 1.01 tr oz
Weight:	31.39 g
Diameter:	38.0 mm
Thickness:	N/A
Edge:	Reeded
Die Axis:	↑↑
Finish:	Proof
Case of Issue:	Red paperboard case, black flocked insert, encapsulated coin, COA

DATE	DESCRIPTION	QUANTITY SOLD	ISSUE PRICE	FINISH	PR-69	PR-70
2014	100th Anniversary of Hockey Canada	7,489	119.95	Proof	120.	—

THE COUGAR SET

TWENTY DOLLARS, THE COUGAR SET, 2014.

Common Obverse

Obverse Selectively Gold Plated

Designers and Engravers:

Obv.:	Susanna Blunt, Susan Taylor
Rev.:	See reverse illustrations
Composition:	99.99% Ag
Silver content:	31.39 g, 1.01 tr oz
Weight:	31.39 g
Diameter:	38.0 mm
Thickness:	N/A
Edge:	Reeded
Die Axis:	↑↑
Finish:	Proof
Case of Issue:	
Singly:	Maroon clam style case, black flocked insert, encapsulated coin, COA
Subscription:	3-hole wood case, black flocked insert, encapsulated coins, COA

Atop A Mountain
Designer: Glen Loates
Engraver: RCM Staff

Perched On A Maple Tree
Designer: Glen Loates
Engraver: RCM Staff

Pouncing In The Snow
Designer: Maurade Bayton
Engraver: RCM Staff

DATE	DESCRIPTION	QUANTITY SOLD	ISSUE PRICE	FINISH	PR-69	PR-70
2014	Atop A Mountain	4,884	89.95	Proof	90.	—
2014	Perched On A Maple Tree, Coloured	3,845	99.95	Proof	90.	—
2014	Pouicing In The Snow, Selectively Gold Plated	3,605	114.95	Proof	90.	—

THE SEVEN SACRED TEACHINGS SET

TWENTY DOLLARS, THE SEVEN SACRED TEACHINGS SET, 2014.

Reflecting the wisdom gleaned by the Anishinaabe people, this seven coin set features the Woodland style artwork of Métis artist Nathalie Berti

Common Obverse

Love
Engraver: Konrad Wachelko

Respect
Engraver: A. Tirabasso, E. Boyer

Courage
Engraver: Steven Stewart

Wisdom
Engraver: RCM Staff

Honesty
Engraver: RCM Staff

Humility
Engraver: RCM Staff

Truth
Engraver: RCM Staff

Designers:
Obv.:   Susanna Blunt
Rev.:   Nathalie Bertin
Composition: 99.99% Ag, Selectively gold plated
Silver content: 31.83 g, 1.02 tr oz
Weight: 31.83 g
Diameter: 40.0 mm
Thickness: 2.9 mm
Case of Issue: Maroon clam style case, black flocked insert, encapsulated coin, with custom beauty box, COA

Engravers:
Obv.:   Susan Taylor
Rev.:   See reverse illustrations

Edge: Reeded
Die Axis: ↑↑
Finish: Proof

DATE	DESCRIPTION	QUANTITY SOLD	ISSUE PRICE	FINISH	PR-69	PR-70
2014	Love	6,761	109.95	Proof	100.	—
2014	Respect	5,404	109.95	Proof	100.	—
2014	Courage	3,443	109.95	Proof	100.	—
2014	Wisdom	4,211	109.95	Proof	100.	—
2014	Honesty	4,000*	109.95	Proof	100.	—
2014	Humility	4,121	109.95	Proof	100.	—
2014	Truth	4,337	109.95	Proof	100.	—

* The actual mintage figure for Honesty is missing in the 2014 Annual Report. The mintage shown is an estimate.

MAJESTIC ANIMALS SERIES

WENTY DOLLARS, THE MAJESTIC MOOSE, 2015.

Designers and Engravers:
Obv.:	Susanna Blunt, Susan Taylor
Rev.:	Claudio D'Angelo, RCM Staff

Composition: 99.99% Ag, Coloured
Silver content: 31.39 g, 1.01 tr oz
Weight: 31.39 g
Diameter: 38.0 mm
Thickness: N/A
Edge: Reeded
Die Axis: ↑↑
Finish: Proof
Case of Issue: Maroon clam style case, black flocked insert, encapsulated coin, COA

WENTY DOLLARS, BIGHORN SHEEP, 2015.

Designers and Engravers:
Obv.:	Susanna Blunt, Susan Taylor
Rev.:	Maurade Baynton, RCM Staff

Composition: 99.99% Ag, Coloured
Silver content: 31.39 g, 1.01 tr oz
Weight: 31.39 g
Diameter: 38.0 mm
Thickness: N/A
Edge: Reeded
Die Axis: ↑↑
Finish: Proof
Case of Issue: Maroon clam style case, black flocked insert, encapsulated coin, COA

WENTY DOLLARS, MISTY MORNING MULE DEER, 2015.

Designers and Engravers:
Obv.:	Susanna Blunt, Susan Taylor
Rev.:	Trevor Tennant

Composition: 99.99% Ag, Coloured
Silver content: 31.83 g, 1.02 tr oz
Weight: 31.39 g
Diameter: 38 mm
Thickness: N/A
Edge: Reeded
Die Axis: ↑↑
Finish: Proof
Case of Issue: Maroon clamshell with custom beauty box, COA

DATE	DESCRIPTION	QUANTITY SOLD	ISSUE PRICE	FINISH	PR-69	PR-70
2015	The Majestic Moose	7,492	99.95	Proof	100.	—
2015	Bighorn Sheep	6,500	99.95	Proof	100.	—
2015	Misty Morning Mule Deer	6,500	99.95	Proof	100.	—

MAJESTIC ANIMALS SERIES (cont.)

TWENTY DOLLARS, MAJESTIC ELK, 2015.

Designers and Engravers:

Obv.:	Susanna Blunt, Susan Taylor
Rev.:	Maurade Baynton
Composition:	99.99% Ag
Silver content:	31.39 g, 1.01 tr oz
Weight:	31.39 g
Diameter:	38 mm
Thickness:	N/A
Edge:	Reeded
Die Axis:	↑↑
Finish:	Proof
Case of Issue:	Maroon clamshell with custom beauty box, COA

TWENTY DOLLARS, IMPOSING ALPHA WOLF, 2015.

Designers and Engravers:

Obv.:	Susanna Blunt, Susan Taylor
Rev.:	Maurade Baynton
Composition:	99.99% Ag, Coloured
Silver content:	31.39 g, 1.01 tr oz
Weight:	31.39 g
Diameter:	38 mm
Thickness:	N/A
Edge:	Reeded
Die Axis:	↑↑
Finish:	Proof
Case of Issue:	Maroon clamshell with custom beauty box, COA

DATE	DESCRIPTION	QUANTITY SOLD	ISSUE PRICE	FINISH	PR-69	PR-70
2015	Majestic Elk	6,501	99.95	Proof	100.	—
2015	Imposing Alpha Wolf	6,499	99.95	Proof	100.	—

TWENTY DOLLARS, THE WOLF, 2015.

Designers and Engravers:

Obv.:	Susanna Blunt, Susan Taylor
Rev.:	Pierre Leduc, RCM Staff
Composition:	99.99% Ag
Silver content:	31.39 g, 1.01 tr oz
Weight:	31.39 g
Diameter:	38.0 mm
Thickness:	N/A
Edge:	Reeded
Die Axis:	↑↑
Finish:	Proof
Case of Issue:	Maroon clam style case, black flocked insert, encapsulated coin, COA

DATE	DESCRIPTION	QUANTITY SOLD	ISSUE PRICE	FINISH	PR-69	PR-70
2015	The Wolf	7,497	99.95	Proof	100.	—

TWENTY DOLLARS, ICE DANCER, 2015.

Designers and Engravers:

Obv.:	Susanna Blunt, Susan Taylor
Rev.:	Douglas R. Laird, RCM Staff

Composition: 99.99% Ag, Coloured
Silver content: 31.39 g, 1.01 tr oz
Weight: 31.39 g
Diameter: 38.0 mm
Thickness: N/A
Edge: Reeded
Die Axis: ↑↑
Finish: Proof
Case of Issue: Maroon clam style case, black flocked insert, encapsulated coin, COA

DATE	DESCRIPTION	QUANTITY SOLD	ISSUE PRICE	FINISH	PR-69	PR-70
2015	Ice Dancer	6,357	99.95	Proof	100.	—

TWENTY DOLLARS, BEAVER AT WORK, 2015.

Designers and Engravers:

Obv.:	Susanna Blunt, Susan Taylor
Rev.:	John Mardon, RCM Staff

Composition: 99.99% Ag, Coloured
Silver content: 31.39 g, 1.01 tr oz
Weight: 31.39 g
Diameter: 38.0 mm
Thickness: N/A
Edge: Reeded
Die Axis: ↑↑
Finish: Proof
Case of Issue: Maroon clam style case, black flocked insert, encapsulated coin, COA

DATE	DESCRIPTION	QUANTITY SOLD	ISSUE PRICE	FINISH	PR-69	PR-70
2015	Beaver At Work	6,538	99.95	Proof	90.	—

TWENTY DOLLARS, GEORGE-ÉTIENNE CARTIER, 2015.

Commemorating Canada's first Minister of Militia and Defence, George-Étienne Cartier is depicted in front of Province House, in Charlottetown, the site of the 1864 Charlottetown Conference.

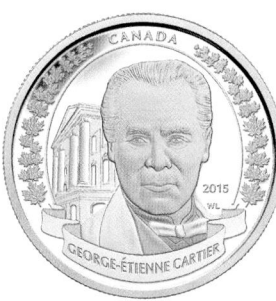

Designers and Engravers:

Obv.:	Susanna Blunt, Susan Taylor
Rev.:	William Lazos, RCM Staff

Composition: 99.99% Ag
Silver content: 31.39 g, 1.01 tr oz
Weight: 31.39 g
Diameter: 38.0 mm
Thickness: N/A
Edge: Reeded
Die Axis: ↑↑
Finish: Proof
Case of Issue: Maroon clam style case, black flocked insert, encapsulated coin, COA

DATE	DESCRIPTION	QUANTITY SOLD	ISSUE PRICE	FINISH	PR-69	PR-70
2015	George-Étienne Cartier	1,268	89.95	Proof	90.	—

TWENTY DOLLARS, SIR JOHN A. MACDONALD, 2015.

Designers and Engravers:

Obv.:	Susanna Blunt, Susan Taylor
Rev.:	William Lazos, RCM Staff

Composition:	99.99% Ag
Silver content:	31.39 g, 1.01 tr oz
Weight:	31.39 g
Diameter:	38.0 mm
Thickness:	N/A
Edge:	Reeded
Die Axis:	↑↑
Finish:	Proof
Case of Issue:	Maroon clam style case, black flocked insert, encapsulated coin, COA

DATE	DESCRIPTION	QUANTITY SOLD	ISSUE PRICE	FINISH	PR-69	PR-70
2015	Sir John A. MacDonald	2,865	89.95	Proof	90.	—

NORTH AMERICAN SPORTFISH SERIES

TWENTY DOLLARS, NORTH AMERICAN SPORTFISH SET, 2015.

Designers and Engravers:

Obv.:	Susanna Blunt, Susan Taylor
Rev.:	Curtis Atwater, RCM Staff

Composition:	99.99% Ag
Silver content:	31.39 g, 1.01 tr oz
Weight:	31.39 g
Diameter:	38.0 mm
Thickness:	3.1 mm
Edge:	Plain Edge Lettering, "9999 FINE SILVER 1OZ 9999 ARGENT PUR 1 OZ"
Die Axis:	↑↑
Finish:	Proof

Common Obverse   Largemouth Bass

Northern Pike   Walleye   Rainbow Trout

Case of Issue: Singly: Maroon clam style case, black flocked insert, encapsulated coin, COA, custom box
              Subscription: Four coin walnut wooden case, black flocked insert, encapsulated coins, COA

DATE	DESCRIPTION	QUANTITY SOLD	ISSUE PRICE	FINISH	PR-69	PR-70
2015	Largemouth Bass	6,490	99.95	Proof	100.	—
2015	Northern Pike	6,409	99.95	Proof	100.	—
2015	Walleye	6,375	99.95	Proof	100.	—
2015	Rainbow Trout	6,612	99.95	Proof	100.	—

FIRST WORLD WAR: BATTLEFRONT SERIES

TWENTY DOLLARS, FIRST WORLD WAR: BATTLEFRONT SET, 2015-2017.

Featuring the effigy of King George V, the Battlefront Series commemorates the contributions of Canadians during the First World War. It was after Second Battle of Ypres that John McCrae penned *In Flanders Fields*.

Common Obverse	**The Battle of Neuve-Chapelle** Designer: Joel Kimmel	**The Second Battle of Ypres** Designer: Silvia Pecota

The Battle of Beaumont-Hamel Designer: Silvia Pecota	**The Somme Offensive** Designer: Glen Loates	**The Battle of Vimy Ridge** Designer: Pandora Young	**The Battle of Passchendaele** Designer: Pandora Young

Designers
Obv.: Sir E.B. Mackennal
Rev.: See reverse illustrations
Composition: 99.99% Ag, Selectively gold plated
Thickness: N/A
Silver content: 31.39 g, 1.01 tr oz
Weight: 31.39 g
Diameter: 38.0 mm
Finish: Proof with selective gold plating
Case of Issue: Maroon clam style case, black flocked insert, encapsulated coin, COA, custom box

Engravers:
Obv.: RCM Staff
Rev.: RCM Staff

Edge: Reeded
Die Axis: ↑↑

DATE	DESCRIPTION	QUANTITY SOLD	ISSUE PRICE	FINISH	PR-69	PR-70
2015	The Battle of Neuve-Chapelle	3,224	109.95	Proof	110.	—
2015	The Second Battle of Ypres	3,397	109.95	Proof	110.	—
2016	The Battle of Beaumont-Hamel	3,517	109.95	Proof	110.	—
2016	The Somme Offensive	3,247	109.95	Proof	110.	—
2017	The Battle of Vimy Ridge	10,000	112.95	Proof	115.	—
2017	The Battle of Passchendaele	10,000	112.95	Proof	115.	—

TWENTY DOLLARS, HOLIDAY REINDEER, 2015.

This coin delivers a magical scene that every child hopes to see—reindeer and a sled waiting on a rooftop while Santa's inside delivering gifts.

Designers and Engravers:

Obv.:	Susanna Blunt, Susan Taylor
Rev.:	Lisa Thomson-Khan
Composition:	99.99% Ag
Silver content:	31.39 g, 1.01 tr oz
Weight:	31.39 g
Diameter:	38.0 mm
Thickness:	N/A
Edge:	Reeded
Die Axis:	↑↑
Finish:	Proof
Case of Issue:	Maroon clam style case, black flocked insert, encapsulated coin, COA

DATE	DESCRIPTION	QUANTITY SOLD	ISSUE PRICE	FINISH	PR-69	PR-70
2015	Holiday Reindeer	4,579	114.95	Proof	115.	—

TWENTY DOLLARS, WEDDING, 2015.

Designers and Engravers:

Obv.:	Susanna Blunt, Susan Taylor
Rev.:	Joel Kimmel, RCM Staff
Composition:	99.99% Ag, Sel. gold plated
Silver content:	31.83 g, 1.02 tr oz
Weight:	31.83 g
Diameter:	40.0 mm
Thickness:	N/A
Edge:	Reeded
Die Axis:	↑↑
Finish:	Proof
Case of Issue:	Maroon clam style case, black flocked insert, encapsulated coin, COA

DATE	DESCRIPTION	QUANTITY SOLD	ISSUE PRICE	FINISH	PR-69	PR-70
2015	Wedding	7,414	109.95	Proof	100.	—

TWENTY DOLLARS, 100TH ANNIVERSARY OF *IN FLANDERS FIELDS*, 2015.

Featuring the effigy of King George V, this coin pays tribute to John McCrae's poem.

Designers and Engravers:

Obv.:	Sir E.B. MacKennal, RCM Staff
Rev.:	Lauric McGaw, RCM Staff
Composition:	99.99% Ag
Silver content:	31.39 g, 1.01 tr oz
Weight:	31.39 g
Diameter:	38.0 mm
Thickness:	N/A
Edge:	Reeded
Case of Issue:	Maroon clam style case, black flocked insert, encapsulated coin, COA, custom box

Die Axis : ↑↑ **Finish:** Proof

DATE	DESCRIPTION	QUANTITY SOLD	ISSUE PRICE	FINISH	PR-69	PR-70
2015	100th Anniv. of *In Flanders Fields*	5,367	89.95	Proof	90.	—

SECOND WORLD WAR: BATTLEFRONT SERIES

TWENTY DOLLARS, SECOND WORLD WAR: BATTLEFRONT SERIES, 2015-2018.
The Second World War Battlefront series honours Canada's participation in key battles during the Second World War. A 10-coin subscription, ending in 2020.

Common Obverse

The Battle of Britain 2015 (1940-)
Designer: Ardell Bourgeois
Engraver: T.H. Paget

Designers and Engravers:

Obv.:	See reverse illustrations		
Rev.:	See reverse illustrations		
Composition:	99.99% Ag		
Silver content:	31.39 g, 1.01 tr oz		
Weight:	31.39 g	Edge:	Reeded
Diameter:	38.0 mm	Die Axis:	↑↑
Thickness:	N/A	Finish:	Proof
Case of Issue:	Maroon clam style case,		
	black flocked insert, encapsulated coin, COA		

2016 The Battle of Hong Kong
Designer: Joel Kimmel
Engraver: T.H. Paget

2017 The Battle of Dieppe
Designer: Alan Daneil
Engraver: T.H. Paget

2017 The Bombing War
Designer: Glen Loates
Engraver: T.H. Paget

2018 The Battle of the Atlantic
Designer: Neil Hamelin
Engraver: T.H. Paget

DATE	DESCRIPTION	QUANTITY SOLD	ISSUE PRICE	FINISH	PR-69	PR-70
2015 (1940-)	The Battle of Britain	6,543	89.95	Proof	90.	—
2016	The Battle of Hong Kong	4,110	89.95	Proof	90.	—
2017	The Battle of Dieppe	7,500	92.95	Proof	95.	—
2017	The Bombing War	7,500	92.95	Proof	95.	—
2018	The Battle of the Atlantic	7,500	94.95	Proof	95.	—

FORESTS OF CANADA SERIES

TWENTY DOLLARS, FORESTS OF CANADA SERIES, 2015.

The Forests of Canada Series was also offered as an 4-coin subscription.

Common Obverse

Designers and Engravers:

Obv.:	Susanna Blunt, Susan Taylor
Rev.:	See reverse illustrations, RCM Staff
Composition:	99.99% Ag, Coloured
Silver content:	31.39 g, 1.01 tr oz
Weight:	31.39 g
Diameter:	38.0 mm
Case of Issue:	Maroon clam style case, black flocked insert, encapsulated coin, COA

Thickness:	N/A
Edge:	Reede
Die Axis:	↑↑
Finish:	Proof

Carolinian Tulip-Tree	Coast Shore Pine	Columbian Yew Tree	Boreal Balsam Poplar
Designer: Julius Csotonyi	Designer: Margaret Best	Designer: Julius Csotonyi	Designer: Margaret Best

DATE	DESCRIPTION	QUANTITY SOLD	ISSUE PRICE	FINISH	PR-69	PR-70
2015	Carolinian Tulip-Tree	3,100	99.95	Proof	100.	—
2015	Coast Shore Pine	3,117	99.95	Proof	100.	—
2015	Columbian Yew Tree	2,781	99.95	Proof	100.	—
2015	Boreal Balsam Poplar	2,271	99.95	Proof	100.	—

TWENTY DOLLARS, CANADIAN ICONS: POLAR BEAR, 2015.

Designers and Engravers:

Obv.:	Susanna Blunt, Susan Taylor
Rev.:	Cindy Deborah Sorley-Keichinger
Composition:	99.99% Ag, with Jade
Silver content:	31.39 g, 1.01 tr oz
Weight:	31.39 g
Diameter:	38 mm
Thickness:	N/A
Edge:	Reeded
Die Axis:	↑↑
Finish:	Proof with jade
Case of Issue:	Maroon clamshefll with custom beauty box, COA

DATE	DESCRIPTION	QUANTITY SOLD	ISSUE PRICE	FINISH	PR-69	PR-70
2015	Canadian Icons: Polar Bear	4,910	114.95	Proof	115.	—

THE CANADIAN HOME FRONT SERIES

WENTY DOLLARS, THE CANADIAN HOME FRONT, 2015-2016.

Featuring the effigy of King George V, this coin pays tribute to the contribution facilitated by the railways during the war effort.

2015 Obverse

2016 Obverse

Designers and Engravers:

Obv.:	Susanna Blunt, Susan Taylor
Rev.:	See reverse illustrations

Composition: 99.99% Ag
Silver content: 31.39 g, 1.01 tr oz
Weight: 31.39 g   **Edge:** Reeded
Diameter: 38.0 mm   **Die Axis:** ↑↑
Thickness: N/A   **Finish:** Proof
Case of Issue: Maroon clam style case, black flocked insert, encapsulated coin, COA, custom box

Transcontinental Railroad
Designer: David A. Oram

Canada's First Submarine During The First World War
Designer: Yves Bérubé

British Commonwealth Air Training Plan
Designer: David A. Oram

Patrol Against U-Boats
Designer: Bonnie Ross

DATE	DESCRIPTION	QUANTITY SOLD	ISSUE PRICE	FINISH	PR-69	PR-70
2015	Transcontinental Railroad	4,490	89.95	Proof	90.	—
2015	Canada's First Submarine During the First World War	3,193	89.95	Proof	90.	—
2016	British Commonwealth Air Training Plan	3,206	89.95	Proof	90.	—
2016	Patrol Against U-Boats	2,819	89.95	Proof	90.	—

ote: Coins illustrated smaller than actual size.

UNESCO AT HOME & ABROAD SET

TWENTY DOLLARS, UNESCO AT HOME & ABROAD, 2015.

In 2015, a $50 gold version of the Mount Fuji & The Canadian Rockies was also issued (see page 433)

| Common Obverse | Wood Buffalo National Park and Sichuan Giant Panda Santuaries Designer: Lauren Crawshaw | Mount Fuji & The Canadian Rockies Designer: Trevor Tennant |

Designers:
Obv.: Susanna Blunt
Rev.: See reverse illustrations
Composition: 99.99% Ag
Weight: 31.39 g
Diameter: 38.0 mm
Thickness: N/A
Case of Issue: Maroon clamshell with custom beauty box, COA.

Engravers:
Obv.: Susan Taylor
Rev.: See reverse illustrations
Silver content: 31.39 g, 1.01 tr oz
Edge: Reeded
Die Axis: ↑↑
Finish: Proof

DATE	DESCRIPTION	QUANTITY SOLD	ISSUE PRICE	FINISH	PR-69	PR-70
2015	Wood Buffalo National Park and Sichuan Giant Panda Sanctuaries	2,157	89.95	Proof	80.	—
2015	Mount Fuji & The Canadian Rockies	3,373	89.95	Proof	80.	—

TORONTO 2015™ PAN AM/PARAPAN AM GAMES SET

TWENTY DOLLARS, TORONTO 2015™ PAN AM/PARAPAN AM GAMES, 2015.

| Common Obverse | Toronto 2015™ Pan Am/Parapan Am Games: In the Spirit of Sports Designer: Tony Bianco | Toronto 2015™ Pan Am/Parapan Am Games: United We Play!™ Designer: Christi Belcourt |

Designers:
Obv.: Susanna Blunt
Rev.: See reverse illustrations
Composition: 99.99% Ag
Weight: 31.39 g
Diameter: 38.0 mm
Thickness: N/A
Case of Issue: Maroon clamshell with custom beauty box. COA.

Engravers:
Obv.: Susan Taylor
Rev.: See reverse illustrations
Silver content: 31.39 g, 1.01 tr oz
Edge: Reeded
Die Axis: ↑↑
Finish: Proof

DATE	DESCRIPTION	QUANTITY SOLD	ISSUE PRICE	FINISH	PR-69	PR-70
2015	Toronto 2015™ Pan Am/Parapan Am Games: In The Spirit of Sports	1,779	124.95	Proof	125.	—
2015	Toronto 2015™ Pan Am/Parapan Am Games: United We Play!™	1,857	124.95	Proof	125.	—

TWENTY DOLLARS, 70TH ANNIVERSARY OF THE END OF THE ITALIAN CAMPAIGN, 2015.

Designers and Engravers:
Obv.:	Susanna Blunt, Susan Taylor
Rev.:	Joel Kimmel

Composition: 99.99% Ag
Silver content: 31.39 g, 1.01 tr oz
Weight: 31.39 g
Diameter: 38 mm
Thickness: N/A
Edge: Reeded
Die Axis: ↑↑
Finish: Proof
Case of Issue: Paper diorama with custom beauty box, COA

DATE	DESCRIPTION	QUANTITY SOLD	ISSUE PRICE	FINISH	PR-69	PR-70
2015	70th Anniversary of the End of the Italian Campaign	3,996	109.95	Proof	110.	—

WEATHER PHENOMENON SERIES

TWENTY DOLLARS, WEATHER PHENOMENON, 2015-2017.

Common Obverse

Designers and Engravers:
Obv.:	Susanna Blunt, Susan Taylor
Rev.:	Tony Bianco, Arnold Nogy

Composition: 99.99% Ag
Silver content: 31.39 g, 1.01 tr oz
Weight: 31.39 g
Diameter: 38.0 mm
Thickness: N/A
Edge: Reeded
Die Axis: ↑↑
Finish: Proof
Case of Issue: Maroon clamshell with black beauty box, COA.

 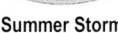   

Summer Storm	Winter Freeze	Radiant Rainbow	Fiery Sky

DATE	DESCRIPTION	QUANTITY SOLD	ISSUE PRICE	FINISH	PR-69	PR-70
2015	Weather Phenomenon: Summer Storm	7,983	99.95	Proof	100.	—
2015	Weather Phenomenon: Winter Freeze	7,043	99.95	Proof	100.	—
2016	Weather Phenomenon: Radiant Rainbow	7,890	99.95	Proof	100.	—
2017	Weather Phenomenon: Fiery Sky	7,643	99.95	Proof	100	—

TWENTY DOLLARS, MAPLE LEAF REFLECTION, 2015.

Designers and Engravers:

Obv.:	Susanna Blunt, Susan Taylor
Rev.:	Lilyane Caulombe
Composition:	99.99% Ag
Silver content:	31.39 g, 1.01 tr oz
Weight:	31.39 g
Diameter:	38 mm
Thickness:	N/A
Edge:	Reeded
Die Axis:	↑↑
Finish:	Proof
Case of Issue:	Maroon clamshefll with custom beauty box, COA

DATE	DESCRIPTION	QUANTITY SOLD	ISSUE PRICE	FINISH	PR-69	PR-70
2015	Maple Leaf Reflection	5,502	99.95	Proof	100.	—

GRIZZLY BEAR SERIES

TWENTY DOLLARS, GRIZZLY BEAR, 2015-2016.

Common Obverse

Designers and Engravers:

Obv.:	Susanna Blunt, Susan Taylor		
Rev.:	Lauren Crawshaw		
Composition:	99.99% Ag		
Silver content:	31.39 g, 1.01 tr oz		
Weight:	31.39 g	**Edge:**	Plain, with edge letterir
Diameter:	38.0 mm	**Die Axis:**	↑↑
Thickness:	N/A	**Finish:**	Proof
Case of Issue:	Maroon clamshell with custom beauty box, COA		

The Catch	Togetherness	Family	The Battle

DATE	DESCRIPTION	QUANTITY SOLD	ISSUE PRICE	FINISH	PR-69	PR-70
2015	Grizzly Bear: The Catch	5,280	99.95	Proof	90.	—
2015	Grizzly Bear: Togetherness	5,145	99.95	Proof	90.	—
2015	Grizzly Bear: Family	4,617	99.95	Proof	90.	—
2016	Grizzly Bear: The Battle	3,418	99.95	Proof	90.	—

WENTY DOLLARS, THE CANADIAN MAPLE LEAF (SHAPED), 2015.

Celebrate Canada's pride with this RCM first one-of-a-kind, maple leaf-shaped coin!

Designers and Engravers:

Obv.:	Susanna Blunt, Susan Taylor
Rev.:	Marcos Hallam
Composition:	99.99% Ag
Silver content:	31.5 g, 1.01 tr oz
Weight:	31.5 g
Diameter:	40.0 mm
Thickness:	N/A
Edge:	Reeded
Die Axis:	↑↑
Finish:	Proof
Case of Issue:	Custom Maple leaf shaped presentation case, COA

DATE	DESCRIPTION	QUANTITY SOLD	ISSUE PRICE	FINISH	PR-69	PR-70
2015	The Canadian Maple Leaf	14,939	149.95	Proof	160.	—

WENTY DOLLARS, TOM THOMSON: SPRING ICE (1916), 2015.

Designers and Engravers:

Obv.:	Susanna Blunt, Susan Taylor
Rev.:	Tom Thomson, RCM Staff
Composition:	99.99% Ag, Selective gold plating
Silver content:	31.39 g, 1.01 tr oz
Weight:	31.39 g
Diameter:	38 mm
Thickness:	N/A
Edge:	Reeded
Die Axis:	↑↑
Finish:	Proof
Case of Issue:	Maroon clamshefll with standard beauty box, COA

DATE	DESCRIPTION	QUANTITY SOLD	ISSUE PRICE	FINISH	PR-69	PR-70
2015	Tom Thomson: Spring Ice (1916)	1,572	114.95	Proof	115.	—

WENTY DOLLARS, A HISTORIC REIGN, 2015.

Designers and Engravers:

Obv.:	Susanna Blunt, Susan Taylor
Rev.:	Cathy Bursey Sabourin
Composition:	99.99% Ag, Coloured
Silver content:	31.39 g, 1.01 tr oz
Weight:	31.39 g
Diameter:	38 mm
Thickness:	N/A
Edge:	Reeded
Die Axis:	↑↑
Finish:	Proof
Case of Issue:	Maroon clamshefll with black beauty box, COA

DATE	DESCRIPTION	QUANTITY SOLD	ISSUE PRICE	FINISH	PR-69	PR-70
2015	A Historic Reign	7,472	109.95	Proof	110.	—

MASTERS CLUB EXCLUSIVE SCALLOP-EDGE SERIES

TWENTY DOLLARS, MASTERS CLUB EXCLUSIVE, 2015-2017.

Designers and Engravers:

Obv.:	Susanna Blunt, Susan Taylor
Rev.:	Tony Bianco

Composition: 99.99% Ag
Silver content: 26.51 g, 0.85 tr oz
Weight: 26.51 g
Diameter: 38 mm
Thickness: N/A
Edge: Plain
Die Axis: ↑↑
Finish: Proof
Case of Issue: Wooden box with graphic beauty box, COA

2015 Master of the Sky: Canada Goose

2016 Master of the Sea: The Orca

2017 Master of the Land: The Timber Wolf

DATE	DESCRIPTION	QUANTITY SOLD	ISSUE PRICE	FINISH	PR-69	PR-70
2015	Master of the Sky: Canada Goose	5,972	99.95	Proof	90.	—
2016	Master of the Sea: The Orca	5,660	99.95	Proof	100.	—
2017	Master of the Land: The Timber Wolf	6,000	102.95	Proof	100.	—

Note: This series was exclusively sold to the Mint Master's Club Members only.

TWENTY DOLLARS, LOONEY TUNES™: MERRIE MELODIES, 2015.

Designers and Engravers:

Obv.:	Susanna Blunt, Susan Taylor
Rev.:	Warner Bros.

Composition: 99.99% Ag
Silver content: 31.39 g, 1.01 tr oz
Weight: 31.39 g
Diameter: 38 mm
Thickness: N/A
Edge: Reeded
Die Axis: ↑↑
Finish: Proof
Case of Issue: ACME Crate with custom beauty box, COA

DATE	DESCRIPTION	QUANTITY SOLD	ISSUE PRICE	FINISH	PR-69	PR-70
2015	Merrie Melodies	12,275	109.95	Proof	110.	—

LOONEY TUNES™ SET

TWENTY DOLLARS, LOONEY TUNES™, 2015.

Common Obverse

Designers and Engravers:

Obv.:	Susanna Blunt, Susan Taylor
Rev.:	Warner Bros.
Composition:	99.99% Ag
Silver content:	31.39 g, 1.01 tr oz
Weight:	31.39 g
Diameter:	40.0 mm
Thickness:	N/A
Edge:	Reeded
Die Axis:	↑↑
Finish:	Proof
Case of Issue:	Wooden box with custom beauty box, COA.

Sylvester

Bugs Bunny

Daffy Duck

Tweety

DATE	DESCRIPTION	QUANTITY SOLD	ISSUE PRICE	FINISH	PR-69	PR-70
2015	Sylvester, Bugs, Daffy, Tweety (4-coin set only)	4,568	419.95	Proof	400.	—
2015	Looney Tunes: Sylvester	3,556				
2015	Looney Tunes: Bugs Bunny	11,390				
2015	Looney Tunes: Daffy Duck	3,627				
2015	Looney Tunes: Tweety	3,686				

Note: These coins were sold as a 4-coin set, though mintages indicate otherwise.

TWENTY DOLLARS, A CELEBRATION OF HER MAJESTY'S 90TH BIRTHDAY, 2016.

Designers and Engravers:

Obv.:	Susanna Blunt, Susan Taylor
Rev.:	Tony Bianco
Composition:	99.99% Ag,
Silver content:	31.39 g, 1.02 tr oz
Weight:	31.39 g
Diameter:	38 mm
Thickness:	N/A
Edge:	Reeded
Die Axis:	↑↑
Finish:	Proof
Case of Issue:	Maroon clamshell with black beauty box, COA

DATE	DESCRIPTION	QUANTITY SOLD	ISSUE PRICE	FINISH	PR-69	PR-70
2016	A Celebration of Her Majesty's 90th Birthday	7,006	99.95	Proof	200.	—

THE UNIVERSE SET

TWENTY DOLLARS, THE UNIVERSE, 2016.

| Common Obverse | The Universe: Observatoire du Mont-Mégantic, Quebec Designer: Loîc Beaumont-Tremblay | The Universe: The Burke-Gaffney Observatory, N.S. Glow-in-the-Dark Glass with Opal Designer: Joel Kimmel and Loic Beaumont-Tremblay | The Universe: NRC Dominion Radio Astrophysical Observatory (DRAO), B.C. Glow-in-the-Dark Glass with Silver Fume Designer: Ardell Bourgeois |

Designers:
  Obv.:   Susanna Blunt
  Rev.:   See reverse illustrations
Composition: 99.99% Ag, Coloured, Glow paint
Silver content: 31.39 g, 1.01 tr oz
Weight: 31.39 g
Diameter: 38.0 mm
Thickness: N/A
Case of Issue: Maroon clamshell with black beauty box, COA.

Engravers:
  Obv.:   Susan Taylor
  Rev.:   See reverse illustrations

Edge: Reeded
Die Axis: ↑↑
Finish: Proof, colour and borosilicate glass

DATE	DESCRIPTION	QUANTITY SOLD	ISSUE PRICE	FINISH	PR-69	PR-70
2016	The Universe: Observatoire du Mont-Mégantic, Quebec	8,311	149.95	Proof	150.	—
2016	The Universe: The Burke-Gaffney Observatory, N.S.	5,536	149.95	Proof	150.	—
2016	The Universe: NRC Dominion Radio Astrophysical Observatory (DRAO), B.C.	4,471	149.95	Proof	150.	—

TWENTY DOLLARS, VENETIAN GLASS ANGEL, 2016.

Designers and Engravers:
  Obv.:   Susanna Blunt
  Rev.:   Julius Csotonyi
Composition: 99.99% Ag
Silver content: 31.39 g, 1.01 tr oz
Weight: 31.39 g
Diameter: 38 mm
Thickness: N/A
Edge: Reeded
Die Axis: ↑↑
Finish: Proof with Murano glass
Case of Issue: Maroon clamshell with graphic beauty box COA.

DATE	DESCRIPTION	QUANTITY SOLD	ISSUE PRICE	FINISH	PR-69	PR-70
2016	Venetian Glass Angel	7,973	149.95	Proof	150.	—

CANADIAN LANDSCAPE SERIES

WENTY DOLLARS, CANADIAN LANDSCAPE, 2016

Common Obverse

Designers and Engravers:

Obv.:	Susanna Blunt, Susan Taylor
Rev.:	Stéphanie Gauvin

Composition: 99.99% Ag, with Colour
Silver content: 31.83 g, 1.02 tr oz
Weight: 31.83 g
Diameter: 40.0 mm
Thickness: N/A
Case of Issue: Maroon clamshell with standard beauty box, COA.

Edge: Reeded
Die Axis: ↑↑
Finish: Proof

The Rockies

The Lake

Ski Chalet

Reaching the Top

DATE	DESCRIPTION	QUANTITY SOLD	ISSUE PRICE	FINISH	PR-69	PR-70
2016	Canadian Landscape Series: The Rockies	3,005	99.95	Proof	100.	—
2016	Canadian Landscape Series: The Lake	2,673	99.95	Proof	100.	—
2016	Canadian Landscape Series: Ski Chalet	2,479	99.95	Proof	100.	—
2016	Canadian Landscape Series: Reaching the Top	2,136	99.95	Proof	100.	—

WENTY DOLLARS, SNOWY OWL, 2016.

Designers and Engravers:

Obv.:	Susanna Blunt, Susan Taylor
Rev.:	Douglas Laird

Composition: 99.99% Ag,
Silver content: 31.39 g, 1.02 tr oz
Weight: 31.39 g
Diameter: 38 mm
Thickness: N/A
Edge: Reeded
Die Axis: ↑↑
Finish: Proof
Case of Issue: Maroon clamshell with black beauty box, COA

DATE	DESCRIPTION	QUANTITY SOLD	ISSUE PRICE	FINISH	PR-69	PR-70
2016	Snowy Owl	6,498	99.95	Proof	100.	—

GEOMETRY IN ART SET

TWENTY DOLLARS, GEOMETRY IN ART, 2016.

Common Obverse

The Loon

The Polar Bear

The Caribou

The Beaver

The Maple Leaf

Designers:		**Engravers:**	
Obv.:	Susanna Blunt	Obv.:	Susan Taylor
Rev.:	Calder Moore	Rev.:	Calder Moore
Composition:	99.99% Ag, Coloured		
Silver content:	31.83 g, 1.02 tr oz		
Weight:	31.83 g	**Edge:**	Reeded
Diameter:	40.0 mm	**Die Axis:**	↑↑
Thickness:	N/A	**Finish:**	Proof
Case of Issue:	Maroon clamshell with graphic beauty box. Also available as a subscription with black wooden box, COA.		

DATE	DESCRIPTION	QUANTITY SOLD	ISSUE PRICE	FINISH	PR-69	PR-70
2016	Geometry in Art: The Loon	6,671	99.95	Proof	100.	—
2016	Geometry in Art: The Polar Bear	6,838	99.95	Proof	100.	—
2016	Geometry in Art: The Caribou	6,459	99.95	Proof	100.	—
2016	Geometry in Art: The Beaver	5,471	99.95	Proof	100.	—
2016	Geometry in Art: The Maple Leaf	5,678	99.95	Proof	100.	—

AIRCRAFT OF THE FIRST WORLD WAR SET

WENTY DOLLARS, AIRCRAFT OF THE FIRST WORLD WAR, 2016.

Common Obverse

Designers			Engravers:	
Obv.:	Susanna Blunt		Obv.:	Susan Taylor
Rev.:	David A. Oram		Rev.:	David A. Oram
Composition:	99.99% Ag, Coloured			
Silver content:	31.83 g, 1.02 tr oz			
Weight:	31.83 g		**Edge:**	Reeded
Diameter:	40.0 mm		**Die Axis:**	↑↑
Thickness:	N/A		**Finish:**	Proof
Case of Issue:	Maroon clamshell with black beauty box, COA.			

The Royal Aircraft Factory S.E.5A

The Sopwith Triplane

Curtiss H-12

DATE	DESCRIPTION	QUANTITY SOLD	ISSUE PRICE	FINISH	PR-69	PR-70
2016	Aircraft of the First World War: The Royal Aircraft Factory S.E.5A	7,253	99.95	Proof	100.	—
2016	Aircraft of the First World War: The Sopwith Triplane	5,643	99.95	Proof	100.	—
2016	Aircraft of the First World War: Curtiss H-12	5,013	99.95	Proof	100.	—

WENTY DOLLARS, MOTHER EARTH, 2016.

Designers and Engravers:	
Obv.:	Susanna Blunt, Susan Taylor
Rev.:	Alexandra Lefort
Composition:	99.99% Ag,
Silver content:	31.39 g, 1.02 tr oz
Weight:	31.39 g
Diameter:	38 mm
Thickness:	N/A
Edge:	Reeded
Die Axis:	↑↑
Finish:	Proof
Case of Issue:	Maroon clamshell with black beauty box, COA

DATE	DESCRIPTION	QUANTITY SOLD	ISSUE PRICE	FINISH	PR-69	PR-70
2016	Mother Earth	6,989	104.95	Proof	180.	—

TWENTY DOLLARS, FOUR-LEAF CLOVER, 2016.

Designers and Engravers:

Obv.:	Susanna Blunt, Susan Taylor
Rev.:	Lilyane Coulombe
Composition:	99.99% Ag, Enameled
Silver content:	31.83 g, 1.02 tr oz
Weight:	31.39 g
Diameter:	38 mm
Thickness:	N/A
Edge:	Reeded
Die Axis:	↑↑
Finish:	Proof
Case of Issue:	Maroon clamshell with black beauty box, COA

DATE	DESCRIPTION	QUANTITY SOLD	ISSUE PRICE	FINISH	PR-69	PR-70
2016	Four-Leaf Clover	5,888	109.95	Proof	110.	—

CANADIAN SALMONIDS SET

TWENTY DOLLARS, CANADIAN SALMONIDS, 2016

Common Obverse

Designers :

			Engravers:	
Obv.:	Susanna Blunt		Obv.:	Susan Taylor
Rev.:	Curtis Atwater		Rev.:	Curtis Atwater
Composition:	99.99% Ag, with Colour			
Silver content:	31.83 g, 1.02 tr oz			
Weight:	31.83 g		**Die Axis:**	↑↑
Diameter:	40.0 mm		**Edge:**	Reeded
Thickness:	N/A		**Finish:**	Proof
Case of Issue:	Maroon clamshell with black beauty box. Available as a subscription, with fishing lure, COA.			

Atlantic Salmon   **Arctic Char**   **Sockeye Salmon**

DATE	DESCRIPTION	QUANTITY SOLD	ISSUE PRICE	FINISH	PR-69	PR-70
2016	Canadian Salmonids: Atlantic Salmon	4,520	99.95	Proof	100.	—
2016	Canadian Salmonids: Arctic Char	4,535	99.95	Proof	100.	—
2016	Canadian Salmonids: Sockeye Salmon	4,059	99.95	Proof	100.	—

TWENTY DOLLARS, *BATMAN V SUPERMAN: DAWN OF JUSTICE™ – THE TRINITY*, 2016.

Designers and Engravers:
Obv.:	Susanna Blunt, Susan Taylor
Rev.:	DC Comics

Composition:	99.99% Ag, Coloured
Silver content:	31.83 g, 1.02 tr oz
Weight:	31.83 g
Diameter:	40 mm
Thickness:	N/A
Edge:	Reeded
Die Axis:	↑↑
Finish:	Proof
Case of Issue:	Premium presentation case, COA

DATE	DESCRIPTION	QUANTITY SOLD	ISSUE PRICE	FINISH	PR-69	PR-70
2016	*Batman v Superman: Dawn of Justice™ – The Trinity*	8,302	109.95	Proof	110.	—

TRADITIONAL UKRAINIAN PYSANKA

TWENTY DOLLARS, TRADITIONAL UKRAINIAN PYSANKA, 2016-2018.

Though many cultures regard the egg as one of spring's most enduring symbols, few do so as beautifully as the Ukrainian people, whose pysanka is a reminder of life's beginnings and the potential inherent in every living thing.

2016-2017 Common Obverse	2016 Traditional Pysanka	2017 Traditional Pysanka	2018 Obverse	2018 Golden Spring Pysanka

Designers:
Obv.:	Susanna Blunt

Composition:	99.99% Ag, Coloured
Silver content:	31.39 g, 1.01 tr oz
Weight:	31.39 g - 31.82 g
Diameter:	45 mm long x 33 mm wide
Thickness:	N/A
Case of Issue:	Maroon clamshell with black beauty box, COA

Engravers:
Rev.:	Ann C. Morash

Die Axis:	↑↑
Edge:	Interrupted reeding
Finish:	2016-2017: Proof
	2018: Proof with reverse gold plating

DATE	DESCRIPTION	QUANTITY SOLD	ISSUE PRICE	FINISH	PR-69	PR-70
2016	Traditional Ukrainian Pysanka	4,000	114.95	Proof	500.	—
2017	Traditional Ukrainian Pysanka	5,000	114.95	Proof	200.	—
2018	Golden Spring Pysanka	5,000	129.95	Proof	150.	—

TWENTY DOLLARS, CELEBRATING THE 40TH SEASON OF THE *TORONTO BLUE JAYS*™, 2016.

Designers and Engravers:

Obv.:	Susanna Blunt, Susan Taylor
Rev.:	Joel Kimmel
Composition:	99.99% Ag, Coloured
Silver content:	31.39 g, 1.01 tr oz
Weight:	31.39 g
Diameter:	38 mm
Thickness:	N/A
Edge:	Reeded
Die Axis:	↑↑
Finish:	Proof
Case of Issue:	Maroon clamshell with full colour beauty box, COA

DATE	DESCRIPTION	QUANTITY SOLD	ISSUE PRICE	FINISH	PR-69	PR-70
2016	Celebrating the 40th Anniversary of the *Toronto Blue Jays*™	11,507	99.95	Proof	100.	—

THE MIGRATORY BIRDS CONVENTION SET

TWENTY DOLLARS, THE MIGRATORY BIRDS CONVENTION, 2016

Common Obverse

Designers and Engravers:

Obv.:	Susanna Blunt, Susan Taylor
Rev.:	Claudio D'Angelo
Composition:	99.99% Ag, with Colour
Silver content:	31.83 g, 1.0 tr oz
Weight:	31.39 g
Diameter:	38 mm
Thickness:	N/A
Edge:	Reeded
Die Axis:	↑↑
Finish:	Proof
Case of Issue:	Maroon clamshell with custom beauty box, COA.

The Mountain Bluebird	The American Avocet	The American Goldfinch	The Pileated Woodpecker

DATE	DESCRIPTION	QUANTITY SOLD	ISSUE PRICE	FINISH	PR-69	PR-70
2016	The Mountain Bluebird	5,353	99.95	Proof	100.	—
2016	The American Avocet	4,138	99.95	Proof	100.	—
2016	The American Goldfinch	4,599	99.95	Proof	100.	—
2016	The Pileated Woodpecker	4,480	99.95	Proof	100.	—

ICONIC CANADA SERIES

WENTY DOLLARS, ICONIC CANADA, 2016-2017.

| 2016 Obverse | 2016: The Polar Bear
Designer: Julius Csotonyi | 2017 Obverse | 2017: The Grizzly Bear
Designer: W. Allan Hancock |

Designers:
Obv.:   Susanna Blunt
Rev.:   See reverse illustrations
Composition: 99.99% Ag, Coloured
Silver content: 31.39 g, 1.01 tr oz
Weight: 31.39 g
Diameter: 38 mm
Case of Issue: Maroon clamshell with custom beauty box, COA

Engravers:
Rev.:   Susan Taylor

Thickness: N/A
Edge: Reeded
Die Axis: ↑↑
Finish: Proof

DATE	DESCRIPTION	QUANTITY SOLD	ISSUE PRICE	FINISH	PR-69	PR-70
2016	Iconic Canada: The Polar Bear	3,958	109.95	Proof	110.	—
2017	Iconic Canada: The Grizzly Bear	4,000	113.95	Proof	115.	—

Note: These coins were exclusively sold to the Mint Master's Club Members only.

LITTLE CREATURES SERIES

WENTY DOLLARS, LITTLE CREATURES: SNAIL, 2016-2018.

| Common Obverse | 2016 Snail | 2017 Dogbane Beetle | 2018 Monarch Caterpillar |

Designers:
Obv.:   Susanna Blunt
Rev.:   Maurice Gervais
Composition: 99.99% Ag, Coloured
Weight: 31.39 g
Diameter: 38 mm
Thickness: N/A
Case of Issue: Maroon clamshell with black beauty box, COA

Engravers:
Obv.:   Susan Taylor

Silver content: 31.39 g, 1.01 tr oz
Edge: Reeded
Die Axis: ↑↑
Finish: Proof

DATE	DESCRIPTION	QUANTITY SOLD	ISSUE PRICE	FINISH	PR-69	PR-70
2016	Little Creatures: Snail	8,007	149.95	Proof	130.	—
2017	Little Creatures: Dogbane Beetle	8,500	151.95	Proof	150.	—
2018	Little Creatures: Monarch Caterpillar	5,000	154.95	Proof	155.	—

MAJESTIC ANIMAL SERIES

TWENTY DOLLARS, MAJESTIC ANIMAL, 2016-2017.

Common Obverse

Regal Red-Tailed Hawk
Designer: Emily S. Damstra

Designers and Engravers:

Obv.:	Susanna Blunt, Susan Taylor
Rev.:	See reverse illustrations
Composition:	99.99% Ag, Coloured
Silver content:	31.83 g, 1.02 tr oz
Weight:	31.83 g
Diameter:	38 mm
Thickness:	N/A
Edge:	Reeded
Die Axis:	↑↑
Finish:	Proof
Case of Issue:	Maroon clamshell with custom beauty box Also sold as a subscription, with black beauty box, COA.

The Commanding Canadian Lynx
Designer: Denis Mayer Jr.

The Baronial Bald Eagle
Designer: Glen Loates

The Benevolent Bison
Designer: Doug Comeau

The Bold Black Bear
Designer: Pierre Leduc

DATE	DESCRIPTION	QUANTITY SOLD	ISSUE PRICE	FINISH	PR-69	PR-70
2016	Regal Red-Tailed Hawk	5,648	99.95	Proof	100.	—
2016	The Commanding Canadian Lynx	5,821	99.95	Proof	100.	—
2016	The Baronial Bald Eagle	5,545	99.95	Proof	100.	—
2016	The Benevolent Bison	4,965	99.95	Proof	100.	—
2017	The Bold Black Bear	5,145	99.95	Proof	100.	—

TWENTY DOLLARS, *STAR TREK*™: ENTERPRISE, 2016.

Designers and Engravers:

Obv.:	Susanna Blunt, Susan Taylor
Rev.:	RCM Staff
Composition:	99.99% Ag, Coloured
Silver content:	31.39 g, 1.01 tr oz
Weight:	31.39 g
Diameter:	38 mm
Thickness:	N/A
Edge:	Reeded
Die Axis:	↑↑
Finish:	Proof
Case of Issue:	Maroon clamshell with graphic beauty box, COA

DATE	DESCRIPTION	QUANTITY SOLD	ISSUE PRICE	FINISH	PR-69	PR-70
2016	*Star Trek*™: Enterprise	11,491	109.95	Proof	110.	—

LANDSCAPE ILLUSION SERIES

TWENTY DOLLARS, LANDSCAPE ILLUSION, 2016-2017.

Common Obverse

Mountain Goat

Designers and Engravers:

Obv.:	Susanna Blunt, Susan Taylor
Rev.:	Julius T. Csotonyi
Composition:	99.99% Ag, Coloured
Silver content:	31.83 g, 1.02 tr oz
Weight:	31.83 g
Diameter:	38 mm
Thickness:	N/A
Edge:	Reeded
Die Axis:	↑↑
Finish:	Proof
Case of Issue:	sold as a subscription, white box with custom beauty box, COA.

Butterfly

Salmon

Pronghorn Antelope

Snowy Owl

DATE	DESCRIPTION	QUANTITY SOLD	ISSUE PRICE	FINISH	PR-69	PR-70
2016	Mountain Goat	3,517	99.95	Proof	100.	—
2016	Butterfly	3,871	99.95	Proof	100.	—
2016	Salmon	3,121	99.95	Proof	100.	—
2017	Pronghorn Antelope	2,903	99.95	Proof	100.	—
2017	Snowy Owl	2,794	99.95	Proof	100.	—

TWENTY DOLLARS, CANADA'S COLOURFUL MAPLE LEAF (SHAPED), 2016.

Designers and Engravers:

Obv.:	Susanna Blunt, Susan Taylor
Rev.:	Maurice Gervais
Composition:	99.99% Ag, Coloured
Silver content:	31.5 g, 1.01 tr oz
Weight:	31.5 g
Diameter:	42 mm x 43 mm
Thickness:	N/A
Edge:	Plain
Die Axis:	↑↑
Finish:	Proof
Case of Issue:	Custom Maple leaf shaped presentation case, COA

DATE	DESCRIPTION	QUANTITY SOLD	ISSUE PRICE	FINISH	PR-69	PR-70
2016	Canada's Colourful Maple Leaf	11,407	154.95	Proof	155.	—

TWENTY DOLLARS, JEWEL OF THE RAIN: BIGLEAF MAPLE, 2016-2017.

| 2016 Obverse | Jewel of the Rain:
Bigleaf Maple
Des.: Caren Heine | 2017 Obverse | Jewel of the Rain:
Sugar Maple Leaves
Des.: Lisa Thomson-Khan |

Designers:
Obv.:   Susanna Blunt
Rev.:   See reverse illustrations
Composition: 99.99% Ag, Coloured
Silver content: 31.39 g, 1.01 tr oz
Weight: 31.39 g
Diameter: 38 mm
Thickness: N/A
Case of Issue: Maroon clamshell with black beauty box, COA

Engravers:
Obv.:   Susan Taylor

Edge: Reeded
Die Axis: ↑↑
Finish: Proof

DATE	DESCRIPTION	QUANTITY SOLD	ISSUE PRICE	FINISH	PR-69	PR-70
2016	Jewel of the Rain: Bigleaf Maple	4,482	124.95	Proof	125.	—
2017	Jewel of the Rain: Sugar Maple Leaves	4,500	129.95	Proof	130.	—

TWENTY DOLLARS, MAPLE LEAF MAZE, 2016.

Designers and Engravers:
Obv.:   Susanna Blunt, Susan Taylor
Rev.:   Maurice Gervais
Composition: 99.99% Ag, Coloured
Silver content: 31.39 g, 1.01 tr oz
Weight: 31.39 g
Diameter: 38 mm
Thickness: N/A
Edge: Reeded
Die Axis: ↑↑
Finish: Proof
Case of Issue: Maroon clamshell with black beauty box, COA

DATE	DESCRIPTION	QUANTITY SOLD	ISSUE PRICE	FINISH	PR-69	PR-70
2016	Maple Leaf Maze	6,647	114.95	Proof	115.	—

DC COMICS™ ORIGINALS SERIES

WENTY DOLLARS, *DC COMICS™ ORIGINALS*, 2016

Common Obverse

Designers and Engravers:
Obv.:	Susanna Blunt, Susan Taylor
Rev.:	DC Comics, RCM Staff

Composition: 99.99% Ag, with Colour
Silver content: 31.83 g, 1.02 tr oz
Weight: 31.83 g
Diameter: 40.0 mm
Thickness: N/A
Edge: Reeded
Die Axis: ↑↑
Finish: Proof
Case of Issue: One-of-a-kind collector case features a glow-in-the-dark BATMAN™ emblem!, COA

DC Comics™ Originals:
The Man of Steel™

DC Comics™ Originals:
The Amazing Amazon

DC Comics™ Originals:
The Dark Knight™

DC Comics™ Originals:
The Trinity

DATE	DESCRIPTION	QUANTITY SOLD	ISSUE PRICE	FINISH	PR-69	PR-70
2016	DC Comics™ Originals: The Man of Steel™	3,088	109.95	Proof	110.	—
2016	DC Comics™ Originals: The Amazing Amazon	4,396	109.95	Proof	110.	—
2016	DC Comics™ Originals: The Dark Knight™	2,889	109.95	Proof	110.	—
2016	DC Comics™ Originals: The Trinity	2,132	112.95	Proof	110.	—

Note: Coins illustrated smaller than actual size.

WENTY DOLLARS, DIWALI: FESTIVAL OF LIGHTS, 2016.
A $200 gold coin with the same design was issued in 2015 (see page 460).

Designers and Engravers:
Obv.:	Susanna Blunt, Susan Taylor
Rev.:	Sarindar Dhaliwal

Composition: 99.99% Ag, Coloured
Silver content: 31.39 g, 1.01 tr oz
Weight: 31.39 g
Diameter: 38 mm
Thickness: N/A
Edge: Reeded
Die Axis: ↑↑
Finish: Proof
Case of Issue: Maroon clamshell with black beauty box, COA

DATE	DESCRIPTION	QUANTITY SOLD	ISSUE PRICE	FINISH	PR-69	PR-70
2016	Diwali: Fesitval of Lights	2,981	91.95	Proof	90.	—

ICONIC STAR TREK™ SCENES

TWENTY DOLLARS, ICONIC *STAR TREK*™ SCENES, 2016

Part of the Royal Canadian Mint's celebration of the 50th Anniversary of *Star Trek* — a television series that is beloved by generations of Canadians and whose vision of the future helped inspire innovation in our time!

| Common Obverse | *Star Trek*™: The City on the Edge of Forever | *Star Trek*™: Mirror Mirror | *Star Trek*™: The Trouble With Tribbles |

Designers:
Obv.:	Susanna Blunt
Rev.:	RCM Staff

Composition: 99.99% Ag, with Colour
Silver content: 31.39 g, 1.01 tr oz
Weight: 31.39 g
Diameter: 38.0 mm
Thickness: N/A
Case of Issue: Graphic beauty box.

Engravers:
Obv.:	Susan Taylor
Rev.:	RCM Staff

Edge: Reeded
Die Axis: ↑↑
Finish: Proof

DATE	DESCRIPTION	QUANTITY SOLD	ISSUE PRICE	FINISH	PR-69	PR-70
2016	*Star Trek*: The City on the Edge of Forever	5,204	109.95	Proof	110.	—
2016	*Star Trek*: Mirror Mirror	5,093	109.95	Proof	110.	—
2016	*Star Trek*: The Trouble With Tribbles	5,245	109.95	Proof	110.	—

Note: Coins illustrated smaller than actual size.

TWENTY DOLLARS, A ROYAL TOUR, 2016.

Designers and Engravers:
Obv.:	Susanna Blunt, Susan Taylor
Rev.:	Chris Jelf

Composition: 99.99% Ag, Coloured
Silver content: 31.39 g, 1.01 tr oz
Weight: 31.39 g
Diameter: 38 mm
Thickness: N/A
Edge: Reeded
Die Axis: ↑↑
Finish: Proof
Case of Issue: Maroon clamshell with black beauty box, COA

DATE	DESCRIPTION	QUANTITY SOLD	ISSUE PRICE	FINISH	PR-69	PR-70
2016	A Royal Tour	6,542	109.95	Proof	110.	—

WENTY DOLLARS, THE COLOURFUL WINGS OF A BUTTERFLY, 2016.

Designers and Engravers:

Obv.:	Susanna Blunt, Susan Taylor
Rev.:	Bonnie Ross

Composition: 99.99% Ag, Coloured
Silver content: 31.39 g, 1.01 tr oz
Weight: 31.39 g
Diameter: 38 mm
Thickness: N/A
Edge: Reeded
Die Axis: ↑↑
Finish: Proof
Case of Issue: Maroon clamshell with black beauty box, COA

DATE	DESCRIPTION	QUANTITY SOLD	ISSUE PRICE	FINISH	PR-69	PR-70
2016	The Colourful Wings of a Butterfly	2,682	158.95	Proof	160.	—

CANADIAN KALEIDOSCOPE SERIES

WENTY DOLLARS, CANADIANA KALEIDSCOPE: 2016-2017.

Tumbled glass and coloured shapes create amazing patterns inside a kaleidoscope, and this breakthrough new series explores the incredible esigns that can be achieved when great Canadian icons become the focus of the kaleidoscope's reflective magic.

   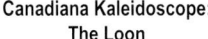 

Common Obverse	**Canadiana Kaleidoscope: Polar Bear**	**Canadiana Kaleidoscope: The Loon**	**Canadiana Kaleidoscope: Maple Leaf**

esigners:

Obv.:	Susanna Blunt
Rev.:	Calder Moore

omposition: 99.99% Ag
ilver content: 31.85 g, 1.02 tr oz
eight: 31.85 g
iameter: 60.0 mm
hickness: N/A
ase of Issue: Maroon clamshell with black beauty box.

Engravers:

Obv.:	Susan Taylor
Rev.:	Calder Moore

Edge: Plain
Die Axis: ↑↑
Finish: Proof

DATE	DESCRIPTION	QUANTITY SOLD	ISSUE PRICE	FINISH	PR-69	PR-70
2016	Canadiana Kaleidoscope: Polar Bear	3,626	117.95	Proof	120.	—
2017	Canadiana Kaleidoscope: The Loon	7,500	117.95	Proof	120.	—
2017	Canadiana Kaleidoscope: Maple Leaf	7,500	117.95	Proof	120.	—

ote: Coins illustrated smaller than actual size.

TWENTY DOLLARS, NATURE'S ADORNMENTS: DRAGONFLY, 2017.

Designers and Engravers:

Obv.:	Susanna Blunt, Susan Taylor
Rev.:	Emily Damstra
Composition:	99.99% Ag, Coloured
Silver content:	31.39 g, 1.01 tr oz
Weight:	31.39 g
Diameter:	38 mm
Thickness:	N/A
Edge:	Reeded
Die Axis:	↑↑
Finish:	Proof
Case of Issue:	Maroon clamshell with graphic beauty box, COA

DATE	DESCRIPTION	QUANTITY SOLD	ISSUE PRICE	FINISH	PR-69	PR-70
2017	Nature's Adornments: Dragonfly	2,749	148.95	Proof	150.	—

UNDER THE SEA SERIES

TWENTY DOLLARS, UNDER THE SEA, 2017.

This three-coin series features unique marine species found in Canadian waters.

Common Obverse	Seahorse	Sea Star	Sea Turtle

Designers:

Obv.:	Susanna Blunt
Rev.:	Maurice Gervais
Composition:	99.99% Ag, Coloured
Weight:	31.39 g
Diameter:	38 mm
Thickness:	N/A
Case of Issue:	Maroon clamshell with black beauty box, COA

Engravers:

Obv.:	Susan Taylor

Silver content:	31.39 g, 1.01 tr oz
Edge:	Reeded
Die Axis:	↑↑
Finish:	Proof

DATE	DESCRIPTION	QUANTITY SOLD	ISSUE PRICE	FINISH	PR-69	PR-70
2017	Under the Sea: Seahorse	3,360	151.95	Proof	150.	—
2017	Under the Sea: Sea Star	7,500	151.95	Proof	150.	—
2017	Under the Sea: Sea Turtle	7,500	151.95	Proof	150.	—

WENTY DOLLARS, SNOWFLAKE, 2017.

Designers and Engravers:

Obv.:	Susanna Blunt, Susan Taylor
Rev.:	Don Komarechka

Composition: 99.99% Ag, Coloured
Silver content: 31.39 g, 1.01 tr oz

Weight:	31.39 g	**Edge:**	Reeded
Diameter:	38 mm	**Die Axis:**	↑↑
Thickness:	N/A	**Finish:**	Proof

Case of Issue: Maroon clamshell with black beauty box, COA

DATE	DESCRIPTION	QUANTITY SOLD	ISSUE PRICE	FINISH	PR-69	PR-70
2017	Snowflake	5,026	113.95	Proof	115.	—

WENTY DOLLARS, SNOW-COVERED TREES, 2017.

Designers and Engravers:

Obv.:	Susanna Blunt, Susan Taylor
Rev.:	Tony Bianco

Composition: 99.99% Ag, Coloured
Silver content: 31.39 g, 1.01 tr oz

Weight:	31.39 g	**Edge:**	Reeded
Diameter:	38 mm	**Die Axis:**	↑↑
Thickness:	N/A	**Finish:**	Proof

Case of Issue: Maroon clamshell with black beauty box, COA

DATE	DESCRIPTION	QUANTITY SOLD	ISSUE PRICE	FINISH	PR-69	PR-70
2017	Snow-Covered Trees	3,114	152.95	Proof	150.	—

WENTY DOLLARS, BRILLIANT BIRCH LEAVES WITH DRUSY STONE, 2017.

Designers and Engravers:

Obv.:	Susanna Blunt, Susan Taylor
Rev.:	Tony Bianco

Composition: 99.99% Ag, Coloured
Silver content: 31.39 g, 1.01 tr oz
Weight: 31.39 g
Diameter: 38 mm
Thickness: N/A
Edge: Reeded
Die Axis: ↑↑
Finish: Proof
Case of Issue: Maroon clamshell with black beauty box, COA

DATE	DESCRIPTION	QUANTITY SOLD	ISSUE PRICE	FINISH	PR-69	PR-70
2017	Brilliant Birch Leaves with Drusy Stone	1,878	161.95	Proof	160.	—

TWENTY DOLLARS, THE NUTTY SQUIRREL AND THE MIGHTY OAK, 2017.

Designers and Engravers:

Obv.:	Susanna Blunt, Susan Taylor
Rev.:	Tony Bianco
Composition:	99.99% Ag, Coloured
Silver content:	31.39 g, 1.01 tr oz
Weight:	31.39 g
Diameter:	38 mm
Thickness:	N/A
Edge:	Reeded
Die Axis:	↑↑
Finish:	Proof
Case of Issue:	Maroon clamshell with black beauty box, COA

DATE	DESCRIPTION	QUANTITY SOLD	ISSUE PRICE	FINISH	PR-69	PR-70
2017	The Nutty Squirrel and the Mighty Oak	2,131	116.95	Proof	115.	—

THREE-DIMENSIONAL SERIES

TWENTY DOLLARS, THREE-DIMENSIONAL, 2017-2018.

Common Obverse   3-D Breaching Whale   3-D Leaping Cougar   3-D Approaching Canada Goose

Designers:

			Engravers:	
Obv.:	Susanna Blunt		Obv.:	Susan Taylor
Rev.:	Matt Bowen			
Composition:	99.99% Ag, Coloured			
Silver content:	31.39 g, 1.01 tr oz			
Weight:	31.39 g		**Edge:**	Reeded
Diameter:	38 mm		**Die Axis:**	↑↑
Thickness:	N/A		**Finish:**	Proof
Case of Issue:	Maroon clamshell with black beauty box, COA			

DATE	DESCRIPTION	QUANTITY SOLD	ISSUE PRICE	FINISH	PR-69	PR-70
2017	Three-Dimensional Breaching Whale	4,657	117.95	Proof	120.	—
2017	Three-Dimensional Leaping Cougar	6,000	117.95	Proof	120.	—
2018	Three-Dimensional Approaching Canada Goose	6,000	117.95	Proof	120.	—

GLISTENING NORTH SERIES

WENTY DOLLARS, GLISTENING NORTH, 2017.

A collectible work of art that celebrates the beauty of Northern Canada and its wildlife! An RCM first — selective use of Diamond Glitter adds an tensely glittering effect that recreates the light-reflecting qualities of the coloured snow and ice.

Common Obverse

The Polar Bear
Designer: Glen Loates

The Arctic Tern
Designer: Derek C. Wicks

The Arctic Wolf
Designer: Maurade Baynton

esigners:
Obv.: Susanna Blunt
Rev.: See reverse illustrations
omposition: 99.99% Ag
lver content: 31.39 g, 1.01 tr oz
eight: 31.39 g
iameter: 38.0 mm
hickness: N/A
ase of Issue: Maroon clamshell with black beauty box. COA.

Engravers:
Obv.: Susan Taylor
Rev.: See reverse illustrations

Edge: Reeded
Die Axis: ↑↑
Finish: Proof

DATE	DESCRIPTION	QUANTTY SOLD	ISSUE PRICE	FINISH	PR-69	PR-70
2017	Glistening North: The Polar Bear	4,595	114.95	Proof	115.	—
2017	Glistening North: The Arctic Tern	7,500	114.95	Proof	115.	—
2017	Glistening North: The Arctic Wolf	5,000	119.95	Proof	120.	—

WENTY DOLLARS, CANADIAN UNDERWATER LIFE, 2017.

This unique coin takes you beneath the waves to discover the amazing underwater worlds that lie off Canada's coasts. The 3D "water" droplet on is coin highlights six of the ocean's residents who face significant challenges caused by human activity.

Designers and Engravers:
Obv.: Susanna Blunt, Susan Taylor
Rev.: Alexandra Lefort
Composition: 99.99% Ag, Coloured
Silver content: 31.39 g, 1.01 tr oz
Weight: 31.39 g
Diameter: 38 mm
Thickness: N/A
Edge: Reeded
Die Axis: ↑↑
Finish: Proof
Case of Issue: Maroon clamshell with black beauty box, COA

DATE	DESCRIPTION	QUANTITY SOLD	ISSUE PRICE	FINISH	PR-69	PR-70
2017	Canadian Underwater Life	4,581	106.95	Proof	110.	—

NATURE'S IMPRESSIONS SERIES

TWENTY DOLLARS, NATURE'S IMPRESSIONS, 2017-2018.

Striking edge patterning features animal prints that are carefully engraved all along the coin's edge in a continuous pattern — a creative tie-in the reverse image itself.

Common Obverse

Woodland Caribou

Polar Bear

Wolf

Designers:
   Obv.:   Susanna Blunt
   Rev.:   Claudio D'Angelo
Composition: 99.99% Ag
Weight: 31.39 g
Diameter: 38.0 mm
Thickness: N/A
Case of Issue: Maroon clamshell with custom beauty box. COA.

Engravers:
   Obv.:   Susan Taylor
   Rev.:   RCM Staff
Silver content: 31.39 g, 1.01 tr oz
Edge: Plain with edge pattern
Die Axis: ↑↑
Finish: Proof

DATE	DESCRIPTION	QUANTITY SOLD	ISSUE PRICE	FINISH	PR-69	PR-70
2017	Nature's Impressions: Woodland Caribou	2,696	102.95	Proof	100.	—
2017	Nature's Impressions: Polar Bear	503	102.95	Proof	100.	—
2018	Nature's Impressions: Wolf	5,500	104.95	Proof	105.	—

TWENTY DOLLARS, BEST WISHES ON YOUR WEDDING DAY!, 2017-2018.

Selective pink gold plating brings to life the intricately patterned heart on the reverse, as well as the effigy of Her Majesty Queen Elizabeth II on the obvers

2017-2018 Common Obverse

2017 Best Wishes

2018 Best Wishes

Designers:
   Obv.:   Susanna Blunt
   Rev.:   Sylvie Daigneault
Composition: 99.99% Ag, Coloured
Weight: 31.83 g
Diameter: 40 mm
Thickness: N/A
Case of Issue: Premium graphic box, COA.

Engravers:
   Obv.:   Susan Taylor
   Rev.:   RCM Staff
Silver content: 31.83 g, 1.02 tr oz
Edge: Reeded
Die Axis: ↑↑
Finish: Proof

DATE	DESCRIPTION	MINTAGE	ISSUE PRICE	FINISH	PR-69	PR-70
2017	Best Wishes On Your Wedding Day!	10,000	112.95	Proof	110.	—
2018	Best Wishes On Your Wedding Day!	10,000	114.95	Proof	115.	—

AIRCRAFT OF THE SECOND WORLD WAR SERIES

TWENTY DOLLARS, AIRCRAFT OF THE SECOND WORLD WAR, 2017.

The Aircraft of the Second World War series salutes three of the most iconic aircraft flown between 1939 and 1945. Whether used to defend the homeland, in combat overseas or as part of the British Commonwealth Air Training Plan here in Canada, these aircraft are remembered as important symbols of Canadian valour and sacrifice.

Common Obverse

Designers and Engravers:

Obv.:	Susanna Blunt, Susan Taylor
Rev.:	David A. Oram

Composition: 99.99% Ag
Silver content: 31.83 g, 1.02 tr oz

Weight:	31.83 g	**Edge:**	Reeded
Diameter:	40.0 mm	**Die Axis:**	↑↑
Thickness:	N/A	**Finish:**	Proof

Case of Issue: Maroon clamshell with black beauty box. COA.

Hawker Hurricane

Avro Anson

Consolidated Canso

DATE	DESCRIPTION	QUANTITY SOLD	ISSUE PRICE	FINISH	PR-69	PR-70
2017	Aircraft of the Second World War: Hawker Hurricane	500	102.95	Proof	100.	—
2017	Aircraft of the Second World War: Avro Anson	7,500	102.95	Proof	100.	—
2017	Aircraft of the Second World War: Consolidated Canso	7,500	102.95	Proof	100.	—

NOCTURNAL BY NATURE SERIES

TWENTY DOLLARS, NOCTURNAL BY NATURE, 2017-2018.

An innovative RCM FIRST: The first-time use of black rhodium plating, one of Earth's rarest precious metals, lends itself perfectly to recreating t
dark night sky, yet allows the moon's uniquely frosted finish to shine through.

| Common Obverse | The Barn Owl
Des.: Jamie Desrochers | The Little Brown Bat
Des.: Calder Moore | The Howling Wolf
Claude Thivierge |

Designers:		Engravers:	
Obv.:	Susanna Blunt	Obv.:	Susan Taylor
Rev.:	See reverse illustratioint	Rev.:	RCM Staff
Composition:	99.99% Ag		
Silver content:	31.39 g, 1.02 tr oz		
Weight:	31.39 g	Edge:	Plain
Diameter:	38 mm	Die Axis:	↑↑
Thickness:	N/A	Finish:	Matte Proof
Case of Issue:	Maroon clamshell with black beauty box, COA.		

DATE	DESCRIPTION	MINTAGE	ISSUE PRICE	FINISH	PR-69	PR-70
2017	Nocturnal By Nature: The Barn Owl	7,000	119.95	Matte Proof	120.	—
2017	Nocturnal By Nature: The Little Brown Bat	7,000	119.95	Matte Proof	120.	—
2018	Nocturnal By Nature: The Howling Wolf	7,000	119.95	Matte Proof	120.	—

TWENTY DOLLARS, PEARL FLOWERS, 2017.

Designers and Engravers:	
Obv.:	Susanna Blunt
Rev.:	Margaret Best
Composition:	99.99% Ag, Coloured
Silver content:	31.39 g, 1.01 tr oz
Weight:	31.39 g
Diameter:	38 mm
Thickness:	N/A
Edge:	Reeded
Die Axis:	↑↑
Finish:	Proof
Case of Issue:	Maroon clamshell with black beauty box, CC

DATE	DESCRIPTION	MINTAGE	ISSUE PRICE	FINISH	PR-69	PR-70
2017	Pearl Flowers	6,000	119.95	Proof	120.	—

ANCIENT CANADA SERIES

TWENTY DOLLARS, ANCIENT CANADA, 2017-2018.

Millions of years ago, the Canadian landscape was teeming with prehistoric species whose remains lie in the rocks that bridge our era with theirs. This is Ancient Canada! Through unique striking techniques and an antique finish, take a closer look at life before us through its depiction of the fossilized remains.

 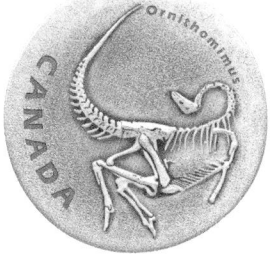 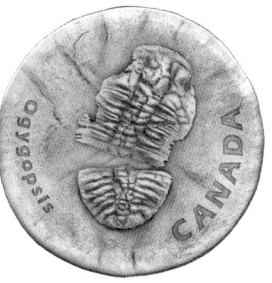 

| Common Obverse | Image based on fossil specimen TMP 1995.110.1 curated at the Royal Tyrrell Museum | Image based on fossil specimen TMP 1995.110.1 curated at the Royal Tyrrell Museum | Image based on fossil specimen curated at the Royal Tyrrell Museum |

Designers:
Obv.: Susanna Blunt
Rev.: See reverse illustration
Composition: 99.99% Ag
Silver content: 31.39 g, 1.02 tr oz
Weight: 31.39 g
Diameter: 38 mm (approx.)
Thickness: N/A
Case of Issue: Floating frame with black beaty box.

Engravers:
Obv.: Susan Taylor
Rev.: RCM Staff

Edge: Plain
Die Axis: ↑↑
Finish: Antique

DATE	DESCRIPTION	MINTAGE	ISSUE PRICE	FINISH	PR-69	PR-70
2017	Ancient Canada: *Ornithomimus*	5,500	134.95	Antique	135.	—
2017	Ancient Canada: *Ogygopsis*	5,500	134.95	Antique	135.	—
2018	Ancient Canada: *Gorgosaurus*	5,500	134.95	Antique	135.	—

TWENTY DOLLARS, *STAR TREK*™: THE BORG, 2017.

Designers and Engravers:
Obv.: Susanna Blunt
Rev.: RCM Staff
Composition: 99.99% Ag, Coloured
Silver content: 31.39 g, 1.01 tr oz
Weight: 31.39 g
Diameter: 38 mm
Thickness: N/A
Edge: Reeded
Die Axis: ↑↑
Finish: Proof
Case of Issue: Maroon clamshell with graphic beauty box, COA

DATE	DESCRIPTION	MINTAGE	ISSUE PRICE	FINISH	PR-69	PR-70
2017	*Star Trek*™: The Borg	10,000	112.95	Proof	115.	—

CANADIAN HONOURS SERIES

TWENTY DOLLARS, CANADIAN HONOURS, 2017-2018.
A 5-coin series explores the highest honours in Canada's Honours System.

Common Obverse

Sacrifice Medal

45th Anniversary of the Order of Military Merit

50th Anniversary of the Order of Canada

45th Anniversary of the Cross of Valour

25th Anniversary of the Star of Military Valour

Designers:		**Engravers:**	
Obv.:	Susanna Blunt	Obv.:	Susan Taylor
Rev.:	Various artists		
Composition:	99.99% Ag, Coloured		
Silver content:	31.83 g, 1.02 tr oz		
Weight:	31.83 g	**Edge:**	Reeded
Diameter:	40 mm	**Die Axis:**	↑↑
Thickness:	N/A	**Finish:**	Proof
Case of Issue:	Maroon clamshell with black beauty box, COA		

DATE	DESCRIPTION	MINTAGE	ISSUE PRICE	FINISH	PR-69	PR-70
2017	Canadian Honours: Sacrifice Medal	5,500	109.95	Proof	110.	—
2017	Canadian Honours: 45th Anniversary of the Order of the Military Merit	5,500	109.95	Proof	110.	—
2017	Canadian Honours 50th Anniversary of the Order of Canada	5,500	109.95	Proof	110.	—
2017	Canadian Honours 45th Anniversary of the Cross of Valour	5,500	109.95	Proof	110.	—
2018	Canadian Honours 25th Anniversary of the Star of Military Valour	5,500	109.95	Proof	110.	—

EN PLEIN AIR SERIES

TWENTY DOLLARS, EN PLEIN AIR, 2017-2018.

Common Obverse

Springtime Gifts

Maritime Memories

A Paddle Awaits

Designers:		Engravers:	
Obv.:	Susanna Blunt	Obv.:	Susan Taylor
Rev.:	Elizabeth Sim	Rev.:	RCM Staff
Composition:	99.99% Ag, Coloured	Thickness:	N/A
Silver content:	31.85 g, 1.02 tr oz	Edge:	Plain
Weight:	31.85 g	Die Axis:	↑↑
Diameter:	60 mm	Finish:	Proof
Case of Issue:	Maroon clamshell with black beauty box, COA		

Note: Coins illustrated smaller than actual size.

DATE	DESCRIPTION	MINTAGE	ISSUE PRICE	FINISH	PR-69	PR-70
2017	En Plein Air:Springtime Gifts	5,500	119.95	Proof	120.	—
2017	En Plein Air: Maritime Memories	5,500	119.95	Proof	120.	—
2017	En Plein Air: A Paddle Awaits	5,500	119.95	Proof	120.	—

TWENTY DOLLARS, CANOE TO TRANQUIL TIMES, 2017.

This coin pays tribute to the enduring, engaging canoe — an ingenious creation from the past that is now a modern icon of Canada. The RCM's second coin featuring a wood piece — now with selective colour.

Designers and Engravers:	
Obv.:	Susanna Blunt
Rev.:	Margaret Best
Composition:	99.99% Ag, Coloured
Silver content:	31.39 g, 1.01 tr oz
Weight:	31.39 g
Diameter:	38 mm
Thickness:	N/A
Edge:	Reeded
Die Axis:	↑↑
Finish:	Proof
Case of Issue:	Maroon clamshell with black beauty box, COA

DATE	DESCRIPTION	MINTAGE	ISSUE PRICE	FINISH	PR-69	PR-70
2017	Canoe to Tranquil Times	4,500	124.95	Proof	125.	—

CANADA'S COASTS SERIES

TWENTY DOLLARS, CANADA'S COASTS SERIES, 2017.

Follow the setting sun across each coin in the series – each sunset features its own disctinct colours.

| Common Obverse | Pacific Coast | Atlantic Coast | Arctic Coast |

Designers:
   Obv.:   Susanna Blunt
   Rev.:   Curtis Atwater
Composition: 99.99% Ag, Coloured
Silver content: 31.39 g, 1.01 tr oz
Weight: 31.39 g
Diameter: 38 mm
Thickness: N/A
Case of Issue: Maroon clamshell with black beauty box, COA

Engravers:
   Obv.:   Susan Taylor
   Rev.:   RCM Staff

Edge: Reeded
Die Axis: ↑↑
Finish: Proof

DATE	DESCRIPTION	MINTAGE	ISSUE PRICE	FINISH	PR-69	PR-70
2017	Pacific Coast	7,500	109.95	Proof	110.	—
2017	Atlantic Coast	7,500	109.95	Proof	110.	—
2017	Arctic Coast	7,500	109.95	Proof	110.	—

TWENTY DOLLARS, A PLATINUM CELEBRATION, 2017.

On November 20, 2017, Her Majesty Queen Elizabeth II and His Royal Highness Prince Philip, Duke of Edinburgh, celbrated their 70th weddi anniversary. The Royal Canadian Mint marked this occasion with a special keepsake coin that will be prized by royalty watchers, historians, collectc and art connoisseurs alike.

Designers and Engravers:
   Obv.:   Susanna Blunt
   Rev.:   Derek Wicks
Composition: 99.99% Ag
Silver content: 31.39 g, 1.01 tr oz
Weight: 31.39 g
Diameter: 38 mm
Thickness: N/A
Edge: Reeded
Die Axis: ↑↑
Finish: Proof
Case of Issue: Maroon clamshell with black beauty box, CO

DATE	DESCRIPTION	MINTAGE	ISSUE PRICE	FINISH	PR-69	PR-70
2017	A Platinum Celebration	7,500	104.95	Proof	105.	—

LOCOMOTIVES ACROSS CANADA SERIES

TWENTY DOLLARS, LOCOMOTIVES ACROSS CANADA, 2017.

Common Obverse	The 4-4-0 Des.: David A. Oram	RS-20 Des.: John Mantha	GE ES44AC Des.: John Mantha

Designers:
Obv.: Susanna Blunt
Rev.: See reverse illustrations
Composition: 99.99% Ag, Selective gold plating
Silver content: 31.39 g, 1.01 tr oz
Weight: 31.39 g
Diameter: 38 mm
Thickness: N/A
Case of Issue: Maroon clamshell with black beauty box, COA

Engravers:
Obv.: Susan Taylor
Rev.: RCM Staff

Edge: Reeded
Die Axis: ↑↑
Finish: Proof

DATE	DESCRIPTION	MINTAGE	ISSUE PRICE	FINISH	PR-69	PR-70
2017	Locomotives Across Canada: The 4-4-0	7,500	112.95	Proof	115.	—
2017	Locomotives Across Canada: RS 20	7,500	112.95	Proof	115.	—
2017	Locomotives Across Canada: GE ES44AC	7,500	112.95	Proof	115.	—

TWENTY DOLLARS, GILDED SILVER MAPLE LEAF (SHAPED), 2017.

Designers and Engravers:
Obv.: Susanna Blunt, Susan Taylor
Rev.: Joel Kimmel
Composition: 99.99% Ag, Selective gold plating
Silver content: 31.39 g, 1.01 tr oz
Weight: 31.39 g
Diameter: 42 mm x 43 mm
Thickness: N/A
Edge: Plain
Die Axis: ↑↑
Finish: Proof
Case of Issue: Maroon clamshefll with black beauty box, COA

DATE	DESCRIPTION	MINTAGE	ISSUE PRICE	FINISH	PR-69	PR-70
2017	Gilded Silver Maple Leaf	10,000	161.95	Proof	160.	—

MOTHER NATURE'S MAGNIFICATION SERIES

TWENTY DOLLARS, MOTHER NATURE'S MAGNIFICATION, 2017-2018.

Common Obverse	Beauty Under The Sun Des.: Alexandra Lefort	Morning Dew Des.: Mrgaret Best

Designers:		Engravers:	
Obv.:	Susanna Blunt	Obv.:	Susan Taylor
Rev.:	See reverse illustrations	Rev.:	RCM Staff
Composition:	99.99% Ag, Coloured		
Silver content:	31.39 g, 1.01 tr oz		
Weight:	31.39 g	Edge:	Reeded
Diameter:	38 mm	Die Axis:	↑↑
Thickness:	N/A	Finish:	Proof
Case of Issue:	Maroon clamshell with black beauty box, COA		

DATE	DESCRIPTION	MINTAGE	ISSUE PRICE	FINISH	PR-69	PR-70
2017	Mother Nature's Magnification: Beauty Under The Sun	7,500	106.95	Proof	110.	—
2017	Mother Nature's Magnification: Morning Dew	7,500	106.95	Proof	110.	—

BEJEWELED BUGS SERIES

TWENTY DOLLARS, BEJEWELED BUGS, 2017.

Common Obverse	Bejeweled Bugs: Butterfly	Bejeweled Bugs: Bee

Designers:		Engravers:	
Obv.:	Susanna Blunt	Obv.:	Susan Taylor
Rev.:	Jori van der Linde	Rev.:	RCM Staff
Composition:	99.99% Ag	Silver content:	31.39 g, 1.01 tr oz
Weight:	31.39 g	Edge:	Reeded
Diameter:	38.0 mm	Die Axis:	↑↑
Thickness:	N/A	Finish:	Proof
Case of Issue:	Maroon clamshell with black beauty box, COA.		

DATE	DESCRIPTION	MINTAGE	ISSUE PRICE	FINISH	PR-69	PR-70
2017	Bejeweled Bugs: Butterfly	4,000	174.95	Proof	175.	—
2017	Bejeweled Bugs: Bee	4,000	174.95	Proof	175.	—

FROM SEA TO SEA TO SEA SERIES

TWENTY DOLLARS, FROM SEA TO SEA TO SEA, 2017-2018.

Canada's national motto pays tribute to the oceans that border our land, for these waters — and the life within them — have long nurtured, challenged and fascinated Canadians. The rich diversity of life in the Pacific, Arctic and Atlantic Oceans are an important part of Canada's maritime heritage, and is at the heart of a three-coin series.

Common Obverse

Atlantic Starfish

Pacific Salmon

Arctic Beluga Whale

Designers:		
Obv.:	Susanna Blunt	
Rev.:	Tony Bianca	
Composition:	99.99% Ag, Selective gold plating	
Silver content:	31.39 g, 1.01 tr oz	
Weight:	31.39 g	
Diameter:	38 mm	
Thickness:	N/A	
Case of Issue:	Maroon clamshell with black beauty box, COA.	

Engravers:	
Obv.:	Susan Taylor
Rev.:	RCM Staff
Edge:	Reeded
Die Axis:	↑↑
Finish:	Proof

DATE	DESCRIPTION	MINTAGE	ISSUE PRICE	FINISH	PR-69	PR-70
2017	From Sea to Sea to Sea: Atlantic Starfish	7,500	112.95	Proof	115.	—
2017	From Sea to Sea to Sea: Pacific Salmon	7,500	112.95	Proof	115.	—
2018	From Sea to Sea to Sea: Arctic Beluga Whale	7,500	112.95	Proof	115.	—

TWENTY DOLLARS, HOT AIR BALLOONS, 2017.

Designers and Engravers:	
Obv.:	Susanna Blunt
Rev.:	Calder Moore
Composition:	99.99% Ag
Silver content:	31.82 g, 1.02 tr oz
Weight:	31.82 g
Diameter:	45 long x 33 wide mm
Thickness:	N/A
Edge:	Interrupted Reeding
Die Axis:	↑↑
Finish:	Proof
Case of Issue:	Maroon clamshell with black beauty box, COA

DATE	DESCRIPTION	MINTAGE	ISSUE PRICE	FINISH	PR-69	PR-70
2017	Hot Air Balloons	5,000	114.95	Proof	115.	—

TWENTY DOLLARS, PUZZLE COIN, CANADA 150, 2017.

Like a puzzle, Confederation came together piece by piece, every part clicking into place over time, the end result far greater than the sum of parts. Diverse geographies, natural wonders and resources coming together from coast to coast to coast. A multitude of traditions, languages, an skills blurring distinct cultural lines. History may have recorded the beginning of Confederation 150 years ago, but for today's citizens, Canada c begin anywhere on this nation's ever-evolving continuum. This puzzle coin is an outstanding, first-ever achievement at the Mint, and a unique portr of Canada that will be the highlight of the most distinctive collections.

Each piece of the puzzle has a face value of $50 (central coin) and $20 (each of the jigsaw pieces). See page 392 for the $50

Designers and Engravers:

Obv.:	Susanna Blunt
Rev.:	Cathy Bursey-Sabourin
Composition:	99.99% Ag, Selective gold plating, coloured
Silver content:	502.47 g, 16.16 tr oz
Weight:	502.47 g (complete puzzle set)
Diameter:	123.7 mm
Finished Size:	184 mm x 184 mm
Thickness:	N/A
Edge:	Interrupted Reeding
Die Axis:	↑↑
Finish:	Proof
Case of Issue:	Wood case with black beauty box, COA

DATE	DESCRIPTION	MINTAGE	ISSUE PRICE	FINISH	PR-69	PR-70
2017	Puzzle Coin, Canada 150	800	1,867	Proof	2,200.	—

Note: This coin was only sold as a complete set of 14 puzzle pieces, plus a central coin.

TWENTY DOLLARS, 100TH ANNIVERSARY OF THE TORONTO MAPLE LEAFS®, 2017.

Designers and Engravers:

Obv.:	Susanna Blunt
Rev.:	Steven Rosati
Composition:	99.99% Ag
Silver content:	31.39 g, 1.01 tr oz
Weight:	31.39 g
Diameter:	38 mm
Thickness:	N/A
Edge:	Reeded
Die Axis:	↑↑
Finish:	Proof
Case of Issue:	Maroon clamshell with black beauty box, CO

DATE	DESCRIPTION	MINTAGE	ISSUE PRICE	FINISH	PR-69	PR-70
2017	100th Anniversary of the Toronto Maple Leafs®	15,000	119.95	Proof	120.	—

WENTY DOLLARS, CANADA: PROTECTING OUR FUTURE, 2017.

Designers and Engravers:

Obv.:	Susanna Blunt
Rev.:	Corrine Hunt
Composition:	99.99% Ag, Hologram
Silver content:	31.39 g, 1.01 tr oz
Weight:	31.39 g
Diameter:	38 mm
Thickness:	N/A
Edge:	Reeded
Die Axis:	↑↑
Finish:	Proof
Case of Issue:	Maroon clamshell with black beauty box, COA

DATE	DESCRIPTION	MINTAGE	ISSUE PRICE	FINISH	PR-69	PR-70
2017	Canada: Protecting Our Future	6,000	114.95	Proof	115.	—

WENTY DOLLARS, ICE CRYSTALS, 2018.

Designers and Engravers:

Obv.:	Susanna Blunt
Rev.:	Don Komarechka
Composition:	99.99% Ag
Silver content:	31.39 g, 1.01 tr oz
Weight:	31.39 g
Diameter:	38 mm
Thickness:	N/A
Edge:	Reeded
Die Axis:	↑↑
Finish:	Proof
Case of Issue:	Maroon clamshell with black beauty box, COA

DATE	DESCRIPTION	MINTAGE	ISSUE PRICE	FINISH	PR-69	PR-70
2018	Ice Crystals	6,000	113.95	Proof	115.	—

WENTY DOLLARS, TREE OF LIFE, 2018.

Designers and Engravers:

Obv.:	Susanna Blunt
Rev.:	Steve Hepburn
Composition:	99.99% Ag
Silver content:	31.39 g, 1.01 tr oz
Weight:	31.39 g
Diameter:	38 mm
Thickness:	N/A
Edge:	Reeded
Die Axis:	↑↑
Finish:	Proof
Case of Issue:	Maroon clamshell with black beauty box, COA

DATE	DESCRIPTION	MINTAGE	ISSUE PRICE	FINISH	PR-69	PR-70
2018	Tree of Life	6,500	119.95	Proof	120.	—

TWENTY DOLLARS, HOLIDAY REINDEER, 2018.

Designers and Engravers:

Obv.:	Susanna Blunt
Rev.:	Anna Bucciarelli
Composition:	99.99% Ag
Silver content:	31.39 g, 1.01 tr oz
Weight:	31.39 g
Diameter:	38 mm
Thickness:	N/A
Edge:	Reeded
Die Axis:	↑↑
Finish:	Proof
Case of Issue:	Maroon clamshell with black beauty box, CO

DATE	DESCRIPTION	MINTAGE	ISSUE PRICE	FINISH	PR-69	PR-70
2018	Holiday Reindeer	5,000	152.95	Proof	155.	—

TWENTY DOLLARS, CANADA'S ICONIC INUKSHUK: GUIDING THE WAY, 2018.

Designers and Engravers:

Obv.:	Susanna Blunt
Rev.:	Tony Bianco
Composition:	99.99% Ag, Reverse gold plating
Silver content:	31.39 g, 1.01 tr oz
Weight:	31.39 g
Diameter:	38 mm
Thickness:	N/A
Edge:	Reeded
Die Axis:	↑↑
Finish:	Proof
Case of Issue:	Maroon clamshell with black beauty box, CO

DATE	DESCRIPTION	MINTAGE	ISSUE PRICE	FINISH	PR-69	PR-70
2018	Canada's Iconic Inukshuk: Guiding The Way	5,000	114.95	Proof	115.	—

TWENTY DOLLARS, LUCKY CLOVER, 2018.

Designers and Engravers:

Obv.:	Susanna Blunt
Rev.:	Lisa Thomson Khan
Composition:	99.99% Ag
Silver content:	31.39 g, 1.01 tr oz
Weight:	31.39 g
Diameter:	38 mm
Thickness:	N/A
Edge:	Reeded
Die Axis:	↑↑
Finish:	Proof
Case of Issue:	Maroon clamshell with black beauty box, CO

DATE	DESCRIPTION	MINTAGE	ISSUE PRICE	FINISH	PR-69	PR-70
2018	Lucky Clover	6,500	104.95	Proof	105.	—

NORSE FIGUREHEADS SERIES

TWENTY DOLLARS, NORSE FIGUREHEADS, 2018.

From about AD 800 to 1050, they were the masters of the seas whose voyages defined trade, discovery and conquest in the Viking Age, and whose seafaring abilities led them to Canada's eastern shore. Step back in time with a three-coin series that re-imagines the elaborate figureheads at the prow legendary Viking longships, which embodied Norse craftsmanship and maritime supremacy in their time.

| Common Obverse | Norse Figureheads:
Northern Fury
Des.: Patrick Bélanger | Norse Figureheads:
Viking Voyage
Des.: Neil Hamelin | Norse Figureheads:
The Dragon's Sail
Des.: Jean-Pierre Vallée |

Designers:
 Obv.:   Susanna Blunt
 Rev.:   See reverse illustrations
Composition: 99.99% Ag,
Silver content: 31.39 g, 1.01 tr oz
Weight: 31.39 g
Diameter: 38 mm
Thickness: N/A
Case of Issue: Maroon clamshell with a standard black beauty box, COA.

Engravers:
 Obv.: Susan Taylor
 Rev.: RCM Staff

Edge: Reeded
Die Axis: ↑↑
Finish: Proof

DATE	DESCRIPTION	MINTAGE	ISSUE PRICE	FINISH	PR-69	PR-70
2018	Norse Figureheads: Northern Fury	6,000	104.95	Proof	105.	—
2018	Norse Figureheads: Viking Voyage	6,000	104.95	Proof	105.	—
2018	Norse Figureheads: The Dragon's Sail	6,000	104.95	Proof	105.	—

TWENTY DOLLARS, ROYAL PORTRAIT, 2018.

The Royal Canadian Mint proudly presents a picture-perfect coin that is both a birthday celebration for His Royal Highness the Prince of Wales and touching tribute to Her Majesty as monarch and matriarch. The photograph reproduced on the reverse (©Cecil Beaton/Victoria and Albert Museum, London/Londres) was made possible by a colour application over engraved relief, which adds textural elements to an already captivating image taken December 1948 at Buckingham Palace.

Designers and Engravers:
 Obv.:   Susanna Blunt
 Rev.:   Maurice Gervais
Composition: 99.99% Ag
Silver content: 31.39 g, 1.01 tr oz
Weight: 31.39 g
Diameter: 38 mm
Thickness: N/A
Edge: Reeded
Die Axis: ↑↑
Finish: Proof
Case of Issue: Maroon clamshell with black beauty box, COA

DATE	DESCRIPTION	MINTAGE	ISSUE PRICE	FINISH	PR-69	PR-70
2018	Royal Portrait	7,500	109.95	Proof	110.	—

MAJESTIC WILDLIFE SERIES

TWENTY DOLLARS, MAJESTIC WILDLIFE, 2018.

The Majestic Wildlife three-coin series will fascinate collectors with a view of Canada's most captivating wildlife.

Common Obverse

Majestic Wildlife:
Courageous Cougar
Des.: Pierre Leduc

Majestic Wildlife:
Wandering White-Tailed Deer
Des.: Maurade Baynton

Majestic Wildlife:
Mettlesome Mountain Goat
Des.: Pierre Leduc

Designers:		**Engravers:**	
Obv.:	Susanna Blunt	Obv.:	Susan Taylor
Rev.:	See reverse illustrations	Rev.:	RCM Staff
Composition:	99.99% Ag,		
Silver content:	31.39 g, 1.01 tr oz		
Weight:	31.39 g	**Edge:**	Reeded
Diameter:	38 mm	**Die Axis:**	↑↑
Thickness:	N/A	**Finish:**	Proof
Case of Issue:	Maroon clamshell with a standard black beauty box, COA.		

DATE	DESCRIPTION	MINTAGE	ISSUE PRICE	FINISH	PR-69	PR-70
2018	Majestic Wildlife: Courageous Cougar	6,000	104.95	Proof	105.	—
2018	Majestic Wildlife: Wandering White-Tailed Deer	6,000	104.95	Proof	105.	—
2018	Majestic Wildlife: Mettlesome Mountain Goat	6,000	104.95	Proof	105.	—

TWENTY DOLLARS, CANADA'S UNEXPLAINED PHENOMENA: THE FALCON LAKE INCIDENT, 2018.

The Falcon Lake Incident is one of Canada's most well known UFO encounters, and a fascinating mystery that is still unexplained! With an unusual shaped contour that hints at an otherworldly theme, this ovoid coin recounts the Falcon Lake Incident in vivid colour, with black-light activated features that add a preternatural glow to the unknown craft.

Designers and Engravers:	
Obv.:	Susanna Blunt
Rev.:	Joel Kimmel
Composition:	99.99% Ag
Silver content:	31.82 g, 1.02 tr oz
Weight:	31.82 g
Diameter:	45 long x 22 wide mm
Thickness:	N/A
Edge:	Interrupted reeding
Die Axis:	↑↑
Finish:	Proof
Case of Issue:	Maroon clamshell with black beauty box, COA

DATE	DESCRIPTION	MINTAGE	ISSUE PRICE	FINISH	PR-69	PR-70
2018	Canada's Unexplained Phenomena: The Falcon Lake Incident	4,000	129.95	Proof	350.	—

GEOMETRIC FAUNA SERIES

WENTY DOLLARS, GEOMETRIC FAUNA , 2018.

Each of these beloved icons of the Canadian wilderness is comprised of carefully positioned polygon shapes that are characteristic of low poly art, efore merging with a more true-to-life depiction.

| Common Obverse | Grey Wolves | Snowy Owls | Orcas |

esigners:		**Engravers:**
Obv.:	Susanna Blunt	Obv.:	Susan Taylor
Rev.:	Claude Thivierge		
omposition:	99.99% Ag		
Ilver content:	31.83 g, 1.02 tr oz		
Veight:	31.83 g	**Edge:**	Reeded
iameter:	38 mm	**Die Axis:**	↑↑
hickness:	N/A	**Finish:**	Proof
ase of Issue:	Maroon clamshell with black beauty box, COA		

DATE	DESCRIPTION	MINTAGE	ISSUE PRICE	FINISH	PR-69	PR-70
2018	Geometric Fauna: Grey Wolves	6,000	104.95	Proof	105.	—
2018	Geometric Fauna: Snowy Owls	6,000	104.95	Proof	105.	—
2018	Geometric Fauna: Orcas	6,000	104.95	Proof	105.	—

WENTY DOLLARS, FROZEN IN ICE — WOOLLY MAMMOTH, 2018.

Frozen In Ice: a colourful window in time! Amazing Ice Age species that once roamed North America, this unique coin captures a herd of *Mammuthus rimigenius* — the iconic woolly mammoth — in detailed engraving and selective colour under a frosted chunk of "ice."

Designers and Engravers:	
Obv.:	Susanna Blunt
Rev.:	Glen Loates
Composition:	99.99% Ag, Selective colour
Silver content:	31.39 g, 1.01 tr oz
Weight:	31.39 g
Diameter:	38 mm
Thickness:	N/A
Edge:	Reeded
Die Axis:	↑↑
Finish:	Proof
Case of Issue:	Maroon clamshell with black beauty box, COA

DATE	DESCRIPTION	MINTAGE	ISSUE PRICE	FINISH	PR-69	PR-70
2018	Frozen In Ice — Woolly Mammoth	5,000	109.95	Proof	110.	—

TWENTY DOLLARS, QUEEN ELIZABETH II's MAPLE LEAVES BROOCH, 2018.

During the Queen's most recent visit in 2010, she wore a maple leaves brooch that was originally presented to her grandmother, Queen Mary (the Duchess) during the royal tour in 1901. The Queen was inspired to wear it as an outward expression of the warmth she feels for her second home — th home of the maple leaf. This beautiful coin returns that gesture with an exquiite reproduction of the brooch she wore.

Designers and Engravers:

Obv.:	Susanna Blunt
Rev.:	Maurade Baynton
Composition:	99.99% Ag, Selective colour with Swarovski® pearl
Silver content:	31.39 g, 1.01 tr oz
Weight:	31.39 g
Diameter:	38 mm
Thickness:	N/A
Edge:	Reeded
Die Axis:	↑↑
Finish:	Proof
Case of Issue:	Maroon clamshell with black beauty box, CO/

DATE	DESCRIPTION	MINTAGE	ISSUE PRICE	FINISH	PR-69	PR-70
2018	Queen Elizabeth II's Maple Leaves Brooch	5,500	119.95	Proof	120.	—

TWENTY DOLLARS, A MODERN ALLEGORY: BOREALIA, 2018.

The symbolic figurehead, Borealia, is a modern take on a classic allegory, one that represents the collective spirit of Canadians in today's worl hopeful and steady in our resolve, as we rise to meet the challenges that lie ahead.

Designers and Engravers:

Obv.:	Susanna Blunt
Rev.:	Rebecca Yanovskaya
Composition:	99.99% Ag, Gold plating
Silver content:	31.39 g, 1.01 tr oz
Weight:	31.39 g
Diameter:	38 mm
Thickness:	N/A
Edge:	Reeded
Die Axis:	↑↑
Finish:	Proof
Case of Issue:	Maroon clamshell with black beauty box, CO/

DATE	DESCRIPTION	MINTAGE	ISSUE PRICE	FINISH	PR-69	PR-70
2018	A Modern Allegory: Borealia	5,000	114.95	Proof	115.	—

TWENTY DOLLARS, CAPTAIN CANUCK, 2018.

Captain Canuck personifies the spirit of Canadians by embodying self-sacrifice, determination and integrity – and all with a full dose of humility and compassio

Designers and Engravers:

Obv.:	Susanna Blunt
Rev.:	richard Comely
Composition:	99.99% Ag, Selective colour
Silver content:	31.56 g, 1.01 tr oz
Weight:	31.56 g
Diameter:	49.80 mm x 28.60 mm
Thickness:	N/A
Edge:	Plain
Die Axis:	↑↑
Finish:	Proof
Case of Issue:	Maroon clamshell with graphic beauty box, CO

DATE	DESCRIPTION	MINTAGE	ISSUE PRICE	FINISH	PR-69	PR-70
2018	Captain Canuck	3,500	119.95	Proof	120.	—

WENTY DOLLARS, THE ROYAL WEDDING OF HRH PRINCE HARRY AND MEGHAN MARKLE, 2018.

Canada's official Royal Wedding commemorative coin presents a sparkling congratulatory message on its reverse, where the portait of HRH Prince enry (Harry) and Ms. Meghan Markle is accompanied by genuine Swarovski® crystals that represent the royal engagement ring.

Designers and Engravers:
Obv.:	Susanna Blunt
Rev.:	Joel Kimmel
Composition:	99.99% Ag, Swarovski® crystals
Silver content:	31.39 g, 1.01 tr oz
Weight:	31.39 g
Diameter:	38 mm
Thickness:	N/A
Edge:	Reeded
Die Axis:	↑↑
Finish:	Proof
Case of Issue:	Maroon clamshell with graphic beauty box, COA

DATE	DESCRIPTION	MINTAGE	ISSUE PRICE	FINISH	PR-69	PR-70
2018	The Royal Wedding of HRH Prince Henry and Meghan Markle	15,000	104.95	Proof	105.	—

TWENTY DOLLAR DERIVATIVES

DATE	DESCRIPTION	QUANTITY SOLD	ISSUE PRICE	ISSUER	FINISH	MARKET PRICE
1998	**Year of the Tiger**, Fifteen dollar coin; Souvenir stamp sheet; Presentation album	8,000	88.88	RCM, CP	PR-69	150.
1998	**Twenty Dollars** Argus and Waterbomber boxed with cardboard model	N/A	N/A	RCM	PR-69	250.
2004	**Twenty Dollars** Northern Lights twenty dollar coin mounted in a frame with a large image of the Northern Lights	N/A	399.00	RCM	PR-69	175.
2012	**Twenty Dollars**, The Queen's Diamond Jubilee, The Royal Cypher, Queen Elizabeth II and Prince Philip; 3-coin wooden collector box, within a beauty box with Diamond Jubilee Cypher	1,809	274.95	RCM	PR-69	200.
2012	**Twenty Dollars** Queen Elizabeth II and Prince Philip, Three-coin case holding UK £5, Australian 50¢, Canadian $20,	4,000	399.95	RCM	PR-69	250.
2015	**Baby Burrowing Owl Coin and Stamp Set**, Twenty dollar coin and stamped postcard	7,500	109.95	RCM/PO	PR-69	100.
2015	**Baby Puffin Coin and Stamp Set**, Twenty dollar coin and stamped postcard	7,500	109.95	RCM/PO	PR-69	100.
2015	**Baby Beaver Coin and Stamp Set**, Twenty dollar coin and stamped postcard	7,500	109.95	RCM/PO	PR-69	100.

TWENTY-FIVE DOLLARS

TWENTY-FIVE DOLLARS, VANCOUVER 2010 OLYMPIC WINTER GAMES, 2007-2009.
ISSUES OF 2007.

2007 Obverse

Curling
Designer: Steve Hepburn
Engraver: Stan Witten

Ice Hockey
Designer: Steve Hepburn
Engraver: William Woodruff

Athletes' Pride
Designer: Shelagh Armstrong
Engraver: Christie Paquet

Biathlon
Designer: Bonnie Ross
Engraver: Stan Witten

Alpine Skiing
Designer: Brian Hughes
Engraver: Stan Witten

Designers:
 Obv.: Susanna Blunt
 Rev.: See reverse illustrations
Composition: 92.5% Ag, 7.5% Cu, Selective hologram
Silver content: 25.7 g, 0.826 tr oz
Weight: 27.78 g
Diameter: 40.0 mm
Thickness: 2.5 mm
Case of Issue: Singly: Black leatherette clam case; black flocked insert, encapsulated coin, COA, Olympic theme sleeve
     Set: Black leatherette, 15-hole, square clam style case; two black flocked inserts (one with seven indentations, the other with eight); encapsulated coins; COA for each coin; Olympic theme sleeve

Engravers:
 Obv.: Susan Taylor
 Rev.: See reverse illustrations
Edge: Reeded
Die Axis: ↑↑
Finish: Proof

DATE	DESCRIPTION	ISSUE DATE	QUANTITY SOLD	ISSUE PRICE	FINISH	PR-69	PR-70
2007	Curling	Feb. 23, 2007	19,531	69.95	Proof	50.	—
2007	Ice Hockey	April 14, 2007	22,512	69.95	Proof	50.	—
2007	Athletes' Pride	July 11, 2007	21,886	69.95	Proof	50.	—
2007	Biathlon	Sept. 12, 2007	16,003	69.95	Proof	50.	—
2007	Alpine Skiing	Oct. 24, 2007	13,500	69.95	Proof	50.	—

WENTY-FIVE DOLLARS, VANCOUVER 2010 OLYMPIC WINTER GAMES, 2007-2009 (cont.).

SSUES OF 2008.

2008 Obverse

Snowboarding
Designer: Steve Hepburn
Engraver: Konrad Wachelko

Freestyle Skiing
Designer: John Mardon
Engraver: Christie Paquet

Home of the 2010 Olympic Winter Games
Designer: Shelagh Armstrong
Engraver: Marcos Hallam

Figure Skating
Designer: Steve Hepburn
Engraver: José Osio

Bobsleigh
Designer: Bonnie Ross
Engraver: Stan Witten

Designers:
  Obv.:   Susanna Blunt
  Rev.:   See reverse illustrations

Engravers:
  Obv.:   Susan Taylor
  Rev.:   See reverse illustrations

Composition: 92.5% Ag, 7.5% Cu, Selective hologram
Silver content: 25.7 g, 0.826 tr oz
Weight: 27.78 g
Diameter: 40.0 mm
Thickness: 2.5 mm

Edge: Reeded
Die Axis: ↑↑
Finish: Proof

Case of Issue: Singly: Black leatherette clam case; black flocked insert, encapsulated coin, COA, Olympic theme sleeve
              Set: Black leatherette, 15-hole, square clam style case; two black flocked inserts (one with seven
                      indentations, the other with eight); encapsulated coins; COA for each coin; Olympic theme sleeve

DATE	DESCRIPTION	ISSUE DATE	QUANTITY SOLD	ISSUE PRICE	FINISH	PR-69	PR-70
2008	Snowboarding	Feb. 20, 2008	6,377	71.95	Proof	50.	—
2008	Freestyle Skiing	April 16, 2008	12,428	71.95	Proof	50.	—
2008	Home of the 2010 Olympic Winter Games	July 23, 2008	12,606	71.95	Proof	50.	—
2008	Figure Skating	Sept. 10, 2008	18,930	71.95	Proof	50.	—
2008	Bobsleigh	Oct. 29, 2008	8,800	71.95	Proof	50.	—

TWENTY-FIVE DOLLARS, VANCOUVER 2010 OLYMPIC WINTER GAMES, 2007-2009 (cont.).

ISSUES OF 2009.

2009 Obverse

Speed Skating
Designer: Tony Bianco
Engraver: William Woodruff

Cross Country Skiing
Designer: Brian Hughes
Engraver: William Woodruff

Olympic Spirit
Designer: Shelagh Armstrong
Engraver: Stan Witten

Skeleton
Designer: Tony Bianco
Engraver: Stan Witten

Ski Jumping
Designer: John Mardon
Engraver: Konrad Wachelko

Designers:
Obv.: Susanna Blunt
Rev.: See reverse illustrations
Composition: 92.5% Ag, 7.5% Cu, Selective hologram
Silver content: 25.7 g, 0.826 tr oz
Weight: 27.78 g
Diameter: 40.0 mm
Thickness: 2.5 mm

Engravers:
Obv.: Susan Taylor
Rev.: See reverse illustrations

Edge: Reeded
Die Axis: ↑↑
Finish: Proof

Case of Issue:
Singly: Black leatherette clam case; black flocked insert, encapsulated coin, COA, Olympic theme sleeve
Set: Black leatherette, 15-hole, square clam style case; two black flocked inserts (one with seven indentations, the other with eight); encapsulated coins; COA for each coin; Olympic theme sleeve

DATE	DESCRIPTION	ISSUE DATE	QUANTITY SOLD	ISSUE PRICE	FINISH	PR-69	PR-70
2009	Speed Skating	Feb. 18, 2009	27,827	71.95	Proof	50.	—
2009	Cross Country Skiing	April 15, 2009	14,292	71.95	Proof	50.	—
2009	Olympic Spirit	June 17, 2009	10,224	71.95	Proof	50.	—
2009	Skeleton	Aug.. 5, 2009	10,582	71.95	Proof	50.	—
2009	Ski Jumping	Oct. 7, 2009	11,365	71.95	Proof	50.	—
2007-2010	Set of 15 coins	—	4,764	—	Proof	700.	—

WENTY-FIVE DOLLARS, TORONTO CITY MAP, 2011.

The reverse design of this coin depicts the City of Toronto as seen through the visor of an astronaut. These coins were struck in Switzerland.

Designers:		Engravers:	
Obv.:	Susanna Blunt	Obv.:	Susan Taylor
Rev.:	Google Earth	Rev.:	RCM Staff

Composition: 99.99% Ag, Selectively gold plated
Silver content: 62.41 g, 2.01 tr oz
Weight: 62.41 g
Diameter: 60.0 mm
Thickness: 2.5 mm
Case of Issue: Maroon leatherette clam style case, black flocked insert, encapsulated coin, COA

Edge:	Reeded
Die Axis:	↑↑
Finish:	Proof

DATE	DESCRIPTION	QUANTITY SOLD	ISSUE PRICE	FINISH	PR-69	PR-70
2011	Toronto City Map	3,948	179.95	Proof	210.	—

TWENTY-FIVE DOLLARS, WAYNE AND WALTER GRETZKY, 2011.

The reverse design on this coin features Wayne Gretzky (the Great One) in action, with a cameo of his father Walter.

Designers and Engravers:

Obv.:	Susanna Blunt, Susan Taylor
Rev.:	Glen Green, Konrad Wachelko, José Osio

Composition: 99.99% Ag, (Hologram of jersey number 99)
Silver content: 31.39 g, 1.01 tr oz
Weight: 31.39 g   **Edge:** Reeded
Diameter: 38.0 mm   **Die Axis:** ↑↑
Thickness: 3.2 mm   **Finish:** Proof
Case of Issue: Maroon leatherette clam style case, black flocked insert, encapsulated coin, COA

DATE	DESCRIPTION	QUANTITY SOLD	ISSUE PRICE	FINISH	PR-69	PR-70
2011	Wayne and Walter Gretzky	6,715	99.99	Proof	85.	—

O CANADA SET ONE

TWENTY-FIVE DOLLARS, O CANADA SET ONE, 2013.

These coins from the O Canada Set focus on iconic Canadian images as seen through our rich animal history. For other coins in the O Canada S● see pages 207-208 and 354, 428.

Common Obverse

The Beaver
Engraver: José Osio

The Polar Bear
Engraver: Alex Tirabasso

The Wolf
Engraver: RCM Staff

The Caribou
Engraver: Susan Taylor

The Orca
Engraver: José Osio

Designers:			**Engravers:**	
Obv.:	Susanna Blunt		Obv.:	Susan Taylor
Rev.:	Pierre Leduc		Rev.:	See reverse illustrations
Composition:	99.99% Ag			
Silver content:	31.1 g, 1.00 tr oz			
Weight:	31.1 g		**Edge:**	Reeded
Diameter:	38.0 mm		**Die Axis:**	↑↑
Thickness:	3.0 mm		**Finish:**	Proof

Case of Issue: Singly: Maroon clam style case, black flocked insert, encapsulated coin, COA, custom coloured box
Subscription: Brown wooden case, 5-hole black flocked insert, encapsulated coins, COA

DATE	DESCRIPTION	QUANTITY SOLD	ISSUE PRICE	FINISH	PR-69	PR-70
2013	The Beaver	8,354	89.95	Proof	65.	—
2013	The Polar Bear	8,299	89.95	Proof	65.	—
2013	The Wolf	8,039	89.95	Proof	65.	—
2013	The Caribou	7,580	89.95	Proof	65.	—
2013	The Orca	6,342	89.95	Proof	65.	—

WENTY-FIVE DOLLARS, GRANDMOTHER MOON MASK, 2013.

The moon is a sacred symbol that appears in countless First Nations traditions and is depicted in this ultra high relief finish.

Designers and Engravers:

Obv.:	Susanna Blunt, Susan Taylor
Rev.:	Richard. Cochrane, Eric Boyer, Nicholas Martin

Composition: 99.99% Ag
Silver content: 30.5 g, 0.98 tr oz

Weight:	30.5 g	**Edge:**	Plain
Diameter:	36.2 mm	**Die Axis:**	↑↑
Thickness:	3.0 mm	**Finish:**	Proof

Case of Issue: Maroon leatherette clam style case, black flocked insert, encapsulated coin, COA

DATE	DESCRIPTION	QUANTITY SOLD	ISSUE PRICE	FINISH	PR-69	PR-70
2013	Grandmother Moon Mask	5,996	149.95	Proof	120.	—

WENTY-FIVE DOLLARS, MISS CANADA: AN ALLEGORY, 2013.

"Miss Canada" was first introduced in 1867.

Designers and Engravers:

Obv.:	Susanna Blunt, Susan Taylor
Rev.:	Laurie McGaw, RCM Staff

Composition: 99.99% Ag
Silver content: 31.39 g, 1.01 tr oz

Weight:	31.39 g		
Diameter:	38.0 mm	**Edge:**	Reeded
Thickness:	3.2 mm	**Die Axis:**	↑↑
Finish:	Proof		

Case of Issue: Maroon leatherette clam style case, black flocked insert, encapsulated coin, COA

DATE	DESCRIPTION	QUANTITY SOLD	ISSUE PRICE	FINISH	PR-69	PR-70
2013	Miss Canada: An Allegory	5,503	89.95	Proof	75.	—

WENTY-FIVE DOLLARS, MATRIARCH MOON MASK, 2014.

First Nations culture is rich with profound wisdom that eloquently expresses the interconnectedness between humanity and nature.

Designers and Engravers:

Obv.:	Susanna Blunt, Susan Taylor
Rev.:	Carol Young, RCM Staff

Composition: 99.99% Ag
Silver content: 30.76 g, 0.988 tr oz

Weight:	30.76 g		
Diameter:	36.15 mm	**Edge:**	Reeded
Thickness:	3.2 mm	**Die Axis:**	↑↑
Finish:	Proof		

Case of Issue: Maroon leatherette clam style case, black flocked insert, encapsulated coin, COA

DATE	DESCRIPTION	QUANTITY SOLD	ISSUE PRICE	FINISH	PR-69	PR-70
2014	Matriarch Moon Mask	5,999	149.95	Proof	120.	—

O CANADA SET TWO

TWENTY-FIVE DOLLARS, O CANADA SET TWO, 2014.

Common Obverse

The Igloo
Designer: Yves Bérubé
Engraver: Konrad Wachelko

Scenic Skiing in Canada
Designer: RCM Staff
Engraver: RCM Staff

Under the Maple Tree
Designer: Claudio D'Angelo
Engraver: RCM Staff

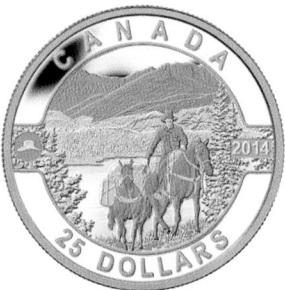

Cowboy in the Canadian Rockies
Designer: Bernie Brown
Engraver: RCM Staff

The Arctic Fox and the
Northern Lights
Designer: Julius Csotonyi
Engraver: Cecily Mok

Designers:		**Engravers:**	
Obv.:	Susanna Blunt	Obv.:	Susan Taylor
Rev.:	See reverse illustrations	Rev.:	RCM Staff

Composition: 99.99% Ag
Silver content: 31.0 g, 1.0 tr oz
Weight: 31.0 g
Diameter: 38.0 mm   **Edge:** Reeded
Thickness: 3.2 mm   **Die Axis:** ↑↑
Case of Issue: **Finish:** Proof

Singly: Maroon clam style case, black flocked insert, encapsulated coin, COA, custom coloured box
Set: Walnut display case, 5-hole black flocked insert, encapsulated coins, COA

DATE	DESCRIPTION	QUANTITY SOLD	ISSUE PRICE	FINISH	PR-69	PR-70
2014	The Igloo	6,013	89.95	Proof	75.	—
2014	Scenic Skiing in Canada	6,016	89.95	Proof	75.	—
2014	Under the Maple Tree	5,972	89.95	Proof	75.	—
2014	Cowboy in the Canadian Rockies	6,110	89.95	Proof	75.	—
2014	The Arctic Fox and the Northern Lights	6,748	89.95	Proof	75.	—

TWENTY-FIVE DOLLARS, 75TH ANNIVERSARY OF THE FIRST ROYAL VISIT, 2014.

Struck in ultra-high relief, the coin celebrates King George VI and Queen Elizabeth's visit to Canada in 1939.

Designers and Engravers:

Obv.:	Susanna Blunt, Susan Taylor
Rev.:	RCM Staff
Composition:	99.99% Ag
Silver content:	30.76 g, 0.99 tr oz
Weight:	30.76 g
Diameter:	36.0 mm
Thickness:	N/A

Edge:	Plain
Die Axis:	↑↑
Finish:	Proof

Case of Issue: Maroon leatherette clam style case, black flocked insert, encapsulated coin, COA, custom box

DATE	DESCRIPTION	QUANTITY SOLD	ISSUE PRICE	FINISH	PR-69	PR-70
2014	25th Anniversary of the First Royal Visit	3,117	149.95	Proof	130.	—

CHRISTMAS ORNAMENT SERIES

TWENTY-FIVE DOLLARS, CHRISTMAS ORNAMENT, 2014-2015.

Featuring an ultra-high relief, this quadruple-struck coin celebrates the holiday season.

Common Obverse	2014	2015

Designers:

Obv.:	Susanna Blunt
Rev.:	Three Degrees Creative Group Inc.
Composition:	99.99% Ag, Coloured Sheer Effect
Silver content:	30.76 g, 0.99 tr oz
Weight:	30.76 g
Diameter:	36.15 mm
Thickness:	N/A

Engravers:

Obv.:	Susan Taylor
Rev.:	RCM Staff

Edge:	Plain
Die Axis:	↑↑
Finish:	Proof, Antique, Colour Enamel

Case of Issue: Maroon leatherette clam style case, black flocked insert, encapsulated coin, COA

DATE	DESCRIPTION	QUANTITY SOLD	ISSUE PRICE	FINISH	PR-69	PR-70
2014	Christmas Ornament	4,726	129.95	Proof	130.	—
2015	Christmas Ornament	3,007	129.95	Proof	130.	—

TWENTY-FIVE DOLLARS, THE FIERCE CANADIAN LYNX, 2014.

Combining multiple finishes and ultra-high relief, this coin captures the Canada lynx, a feline native to the Boreal forests.

Designers and Engravers:

Obv.:	Susanna Blunt, Susan Taylor
Rev.:	Pierre Leduc, RCM Staff
Composition:	99.99% Ag
Silver content:	30.76 g, 0.99 tr oz
Weight:	30.76 g
Diameter:	36.15 mm
Thickness:	N/A
Case of Issue:	Maroon leatherette clam style case, black flocked insert, encapsulated coin, COA

Edge:	Plain
Die Axis:	↑↑
Finish:	Proof

DATE	DESCRIPTION	QUANTITY SOLD	ISSUE PRICE	FINISH	PR-69	PR-70
2014	The Fierce Canadian Lynx	1,519	149.95	Proof	150.	—

SINGING MOON MASK SET

TWENTY-FIVE DOLLARS, SINGING MOON MASK SET, 2015.

Featuring three distinct finishes, all coins are struck in ultra-high relief and feature the artwork of Andy Everson of the K'omoks and Kwakwaka'wak First Nations in British Columbia.

Common Obverse

Designers and Engravers:

Obv.:	Susanna Blunt, Susan Taylor
Rev.:	Andy Everson, RCM Staff
Composition:	99.99% Ag
Silver content:	30.76 g, 0.99 tr oz
Weight:	30.76 g
Diameter:	36.15 mm
Thickness:	N/A
Edge:	Plain
Die Axis:	↑↑
Finish:	Proof, Antique, Colour Enamel
Case of Issue:	Wooden case, black flocked insert, encapsulated coins, COA, black box

Proof	Proof Antique	Proof Colour Enamel

DATE	DESCRIPTION	QUANTITY SOLD	ISSUE PRICE	FINISH	PR-69	PR-70
2015	Singing Moon Mask, Proof	—	N.I.I.	Proof	120.	—
2015	Singing Moon Mask, Proof Antique	—	N.I.I.	Antique	120.	—
2015	Singing Moon Mask, Proof Colour Enamel	—	N.I.I.	Enamel	120.	—
2015	Set of 3 Coins	2,974	359.95	—	340.	*

STAR CHARTS SET

WENTY FIVE DOLLARS, STAR CHARTS SET, 2015

Based on the artwork of Western Ojibwa artist Cyril Assiniboine, these glow-in-the-dark coins, whose cases when assembled form the Big Dipper, epict the Plains Ojibwa as they hunt a great bear.

Common Obverse

Designers:		Engravers:	
Obv.:	Susanna Blunt	Obv.:	Susan Taylor
Rev.:	Cyril Assiniboine	Rev.:	RCM Staff

Composition: 99.99% Ag
Silver content: 31.83 g, 1.02 tr oz
Weight: 31.83 g   **Edge:** Reeded
Diameter: 40.0 mm   **Die Axis:** ↑↑
Thickness: N/A   **Finish:** Proof
Case of Issue: Maroon leatherette clam style case, black flocked insert, encapsulated coin, COA, custom case

The Great Ascent   The Eternal Pursuit   The Quest   The Wounded Bear

DATE	DESCRIPTION	QUANTITY SOLD	ISSUE PRICE	FINISH	PR-69	PR-70
2015	The Quest	7,445	104.95	Proof	100.	—
2015	The Wounded Bear	6,919	104.95	Proof	100.	—
2015	The Great Ascent	6,162	104.95	Proof	100.	—
2015	The Eternal Pursuit	7,294	104.95	Proof	100.	—

TWENTY-FIVE FOR TWENTY-FIVE SERIES

WENTY-FIVE DOLLARS (½ ounce), FINE SILVER, TWENTY-FIVE FOR TWENTY-FIVE SERIES, 2015-2016.

Common Obverse	50th Anniversary of Canadian Flag Designer: Julius Csotonyi	Winter Fun Designer: Jesse Koreck	Woodland Elf Designer: Jesse Koreck	True North Designer: RCM Staff

Designers:		Engravers:	
Obv.:	Susanna Blunt	Obv.:	Susan Taylor
Rev.:	See reverse illustrations	Rev.:	RCM Staff

Composition: 99.99% Ag, Coloured
Silver content: 7.96 g, 0.25 tr oz
Weight: 7.96 g   **Edge:** Reeded
Diameter: 27.0 mm   **Die Axis:** ↑↑
Thickness: N/A   **Finish:** Specimen
Case of Issue: Vinyl pouch, encapsulated coin, coloured folder

TWENTY-FIVE DOLLARS (½ ounce), FINE SILVER, TWENTY-FIVE FOR TWENTY-FIVE SERIES, 2015-2016, PRICING TABLE.

DATE	DESCRIPTION	QUANTITY SOLD	ISSUE PRICE	FINISH	SP-68	SP-69
2015	50th Anniversary of Canadian Flag	223,373	25.00	Specimen	30.	—
2016	Winter Fun	133,621	25.00	Specimen	30.	—
2016	Woodland Elf	91,428	25.00	Specimen	30.	—
2016	True North	118,410	25.00	Specimen	30.	—

TWENTY-FIVE DOLLARS, THE LIBRARY OF PARLIAMENT, 2016.

This coin marks the 140th anniversary of the outstandingly beautiful Library of Parliament building, which opened February 28th 1876, the only building which survived the 1916 fire that burned the rest of Parliament.

Designers and Engravers:
Obv.: Susanna Blunt, Susan Taylor
Rev.: RCM Staff
Composition: 99.99% Ag
Silver content: 30.75g, 0.99 tr oz
Weight: 30.75 g   **Edge:** Reeded
Diameter: 36.07 mm   **Die Axis:** ↑↑
Thickness: N/A   **Finish:** Proof
Case of Issue: Maroon clamshell with black beauty box

DATE	DESCRIPTION	QUANTITY SOLD	ISSUE PRICE	FINISH	PR-69	PR-70
2016	The Library of Parliament	5,992	159.95	Proof	180.	—

TWENTY-FIVE DOLLARS, 125TH ANNIVERSARY OF THE INVENTION OF BASKETBALL, 2016.

This outstanding coloured convex-shaped coin proudly celebrates the 125th anniversary of a team sport that was invented by a Canadian and has since taken the world by storm!

Designers and Engravers:
Obv.: Susanna Blunt, Susan Taylor
Rev.: Glen Green
Composition: 99.99% Ag, Selective color
Silver content: 30.76 g, 0.99 tr oz
Weight: 30.75 g   **Edge:** Reeded
Diameter: 36.07 mm   **Die Axis:** ↑↑
Thickness: N/A   **Finish:** Proof
Case of Issue: Maroon clamshell with black beauty box.

DATE	DESCRIPTION	QUANTITY SOLD	ISSUE PRICE	FINISH	PR-69	PR-70
2016	125th Anniversary of the Invention of Basketball	6,075	159.95	Proof	160.	—

SCULPTURAL ART OF PARLIAMENT SET

TWENTY-FIVE DOLLARS, SCULPTURAL ART OF PARLIAMENT, 2016.

In the heart of our nation's capital, the hallowed walls of Parliament are home to thousands of carved and sculpted artworks of exceptional beauty.

| Common Obverse | Grotesque Wild Green Man | Grotesque Foliated Green Man | Grotesque Horned Green Man |

Designers:

Obv.: Susanna Blunt
Rev.: Phil White

Composition: 99.99% Ag
Silver content: 30.75 g, 0.99 tr oz
Weight: 30.75 g
Diameter: 36 mm
Thickness: N/A
Case of Issue: Maroon clamshell with black beauty box.

Engravers:

Obv.: Susan Taylor
Rev.: RCM Staff

Edge: Plain
Die Axis: ↑↑
Finish: Proof

DATE	DESCRIPTION	QUANTITY SOLD	ISSUE PRICE	FINISH	PR-69	PR-70
2016	Grotesque Wild Green Man	2,038	149.95	Proof	150.	—
2016	Grotesque Foliated Green Man	1,822	149.95	Proof	150.	—
2016	Grotesque Horned Green Man	1,674	149.95	Proof	150.	—

TWENTY-FIVE DOLLARS, PIEDFORT, THE COAT OF ARMS OF CANADA, 2016.

A timeless celebration of Canada, its people, its history and its heritage through this richly detailed reproduction of a distinguished national symbol.

Designers and Engravers:

Obv.: Susanna Blunt, Susan Taylor
Rev.: RCM Staff

Composition: 99.99% Ag
Silver content: 31.39 g, 1.01 tr oz
Weight: 31.39 g
Diameter: 34 mm
Thickness: N/A
Case of Issue: Maroon clamshell with standard beauty box

Edge: Reeded
Die Axis: ↑↑
Finish: Proof

DATE	DESCRIPTION	QUANTITY SOLD	ISSUE PRICE	FINISH	PR-69	PR-70
2016	The Coat of Arms of Canada	5,985	99.95	Proof	100.	—

TWENTY-FIVE DOLLARS, VIEW OF CANADA FROM SPACE, 2017.

On January 22, 1992, the NASA space shuttle *Discovery* launched from Kennedy Space Center in Cape Canaveral with a crew of seven including neurologist Dr. Roberta Bondar, M.D., Ph.D., who holds the distinction of being Canada's first female astronaut. Proudly celebrating the 25 anniversary of Dr. Bondar's historic mission with this fine silver coin, whose convex shape provides the perfect canvas for recreating a view that is o of this world!

Designers and Engravers:

Obv.:	Susanna Blunt, Susan Taylor
Rev.:	Alexandra Lefort
Composition:	99.99% Ag
Silver content:	30.75 g, 1.01 tr oz
Weight:	30.75 g
Diameter:	36.07 mm
Thickness:	N/A
Case of Issue:	Maroon clamshell with standard beauty box

	Edge:	Reeded
	Die Axis:	↑↑
	Finish:	Proof

DATE	DESCRIPTION	QUANTITY SOLD	ISSUE PRICE	FINISH	PR-69	PR-70
2017	A View of Canada From Space	4,750	159.95	Proof	160.	—

TWENTY-FIVE DOLLARS, FOOTBALL-SHAPED AND CURVED COIN, 2017.

This coin is curved (convex) to resemble an inflated football, ready for play!

 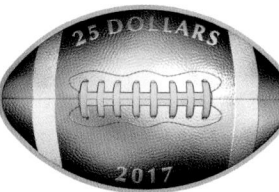

Designers and Engravers:

Obv.:	Susanna Blunt, Susan Taylor
Rev.:	RCM staff
Composition:	99.99% Ag
Silver content:	31.66 g, 1.01 tr oz
Weight:	31.66 g
Diameter:	48 x 30.33 mm
Thickness:	N/A
Case of Issue:	Maroon clamshell with black beauty box

	Edge:	Plain
	Die Axis:	↑↑
	Finish:	Proof

DATE	DESCRIPTION	QUANTITY SOLD	ISSUE PRICE	FINISH	PR-69	PR-70
2017	Football-Shaped and Curved Coin	5,802	161.95	Proof	160.	—

TWENTY-FIVE DOLLARS, 35TH ANNIVERSARY OF TRIVIAL PURSUIT, 2017.

Soon after its 1982 release, Trivial Pursuit took the world by storm when everyone seemed to be clamouring to play the Canadian invention that p their general knowledge to the test! Through this colourful piedfort, the 35th anniversary of a classic board game whose worldwide success has mac it a household name, is proudly celebrated.

Designers and Engravers:

Obv.:	Susanna Blunt, Susan Taylor
Rev.:	RCM staff
Composition:	99.99% Ag
Silver content:	31.39 g, 1.02 tr oz
Weight:	34 g
Diameter:	36.07 mm
Thickness:	N/A
Case of Issue:	Black graphic case with graphic beauty box.

	Edge:	Reeded
	Die Axis:	↑↑
	Finish:	Proof

DATE	DESCRIPTION	QUANTITY SOLD	ISSUE PRICE	FINISH	PR-69	PR-70
2017	35th Anniversary of Trivial Pursuit	4,268	118.95	Proof	120.	—

TWENTY-FIVE DOLLARS, DRAGON BOAT FESTIVAL, 2017-2018.

Ultra-high relief brings the Chinese dragon to life on the reverse, which represents a stunning visual celebration of the annual Dragon Boat Festival celebrated worldwide — including several cities across Canada!

Common Obverse   **2017 Dragon Boat Festival**   **2018 Dragon Boat Festival**

Designers:		**Engravers:**	
Obv.:	Susanna Blunt	Obv.:	Susan Taylor
Rev.:	Simon Ng		
Composition:	99.99% Ag, Selective colour		
Silver content:	30.76 g, 0.99 tr oz		
Weight:	30.76 g	**Edge:**	Plain
Diameter:	36.15 mm	**Die Axis:**	↑↑
Thickness:	N/A	**Finish:**	Proof
Case of Issue:	Maroon clamshell with black beauty box.		

DATE	DESCRIPTION	MINTAGE	ISSUE PRICE	FINISH	PR-69	PR-70
2017	Dragon Boat Festival	6,000	139.95	Proof	140.	—
2018	Dragon Boat Festival	6,000	149.95	Proof	150.	—

TWENTY-FIVE DOLLARS, THE GREAT TRAIL, 2017.

This unique rectangular coin that echoes the shape of a fold-out map, honours the connection of The Great Trail by Trans Canada Trail.

Designers and Engravers:	
Obv.:	S. Blunt, S. Taylor
Rev.:	Steve Hepburn
Composition:	99.99% Ag, Selective colour
Silver content:	47.35 g, 1.5 tr oz
Weight:	47.35 g
Diameter:	49.8 mm x 28.8 mm
Thickness:	N/A.
Edge:	Plain
Die Axis:	↑↑
Finish:	Proof
Case of Issue:	Maroon clamshell with custom beauty box, COA.

DATE	DESCRIPTION	MINTAGE	ISSUE PRICE	FINISH	PR-69	PR-70
2017	The Great Trail	5,500	159.95	Proof	160.	—

TIMELESS ICONS

TWENTY-FIVE DOLLARS, PIEDFORT, TIMELESS ICONS, 2017-2018.

The Royal Canadian Mint reflects on a nation's 150-year journey — and beyond — through the fusion of two iconic symbols that continue to insp... admiration by proudly representing all that is Canada.

| Common Obverse | Beaver | Caribou |

Designers:
  Obv.: Susanna Blunt
  Rev.: Pierre Leduc
Composition: 99.99% Ag, Selectively gold plated
Silver content: 31.39 g, 1.02 tr oz
Weight: 31.39 g
Diameter: 34 mm
Finish: Proof
Case of Issue: Maroon clamshell with standard beauty box, COA

Engravers:
  Obv.: Susan Taylor
  Rev.: RCM Staff

Edge: Reeded
Die Axis: ↑↑

DATE	DESCRIPTION	QUANTITY SOLD	ISSUE PRICE	FINISH	PR-69	PR-70
2017	Timeless Icons: Beaver	1,004	129.95	Proof	130.	—
2018	Timeless Icons: Caribou	7,500	129.95	Proof	130.	—

TWENTY-FIVE DOLLARS, THE GREAT SEAL OF CANADA, 2017.

Imprinted upon our nation's most important documents, the Great Seal of Canada signifies the sanction of the Crown, the authority of the governme... and the authenticity of the document in question. The Royal Canadian Mint proudly pays tribute to a ceremonial and administrative tradition that dat... back to Confederation.

Designers and Engravers:
  Obv.: Susanna Blunt, Susan Taylor
  Rev.: Eric Aldwinckle
Composition: 99.99% Ag, selective gold plating
Silver content: 30.76 g, 1.01 tr oz
Weight: 30.76 g   **Edge:** Plain
Diameter: 36 mm   **Die Axis:** ↑↑
Thickness: N/A   **Finish:** Proof
Case of Issue: Maroon clamshell with standard beauty box, COA

DATE	DESCRIPTION	MINTAGE	ISSUE PRICE	FINISH	PR-69	PR-70
2017	The Great Seal of Canada	6,000	139.95	Proof	140.	—

TWENTY-FIVE DOLLARS, 100TH ANNIVERSARY OF THE NHL, 2017.

The National Hockey League's centennial anniversary is a celebration of 100 years of history that have shaped our beloved winter sport, and the defining moments that are as much a part of Canada's history as they are of the NHL's.

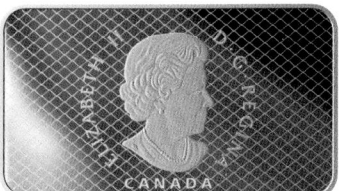 

Designers and Engravers:

Obv.:	S. Blunt, S. Taylor
Rev.:	Julius Csotonyi
Composition:	99.99% Ag
Silver content:	47.35 g, 1.5 tr oz
Weight:	47.35 g
Diameter:	49.8 mm x 28.8 mm
Thickness:	N/A.
Edge:	Plain
Die Axis:	↑↑
Finish:	Proof
Case of Issue:	Maroon clamshell with custom beauty box, COA.

DATE	DESCRIPTION	MINTAGE	ISSUE PRICE	FINISH	PR-69	PR-70
2017	100th Anniversary of the NHL	6,000	139.95	Proof	140.	—

TWENTY-FIVE DOLLARS, CLASSIC HOLIDAY ORNAMENT, 2018.

This coin captures the beauty of a vintage tree ornament using 21st century innovations. It's uniquely concave to echo the curve of early glass balls, punctuated with a Swarovski© crystal. Its chiselled indentations are a 19th-century invention to reflect candlelight.

Designers and Engravers:

Obv.:	Susanna Blunt, Susan Taylor		
Rev.:	Calder Moore		
Composition:	99.99% Ag		
Silver content:	30.75 g, 0.99 tr oz		
Weight:	30.75 g	Edge:	Reeded
Diameter:	36.07 mm	Die Axis:	↑↑
Thickness:	N/A	Finish:	Proof
Case of Issue:	Black clamshell with black beauty box, COA.		

DATE	DESCRIPTION	MINTAGE	ISSUE PRICE	FINISH	PR-69	PR-70
2018	Classic Holiday Ornament	5,500	159.95	Proof	160.	—

TWENTY-FIVE DOLLARS, 180TH ANNIVERSARY OF CANADIAN BASEBALL, 2018.

June 4, 1838: An open pasture, a hand-hewn "club," and a ball made of yarn and calfskin were all that was necessary to stage a match that made sports history. Shaped like a baseball, the reverse of this convex-shaped coin steps back in time 180 years ago, to the first detailed record of a baseball game played in Canada.

Designers and Engravers:

Obv.:	Susanna Blunt, Susan Taylor		
Rev.:	Steve Hepburn		
Composition:	99.99% Ag		
Silver content:	30.75 g, 1.01 tr oz		
Weight:	30.75 g	Edge:	Reeded
Diameter:	36.07 mm	Die Axis:	↑↑
Thickness:	N/A	Finish:	Proof
Case of Issue:	Black clamshell with black beauty box, COA.		

DATE	DESCRIPTION	MINTAGE	ISSUE PRICE	FINISH	PR-69	PR-70
2018	180th Anniversary of Canadian Baseball	5,000	169.95	Proof	170.	—

TWENTY-FIVE DOLLARS, THUNDERBIRD, 2018.

The Thunderbird is one of the most powerful spirits in Northwest Coast mythology. Beautifully engraved in ultra high relief, with a selective touch colour reflects the expressive art style of the Kwakwaka'wakw.

Designers and Engravers:

Obv.:	Susanna Blunt, Susan Taylor
Rev.:	Andy Everson
Composition:	99.99% Ag
Silver content:	30.76 g, 1.01 tr oz
Weight:	30.76 g
Diameter:	36.15 mm
Thickness:	N/A
Case of Issue:	Standard maroon clamshell with black beauty box, COA.

	Edge:	Plain
	Die Axis:	↑↑
	Finish:	Proof

DATE	DESCRIPTION	MINTAGE	ISSUE PRICE	FINISH	PR-69	PR-70
2018	Thunderbird	5,000	149.95	Proof	150.	—

TWENTY-FIVE DOLLARS, *ANCESTOR MOON* MASK, 2018.

A gentle and caring ancestor who watches over the people, lighting the way when travellers are on the water during the night, or illuminating the beach to help people dig for clams in the dark. *Ancestor Moon* is always present, always ready to guide and protect.

Designers and Engravers:

Obv.:	Susanna Blunt, Susan Taylor
Rev.:	Andy Everson
Composition:	99.99% Ag, Selective colour
Silver content:	30.76 g, 1.01 tr oz
Weight:	30.76 g
Diameter:	36.15 mm
Thickness:	N/A
Case of Issue:	Standard maroon clamshell with graphic beauty box, COA.

	Edge:	Plain
	Die Axis:	↑↑
	Finish:	Proof

DATE	DESCRIPTION	MINTAGE	ISSUE PRICE	FINISH	PR-69	PR-70
2018	*Ancestor Moon* Mask	4,000	149.95	Proof	150.	—

Note: The *Ancestor Moon* Mask coin was exclusively sold to the Mint Master's Club Members only.

THIRTY DOLLARS

THIRTY DOLLARS, WELCOME FIGURE (DZUNUK'WA) TOTEM POLE, 2005.

Dzunuk'wa is a giant, hairy, black-bodied, big-breasted, wide-eyed female monster. She is physically strong enough to tear down large trees, ritually powerful enough to resurrect the dead and possesses magical treasures and great wealth.

Designers and Engravers:

Obv.:	Susanna Blunt, Susan Taylor
Rev.:	Richard Hunt, Susan Taylor
Composition:	92.5% Ag, 7.5% Cu
Silver content:	29.137 g, 0.937 tr oz
Weight:	31.50 g
Diameter:	40.0 mm
Thickness:	3.0 mm
Edge:	Reeded
Die Axis:	↑↑
Finish:	Proof
Case of Issue:	Maroon plastic slide case, black plastic insert, encapsulated coin, COA

DATE	DESCRIPTION	QUANTITY SOLD	ISSUE PRICE	FINISH	PR-69	PR-70
2005	Welcome Figure Totem Pole	9,904	79.95	Proof	70.	—

Note: An identical design is utilized on the $300 gold coin for 2005, see page 475.

THIRTY DOLLARS, DOG SLED TEAM, 2006.

Designers and Engravers:

Obv.:	Susanna Blunt, Susan Taylor
Rev.:	Arnold Nogy, José Osio
Composition:	92.5% Ag, 7.5% Cu, Painted
Silver content:	29.137 g, 0.937 tr oz
Weight:	31.50 g
Diameter:	40.0 mm
Thickness:	3.0 mm
Edge:	Reeded
Die Axis:	↑↑
Finish:	Proof
Case of Issue:	Maroon plastic slide case, black plastic insert, encapsulated coin, COA

DATE	DESCRIPTION	QUANTITY SOLD	ISSUE PRICE	FINISH	PR-69	PR-70
2006	Dog Sled Team	7,384	89.95	Proof	150.	—

Note: An identical design is utilized on the $250 gold coin for 2006, see page 465.

NOTE TO COLLECTORS

When the initials N.I.I. appear in the pricing table it indicates the coin was part of a set issued by the Royal Canadian Mint, and not issued individually. Coin designs that are found only in sets offered by the Royal Canadian Mint are listed individually by denomination, and date in Volume Two.

SP-68 / PR-69	This price is based on the item still being in the original package as sold by the Mint.
SP-69 / PR-70	This price is based on the item being graded by a reputable third-party grading company.

NATIONAL WAR MEMORIALS SERIES

THIRTY DOLLARS, NATIONAL WAR MEMORIALS SERIES, 2006-2007.

2006 Obverse
Date on Obverse

2006 National War Memorial
Designer: Vernon March
Engraver: José Osio

2006 Beaumont-Hamel
Newfoundland Memorial
Designer: RCM Staff
Engraver: Susan Taylor

2007 Obverse
Date on Reverse

2007
Canadian National Vimy Memorial
Designer: RCM Staff
Engraver: José Osio

Designers:		**Engravers:**	
Obv.:	Susanna Blunt	Obv.:	Susan Taylor
Rev.:	See reverse illustrations	Rev.:	See reverse illustrations
Composition:	92.5% Ag, 7.5% Cu		
Silver content:	29.137 g, 0.937 tr oz		
Weight:	31.50 g	**Edge:**	Reeded
Diameter:	40.0 mm	**Die Axis:**	↑↑
Thickness:	3.0 mm	**Finish:**	Proof
Case of Issue:	Maroon plastic slide case, black plastic insert, encapsulated coin, COA		

DATE	DESCRIPTION	QUANTITY SOLD	ISSUE PRICE	FINISH	PR-69	PR-70
2006	National War Memorial	8,876	79.95	Proof	80.	—
2006	Beaumont-Hamel Newfoundland Memorial	15,325	79.95	Proof	80.	—
2007 (1917-)	Canadian National Vimy Memorial	5,335	79.95	Proof	80.	—

CANADIAN ACHIEVEMENT SERIES

HIRTY DOLLARS, 5TH ANNIVERSARY OF CANADARM, 2006.

Designers and Engravers:

Obv.:	Susanna Blunt, Susan Taylor
Rev.:	Cecily Mok, Cecily Mok
Composition:	92.5% Ag, 7.5% Cu, Decal
Silver content:	29.137 g, 0.937 tr oz
Weight:	31.50 g
Diameter:	40.0 mm
Thickness:	3.0 mm
Edge:	Reeded
Die Axis:	↑↑
Finish:	Proof
Case of Issue:	Maroon plastic slide case, black plastic insert, encapsulated coin, COA

HIRTY DOLLARS, PANORAMIC PHOTOGRAPHY IN CANADA, NIAGARA FALLS, 2007.

Designers and Engravers:

Obv.:	Susanna Blunt, Susan Taylor
Rev.:	Chris Jordison, RCM Staff
Composition:	92.5% Ag, 7.5% Cu, Hologram
Silver content:	29.137 g, 0.937 tr oz
Weight:	31.50 g
Diameter:	40.0 mm
Thickness:	2.8 mm
Edge:	Reeded
Die Axis:	↑↑
Finish:	Proof
Case of Issue:	Maroon leatherette clam style case, black flocked insert, encapsulated coin, COA

HIRTY DOLLARS, IMAX©, 2008.

Designers and Engravers:

Obv.:	Susanna Blunt, Susan Taylor
Rev.:	IMAX©, RCM Staff
Composition:	92.5% Ag, 7.5% Cu, Hologram
Silver content:	29.137 g, 0.937 tr oz
Weight:	31.50 g
Diameter:	40.0 mm
Thickness:	2.8 mm
Edge:	Reeded
Die Axis:	↑↑
Finish:	Proof
Case of Issue:	Maroon leatherette clam style case, black flocked insert, encapsulated coin, COA

DATE	DESCRIPTION	QUANTITY SOLD	ISSUE PRICE	FINISH	PR-69	PR-70
2006	5th Anniversary of Canadarm, Decal	9,357	79.95	Proof	80.	—
2007	Panoramic Photography in Canada, Niagara Falls, Hologram	5,702	84.95	Proof	80.	—
2008	IMAX®, Hologram	3,861	84.95	Proof	80.	—

ote: For the gold coins in this series see page 477.

THIRTY DOLLARS, INTERNATIONAL YEAR OF ASTRONOMY, 2009.

Designers and Engravers:

Obv.:	Susanna Blunt, Susan Taylor
Rev.:	Colin Mayne, Stan Witten
Composition:	92.5% Ag, 7.5% Cu, Painted
Silver content:	31.22 g, 1.00 tr oz
Weight:	33.75 g
Diameter:	40.0 mm
Thickness:	2.9 mm
Edge:	Reeded
Die Axis:	↑↑
Finish:	Proof
Case of Issue:	Maroon leatherette clam style case, black flocked insert, encapsulated coin, COA

DATE	DESCRIPTION	QUANTITY SOLD	ISSUE PRICE	FINISH	PR-69	PR-70
2009	International Year of Astronomy	7,174	89.95	Proof	90.	—

THIRTY DOLLARS, 100TH ANNIVERSARY OF THE COMPLETION OF THE GRAND TRUNK PACIFIC RAILWAY, 2014.

The Grand Trunk Pacific Railway was completed in 1914 and linked eastern Canada to the Pacific. The same design was issued in a $250 gold coin (see page 466).

Designers:

Obv.:	Susanna Blunt
Rev.:	Joel Kimmel
Composition:	99.99% Ag
Silver content:	56.0 g, 1.80 tr oz
Weight:	56.0 g
Diameter:	54.0 mm
Thickness:	N/A
Case of Issue:	Maroon leatherette clam style case, black flocked insert, encapsulated coin, COA, custom coloured box

Engravers:

Obv.:	Susan Taylor
Rev.:	RCM Staff
Edge:	Reeded
Die Axis:	↑↑
Finish:	Proof

DATE	DESCRIPTION	QUANTITY SOLD	ISSUE PRICE	FINISH	PR-69	PR-70
2014	100th Anniv. Completion of Grand Truck Pacific Railway	500	169.95	Proof	170.	—

THIRTY DOLLARS, CANADA THROUGH THE EYES OF TIM BARNARD, 2014

Des.: Susanna Blunt
Engr.: Susan Taylor

Des.: Tim Bernard
Engr.: RCM Staff

THIRTY DOLLARS, 75TH ANNIVERSARY OF THE DECLARATION OF THE SECOND WORLD WAR, 1939-2014

Des.: Susanna Blunt
Engr.: Susan Taylor

Des.: Silvia Pecota
Engr.: RCM Staff

THIRTY DOLLARS, NATIONAL ABORIGINAL VETERANS MONUMENT, 2014

Des.: Susanna Blunt
Engr.: Susan Taylor

Des.: N. L. Pinay
Engr.: RCM Staff

Designers and Engravers: See illustrations
Composition: 99.99% Ag
Silver content: 62.7 g, 2.00 tr oz
Weight: 62.7 g
Diameter: 54.0 mm
Thickness: 3.0 mm

Edge: Reeded
Die Axis: ↑↑
Finish: Proof
Case of Issue: Maroon leatherette clam style case, black flocked insert, encapsulated coin, COA custom coloured box

DATE	DESCRIPTION	QUANTITY SOLD	ISSUE PRICE	FINISH	PR-69	PR-70
2014	Canada Through the Eyes of Tim Barnard	4,996	169.95	Proof	170.	—
2014 (1939-)	75th Anniv. Declaration of Second World War	4,159	169.95	Proof	170.	—
2014	National Aboriginal Veterans Monument	2,026	169.95	Proof	170.	—

Note: Coins illustrated smaller than actual size.

IN THE MOONLIGHT

THIRTY DOLLARS, IN THE MOONLIGHT, 2015-2016.

Common Obverse

Moonlight Fireflies
Designer: Ervin Mohan

Northern Lights in the Moonlight
Designer: Julius Csotonyl

Designers:		
Obv.:	Susanna Blunt	
Rev.:	See reverse illustrations	
Composition:	99.99% Ag, Selective colour	
Silver content:	62.67 g, 2.0 tr oz	
Weight:	62.67 g	
Diameter:	54.0 mm	
Thickness:	N/A	
Case of Issue:	Maroon clamshell with custom beauty box.	

Engravers:
Obv.:   Susan Taylor

Edge: Reeded
Die Axis: ↑↑
Finish: Proof

DATE	DESCRIPTION	QUANTITY SOLD	ISSUE PRICE	FINISH	PR-69	PR-70
2015	Moonlight Fireflies	3,999	189.95	Proof	240.	—
2016	Northern Lights in the Moonlight	3,999	189.95	Proof	400.	—

THIRTY DOLLARS, CANADA'S MERCHANT NAVY IN THE BATTLE OF THE ATLANTIC, 2015.

Designers and Engravers:
Obv.:   Susanna Blunt, Susan Taylor
Rev.:   Yves Bérubé
Composition: 99.99% Ag
Silver content: 62.67 g, 2.0 tr oz
Weight: 62.67 g
Diameter: 54.0 mm
Thickness: N/A
Edge: Reeded
Die Axis: ↑↑
Finish: Proof
Case of Issue: Maroon clamshell with custom beauty box.

DATE	DESCRIPTION	QUANTITY SOLD	ISSUE PRICE	FINISH	PR-69	PR-70
2015	Canada's Merchant Navy in the Battle of the Atlantic	2,460	169.95	Proof	170.	—

Note: Coins illustrated smaller than actual size.

LOONEY TUNES™ CLASSIC SCENES SERIES

HIRTY DOLLARS, LOONEY TUNES™ CLASSIC SCENES, 2015.

Bugs. Daffy. Tweety. Sylvester. For many Canadians, the mere mention of these names evoke fond childhood memories of spending Saturday mornings in nt of a television, transfixed and spellbound as these characters—and many more—outsmarted each other in situations that could only exist in our imaginations.

| Common Obverse | The Rabbit of Seville | Fast and Furry-ous | Birds Anonymous |

esigners:		**Engravers:**	
Obv.:	Susanna Blunt	Obv.:	Susan Taylor
Rev.:	Warner Bros.	Rev.:	Warner Bros.
omposition:	99.99% Ag		
lver content:	62.67 g, 2.0 tr oz		
eight:	62.67 g	**Edge:**	Reeded
ameter:	54.0 mm	**Die Axis:**	↑↑
hickness:	3.0 mm	**Finish:**	Proof
ase of Issue:	Maroon plastic slide case, black plastic insert, encapsulated coin, COA		

DATE	DESCRIPTION	QUANTITY SOLD	ISSUE PRICE	FINISH	PR-69	PR-70
2015	Looney Tunes™ Classic Scenes: *The Rabbit of Seville*	4,995	189.95	Proof	160.	—
2015	Looney Tunes™ Classic Scenes: *Fast and Furry-ous*	4,877	189.95	Proof	160.	—
2015	Looney Tunes™ Classic Scenes: *Birds Anonymous*	4,965	189.95	Proof	160.	—

ote: Coins illustrated smaller than actual size.

HIRTY DOLLARS, ILLUMINATED CORAL REEF, 2016.

Designers and Engravers:

Obv.:	Susanna Blunt, Susan Taylor
Rev.:	Jesse Koreck
Composition:	99.99% Ag, Selective colour
Silver content:	62.67 g, 2.0 tr oz
Weight:	62.67 g
Diameter:	54.0 mm
Thickness:	N/A
Edge:	Reeded
Die Axis:	↑↑
Finish:	Proof
Case of Issue:	Maroon clamshell with custom beauty box.

DATE	DESCRIPTION	QUANTITY SOLD	ISSUE PRICE	FINISH	PR-69	PR-70
2016	Illuminated Coral Reef	3,995	189.95	Proof	190.	—

THIRTY DOLLARS, POP ART: CELEBRATING THE CANADA GOOSE, 2016.

Designers and Engravers:
Obv.:	Susanna Blunt, Susan Taylor
Rev.:	Andrew Lewis
Composition:	99.99% Ag
Silver content:	62.69 g, 2.0 tr oz
Weight:	62.69 g
Diameter:	50 mm
Thickness:	N/A
Edge:	Reeded
Die Axis:	↑↑
Finish:	Proof
Case of Issue:	Maroon clamshell with custom beauty box.

DATE	DESCRIPTION	QUANTITY SOLD	ISSUE PRICE	FINISH	PR-69	PR-70
2016	Pop Art: Celebrating the Canada Goose	2,332	169.95	Proof	170.	—

THIRTY DOLLARS, *BATMAN V SUPERMAN: DAWN OF JUSTICE*™, 2016.

Designers and Engravers:
Obv.:	Susanna Blunt, Susan Taylor
Rev.:	DC Comics
Composition:	99.99% Ag, Selective colour
Silver content:	62.67 g, 2.0 tr oz
Weight:	62.67 g
Diameter:	54 mm
Thickness:	N/A
Edge:	Reeded
Die Axis:	↑↑
Finish:	Proof
Case of Issue:	Premium presentation case.

DATE	DESCRIPTION	QUANTITY SOLD	ISSUE PRICE	FINISH	PR-69	PR-70
2016	*Batman v Superman: Dawn of Justice*	6,141	189.95	Proof	190.	—

Note: Coins illustrated smaller than actual size.

THIRTY DOLLARS, *STAR TREK*™: FIVE CAPTAINS, 2017.

The Royal Canadian Mint continues its celebration of *Star Trek*™ with a unique glow-in-the-dark coin that brings together the legendary captains who repeatedly rose to the challenges that come with boldly going "where no man has gone before."

 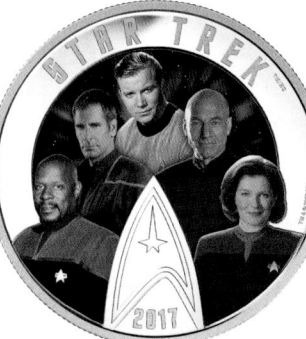

Designers and Engravers:
Obv.:	Susanna Blunt,
Rev.:	RCM Staff
Composition:	99.99% Ag, Selective colour
Silver content:	62.67 g, 1.0 tr oz
Weight:	62.67 g
Diameter:	54.0 mm
Thickness:	N/A
Edge:	Reeded
Die Axis:	↑↑
Finish:	Proof
Case of Issue:	Graphic beauty box.

DATE	DESCRIPTION	MINTAGE	ISSUE PRICE	FINISH	PR-69	PR-70
2017	*Star Trek*™: Five Captains	5,000	194.95	Proof	195.	—

ENDANGERED ANIMAL CUTOUT SERIES

State-of-the-art technology and internationally renowned craftsmanship have come together to produce a uniquely shaped cutout — one that smoothly recreates the animal's iconic outline!

THIRTY DOLLARS, ENDANGERED ANIMAL CUTOUT: WOODLAND CARIBOU, 2017.

Designers and Engravers:

Obv.:	Susanna Blunt, Susan Taylor
Rev.:	Trevor Tennant
Composition:	99.99% Ag,
Silver content:	52.88 g, 1.0 tr oz
Weight:	52.88 g
Diameter:	54.0 mm
Thickness:	N/A
Edge:	Reeded
Die Axis:	↑↑
Finish:	Proof
Case of Issue:	Maroon clamshell with black beauty box, COA.

THIRTY DOLLARS, ENDANGERED ANIMAL CUTOUT: WHOOPING CRANE, 2017.

Designers and Engravers:

Obv.:	Susanna Blunt, Susan Taylor
Rev.:	Trevor Tennant
Composition:	99.99% Ag,
Silver content:	56.30 g, 1.81 tr oz
Weight:	56.30 g
Diameter:	54.0 mm
Thickness:	N/A
Edge:	Reeded
Die Axis:	↑↑
Finish:	Proof
Case of Issue:	Maroon clamshell with black beauty box, COA.

DATE	DESCRIPTION	MINTAGE	ISSUE PRICE	FINISH	PR-69	PR-70
2017	Endangered Animal Cutout: Woodland Cairbou	5,500	189.95	Proof	190.	—
2017	Endangered Animal Cutout: Whooping Crane	5,500	189.95	Proof	190.	—

THIRTY DOLLARS, ZENTANGLE® ART: THE GREAT GREY WOLF, 2017.

This fine silver coin introduces a new take on the traditional image of the fearless predator, by combining varying abstract patterns in a beautifully engraved celebration of life as art.

Designers and Engravers:

Obv.:	Susanna Blunt,
Rev.:	Jori Van Der Linde
Composition:	99.99% Ag,
Silver content:	62.69 g, 1.0 tr oz
Weight:	62.69 g
Diameter:	50.0 mm
Thickness:	N/A
Edge:	Reeded
Finish:	Proof
Case of Issue:	Maroon clamshell with black beauty box.

DATE	DESCRIPTION	MINTAGE	ISSUE PRICE	FINISH	PR-69	PR-70
2017	Zentangle® Art: The Great Grey Wolf	4,000	174.95	Proof	175.	—

ANIMALS IN THE MOONLIGHT SERIES

THIRTY DOLLARS, ANIMALS IN THE MOONLIGHT, 2017.

Featuring luminescent wilderness scenes that reveal the secretive movements of the cougar, lynx, orca and owl that have facinated humanity f
centuries.

Common Obverse

Cougar
Designer: Jan Poynter

Lynx
Designer: Curtis Atwater

Orcas
Designer: Vanessa Miller

Great Horned Owl
Designer: Curtis Atwater

Designers:		**Engravers:**	
Obv.:	Susanna Blunt	Obv.:	Susan Taylor
Rev.:	See reverse illustrations		
Composition:	99.99% Ag, Selective colour	**Thickness:**	N/A
Silver content:	62.67 g, 2.0 tr oz	**Edge:**	Reeded
Weight:	62.67 g	**Die Axis:**	↑↑
Diameter:	54.0 mm	**Finish:**	Proof
Case of Issue:	Maroon clamshell with graphic beauty box, COA.		

DATE	DESCRIPTION	MINTAGE	ISSUE PRICE	FINISH	PR-69	PR-70
2017	Animals in the Moonlight: Cougar	580	189.95	Proof	190.	—
2017	Animals in the Moonlight: Lynx	4,000	189.95	Proof	190.	—
2017	Animals in the Moonlight: Orcas	4,000	189.95	Proof	190.	—
2017	Animals in the Moonlight: Great Horned Owl	4,000	189.95	Proof	190.	—

THIRTY DOLLARS, CELEBRATING CANADA DAY, 2017.

On Canada Day, Parliament Hill is awash in a sea of red and white that is a proud expression of patriotism–especially in 2017, when Canadians came together to celebrate 150 years of Confederation.

Designers and Engravers:

Obv.:	Susanna Blunt,
Rev.:	Jesse Koreck
Composition:	99.99% Ag,
Silver content:	62.67 g, 1.0 tr oz
Weight:	62.67 g
Diameter:	54.0 mm
Thickness:	N/A
Edge:	Reeded
Finish:	Proof
Case of Issue:	Maroon clamshell with graphic beauty box, COA.

DATE	DESCRIPTION	MINTAGE	ISSUE PRICE	FINISH	PR-69	PR-70
2017	Celebrating Canada Day	5,000	189.95	Proof	190.	—

THIRTY DOLLARS, FLORA AND FAUNA OF CANADA, 2017.

A powerful portrait of Canada through the majestic flora and fauna icons speak of the distinctiveness of each province and territory, and the natural beauty that reigns within their boundaries. With a 360-degree design highlighting the spectacular diversity of this nation as a whole.

Designers and Engravers:

Obv.:	Susanna Blunt,
Rev.:	Steve Hepburn
Composition:	99.99% Ag,
Silver content:	62.69 g, 1.0 tr oz
Weight:	62.69 g
Diameter:	50.0 mm
Thickness:	N/A
Edge:	Reeded
Finish:	Proof
Case of Issue:	Maroon clamshell with black beauty box.

DATE	DESCRIPTION	MINTAGE	ISSUE PRICE	FINISH	PR-69	PR-70
2017	Flora and Fauna of Canada	4,000	174.95	Proof	175.	—

PHASES OF THE MOON SET

THIRTY DOLLARS, PHASES OF THE MOON, 3-COIN SET, 2017.

This captivating 3-coin set portrays three moon phases with translucent enamel creating the shadow that defines the new and waxing gibbous moon.

Common
Obverse

Designers and Engravers:

Obv.:	Susanna Blunt, Susan Taylor
Rev.:	Andy Everson
Composition:	99.99% Ag
Silver content:	62.69 g, 2.0 tr oz
Weight:	62.69 g
Diameter:	50.0 mm
Thickness:	N/A
Edge:	Reeded
Die Axis:	↑↑
Finish:	Proof
Case of Issue:	Maroon clamshell with black beauty box, COA

New Moon   Half Moon   Full Moon

DATE	DESCRIPTION	MINTAGE	ISSUE PRICE	FINISH	PR-69	PR-70
2017	Phases of the Moon 3-coin set	3,000	575.95	Proof	575.	—

THIRTY DOLLARS, GOLDEN MAPLE LEAF, 2018.

An RCM first! Introducing the first fine silver coin featuring an 18Kt. gold maple leaf.

Designers and Engravers:

Obv.:	Susanna Blunt,
Rev.:	Michelle Grant
Composition:	99.99% Ag,
Silver content:	62.69 g, 1.0 tr oz
Weight:	62.69 g + 1 g (18 Kt. gold maple leaf)
Diameter:	50.0 mm
Thickness:	N/A
Edge:	Reeded
Finish:	Proof
Case of Issue:	Maroon clamshell with black beauty box, COA.

DATE	DESCRIPTION	MINTAGE	ISSUE PRICE	FINISH	PR-69	PR-70
2018	Golden Maple Leaf	2,750	299.95	Proof	300.	—

GATES OF CANADA SERIES

THIRTY DOLLARS, GATES OF CANADA, 2017-2018.

To some, gates are a way to keep people out—but they can also be a beautiful invitation to enter. The intricate scrollwork on each coin of a filigree gate sets an elegant tone and catches the eye, beckoning you to look at what lies beyond!

2017 Obverse

2018 Obverse

Gate to Enchanted Garden
Des.: Tony Bainco

Halifax Public Gardens
Des.: Margaret Best

The Queen's Gate
Formal Entrance to Parliament Hill
Des.: Cathy Bursey-Sabourin
and Patrick Belanger

Designers:		**Engravers:**	
Obv.:	Susanna Blunt	Obv.:	Susan Taylor
Rev.:	See reverse illustrations		
Composition:	99.99% Ag, Selective colour	**Thickness:**	N/A
Silver content:	62.69 g, 2.0 tr oz	**Edge:**	Reeded
Weight:	62.69 g	**Die Axis:**	↑↑
Diameter:	50.0 mm	**Finish:**	Proof
Case of Issue:	Maroon clamshell with black beauty box, COA.		

DATE	DESCRIPTION	MINTAGE	ISSUE PRICE	FINISH	PR-69	PR-70
2017	Gates of Canada: Gate to Enchanted Garden	5,500	239.95	Proof	240.	—
2018	Gates of Canada: Halifax Public Gardens	5,500	239.95	Proof	240.	—
2018	Gates of Canada: The Queen's Gate	5,500	239.95	Proof	240.	—

ARCTIC ANIMALS AND NORTHERN LIGHTS SERIES

THIRTY DOLLARS, ARCTIC ANIMALS AND NORTHERN LIGHTS, 2018.

This must-have series showcases the Arctic's most celebrated wilderness residents with innovative, glow-in-the-dark designs that reveal how, eve
in the dark of night, this extreme landscape is rife with life—and magic!

Common obverse	Polar Bear	Snowy Owl

Designers:
Obv.:   Susanna Blunt
Rev.:   Trevor Tennant
Composition: 99.99% Ag, Selective colour
Silver content: 62.69 g, 2.0 tr oz
Weight: 62.69 g
Diameter: 50.0 mm
Case of Issue: Maroon clamshell with black beauty box, COA.

Engravers:
Obv.:   Susan Taylor
Thickness: N/A
Edge: Reeded
Die Axis: ↑↑
Finish: Proof

DATE	DESCRIPTION	MINTAGE	ISSUE PRICE	FINISH	PR-69	PR-70
2018	Arctic Animals and Northern Lights: Polar Bear	4,000	189.95	Proof	190.	—
2018	Arctic Animals and Northern Lights: Snowy Owl	4,000	189.95	Proof	190.	—

THIRTY DOLLARS, CAPTAIN COOK AND THE HMS *RESOLUTION*, 2018.

After exploring the South Pacific and crossing the Antarctic Circle during his previous two voyages, Captain James Cook (1728-1779) came north on his thir
epic Pacific voyage, eventually reaching our western shores in 1778.

Designers and Engravers:
Obv.:   Susanna Blunt, Susan Taylor
Rev.:   Neil Hamelin
Composition: 99.99% Ag, Gold plated
Silver content: 62.69 g, 2.0 tr oz
Weight: 62.69 g
Diameter: 50 mm
Thickness: N/A
Edge: Reeded
Die Axis: ↑↑
Finish: Proof
Case of Issue: Maroon clamshellf with a
standard black beauty box, COA.

DATE	DESCRIPTION	MINTAGE	ISSUE PRICE	FINISH	PR-69	PR-70
2018	Captain Cook and the HMS Resolution	4,000	189.95	Proof	190.	—

Note: Coins illustrated smaller than actual size.

100TH ANNIVERSARY OF THE CANADIAN NATIONAL INSTITUTE FOR THE BLIND SET

THIRTY DOLLARS, 100TH ANNIVERARY OF THE CNIB, 2018.

In the wake of the First World War, and the Halifax Explosion that left hundreds blind or partially sighted, seven visionaries saw beyond the tragedy and held fast their ideal that those injured could lead productive lives, nurture their talents, and ultimately fulfill their dreams. As our first coin designed by a partially sighted artist, and the first to feature braille, this keepsake is testament to the power of the Canadian National Institute for the Blind's (CNIB) vision.

  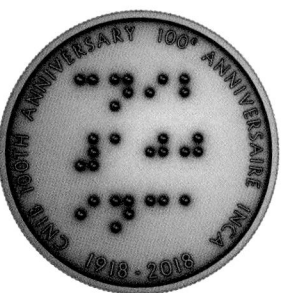 

Designers and Engravers:

Obv.:	Susanna Blunt / Susan Taylor
Rev.:	Meghan Sims

	Coin	**Medallion**
		Bronze
Composition:	99.99% Ag	
Silver content:	62.69 g, 2.0 tr oz	
Weight:	62.69 g	77.17
Diameter:	50.0 mm	52 mm
Thickness:	N/A	
Edge:	Reeded	Plain
Die Axis:	↑↑	↑↑
Finish:	Proof	Antique
Case of Issue:	Maroon clamshell with black beauty box, COA	

DATE	DESCRIPTION	MINTAGE	ISSUE PRICE	FINISH	PR-69	PR-70
2018	100th Anniversary CNIB Coin & Medallion set	3,000	219.95	Proof / Antique	220.	—

THIRTY DOLLARS, *THE JUSTICE LEAGUE™: THE WORLD'S GREATEST SUPER HEROES*, 2018.

The World's Greatest Super Heroes—a strike force of unprecedented power, and the A-team of the DC Universe. Through their different abilities, feats and personalities, each character symbolizes a different ideal: hope (Superman), justice (Batman), truth (Wonder Woman), optimism (The Flash), conviction (Aquaman), and adaptability (Cyborg).

Designers and Engravers:

Obv.:	Susanna Blunt, Susan Taylor
Rev.:	Jason Fabok, Brad Anderson
Composition:	99.99% Ag, Selective colour
Silver content:	62.67 g, 2.0 tr oz
Weight:	62.67 g
Diameter:	54 mm
Thickness:	N/A
Edge:	Reeded
Die Axis:	↑↑
Finish:	Proof
Case of Issue:	Graphic beauty box, COA..

DATE	DESCRIPTION	MINTAGE	ISSUE PRICE	FINISH	PR-69	PR-70
2018	*The Justice League™: The World's Greatest Super Heroes*	6,000	189.95	Proof	190.	—

Note: Coins illustrated smaller than actual size.

FIFTY DOLLARS

FIFTY DOLLARS, THE FOUR SEASONS, 2006.

Designers and Engravers:
Obv.:	S. Blunt, S. Taylor
Rev.:	T. Bianco, J. Osio

Composition: 99.99% Ag
Silver content: 156.34 g, 5.026 tr oz
Weight: 156.36 g
Diameter: 64.8 mm
Thickness: 5.0
Edge: Reeded
Die Axis: ↑↑
Finish: Proof
Case of Issue: Black case, black flocked insert, encapsulated coin, COA

FIFTY DOLLARS, 60TH WEDDING ANNIVERSARY OF QUEEN ELIZABETH AND PRINCE PHILIP, 1947-2007.

Designers and Engravers:
Obv.:	S. Blunt, S. Taylor
Rev.:	S. Hepburn, S. Taylor

Composition: 99.99% Ag
Silver content: 156.34 g, 5.026 tr oz
Weight: 156.36 g
Diameter: 65.0 mm
Thickness: 5.0
Edge: Reeded
Die Axis: ↑↑
Finish: Proof
Case of Issue: Maroon leatherette clam style case, black flocked insert, encapsulated coin, COA

FIFTY DOLLARS, 100TH ANNIVERSARY OF THE ROYAL CANADIAN MINT, 1908-2008.

Designers and Engravers:
Obv.:	S. Blunt, S. Taylor
Rev.:	Konrad Wachelko

Composition: 99.99% Ag
Silver content: 157.65 g, 5.069 tr oz
Weight: 157.67 g
Diameter: 65.0 mm
Thickness: 5.2 mm
Edge: Reeded
Die Axis: ↑↑
Finish: Proof
Case of Issue: Maroon leatherette clam style case, black flocked insert, encapsulated coin, COA

DATE	DESCRIPTION	MINTAGE	ISSUE PRICE	FINISH	PR-69	PR-70
2006	The Four Seasons	1,999	299.95	Proof	350.	—
2007 (1947-)	60th Wedding Anniv. Queen Elizabeth / Prince Philip	1,957	299.95	Proof	300.	—
2008 (1908-)	100th Anniversary of the Royal Canadian Mint	2,078	369.95	Proof	325.	—

FIFTY DOLLARS, 150TH ANNIVERSARY OF THE START OF THE CONSTRUCTION OF THE PARLIAMENT BUILDINGS, 1859-2009.

Designers and Engravers:

Obv.:	S. Blunt, S. Taylor
Rev.:	Cecily Mok

Composition: 99.99% Ag
Silver content: 157.65 g, 5.069 tr oz
Weight: 157.67 g
Diameter: 65.0 mm
Thickness: 5.0 mm
Edge: Reeded
Die Axis: ↑↑
Finish: Proof
Case of Issue: Maroon leatherette clam style case, black flocked insert, encapsulated coin, COA

FIFTY DOLLARS, 75TH ANNIVERSARY OF THE FIRST BANK NOTES ISSUED BY THE BANK OF CANADA, 1935-2010.

The reverse design on this coin is a reproduction of the allegory that appeared on the original 1935 $50 bank note, a seated woman with elements of radio broadcasting to symbolise modern inventions.

Designers and Engravers:

Obv.:	S. Blunt, S. Taylor
Rev.:	Cecily Mok

Composition: 99.99% Ag
Silver content: 157.65 g, 5.069 tr oz
Weight: 157.67 g
Diameter: 65.3 mm
Thickness: 5.0 mm
Edge: Reeded
Die Axis: ↑↑
Finish: Proof
Case of Issue: Maroon leatherette clam style case, black flocked insert, encapsulated coin, COA

FIFTY DOLLARS, VANCOUVER 2010 – LOOK OF THE GAMES, 2010.

Designers and Engravers:

Obv.:	S. Blunt, S. Taylor
Rev.:	Vancourver 2010 Design Team

Composition: 99.99% Ag
Silver content: 157.6 g, 5.069 tr oz
Weight: 157.6 g
Diameter: 65.25 mm
Thickness: N/A
Edge: Reeded
Die Axis: ↑↑
Finish: Proof
Case of Issue: Maroon leatherette clam style case, black flocked insert, encapsulated coin, COA

DATE	DESCRIPTION	QUANTITY SOLD	ISSUE PRICE	FINISH	PR-69	PR-70
2009 (1859-)	150th Anniv. Construction Parliament Buildings	910	459.95	Proof	350.	—
2010 (1935-)	75th Anniv. Bank of Canada Notes	1,991	389.95	Proof	375.	—
2010	Vancouver 2010 – The Look of the Games	2,010	389.95	Proof	450.	—

FIFTY DOLLARS, 100TH ANNIVERSARY OF THE CALGARY STAMPEDE, 2012.

In 1912, working cowboy and trick roper Guy Weadick, inspired by the travelling wild-west shows in the early 1900s, convinced four local ranche to help him produce the first Frontier Days and Cowboy Championship Contest, later to be called the Calgary Stampede. One hundred years late Calgary, Alberta remains home to "the greatest outdoor show on earth".

Designers and Engravers:

Obv.:	S. Blunt, S. Taylor
Rev.:	M. Grant, J. Osio
Composition:	99.99% Ag
Silver content:	157.65 g, 5.069 tr oz
Weight:	157.67 g
Diameter:	65.3 mm
Thickness:	5.0 mm
Edge:	Reeded
Die Axis:	↑↑
Finish:	Proof
Case of Issue:	Maroon leatherette clam style case, black flocked insert, encapsulated coin, COA

FIFTY DOLLARS, THE BEAVER, 2013.

The importance of the beaver in the development of Canada through the fur trade led to its official designation as the national animal in 1975.

Designers and Engravers:

Obv.:	S. Blunt, S. Taylor
Rev.:	E. Damstra, C. Mok
Composition:	99.99% Ag
Silver content:	157.65 g, 5.069 tr oz
Weight:	157.67 g
Diameter:	65.3 mm
Thickness:	5.0 mm
Edge:	Reeded
Die Axis:	↑↑
Finish:	Proof
Case of Issue:	Maroon leatherette clam style case, black flocked insert, encapsulated coin, COA

FIFTY DOLLARS, QUEEN'S CORONATION, 1953-2013.

This coin was issued to commemorate the 60th Anniversary of her Majesty Queen Elizabeth II's accession. The reverse image used for this coin i the official coronation photograph taken by Cecil Beaton, June 2nd, 1953, licensed by the Victoria & Albert Museum in London, England.

Designers and Engravers:

Obv.:	Mary Gillick, Thomas Shingles
Rev.:	See description
Composition:	99.99% Ag
Silver content:	157.65 g, 5.069 tr oz
Weight:	157.67 g
Diameter:	65.3 mm
Thickness:	5.0 mm
Edge:	Reeded
Die Axis:	↑↑
Finish:	Proof, Coloured
Case of Issue:	Maroon leatherette clam style case, black flocked insert, encapsulated coin, COA

DATE	DESCRIPTION	MINTAGE	ISSUE PRICE	FINISH	PR-69	PR-70
2012	100th Anniv. of the Calgary Stampede	1,500	495.95	Proof	450.	—
2013	The Beaver	1,500	519.95	Proof	450.	—
2013 (1953-)	Queen's Coronation	1,499	524.95	Proof	550.	—

FIFTY DOLLARS, *HMS SHANNON* AND *USS CHESAPEAKE*, 1813-2013.

Designers and Engravers:
Obv.:	S. Blunt, S. Taylor
Rev.:	J. Horton, C. Mok

Composition: 99.99% Ag
Silver content: 157.65 g, 5.069 tr oz
Weight: 157.67 g
Diameter: 65.0 mm
Thickness: 5.0 mm
Edge: Reeded
Die Axis: ↑↑
Finish: Proof
Case of Issue: Maroon leatherette clam style case, black flocked insert, encapsulated coin, COA

FIFTY DOLLARS, SWIMMING BEAVER, 2014.

Designers and Engravers:
Obv.:	S. Blunt, S. Taylor
Rev.:	E. Damstra, RCM Staff

Composition: 99.99% Ag
Silver content: 157.65 g, 5.069 tr oz
Weight: 157.67 g
Diameter: 65.3 mm
Thickness: 5.0 mm
Edge: Reeded
Die Axis: ↑↑
Finish: Proof
Case of Issue: Maroon leatherette clam style case, black flocked insert, encapsulated coin, COA

FIFTY DOLLARS, ABORIGINAL STORY: THE LEGEND OF THE SPIRIT BEAR, 2014.

Designers and Engravers:
Obv.:	S. Blunt, S. Taylor
Rev.:	D. Gait, RCM Staff

Composition: 99.99% Ag
Silver content: 157.65 g, 5.069 tr oz
Weight: 157.67 g
Diameter: 65.3 mm
Thickness: 5.0 mm
Edge: Reeded
Die Axis: ↑↑
Finish: Proof
Case of Issue: Maroon leatherette clam style case, black flocked insert, encapsulated coin, COA

DATE	DESCRIPTION	MINTAGE	ISSUE PRICE	FINISH	PR-69	PR-70
2013 (1813-)	*HMS Shannon* and *USS Chesapeake*	1,490	499.85	Proof	450.	—
2014	Swimming Beaver	1,495	519.95	Proof	500.	—
2014	Aboriginal Story: The Legend of the Spirit Bear	700	519.95	Proof	520.	—

FIFTY DOLLARS, MAPLE LEAVES, 2014.

Designers and Engravers:

Obv.:	S. Blunt, S. Taylor
Rev.:	Luc Normandin, RCM Staff

Composition: 99.99% Ag
Silver content: 157.65 g, 5.069 tr oz
Weight: 157.67 g
Diameter: 65.3 mm
Thickness: 5.0 mm
Edge: Reeded
Die Axis: ↑↑
Finish: Proof
Case of Issue: Red lacquered wooden box, black flocked insert, encapsulated coin, COA

FIFTY DOLLARS, LUSTROUS MAPLE LEAVES, 2015.

Designers and Engravers:

Obv.:	S. Blunt, S. Taylor
Rev.:	Michelle Grant, RCM Staff

Composition: 99.99% Ag
Silver content: 157.65 g, 5.069 tr oz
Weight: 157.67 g
Diameter: 65.3 mm
Thickness: 5.0 mm
Edge: Reeded
Die Axis: ↑↑
Finish: Proof, Hologram
Case of Issue: Red lacquered wooden box, black flocked insert, encapsulated coin, COA

DATE	DESCRIPTION	QUANTITY SOLD	ISSUE PRICE	FINISH	PR-69	PR-70
2014	Maple Leaves	1,505	499.95	Proof	500.	—
2015	Lustrous Maple Leaves	2,975	519.95	Proof	550.	—

FIFTY FOR FIFTY SERIES

IFTY DOLLARS, FIFTY FOR FIFTY SERIES, 2014-2016.

Common Obverse

Designers and Engravers:

Obv.:	S. Blunt ,S. Taylor
Rev.:	See reverse illustrations
Composition:	99.99% Ag
Silver content:	15.87 g, .5 tr oz
Weight:	15.87 g
Diameter:	34.0 mm
Thickness:	2.2 mm
Case of Issue:	Clear vinyl pouch in a certificate booklet

Edge:	Reeded
Die Axis:	↑↑
Finish:	Matte Proof

2014	2014	2015	2016
Polar Bear	Snowy Owl	Beaver	Hare
Designer: Emily Damstra	Designer: Trevor Tennant	Designer: Emily Damstra	Designer: Emily Damstra
Engraver: Alex Tirabasso	Engraver: RCM Staff	Engraver: RCM Staff	Engraver: RCM Staff

DATE	DESCRIPTION	QUANTITY SOLD	ISSUE PRICE	FINISH	PR-69	PR-70
2014	Iconic Polar Bear	99,926	50.00	Matte Proof	55.	—
2014	Snowy Owl	89,568	50.00	Matte Proof	55.	—
2015	Beaver	78,133	50.00	Matte Proof	55.	—
2016	Hare	49,545	50.00	Matte Proof	55.	—

Note: Coin illustrated smaller than actual size.

FIFTY DOLLARS, 50TH ANNIVERSARY OF THE CANADIAN FLAG, 2015.

Designers and Engravers:

Obv.:	S. Blunt, S. Taylor
Rev.:	N/A
Composition:	99.99% Ag, Selective colour
Silver content:	47.34 g, 1.5 tr oz
Weight:	47.34 g
Diameter:	49.8 mm x 28.8 mm
Thickness:	N/A.
Edge:	Reeded
Die Axis:	↑↑
Finish:	Proof
Case of Issue:	Maroon clamshell with custom beauty box.

DATE	DESCRIPTION	QUANTITY SOLD	ISSUE PRICE	FINISH	PR-69	PR-70
2015	50th Annivesary of the Canadian Flag	8,843	159.95	Proof	160.	—

FIFTY DOLLARS, 100TH ANNIVERSARY OF *IN FLANDERS FIELDS*, 2015.

Designers and Engravers:

Obv.:	S. Blunt, S. Taylor
Rev.:	Tony Bianco
Composition:	99.99% Ag, Selective colour
Silver content:	157.65 g, 5.069 tr oz
Weight:	157.65 g
Diameter:	65.25 mm
Thickness:	N/A.
Edge:	Reeded
Die Axis:	↑↑
Finish:	Proof
Case of Issue:	Maroon clamshell with custom beauty box.

FIFTY DOLLARS, MURANO MAPLE LEAF – AUTUMN RADIANCE, 2016

Designers and Engravers:

Obv.:	S. Blunt, S. Taylor
Rev.:	Lisa Thomson-Khan
Composition:	99.99% Ag, Selective colour
Silver content:	157.6 g, 5.0 tr oz
Weight:	157.6 g
Diameter:	65.25 mm
Thickness:	N/A.
Edge:	Reeded
Die Axis:	↑↑
Finish:	Proof
Case of Issue:	Red lacquered wooden case with black beauty box.

FIFTY DOLLARS, WANDUTA: PORTRAIT OF A CHIEF, 2016

Designers and Engravers:

Obv.:	S. Blunt, S. Taylor
Rev.:	Darlene Gait
Composition:	99.99% Ag, Selective colour
Silver content:	157.6 g, 5.0 tr oz
Weight:	157.6 g
Diameter:	65.25 mm
Thickness:	N/A.
Edge:	Reeded
Die Axis:	↑↑
Finish:	Proof
Case of Issue:	Maroon clamshell with custom beauty box, COA.

DATE	DESCRIPTION	QUANTITY SOLD	ISSUE PRICE	FINISH	PR-69	PR-70
2015	100th Anniversary of *In Flanders Fields*	1,489	519.95	Proof	520.	—
2016	Murano Maple Leaf – Autumn Radiance	1,993	549.95	Proof	550.	—
2016	Wanduta: Portrait of a Chief	1,195	519.95	Proof	525.	—

MYTHICAL REALMS OF THE HAIDA SET

FIFTY DOLLARS, MYTHICAL REALMS OF THE HAIDA SET, 2016.

Haida Gwaii is a place of astounding natural beauty; a land of ancient legends where mythical beings move about in the guise of familiar animals from our three-dimensional world. This mesmerizing new coin series portrays three of the most powerful supernatural beings from the realms of water, earth and sky.

| Common Obverse | The Orca | The Eagle | The Bear |

Designers:
- Obv.: Susanna Blunt
- Rev.: April White

Composition: 99.99% Ag, Selective color
Silver content: 157.6 g, 5.0 tr oz
Weight: 157.6 g
Diameter: 65.25 mm
Thickness: N/A
Case of Issue: Maroon clamshell with black beauty box.

Note: Coins illiustrated smaller than actual size.

Engravers:
- Obv.: Susan Taylor
- Rev.: April White

Edge: Reeded
Die Axis: ↑↑
Finish: Proof

DATE	DESCRIPTION	QUANTITY SOLD	ISSUE PRICE	FINISH	PR-69	PR-70
2016	Mythical Realms of the Haida Series: The Orca	792	549.95	Proof	550.	—
2016	Mythical Realms of the Haida Series: The Eagle	739	549.95	Proof	550.	—
2016	Mythical Realms of the Haida Series: The Bear	703	549.95	Proof	550.	—

FIFTY DOLLARS, PEACE TOWER CLOCK 90TH ANNIVERSARY, 2017.

At the stroke of noon on July 1, 1927, the Peace Tower Clock made its debut during Confederatin's Diamond Jubilee. Ninety years later, the commanding timepiece and its copper-clad apex are the pride of Canada!

Designers and Engravers:
- Obv.: S. Blunt, S. Taylor
- Rev.: Calder Moore

Composition: 99.99% Ag,
Silver content: 157.6 g, 5.0 tr oz
Weight: 157.6 g
Diameter: 65.25 mm
Thickness: N/A.
Edge: Reeded
Die Axis: ↑↑
Finish: Antique
Case of Issue: Maroon clamshell with black beauty box, COA.

DATE	DESCRIPTION	MINTAGE	ISSUE PRICE	FINISH	PR-69	PR-70
2017	Peace Tower Clock 90th Anniversary	1,200	579.95	Antique	580.	—

FIFTY DOLLARS, MAPLE LEAVES IN MOTION, 2017.

The RCM's largest-ever convex coin! Featured on its reverse a stunning display of swirling maple leaves that, combined with the coin's uniqu
shape and relfective proof finish, take on a three-dimensional appearance.

Designers and Engravers:

Obv.:	S. Blunt, S. Taylor
Rev.:	Lisa Thomson-Khan
Composition:	99.99% Ag,
Silver content:	157.6 g, 5.0 tr oz
Weight:	157.6 g
Diameter:	60 mm
Thickness:	N/A.
Edge:	Reeded
Die Axis:	↑↑
Finish:	Proof
Case of Issue:	Red lacquered box with black beauty box.

FIFTY DOLLARS, MAPLE LEAVES IN MOTION, 2018.

A flurry of maple leaves lends depth and texture to the highly polished antique finish, for a dazzling work of art whose domed shape will stop yo
in your tracks.

Designers and Engravers:

Obv.:	S. Blunt, S. Taylor
Rev.:	Claudio D'Angelo
Composition:	99.99% Ag,
Silver content:	157.6 g, 5.0 tr oz
Weight:	157.6 g
Diameter:	60 mm
Thickness:	N/A.
Edge:	Reeded
Die Axis:	↑↑
Finish:	Antique
Case of Issue:	Red wood lacquered case with black box, COA.

DATE	DESCRIPTION	MINTAGE	ISSUE PRICE	FINISH	PR-69	PR-70
2017	Maple Leaves in Motion	2,000	579.95	Proof	580.	—
2018	Maple Leaves in Motion	1,500	579.95	Antique	580.	—

FTY DOLLARS, WHISPERING MAPLE LEAVES, 2017.

This 3 oz. fine silver coin captures the beauty of maple foilage swaying in a warm breeze, with the additon of reverse gold plating to mimic the lden glow of a summer day.

Designers and Engravers:

Obv.:	S. Blunt, S. Taylor
Rev.:	Clader Moore
Composition:	99.99% Ag,
Silver content:	94.4 g, 3.04 tr oz
Weight:	94.4 g
Diameter:	55 mm
Thickness:	N/A.
Edge:	Reeded
Die Axis:	↑↑
Finish:	Proof
Case of Issue:	Maroon clamshefll with black beauty box, COA.

DATE	DESCRIPTION	MINTAGE	ISSUE PRICE	FINISH	PR-69	PR-70
2017	Whispering Maple Leaves	3,500	299.95	Proof	300.	—

IFTY DOLLARS, 125TH ANNIVERSARY OF THE STANLEY CUP®, 2017.

In 1892, the Governor General of Canada, Lord Stanley, donated a silver bowl for the purpose of fostering a competitive spirit between Canada's nateur hockey teams. The RCM is proud to commemorate the 125th anniversary of the Stanley Cup's origins, with a one-of-a-kind shaped coin that ays tribute to hockey's ultimate prize.

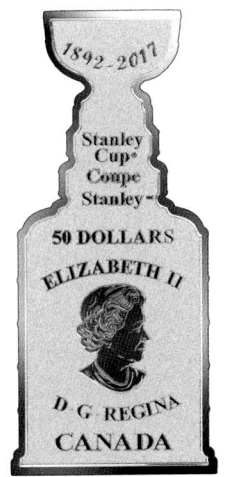 

Designers and Engravers:

Obv.:	S. Blunt, S. Taylor
Rev.:	RCM Staff
Composition:	99.99% Ag,
Silver content:	157.6 g, 5.07 tr oz
Weight:	99.53 g
Height :	58 mm
Thickness:	N/A.
Edge:	Reeded
Die Axis:	↑↑
Finish:	Reverse Proof
Case of Issue:	Rectangular black clamshell with NHL branded beauty box..

DATE	DESCRIPTION	MINTAGE	ISSUE PRICE	FINISH	PR-69	PR-70
2017	125th Anniversary of the Stanley Cup	5,000	359.95	Reverse Proof	360.	—

FIFTY DOLLARS, PUZZLE COIN, CANADA 150, 2017.

Like a puzzle, Confederation came together piece by piece, every part clicking into place over time, the end result far greater than the sum of i parts. Diverse geographies, natural wonders and resources coming together from coast to coast to coast. A multitude of traditions, languages, a skills blurring distinct cultural lines. History may have recorded the beginning of Confederation 150 years ago, but for today's citizens, Canada ca begin anywhere on this nation's ever-evolving continuum. This puzzle coin is an outstanding, first-ever achievement at the Mint, and a unique portra of Canada that will be the highlight of the most distinctive collections.

Each piece of the puzzle has a face value of $50 (central coin) and $20 (each of the jigsaw pieces). See page 342 for the $20

Designers and Engravers:

Obv.:	Susanna Blunt
Rev.:	Cathy Bursey-Sabourin
Composition:	99.99% Ag, Selective gold plating, coloured
Silver content:	502.47 g, 16.16 tr oz
Weight:	502.47 g (complete set
Diameter:	123.7 mm
Finished Size:	184 mm x 184 mm
Thickness:	N/A
Edge:	Interrupted Reeding
Die Axis:	↑↑
Finish:	Proof
Case of Issue:	Wood case with black beauty box, COA

DATE	DESCRIPTION	MINTAGE	ISSUE PRICE	FINISH	PR-69	PR-70
2017	Puzzle Coin, Canada 150	800	1,867	Proof	2,000.	—

Note: This coin was only sold as a complete set of 14 puzzle pieces, plus a central coin.

DC COMICS ORIGINALS

FIFTY DOLLARS, *DC COMICS ORIGINALS*, 2017.

The application of gold plating throughout the reverse (except for *Superman* at the centre) gives this series a rich golden gleam – like the aged sep tint of a page from an old book, but with much more vibrancy to highlight the engraved details!

Common Obverse	*The Brave and The Bold*	*All Star Comics*

Designers:

Obv.:	Susanna Blunt
Rev.:	DC Comics
Composition:	99.99% Ag, Reverse gold plating
Weight:	94.4 g
Diameter:	55 mm
Thickness:	N/A.
Case of Issue:	Maroom clamshell with graphic beauty box, COA.

Engravers:

Obv.:	Susan Taylor
Silver content:	94.4 g, 3.04 tr oz
Edge:	Reeded
Die Axis:	↑↑
Finish:	Proof

DATE	DESCRIPTION	MINTAGE	ISSUE PRICE	FINISH	PR-69	PR-70
2017	DC Comics Originals: *The Brave and The Bold*	3,000	319.95	Proof	320.	—
2017	DC Comics Originals: *All Star Comics*	3,000	319.95	Proof	320.	—

FIFTY DOLLARS, MONARCH MIGRATION, 2017.

Designers and Engravers:
Obv.:	S. Blunt, S. Taylor
Rev.:	Graham Spaull

Composition: 99.99% Ag
Silver content: 94.4 g, 3.04 tr oz
Weight: 94.4 g
Diameter: 55 mm
Thickness: N/A.
Edge: Reeded
Die Axis: ↑↑
Finish: Proof
Case of Issue: Maroon clamshell with black beauty box, COA.

DATE	DESCRIPTION	MINTAGE	ISSUE PRICE	FINISH	PR-69	PR-70
2017	Monarch Migration	3,500	299.95	Proof	300.	—

FIFTY DOLLARS, CANADIAN ICONS, 2017.

From the mountains of Western Canada to the maritime emblems of Atlantic Canada, and the inukshuk that reflects the spirit of the North, they re the classic images that define a nation on this special anniversary year! Experience Canada from coast to coast to coast—and throughout the easons—with an inspirational collage of red-coloured icons that come together to embody a nation's spirit and its pride.

Designers and Engravers:
Obv.:	S. Blunt, S. Taylor
Rev.:	Tami Mayrand

Composition: 99.99% Ag
Silver content: 157.6 g, 5.07 tr oz
Weight: 157.6 g
Diameter: 65.25 mm
Thickness: N/A.
Edge: Reeded
Die Axis: ↑↑
Finish: Proof
Case of Issue: Maroon clamshell with Canada 150 themed black beauty box, COA.

DATE	DESCRIPTION	MINTAGE	ISSUE PRICE	FINISH	PR-69	PR-70
2017	Canadian Icons	1,500	519.95	Proof	520.	—

FIFTY DOLLARS, HOLIDAY SPLENDOUR, 2018.

Individually hand-blown Murano glass poinsettia with a sprinkling of gold foil applied to the centre of this coin will captivate holiday revellers f[...] generations to come.

Designers and Engravers:

Obv.:	S. Blunt, S. Taylor
Rev.:	Marie-Élaine Cusson
Composition:	99.99% Ag
Silver content:	157.6 g, 5.07 tr oz
Weight:	157.6 g
Diameter:	65.25 mm
Thickness:	N/A.
Edge:	Reeded
Die Axis:	↑↑
Finish:	Proof
Case of Issue:	Maroon clamshell with Canada 150 themed black beauty box, COA

DATE	DESCRIPTION	MINTAGE	ISSUE PRICE	FINISH	PR-69	PR-70
2018	Holiday Spendour	1,500	569.95	Proof	570.	—

FIFTY DOLLARS, POLAR BEAR SOAPSTONE SCULPTURE, 2018.

Introducing an unforgettable coin that pairs a traditional soapstone sculpture with contemporary coin-making techniques.

Designers:

Obv.:	Susanna Blunt
Rev.:	Dave Zachary
Composition:	99.99% Ag
Silver content:	157.6 g, 5.07 tr oz
Weight:	157.6 g
Diameter:	65.25 mm
Thickness:	N/A.
Case of Issue:	Wooden circular base with black beauty box, COA.

Engravers:

Obv.:	Susan Taylor
Edge:	Reeded
Die Axis:	↑↑
Finish:	Proof

DATE	DESCRIPTION	MINTAGE	ISSUE PRICE	FINISH	PR-69	PR-70
2018	Polar Bear Soapstone Sculpture	1,300	549.95	Proof	550.	—

THE SAN XING GODS: FU, LU, SHOU SET

FTY DOLLARS, THE SAN XING GODS: FU, LU, SHOU, 2018.

The beneficent San Xing, or Three Stars, dwell auspiciously in Chinese homes and businesses around the world.

Designers and Engravers:

Obv.:	S. Blunt, S. Taylor
Rev.:	Simon Ng
Composition:	99.99% Ag, Selective colour
Silver content:	157.6 g, 5.07 tr oz
Weight:	157.6 g (each coin)
Diameter:	65.25 mm (each coin)
Thickness:	N/A.
Edge:	Reeded
Die Axis:	↑↑
Finish:	Proof
Case of Issue:	Maroon clamshell with black beauty box, COA.

Fu

Lu

Shou

DATE	DESCRIPTION	MINTAGE	ISSUE PRICE	FINISH	PR-69	PR-70
2018	The San Xing Gods: Fu, Lu, Shou 3-coin set	588	1,688.88	Proof	1,700.	—

ONE HUNDRED DOLLARS
ONE HUNDRED FOR ONE HUNDRED SERIES

ONE HUNDRED FOR ONE HUNDRED SERIES, 2013-2016.
These coins are from the $100 for $100 fine silver coin series.

Common Obverse

Bison Stampede
Designer: Cosme Saffioti
Engraver: Christie Paquet

Designers and Engravers:

Obv.:	Susanna Blunt, Susan Taylor	
Rev.:	See reverse illustrations	
Composition:	99.99% Ag	
Silver content:	31.6 g, 1.0 oz	
Weight:	31.6 g	**Edge:**	Reeded
Diameter:	40.0 mm	**Die Axis:**	↑↑
Thickness:	3.0 mm	**Finish:**	Reverse Proof, Matte Proo
Case of Issue:	2013 Bison:	Maroon leatherette clam style case, blac flocked insert, encapsulated coin, COA
	2013-2014:	Customized paper case lined with flock, encapsulated coin, COA
	2015:	Graphic collector's box

The Grizzly
Designer: Claudio D'Angelo
Engraver: Steven Stewart

Majestic Bald Eagle
Designer: Claudio D'Angelo
Engraver: Eric Boyer

Rocky Mountain Bighorn Sheep
Designer: Claudio D'Angelo
Engraver: RCM Staff

Musk Ox
Designer: Laurene Spino
Engraver: RCM Staff

Horse
Designer: Claudio D'Angelo
Engraver: RCM Staff

Cougar
Designer: Claudio D'Angelo
Engraver: RCM Staff

Orca
Designer: Trevor Tennant
Engraver: RCM Staff

The Nobel Elk
Designer: Glen Loates
Engraver: RCM Staff

DATE	DESCRIPTION	QUANTITY SOLD	ISSUE PRICE	FINISH	PR-69	PR-70
2013	Bison Stampede, Reverse Proof	49,986	100.00	Proof	120.	—
2013	The Grizzly, Matte Proof	49,092	100.00	Proof	120.	—
2014	Majestic Bald Eagle, Matte Proof	49,166	100.00	Proof	120.	—
2014	Rocky Mountain Bighorn Sheep, Matte Proof	44,747	100.00	Proof	120.	—
2015	Musk Ox, Matte Proof	43,961	100.00	Proof	120.	—
2015	Horse, Matte Proof	45,151	100.00	Proof	120.	—
2016	Cougar, Matte Proof	38,170	100.00	Proof	120.	—
2016	Orca, Matte Proof	27,717	100.00	Proof	120.	—
2016	The Nobel Elk, Matte Proof	16,377	100.00	Proof	120.	—

NE HUNDRED DOLLARS, 100TH ANNIVERSARY OF THE DECLARATION OF FIRST WORLD WAR, 2014.

Designers and Engravers:
Obv.:	S. Blunt, S. Taylor
Rev.:	Yves Bérubé, RCM Staff

Composition:	99.99% Ag
Silver content:	311.5 g, 10.0 tr oz
Weight:	311.5 g
Diameter:	76.25 mm
Thickness:	N/A
Edge:	Reeded
Die Axis:	↑↑
Finish:	Proof
Case of Issue:	Maple wooden case, black flocked insert, encapsulated coin, COA

NE HUNDRED DOLLARS, MAJESTIC MAPLE LEAVES, 2014.

Designers and Engravers:
Obv.:	S. Blunt, S. Taylor
Rev.:	Pierre Leduc, RCM Staff

Composition:	99.99% Ag
Silver content:	311.5 g, 10.0 tr oz
Weight:	311.5 g
Diameter:	76.25 mm
Thickness:	N/A
Edge:	Reeded
Die Axis:	↑↑
Finish:	Proof
Case of Issue:	Maple wooden case black flocked insert, encapsulated coin, COA

NE HUNDRED DOLLARS, CELEBRATING PHOTOGRAPHER YOUSUF KARSH, ALBERT EINSTEIN SPECIAL THEORY OF RELATIVITY, 2015.

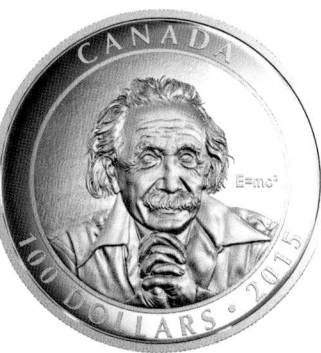

Designers and Engravers:
Obv.:	S. Blunt, S. Taylor
Rev.:	Original photo by Yousuf Karsh, RCM Staff

Composition:	99.99% Ag
Silver content:	311.5 g, 10.0 tr oz
Weight:	311.50 g
Diameter:	76.25 mm
Thickness:	N/A
Edge:	Reeded
Die Axis:	↑↑
Finish:	Proof
Case of Issue:	Maple presentation case with graphic beauty box.

DATE	DESCRIPTION	QUANTITY SOLD	ISSUE PRICE	FINISH	PR-69	PR-70
2014	100th Anniv. of Declaration of First World War	424	899.95	Proof	900.	—
2014	Majestic Maple Leaves	249	899.95	Proof	900.	—
2015	Celebrating Canadian Photographer Yousuf Karsh, Albert Einstein Special Theory of Relativity	1,341	899.95	Proof	900.	—

ONE HUNDRED DOLLARS, 100TH ANNIVERSARY OF *IN FLANDERS FIELDS*, 2015.

Designers and Engravers:

Obv.:	S. Blunt, S. Taylor
Rev.:	Tony Bianco
Composition:	99.99% Ag
Silver content:	311.5 g, 10.0 tr oz
Weight:	311.5 g
Diameter:	76.25 mm
Thickness:	N/A
Edge:	Reeded
Die Axis:	↑↑
Finish:	Proof
Case of Issue:	Wood case with custom beauty box.

DATE	DESCRIPTION	QUANTITY SOLD	ISSUE PRICE	FINISH	PR-69	PR-70
2015	100th Anniversary of *In Flanders Fields*	498	899.95	Proof	900.	—

ONE HUNDRED DOLLARS, VIMY RIDGE, 2017.

Designers and Engravers:

Obv.:	Sir E. B. MacKennal
Rev.:	RCM Staff
Composition:	99.99% Ag
Silver content:	311.54 g, 10.0 tr oz
Weight:	311.54 g
Diameter:	76.25 mm
Thickness:	N/A
Edge:	Reeded
Die Axis:	↑↑
Finish:	Proof
Case of Issue:	Wood case with black beatuy box.

DATE	DESCRIPTION	MINTAGE	ISSUE PRICE	FINISH	PR-69	PR-70
2017	Vimy Ridge	750	999.95	Proof	1,000.	—

SCULPTURE OF MAJESTIC CANADIAN ANIMALS SERIES

NE HUNDRED DOLLARS, SCULPTURE OF MAJESTIC CANADIAN ANIMALS, 2017.

The coin's large diameter (65 mm) provides the perfect pedestal for the silver, gold-plated animal-shaped embellishment emerging from the reverse.

Common obverse	Grizzly Bear	Cougar

Elk	Bighorn Sheep	Wolf

Designers		**Engravers:**	
Obv.:	Susanna. Blunt	Obv.:	Susan Taylor
Rev.:	Karl Lansing		
Composition:	99.99% Ag		
Silver content:	315.71 g, 10.0 tr oz		
Weight:	315.71 g	**Edge:**	Reeded
Diameter:	65 mm	**Die Axis:**	↑↑
Thickness:	N/A	**Finish:**	Proof
Case of Issue:	Wooden circular base with black box.		

DATE	DESCRIPTION	QUANTITY SOLD	ISSUE PRICE	FINISH	PR-69	PR-70
2017	Sculpture of Majestic Canadian Animnals: Grizzly Bear	981	999.95	Proof	1,000.	—
2017	Sculpture of Majestic Canadian Animals: Courgar	1,200	1,099.95	Proof	1,000.	—
2017	Sculpture of Majestic Canadian Animals: Elk	1,200	1,099.95	Proof	1,000.	—
2017	Sculpture of Majestic Canadian Animals: Wolf	1,200	1,099.95	Proof	1,000.	—

COMMEMORATING HISTORICAL CANADIAN CONFEDERATION

ONE HUNDRED DOLLARS, COMMEMORATING HISTORICAL CANADIAN CONFEDERATION, 2017.

This low mintage 3-coin series commemorates the historical importance of Canadian Confederation.

| Common Obverse Designer and Engraver: Susanna Blunt and Leonard Charles Wyon | *Historia Tua Epos Est* The 150th Anniversary of Canadian Confederation Designer: Rebecca Yanovskaya | *Juventas et Patrius Vigor:* The 1867 Confedration Medal Designer: Raymond Delamarre | *A Mari Usque Ad Mare:* The Diamond Jubilee of the Co federation of Canada Medal Designer: J.S. and A.B. Wyon |

Designers
Obv.:   See illustrations
Composition: 99.99% Ag
Silver content: 311.535 g, 10.0 tr oz
Weight: 311.535 g
Diameter: 76.25 mm
Thickness: N/A
Case of Issue: Maroon clamshell with Canada 150 beauty box.

Engravers:
Rev.:   See illustrations

Edge: Reeded
Die Axis: ↑↑
Finish: Proof

DATE	DESCRIPTION	MINTAGE	ISSUE PRICE	FINISH	PR-69	PR-70
2017	*Juventas et Patrius Vigor:* The 1867 Confedration Medal	1,000	899.95	Proof	1,000.	—
2017	*A Mari Usque Ad Mare:* The Diamond Jubilee of the Confederation of Canada Medal	1,000	899.95	Proof	900.	—
2017	*Historia Tua Epos Est* The 150th Anniversary of Canadian Confedertion	1,000	899.95	Proof	900.	—

ONE HUNDRED DOLLARS, DC COMICS ORIGINALS: SUPERMAN'S *SHIELD*, 2017.

Basing itself on the DC Comics style of the 1980s, this series celebrates one of the most established looks for the DC Comics pantheon of *Sup Heroes* — including the *Man of Tomorrow, Superman.*

Designers and Engravers:
Obv.:   S. Blunt, S. Taylor
Rev.:   DC Comics
Composition: 99.99% Ag, transparent enamel
Silver content: 315.2 g, 10.14 tr oz
Weight: 315.2 g
Diameter: 110 mm x 87.5 mm
Thickness: N/A
Edge: Interrupted reeding
Die Axis: ↑↑
Finish: Proof
Case of Issue: Basic clamshell with graphic beauty box, CO

DATE	DESCRIPTION	MINTAGE	ISSUE PRICE	FINISH	PR-69	PR-70
2017	DC Comics Originals: Superman's Shield	1,500	1,149.95	Proof	1,150.	—

NE HUNDRED DOLLARS, *STAR TREK™: U.S.S. ENTERPRISE* NCC-1701, 2017.

Inspired by *Star Trek*'s spirit of innovation, the RCM pushes the boundaries of numismatic art with a remarkable feat of its own: an *Enterprise-* aped coin!

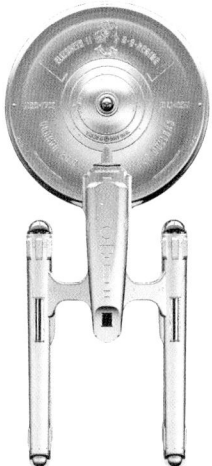
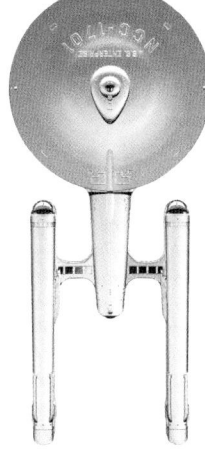

Designers and Engravers:
Obv.:	S. Blunt, S. Taylor
Rev.:	RCM Staff
Composition:	99.99% Ag,
Silver content:	318.81 g, 10.25 tr oz
Weight:	318.81 g
Diameter:	113.2 long x 50.6 wide
Thickness:	N/A
Edge:	Plain
Die Axis:	↑↑
Finish:	Matte Proof
Case of Issue:	Maroon clamshell with graphic beauty box, COA.

DATE	DESCRIPTION	MINTAGE	ISSUE PRICE	FINISH	PR-69	PR-70
2017	*Star Trek™: U.S.S. Enterprise* NCC-1701	1,000	1,199.95	Matte Proof	1,500.	—

NE HUNDRED DOLLARS, THE ANGEL OF VICTORY: 100TH ANNIVERSARY OF THE FIRST WORLD WAR ARMISTICE, 2018.

Signed in 1918 "on the eleventh hour of the eleventh day of the eleventh month," the Armistice of Compiègne put an end to hostilities during the First orld War. This 10 oz. fine silver coin commemorates the centennial of the Armistice, to honour the thousands of men and women from Canada and ewfoundland who lost their lives in the "war to end all wars."

Designers and Engravers:
Obv.:	S. Blunt, S. Taylor
Rev.:	Pandora Young
Composition:	99.99% Ag
Silver content:	311.54 g, 10.0 tr oz
Weight:	311.54 g
Diameter:	76.25 mm
Thickness:	N/A
Edge:	Reeded
Die Axis:	↑↑
Finish:	Proof
Case of Issue:	Maroon clamshell with black beatuy box, COA.

DATE	DESCRIPTION	MINTAGE	ISSUE PRICE	FINISH	PR-69	PR-70
2018	The Angel of Victory: 100th Anniversary of the First World War Armistice	750	999.95	Proof	1,000.	—

ONE HUNDRED TWENTY-FIVE DOLLARS

ONE HUNDRED TWENTY-FIVE DOLLARS, HOWLING WOLF, 2014

Designers and Engravers:
Obv.:	S. Blunt, S. Taylor
Rev.:	Pierre Leduc, RCM Staff

Composition:	99.99% Ag
Silver content:	500.0 g, 16.07 tr oz
Weight:	500.0 g
Diameter:	85.0 mm
Thickness:	N/A
Edge:	Reeded
Die Axis:	↑↑
Finish:	Proof
Case of Issue:	Wooden box, black flocked insert, encapsulated coin, CO

ONE HUNDRED TWENTY-FIVE DOLLARS, CANADIAN HORSE, 2015

Designers and Engravers:
Obv.:	S. Blunt, S. Taylor
Rev.:	Michelle Grant, RCM Staff

Composition:	99.99% Ag
Silver content:	500.0 g, 16.07 tr oz
Weight:	500.0 g
Diameter:	85.0 mm
Thickness:	N/A
Edge:	Reeded
Die Axis:	↑↑
Finish:	Proof
Case of Issue:	Wooden box, black flocked insert, encapsulated coin, CO

ONE HUNDRED TWENTY-FIVE DOLLARS, GROWLING COUGAR, 2015

Designers and Engravers:
Obv.:	S. Blunt, S. Taylor
Rev.:	Pierre Leduc, RCM Staff

Composition:	99.99% Ag
Silver content:	500.0 g, 16.07 tr oz
Weight:	500.0 g
Diameter:	85.0 mm
Thickness:	N/A
Edge:	Reeded
Die Axis:	↑↑
Finish:	Proof
Case of Issue:	Wooden box, black flocked insert, encapsulated coin, CO

DATE	DESCRIPTION	QUANTITY SOLD	ISSUE PRICE	FINISH	PR-69	PR-70
2014	Howling Wolf	998	1,099.95	Proof	1,000.	—
2015	Canadian Horse	504	1,099.95	Proof	1,100.	—
2015	Growling Cougar	651	1,099.95	Proof	1,100.	—

CONSERVATION SET

NE HUNDRED TWENTY-FIVE DOLLARS, CONSERVATION SET, 2015.

Common Obverse	The Whooping Crane Designer: Luc Normandin	The Grey Fox Designer: Laurene Spino	The Narwhal Designer: Curtis Atwater

esigners:
  Obv.:   Susanna Blunt
  Rev.:   See reverse illustrations
omposition: 99.99% Ag
ilver content: 500 g, 16.075 tr oz
eight: 500 g
iameter: 85 mm
hickness: N/A
ase of Issue: Maroon clamshell with black beauty box.

Engravers:
  Obv.:   Susan Taylor

Edge: Reeded
Die Axis: ↑↑
Finish: Proof

DATE	DESCRIPTION	QUANTITY SOLD	ISSUE PRICE	FINISH	PR-69	PR-70
2015	Conservation Series: The Whooping Crane	395	1,099.95	Proof	1,100	—
2015	Conservation Series: The Grey Fox	390	1,099.95	Proof	1,100	—
2015	Conservation Series: The Narwhal	300	1,099.95	Proof	1,100	—

ote: Coins illustrated are smaller than actual size.

NE HUNDRED TWENTY-FIVE DOLLARS, ROARLING GRIZZLY, 2016 AND ELK, 2017.

Common Obverse	2016 Roaring Grizzly	2017 Elk

esigners:
  Obv.:   Susanna Blunt
  Rev.:   Pierre Leduc,
omposition: 99.99% Ag
ilver content: 500.0 g, 16.07 tr oz
eight: 500.0 g
iameter: 85.0 mm
hickness: N/A
ase of Issue: Wooden box with standard beauty box.

Engravers:
  Obv.:   Susan Taylor

Edge: Reeded
Die Axis: ↑↑
Finish: Proof

DATE	DESCRIPTION	QUANTITY SOLD	ISSUE PRICE	FINISH	PR-69	PR-70
2016	Roaring Grizzly Bear	440	1,099.95	Proof	1,100.	—
2017	Elk	650	1,249.95	Proof	1,250.	—

TWO HUNDRED DOLLARS
TWO HUNDRED FOR TWO HUNDRED SERIES

TWO HUNDRED DOLLARS, TWO HUNDRED FOR TWO HUNDRED, 2014-2016.

Common Obverse

2014
Towering Forests of Canada
Designer: Ellen Cowie

2015
Coastal Waters of Canada
Designer: Ellen Cowie

2015
Canada's Rugged Mountains
Designer: Steve Hepburn

2016
Vast Prairies
Designer: Luc Normandin

2016
Canada's Icy Arctic
Designer: Bonnie Ross

Designers:		**Engravers:**	
Obv.:	Susanna Blunt	Obv.:	Susan Taylor
Rev.:	See reverse illustrations		
Composition:	99.99% Ag		
Silver content:	62.69 g, 2.02 tr oz		
Weight:	62.69 g	**Edge:**	Reeded
Diameter:	50.0 mm	**Die Axis:**	↑↑
Thickness:	N/A	**Finish:**	Matte Proof
Case of Issue:	Paperboard case, white flocked insert, encapsulated coin, COA		

DATE	DESCRIPTION	QUANTITY SOLD	ISSUE PRICE	FINISH	PR-69	PR-70
2014	Towering Forests of Canada	19,695	200.00	Matte Proof	220.	—
2015	Coastal Waters of Canada	24,760	200.00	Matte Proof	220.	—
2015	Canada's Rugged Mountains	24,706	200.00	Matte Proof	220.	—
2016	Vast Prairies	11,754	200.00	Matte Proof	220.	—
2016	Canada's Icy Arctic	8,441	200.00	Matte Proof	220.	—

Note: Coins illustrated are smaller than actual size.

TWO HUNDRED FIFTY DOLLARS

VANCOUVER 2010 OLYMPIC WINTER GAMES SERIES, 2007-2010

These are the first coins produced in pure silver by the Royal Canadian Mint with a guaranteed weight of one kilo.

Common Obverse
(Except for date)

Early Canada
Designer: Stan Witten
Engraver: Stan Witten

Towards Confederation
Designer: Susan Taylor
Engraver: Susan Taylor

The Canada of Today
Designer: Design Team of the Vancouver
Organising Committee for the 2010
Olympic and Paralympic Winter Games
Engraver: Konrad Wachelko

Surviving the Flood
Designer: Xwa lac tun (Ricky Harry)
Engraver: Christie Paquet

Designers:		Engravers:	
Obv.:	Susanna Blunt	Obv.:	Susan Taylor
Rev.:	See reverse illustrations	Rev.:	See reverse illustrations
Composition:	99.99% Ag	Thickness:	12.5 mm
Silver content:	1,000.0 g, 32.151 tr oz	Edge:	Plain
Weight:	1,000.0 g (1 kilo)	Die Axis:	↑↑
Diameter:	101.6 mm	Finish:	Proof, Ultra high relief
Case of Issue:	Black display case, black flocked insert, encapsulated coin, COA, Vancouver 2010 Olympic Winter Games theme sleeve		

DATE	DESCRIPTION	ISSUE DATE	QUANTITY SOLD	ISSUE PRICE	FINISH	PR-68	PR-69
2007	Early Canada	Feb. 23, 2007	2,500	1,299.95	Proof	1,600.	—
2008	Towards Confederation	Feb. 20, 2008	2,500	1,599.95	Proof	1,600.	—
2009	The Canada of Today	April 15, 2009	905	1,599.95	Proof	1,600.	—
2009	Surviving the Flood	Nov. 17, 2009	815	1,599.95	Proof	1,600.	—

VANCOUVER 2010 OLYMPIC WINTER GAMES, 2007-2010 (cont.).

TWO HUNDRED FIFTY DOLLARS, THE EAGLE, 2010.

The eagle, an important First Nations symbol, represents power, peace and prestige. This is the first time a coin is offered in three different finishe

Obverse	The Eagle, Proof Enamel

Designers:			Engravers:	
Obv.:	Susanna Blunt		Obv.:	Susan Taylor
Rev.:	Xwa lac tun (Ricky Harry)		Rev.:	Stan Witten
Composition:	99.99% Ag		**Thickness:**	12.5 mm
Silver content:	1,000.0 g, 32.151 tr oz		**Edge:**	Plain
Weight:	1,000.0 g (1 kilo)		**Die Axis:**	↑↑
Diameter:	101.6 mm		**Finish:**	Proof
Case of Issue:	Black display case, black flocked insert, encapsulated coin, COA, Vancouver 2010 Olympic Winter Games theme sleeve			

DATE	DESCRIPTION	ISSUE DATE	QUANTITY SOLD	ISSUE PRICE	FINISH	PR-69	PR-70
2010	The Eagle, Proof	Nov. 19, 2009	349	1,649.95	Proof	1,600.	—
2010	The Eagle, Proof Enamel	Nov. 19, 2009	74	1,649.95	Enamel	1,800.	—
2010	The Eagle, Proof Antique	Nov. 19, 2009	349	1,649.95	Antique	1,600.	—

Note: 1. Identical designs are utilized on the $2,500 gold coins for 2007, 2008, 2009 and 2010, see page 415.
       2. Coins on pages 338-339 are illustrated smaller than actual size.

TWO HUNDRED FIFTY DOLLARS, 125TH ANNIVERSARY OF BANFF NATIONAL PARK, 2010.

Banff National Park was Canada's first national park, and the world's third, spanning 6,641 square kilometres of valleys, mountains, glaciers, forest
meadows, and rivers.

Designers and Engravers:

Obv.:	S. Blunt, S. Taylor
Rev.:	T. Bianco, S. Taylor
Composition:	99.99% Ag
Silver content:	1,000.0 g, 32.151 tr oz
Weight:	1,000.0 g (1 kilo)
Diameter:	101.8 mm
Thickness:	12.5 mm
Edge:	Plain
Die Axis:	↑↑
Finish:	Proof
Case of Issue:	Black display case, black flocked insert, encapsulated coin, CO

DATE	DESCRIPTION	MINTAGE	ISSUE PRICE	FINISH	PR-69	PR-70
2010	125th Anniversary of Banff National Park	525	1,904.95	Proof	1,600.	—

WO HUNDRED FIFTY DOLLARS, 375TH ANNIVERSARY OF THE FIRST EUROPEAN OBSERVATION OF LACROSSE, 2011.
First documented by a Jesuit missionary, Jean de Brébeuf in 1636, lacrosse is sport, legend, culture, and history combined. Lacrosse is the national ummer sport of Canada.

Designers and Engravers:
Obv.:	S. Blunt, S. Taylor
Rev.:	S. Hepburn, C. Paquet
Composition:	99.99% Ag
Silver content:	1,000.0 g, 32.151 tr oz
Weight:	1,000.0 g (1 kilo)
Diameter:	101.8 mm
Thickness:	12.5 mm
Edge:	Plain
Die Axis:	↑↑
Finish:	Proof
Case of Issue:	Black display case, black flocked insert, encapsulated coin, COA

WO HUNDRED FIFTY DOLLARS, YEAR OF THE (WATER) DRAGON, 2012.
The year 2012 is ruled by the Water Dragon. The Water Dragon occurs every sixty years and personifies creativity at it best.

Designers and Engravers:
Obv.:	S. Blunt, S. Taylor
Rev.:	Three Degrees Creative Group Inc., Cecily Mok
Composition:	99.99% Ag
Silver content:	1,000.0 g, 32.151 tr oz
Weight:	1,000.0 g (1 kilo)
Diameter:	101.8 mm
Thickness:	12.5 mm
Edge:	Plain
Die Axis:	↑↑
Finish:	Proof
Case of Issue:	Black display case, black flocked insert, encapsulated coin, COA

WO HUNDRED FIFTY DOLLARS, THE MOOSE FAMILY, ROBERT BATEMAN MOOSE COIN SERIES, 1962-2012.
The reverse design on this coin features a bull moose's head and antlers taken from Robert Bateman's painting The Moose Family. The coin was sued to commemorate the 50th anniversary of the Canadian Wildlife Federation.

Designers and Engravers:
Obv.:	S. Blunt, S. Taylor
Rev.:	Robert Bateman, Stan Witten
Composition:	99.99% Ag
Silver content:	1,000.0 g, 32.151 tr oz
Weight:	1,000.0 g (1 kilo)
Diameter:	102.1 mm
Thickness:	12.5 mm
Edge:	Reeded
Die Axis:	↑↑
Finish:	Proof
Case of Issue:	Maple wood case, black flocked insert, encapsulated coin, COA

DATE	DESCRIPTION	QUANTITY SOLD	ISSUE PRICE	FINISH	PR-69	PR-70
2011	375th Anniv. First European Observation Lacrosse	591	2,195.95	Proof	1,600.	—
2012	Year of the (Water) Dragon	1,616	2,195.95	Proof	2,000.	—
2012 (1962-)	The Moose Family	591	2,249.95	Proof	2,000.	—

TWO HUNDRED FIFTY DOLLARS (kilogram), GEORGE III PEACE MEDAL, 2012.

The presentation of Indian Chief Medals to the First Nations Chiefs in Canada was begun by King Louis XIV of France. This practice was continued bthe Kings and Queens of England as a symbol of maintaining peaceful relations with the Indian Nations. See page 492 for the gold version of this meda

2012 Obverse

Des.: RCM Staff's representation of the
King George III Peace Medal
Engravers: K. Wachelko, M. Bowen
S. Strath, S. Stewart

Designers and Engravers:
- Obv..: See reverse illustration
- Rev.: See reverse illustration

Composition: 99.99% Ag
Thickness: 12.5 mm
Silver content: 1,000.0 g, 32.151 tr oz
Edge: Reeded
Weight: 1,000.0 g (1 kilo)
Die Axis: ↑↑
Diameter: 102.1 mm
Finish: 2012 Proof,
2013 Proof, Selectively gold plate
Case of Issue: Maroon leatherette clam
style case, black flocked
insert, encapsulated coin, CO

TWO HUNDRED FIFTY DOLLARS, THE BATTLE OF QUEENSTON HEIGHTS, 2012.

This coin was issued to commemorate the first major battle in the War of 1812, which resulted in a Canadian victory.

Designers and Engravers:
- Obv.: S. Blunt, S. Taylor
- Rev.: John David Kelly,
  Marcos Hallam

Composition: 99.99% Ag
Silver content: 1,000.0 g, 32.151 tr oz
Weight: 1,000.0 g (1 kilo)
Diameter: 102.1 mm
Thickness: 12.5 mm
Edge: Reeded
Die Axis: ↑↑
Finish: Proof
Case of Issue: Maroon clam style case
black flocked insert,
encapsulated coin, CO

TWO HUNDRED FIFTY DOLLARS, YEAR OF THE DRAGON, 2012.

Designers and Engravers:
- Obv.: S. Blunt, S. Taylor
- Rev.: Three Design Creative
  Group

Composition: 99.99% Ag
Silver content: 1,000.0 g, 32.151 tr oz
Weight: 1,000.0 g (1 kilo)
Diameter: 102.6 mm
Thickness: 12.5 mm
Edge: Pl,ain
Die Axis: ↑↑
Finish: Proof
Case of Issue: Maroon clam style case
black flocked insert,
encapsulated coin, CO

DATE	DESCRIPTION	QUANTITY SOLD	ISSUE PRICE	FINISH	PR-69	PR-70
2012	George III Peace Medal	590	2,249.95	Proof	1,800.	—
2012	The Battle of Queenston Heights	225	2,249.95	Proof	2,000.	—
2013	Year of the Dragon	5,888	2,195.95	Proof	2,000.	—

WO HUNDRED FIFTY DOLLARS, CANADA'S ARCTIC LANDSCAPE, 2013.

Designers and Engravers:
Obv.:	S. Blunt, S. Taylor
Rev.:	W. D. Ward, S. Witten

Composition: 99.99% Ag
Silver content: 1,000.0 g, 32.151 tr oz
Weight: 1,000.0 g (1 kilo)
Diameter: 101.8 mm
Thickness: 12.5 mm
Edge: Reeded
Die Axis: ↑↑
Finish: Proof
Case of Issue: Maple wood case, black flocked insert, encapsulated coin, COA

WO HUNDRED FIFTY DOLLARS, YEAR OF THE SNAKE, 2013.

Designers and Engravers:
Obv.:	S. Blunt, S. Taylor
Rev.:	Three Degrees Creative Group Inc., Christie Paquet

Composition: 99.99% Ag
Silver content: 1,000.0 g, 32.151 tr oz
Weight: 1,000.0 g (1 kilo)
Diameter: 102.1 mm
Thickness: 12.5 mm
Edge: Reeded
Die Axis: ↑↑
Finish: Proof
Case of Issue: Silver satin-like covered case, black flocke insert, encapsulated coin, COA

"WO HUNDRED FIFTY DOLLARS, 250TH ANNIVERSARY OF THE END OF THE SEVEN YEARS WAR, 2013.

The Seven Years War (1756-1763) in North America was fought between the English and French over control of the trade in this section of the world.

Designers and Engravers:
Obv.:	S. Blunt, S. Taylor
Rev.:	Luc Normandin, Konrad Wachelko

Composition: 99.99% Ag
Silver content: 1,000.0 g, 32.151 tr oz
Weight: 1,000.0 g (1 kilo)
Diameter: 102.1 mm
Thickness: 12.5 mm
Edge: Reeded
Die Axis: ↑↑
Finish: Proof
Case of Issue: Maple wood box, black flocked insert, encapsulated coin, COA

DATE	DESCRIPTION	QUANTITY SOLD	ISSUE PRICE	FINISH	PR-69	PR-70
2013	Canada's Arctic Landscape	320	2,249.95	Proof	2,000.	—
2013	Year of the Snake	359	2,249.95	Proof	2,250.	—
2013	250th Anniv., End of the Seven Years War	179	2,249.95	Proof	2,250.	—

TWO HUNDRED FIFTY DOLLARS, BATTLE OF CHATEAUGUAY, WAR OF 1812, 2013.

Designers and Engravers:
Obv.: S. Blunt, S. Taylor
Rev.: H. Julien, J. Osio, E. Boyer
Composition: 99.99% Ag
Silver content: 1,000.0 g, 32.151 tr oz
Weight: 1,000.0 g (1 kilo)
Diameter: 102.1 mm
Thickness: 12.5 mm
Edge: Reeded
Die Axis: ↑↑
Finish: Proof
Case of Issue: Maple wood box, black flocked insert, encapsulated coin, COA

TWO HUNDRED FIFTY DOLLARS, THE CARIBOU, 2013.

Designers and Engravers:
Obv.: S. Blunt, S. Taylor
Rev.: Trevor Tennant, RCM Staff
Composition: 99.99% Ag
Silver content: 1,000.0 g, 32.151 tr oz
Weight: 1,000.0 g (1 kilo)
Diameter: 102.1 mm
Thickness: 12.5 mm
Edge: Reeded
Die Axis: ↑↑
Finish: Proof
Case of Issue: Maple wood box, black flocked insert, encapsulated coin, COA

DATE	DESCRIPTION	QUANTITY SOLD	ISSUE PRICE	FINISH	PR-69	PR-70
2013	Battle of Chateauguay	112	2,249.95	Proof	2,000.	—
2013	The Caribou	146	2,249.95	Proof	2,000.	—

WO HUNDRED FIFTY DOLLARS, YEAR OF THE HORSE, 2014.

Designers and Engravers:

Obv.:	S. Blunt, S. Taylor
Rev.:	Three Degrees Creative Group Inc., RCM Staff

Composition:	99.99% Ag
Silver content:	1,000.0 g, 32.151 tr oz
Weight:	1,000.0 g (1 kilo)
Diameter:	102.1 mm
Thickness:	12.5 mm
Edge:	Reeded
Die Axis:	↑↑
Finish:	Proof
Case of Issue:	Silver satin-like covered case, black flocked insert, encapsulated coin, COA

WO HUNDRED FIFTY DOLLARS, BATTLE OF LUNDY'S LANE, 2014.

Designers and Engravers:

Obv.:	S. Blunt, S. Taylor
Rev.:	Bonnie Ross, RCM Staff

Composition:	99.99% Ag
Silver content:	1,000.0 g, 32.151 tr oz
Weight:	1,000.0 g (1 kilo)
Diameter:	102.1 mm
Thickness:	N/A
Edge:	Reeded
Die Axis:	↑↑
Finish:	Proof
Case of Issue:	Maple wood case, black flocked insert, encapsulated coin, COA

DATE	DESCRIPTION	QUANTITY SOLD	ISSUE PRICE	FINISH	PR-69	PR-70
2014	Year of the Horse	469	2,249.95	Proof	2,250.	—
2014	Battle of Lundy's Lane	225	2,249.95	Proof	2,250.	—

MAPLE LEAF FOREVER SERIES

TWO HUNDRED FIFTY DOLLARS, MAPLE LEAF FOREVER, 2014-2016.

| 2014 | 2015 | 2016 |
| Coloured Enamel | Hologram | Natural Colour & Selective Gold Platning |

Designers:		**Engravers:**	
Obv.:	Susanna Blunt	Obv.:	Susan Taylor
Rev.:	See reverse illustrations		
Composition:	99.99% Ag, Hologram		
Silver content:	1,000.0 g, 32.151 tr oz		
Weight:	1,000.0 g (1 kilo)	**Edge:**	Reeded
Diameter:	102.1 mm	**Die Axis:**	↑↑
Thickness:	N/A	**Finish:**	Proof
Case of Issue:	Maple wood case, black flocked insert, encapsulated coin, COA		

DATE	DESCRIPTION	QUANTITY SOLD	ISSUE PRICE	FINISH	PR-69	PR-70
2014	Maple Leaf Forever, Coloured Enamel	571	2,299.95	Proof	2,300.	—
2015	Maple Leaf Forever, Hologram	500	2,299.95	Proof	2,300.	—
2016	Maple Leaf Forever, Natural Colour & Selective Gold Plating	488	2,299.95	Proof	2,300.	—

Note: Coins illustrated are smaller than actual size.

IN THE EYES OF... SERIES

TWO HUNDRED FIFTY DOLLARS, IN THE EYES OF... 2014-2017.

In The Eyes Of... is a series featuring the distinctive eyes of Canada's wildlife.

Designers and Engravers:

Obv.:	S. Blunt, S. Taylor
Rev.:	See reverse illustrations
Composition:	99.99% Ag
Silver content:	1,000.0 g, 32.151 tr oz
Weight:	1,000.0 g (1 kilo)
Diameter:	102.1 mm
Thickness:	12.5 mm
Edge:	Reeded
Die Axis:	↑↑
Finish:	Proof
Case of Issue:	Maple wood case, black flocked insert, encapsulated coin, COA

2014 – In The Eyes of the Snowy Owl
Designer: A. Nogy

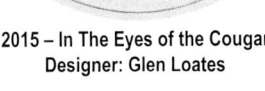  

2015 – In The Eyes of the Cougar
Designer: Glen Loates

2016 – In The Eyes of the Spirit Bear
Designer: Glen Loates

2017 – In The Eyes of the Timber Wolf
Designer: Pierre Leduc

DATE	DESCRIPTION	QUANTITY SOLD	ISSUE PRICE	FINISH	PR-69	PR-70
2014	In The Eyes of the Snowy Owl	500	2,299.95	Proof	2,300.	—
2015	In The Eyes of the Cougar	500	2,299.95	Proof	2,300.	—
2016	In The Eyes of the Spirit Bear	356	2,299.95	Proof	2,300.	—
2017	In The Eyes of the Timber Wolf	400	2,299.95	Proof	2,300.	—

TWO HUNDRED FIFTY DOLLARS, YEAR OF THE SHEEP, 2015.

Designers and Engravers:

Obv.:	S. Blunt, S. Taylor
Rev.:	Three Degrees Creative, RCM Staff
Composition:	99.99% Ag
Silver content:	1,000.0 g, 32.151 tr oz
Weight:	1,000.0 g (1 kilo)
Diameter:	102.1 mm
Thickness:	N/A
Edge:	Reeded
Die Axis:	↑↑
Finish:	Proof, Coloured
Case of Issue:	Silver satin-like covered case, black flocked insert, encapsulated coin COA, custom red sleeve

TWO HUNDRED FIFTY DOLLARS, LOONEY TUNES™: ENSEMBLE CAST, 2015.

Designers and Engravers:

Obv.:	S. Blunt, S. Taylor
Rev.:	Warner Bros.
Composition:	99.99% Ag
Silver content:	1,006.0 g, 32.151 tr oz
Weight:	1,006.0 g (1 kilo)
Diameter:	102.1 mm
Thickness:	N/A
Edge:	Reeded
Die Axis:	↑↑
Finish:	Proof
Case of Issue:	Wooden case with custom beauty box, encapsulated coin, COA

TWO HUNDRED FIFTY DOLLARS, YEAR OF THE MONKEY, 2016.

The year 2016 is ruled by the Monkey, the Chinese zodiac that most closely resembles humankind.

Designers and Engravers:

Obv.:	S. Blunt, S. Taylor
Rev.:	Three Degrees Creative
Composition:	99.99% Ag
Silver content:	1,000.0 g, 32.151 tr oz
Weight:	1,000.0 g (1 kilo)
Diameter:	120 mm
Thickness:	N/A
Edge:	Reeded
Die Axis:	↑↑
Finish:	Proof with enamel
Case of Issue:	Silver satin-like covered case with custom red sleeve.

DATE	DESCRIPTION	QUANTITY SOLD	ISSUE PRICE	FINISH	PR-69	PR-70
2015	Year of the Sheep	310	2,288.88	Proof	2,290.	—
2015	Looney Tunes™ Ensemble Cast	342	2,350.95	Proof	2,350.	—
2016	Year of the Monkey	199	2,288.88	Proof	2,300.	—

TWO HUNDRED FIFTY DOLLARS, ARMS OF CANADA, 2016.

Designers and Engravers:
Obv.:	S. Blunt, S. Taylor
Rev.:	RCM Staff

Composition: 99.99% Ag
Silver content: 1,000.0 g, 32.151 tr oz
Weight: 1,000.0 g (1 kilo)
Diameter: 102 mm
Thickness: N/A
Edge: Reeded
Die Axis: ↑↑
Finish: Proof with antique
Case of Issue: Wood case and black beatuy box.

TWO HUNDRED FIFTY DOLLARS, THE CANADIAN COIN COLLECTION, 2017.

Designers and Engravers:
Obv.:	S. Blunt, S. Taylor
Rev.:	RCM Staff

Composition: 99.99% Ag
Silver content: 1,000.0 g, 32.151 tr oz
Weight: 1,000.0 g (1 kilo)
Diameter: 102.1 mm
Thickness: N/A
Edge: Reeded
Die Axis: ↑↑
Finish: Proof with antique
Case of Issue: Wood case and black beatuy box.

TWO HUNDRED FIFTY DOLLARS, YEAR OF THE ROOSTER, 2017.

Designers and Engravers:
Obv.:	S. Blunt, S. Taylor
Rev.:	Three Degrees Creative

Composition: 99.99% Ag
Silver content: 1,000.0 g, 32.151 tr oz
Weight: 1,000.0 g (1 kilo)
Diameter: 120 mm
Thickness: N/A
Edge: Reeded
Die Axis: ↑↑
Finish: Proof with enamel
Case of Issue: Silver satin-like covered case with custom red sleeve.

DATE	DESCRIPTION	QUANTITY SOLD	ISSUE PRICE	FINISH	PR-69	PR-70
2016	Arms of Canada	411	2,329.95	Proof	2,500.	—
2017	The Canadian Coin Collection	220	2,499.95	Proof with antique	2,500.	—
2017	Year of the Rooster	85	2,288.88	Proof	2,300.	—

TWO HUNDRED FIFTY DOLLARS, A TRIBUTE TO THE FIRST CANADIAN GOLD COIN, 2017.

Designers and Engravers:
Obv.:	S. Blunt, S. Taylor
Rev.:	W. H. J. Blackmore
Composition:	99.99% Ag
Silver content:	1,000.0 g, 32.151 tr oz
Weight:	1,000.0 g (1 kilo)
Diameter:	102.1 mm
Thickness:	N/A
Edge:	Reeded
Die Axis:	↑↑
Finish:	Proof
Case of Issue:	Wood case and black beauty box, COA

TWO HUNDRED FIFTY DOLLARS, MAPLE LEAF FOREVER (SHAPED), 2017.

Designers and Engravers:
Obv.:	S. Blunt, S. Taylor
Rev.:	Lisa Thomson-Khan
Composition:	99.99% Ag
Silver content:	1,000.0 g, 32.151 tr oz
Weight:	1,000.0 g (1 kilo)
Diameter:	150 mm (top to bottom)
Thickness:	N/A
Edge:	Plain
Die Axis:	↑↑
Finish:	Antiqued
Case of Issue:	Wood case and black beauty box, COA

TWO HUNDRED FIFTY DOLLARS, A FIERCE GAZE: *TYRANNOSAURUS REX*, 2018.

Designers and Engravers:
Obv.:	S. Blunt, S. Taylor
Rev.:	Julius Csotonyi
Composition:	99.99% Ag
Silver content:	1,006.0 g, 32.151 tr oz
Weight:	1,006.0 g
Diameter:	102.1 mm
Thickness:	N/A
Edge:	Reeded
Die Axis:	↑↑
Finish:	Proof
Case of Issue:	Wood case and black beauty box, COA

DATE	DESCRIPTION	MINTAGE	ISSUE PRICE	FINISH	PR-69	PR-70
2017	A Tribute to the First Canadian Gold Coin	500	2,329.95	Proof	2,350.	—
2017	Maple Leaf Forever (shaped)	700	2,499.95	Antique	2,500.	—
2018	A Fierce Gaze: *Tyrannosaurus Rex*	400	2,299.95	Proof	2,300.	—

FIVE HUNDRED DOLLAR SILVER COINS

FIVE HUNDRED DOLLARS, THE SPIRIT OF HAIDA GWAII, 2012.

Designers and Engravers:
Obv.: S. Blunt, S. Taylor
Rev.: Bill Reid, C. Saffioti
Composition: 99.99% Ag
Silver content: 5,000.0 g, 160.75 tr oz
Weight: 5,000.0 g, (5 kilos)
Diameter: 180.0 mm
Thickness: N/A
Edge: Reeded
Die Axis: ↑↑
Finish: Proof
Case of Issue: Canadian walnut wood case, black velvet insert, encapsulated coin, COA

FIVE HUNDRED DOLLARS, TSATSISNUKOMI, BC, 2013.

Designers and Engravers:
Obv.: S. Blunt, S. Taylor
Rev.: Emily Carr, C. Paquet, S. Witten
Composition: 99.99% Ag
Silver content: 5,000.0 g, 32.160.7 tr oz
Weight: 5,000.0 g (5 kilos)
Diameter: 180.0 mm
Thickness: N/A
Edge: Reeded
Die Axis: ↑↑
Finish: Proof
Case of Issue: Canadian walnut wood case, acrylic holder, COA in booklet format

FIVE HUNDRED DOLLARS, CANADIAN MONUMENTS: NATIONAL ABORIGINAL VETERANS MONUMENT, 2014.

Designers and Engravers:
Obv.: S. Blunt, S. Taylor
Rev.: N. L. Pinay, RCM Staff
Composition: 99.99% Ag
Silver content: 5,000.0 g, 160.75 tr oz
Weight: 5,000.0 g (5 kilo)
Diameter: 180.0 mm
Thickness: N/A
Edge: Reeded
Die Axis: ↑↑
Finish: Proof
Case of Issue: Walnut wood case, acrylic box encapsulated coin, COA

DATE	DESCRIPTION	QUANTITY SOLD	ISSUE PRICE	FINISH	PR-69	PR-70
2012	The Spirit of Haida Gwaii	95	9,999.95	Proof	9,000.	—
2013	Tsatsisnukomi, BC, 1912	99	10,500.00	Proof	9,000.	—
2014	National Aboriginal Veterans Monument	111	10,500.00	Proof	9,000.	—

FIVE HUNDRED DOLLARS, *THE DANCE SCREEN (THE SCREAM TOO)*, 2015.

Designers and Engravers:

Obv.:	S. Blunt, S. Taylor
Rev.:	James Hart

Composition:	99.99% Ag
Silver content:	5,000.0 g, 32.160.7 tr oz
Weight:	5,000.0 g (5 kilos)
Diameter:	180.0 mm
Thickness:	N/A
Edge:	Reeded
Die Axis:	↑↑
Finish:	Proof
Case of Issue:	Canadian walnut wood case, acrylic holder, COA in booklet format

FIVE HUNDRED DOLLARS, *CHARLES EDENSHAW: ARGILLITE CHEST*, 2016.

This five-kilogram masterpiece brings you one of the greatest works from the Pacific Northwest: the argillite chest by Charles Edenshaw (1839 – 1924), a renowned artist and pivotal guardian of Haida culture.

Designers and Engravers:

Obv.:	Susanna Blunt
Rev.:	RCM Engravers

Composition:	99.99% Ag
Silver content:	5,000.0 g, 160.755 tr oz
Weight:	5,000.0 g (5 kilos)
Diameter:	180 mm
Thickness:	N/A
Edge:	Reeded
Die Axis:	↑↑
Finish:	Proof
Case of Issue:	Wooden display case.

FIVE HUNDRED DOLLARS, CANADA 150 FROM COAST TO COAST TO COAST, 2017.

From the soaring peaks of Western Canada to the stately lighthouses of the East Coast and the majestic wilderness of the Canadian North, some of the most iconic images of Canada are truly timeless and never cease to inspire pride.

Designers and Engravers:

Obv.:	Susanna Blunt
Rev.:	Steve Hepburn

Composition:	99.99% Ag
Silver content:	5,000.0 g, 160.755 tr oz
Weight:	5,000.0 g (5 kilos)
Diameter:	180 mm
Thickness:	N/A
Edge:	Reeded
Die Axis:	↑↑
Finish:	Proof
Case of Issue:	Wooden display case, COA.

DATE	DESCRIPTION	MINTAGE	ISSUE PRICE	FINISH	PR-69	PR-70
2015	*The Dance Screen (The Scream Too)*	86	10,500.00	Proof	10,500.	—
2016	*Charles Edenshaw: Argillite Chest*	100	10,699.95	Proof	10,700.	—
2017	Canada 150 From Coast to Coast to Coast	100	10,699.95	Proof	10,700.	—

Note: Coins illustrated smaller than actual size.

SILVER SPECIAL ISSUE SETS

ARCTIC FOX FINE SILVER COIN SET, 2004.

The first fractional fine silver coins feature wildlife designs that were originally created for platinum proof coins. The Arctic Fox first appeared on the platinum proof coins of 1993.

Designers and Engravers:
Obv.: S. Blunt, S. Taylor
Rev.: Claude D'Angelo
Rev.: $5 – Susan Taylor
$4 – Sheldon Beveridge
$3 – Ago Aarand
$2 – Ago Aarand
Specifications: See page 595
Silver content: 1.85 tr oz
Finish: Proof, Frosted relief against a mirror background
Case of Issue: Black case, multicoloured outer sleeve

CANADA LYNX FINE SILVER COIN SET, 2005.

Designers and Engravers:
Obv.: S. Blunt, S. Taylor
Rev.: Michael Dumas
Rev.: $5 – Susan Taylor
$4 – Cosme Saffioti
$3 – Stan Witten
$2 – Ago Aarand
Specifications: See page 595
Silver content: 1.85 tr oz
Finish: Proof, Frosted relief against a mirror background
Case of Issue: N/A

BALD EAGLE FINE SILVER COIN SET, 2015.

Designers and Engravers:
Obv.: S. Blunt, S. Taylor
Rev.: Michael Dumas
Rev.: Derek C. Wicks
Specifications: See page 595
Silver content: 1.85 tr oz
Finish: Proof, Frosted relief against a mirror background
Case of Issue: Maple wood case with a graphic beauty box.

CANADA WOLF FINE SILVER COIN SET, 2016.

Designers and Engravers:
Obv.: S. Blunt, S. Taylor
Rev.: Pierre Leduc
Specifications: See page 595
Silver content: 1.85 tr oz
Finish: Proof, Frosted relief against a mirror background
Case of Issue: Maple wood case with graphic beauty box.

DATE	DESCRIPTION	QUANTITY SOLD	ISSUE PRICE	FINISH	PR-69	PR-70
2004	Arctic Fox, Set of 4 coins	14,566	89.95	Proof	140.	—
2005	Canada Lynx, Set of 4 coins	7,942	89.95	Proof	160.	—
2015	Bald Eagle, Set of 4 coins	7,500	199.95	Proof	200.	—
2016	Wolf, Set of 4 coins	7,500	199.95	Proof	200.	—

Note: The Silver Special Issues sets are illustrated smaller than actual size.

GOLD COINS

ONE CENT GOLD COIN

ONE CENT, FAREWELL TO THE PENNY, 2012.

This coin was issued in commemoration of the last strike of the Canadian one-cent coin on May 4th, 2011.

Actual Size

Designers and Engravers:
Obv.:	Susanna Blunt, Susan Taylor
Rev.:	G. E. Kruger-Gray, RCM Staff

Composition:	99.99% Au		
Gold content:	1.27 g, 0.04 tr oz		
Weight:	1.27 g		
Diameter:	13.9 mm	**Edge:**	Plain
Thickness:	0.7 mm	**Die Axis:**	↑↑
Finish:	Proof		
Case of Issue:	Maroon leatherette clam style case, black flock insert, encapsulated coin, COA, custom coloured box		

DATE	DESCRIPTION	QUANTITY SOLD	ISSUE PRICE	FINISH	PR-69	PR-70
2012	The Penny	11,251	129.95	Proof	130.	—

TWENTY-FIVE CENT GOLD COINS

TWENTY-FIVE CENTS, COMMEMORATIVE GOLD COINS, 2010-2015.

Actual Size

Designers:
Obv.:	Susanna Blunt		
Rev.:	See reverse illustrations		
Composition:	99.99% Au		
Gold content:	0.5 g, 0.016 tr oz		
Weight:	0.5 g		
Diameter:	11.0 mm		
Case of Issue:	Maroon leatherette clam style case, black flocked insert, encapsulated coin, COA		

Engravers:
Rev.:	Susan Taylor
Rev.:	See reverse illustrations
Thickness:	0.5-0.6 mm
Edge:	Reeded
Die Axis:	↑↑
Finish:	Proof

2010 Obverse with "P" Mint Mark	2010 Caribou Des.: E. Hahn Engr.: RCM Staff	2011-2015 Obverse without "P" Mint Mark	2011 Cougar Des.: E. Damstra Engr.: W. Woodruff	2013 Hummingbird Des.: C. D'Angelo Engr.: S. Strath

2014 Rocky Mountain Bighorn Sheep Des.: E. Damstra Engr.: S. Stewart	2014 Eastern Chipmunk Des.: Tony Bianco Engr.: S. Strath	2015 Grizzly Bear Des.: Emily Damstra Engr.: RCM Staff	2015 Rock Rabbit Des.: Derek Wicks Engr.: RCM Staff	2015 Diwali: Festival of Lights Des.: Sarindar Dhaliwal Engr.: RCM Staff

WENTY-FIVE CENTS, COMMEMORATIVE GOLD COINS, 2010-2015, PRICING TABLE.

DATE	DESCRIPTION	QUANTITY SOLD	ISSUE PRICE	FINISH	PR-69	PR-70
2010	Caribou	9,955	74.95	Proof	80.	—
2011	Cougar	8,627	79.95	Proof	80.	—
2013	The Hummingbird	9,993	79.95	Proof	80.	—
2014	Rocky Mountain Bighorn Sheep	6,054	79.95	Proof	80.	—
2014	Eastern Chipmunk	9,400	79.95	Proof	80.	—
2015	Grizzly Bear	4,069	79.95	Proof	80.	—
2015	Rock Rabbit	5,927	79.95	Proof	80.	—
2015	Diwali: Fesitival of Lights	2,783	79.95	Proof	80.	—

TWENTY-FIVE CENT GOLD COINS PREDATOR VS. PREY SERIES

WENTY-FIVE CENTS, GOLD COINS PREDATOR VS. PREY, 2016-2017.

Actual Size

2016
Traditional Arctic Fox
Des.: Pierre Leduc

2017
Traditional Arctic Hare
Des.: Pierre Leduc

2017
Inuit Arctic Fox
Des.: Andrew Qappik

2017
Inuit Arctic Hare
Des.: Andrew Qappik

Designers:
  Obv.: Susanna Blunt
  Rev.: See reverse illustrations
Composition: 99.99% Au
Gold content: 0.5 g, 0.016 tr oz
Weight: 0.5 g
Diameter: 11.0 mm
Case of Issue: Maroon leatherette clam style case, black flocked insert, encapsulated coin, COA

Engravers:
  Rev.: Susan Taylor
  Rev.: See reverse illustrations
Thickness: 0.5-0.6 mm
Edge: Reeded
Die Axis: ↑↑
Finish: Proof

DATE	DESCRIPTION	QUANTITY SOLD	ISSUE PRICE	FINISH	PR-69	PR-70
2016	Predator vs. Prey: Traditional Arctic Fox	6,497	79.95	Proof	80.	—
2017	Predator vs. Prey: Traditional Arctic Hare	6,065	79.95	Proof	80.	—
2017	Predator vs. Prey: Inuit Arctic Fox	5,525	79.95	Proof	80.	—
2017	Predator vs. Prey: Inuit Arctic Hare	4,444	79.95	Proof	80.	—

FIFTY CENT GOLD COINS

FIFTY CENT (1/25 OUNCE) ISSUES, 2004-2012.

The 1/25 oz gold coin is the smallest ever produced by the Royal Canadian Mint.

Designers:
Obv.:	Susanna Blunt
Rev.:	See reverse illustrations

Composition: 99.99% Au
Gold content: 1.27 g, 0.041 tr oz
Weight: 1.27 g
Diameter: 13.9 mm
Thickness: 0.6 mm

Engravers:
Obv.:	Susan Taylor
Rev.:	See reverse illustrations

Edge: Reeded
Die Axis: ↑↑
Finish: Proof

Case of Issue:
2004:	Maroon leatherette case, black flocked insert, encapsulated coin, COA
2005-2006:	Maroon plastic slide case, black plastic insert, encapsulated coin, COA
2007-2012:	Maroon leatherette clam style case, black flocked insert, encapsulated coin, COA

Actual Size

| Common Obverse | 2004
Majestic Moose
Des. and Engr.:
José Osio | 2005
Voyageur
Des.: E. Hahn
Engr.: Stan Witten | 2006
Cowboy
Des.: M. Grant
Engr.: Stan Witten | 2007
Wolf
Des. and Engr.:
William Woodruff |

| 2008
De Havilland
Beaver
Des.: P. Mossman
Engr.: K. Wachelko | 2009
Red Maple Leaves
Des. and Engr.:
Christie Paquet | 2010
R.C.M.P.
Des.: J. Griffin-Scott
Engr.: K. Wachelko | 2011
Canada Geese
Des.: E. Damstra
Engr.: K. Wachelko | 2012
The Bluenose
Des.: From the late
Nova Scotia artist
P. MacCready's
watercolour
painting
Engr.: S. Witten |

DATE	DESCRIPTION	QUANTITY SOLD	ISSUE PRICE	FINISH	PR-69	PR-70
2004	Majestic Moose, 25th Anniv. Gold Maple Leafs	24,992	69.95	Proof	140.	—
2005	70th Anniversary of Voyageur Design	13,933	69.95	Proof	120.	—
2006	Cowboy	13,524	69.95	Proof	120.	—
2007	Wolf	12,514	81.95	Proof	160.	—
2008	De Havilland Beaver	13,526	85.95	Proof	120.	—
2009	Red Maple Leaves	11,854	99.95	Proof	120.	—
2010	Royal Canadian Mounted Police	9,594	109.95	Proof	120.	—
2011	Canada Geese	7,498	109.95	Proof	120.	—
2012	The Bluenose	13,524	129.95	Proof	120.	—

FTY CENTS, THE BOREAL FOREST, 2011.

The Boreal Forest is a vast woodland that circumvents the globe across the northern hemisphere, and 2011 was declared International Year of the Forest. These are 1/25 ounce coins.

2011   BOREAL FOREST

2011   ORCA WHALE

2011   WOOD BISON

2011   PEREGRINE FALCON

Actual Size

Designers:		**Engravers:**	
Obv.:	Susanna Blunt	Obv.:	Susan Taylor
Rev.:	Corrine Hunt	Rev.:	Boreal Forest / Peregrine Falcon: Marcos Hallam
Composition:	99.99% Au		Orca Whale: Cecily Mok,
Gold content:	1.27 g, 0.04 tr oz		Wood Bison: Konrad Wachelko
Weight:	1.27 g	**Edge:**	Reeded
Diameter:	13.8 to 13.9 mm	**Die Axis:**	↑↑
Thickness:	0.6 mm	**Finish:**	Proof
Case of Issue:	Maroon leatherette clam style case, black flocked insert, encapsulated coin, COA		

DATE	DESCRIPTION	QUANTITY SOLD	ISSUE PRICE	FINISH	PR-69	PR-70
2011	Boreal Forest	1,859	139.95	Proof	120.	—
2011	Orca Whale	1,729	139.95	Proof	120.	—
2011	Wood Bison	1,678	139.95	Proof	120.	—
2011	Peregrine Falcon	1,686	139.95	Proof	120.	—

FIFTY CENTS, COMMEMORATIVE GOLD COINS, 2012-2017.

Actual Size

Designers:		Engravers:	
Obv.:	Susanna Blunt	Obv.:	Susan Taylor
Rev.:	See reverse illustrations	Rev.:	See reverse illustration
Composition:	99.99% Au	Thickness:	0.5 to 0.7 mm
Gold content:	1.27 g, 0.04 tr oz	Edge:	Reeded
Weight:	1.27 g	Die Axis:	↑↑
Diameter:	13.9 mm	Finish:	Proof
Case of Issue:	Maroon leatherette clam style case, black flocked insert, encapsulated coin, COA		

Common Obverse

2012
150th Anniv. of the
Caribou Gold Rush
Des.: Tony Bianco
Engr.: C. Paquet

2013
Owl Shaman
Holding Goose
Des.: J. Nowkawalk
Engr.: S. Stewart

2013
Bald Eagle
Des.: Trevor Tennant
Engr.: Cecily Mok
Actual size

2013
300th Anniv. of
Louisbourg
Des.: Peter Gough
Engr.: RCM Staff

2013
Starfish
Des.: E. Damstra
Engr.: S. Strath

2014
Canada's Classic Beaver
Des. G.E. Kruger Gray
Engr. M. Bowan

2014
Osprey
Des.: RCM Staff
Engr.: K. Wachelko

2014
Seahorse
Des.: Emily Damstra
Engr.: M. Hallam

2014
Quebec/Charlottetown
Conferences
Des.: M. Bowen
Engr.: RCM Staff

2015
Owl
Des.: A. Nogy
Engr.: RCM Staff

2015
Maple Leaf
Des.: P. Leduc
Engr.: RCM Staff

2015
Sea Creatures: Lobster
Des.: Emily Damstra
Engr.: RCM Staff

2017
The Silver Maple Leaf
Des.: Margaret Best
Engr.: RCM Staff

DATE	DESCRIPTION	QUANTITY SOLD	ISSUE PRICE	FINISH	PR-69	PR-70
2012	150th Anniv. of the Caribou Gold Rush	5,988	129.95	Proof	120.	—
2013	Owl Shaman Holding Goose	5,736	129.95	Proof	120.	—
2013	Bald Eagle	9,712	129.95	Proof	130.	—
2013	300th Anniv. of Louisbourg	3,409	129.95	Proof	130.	—
2013	Sea Creatures: Starfish	4,287	129.95	Proof	130.	—
2014	Canada's Classic Beaver	7,500	129.95	Proof	130.	—
2014	Osprey	4,096	129.95	Proof	130.	—
2014	Sea Creatures: Seahorse	3,049	129.95	Proof	130.	—
2014 (1884-)	150th Anniv. Quebec/Charlottetown Conferences	4,746	129.95	Proof	130.	—
2015	Owl	3,592	129.95	Proof	130.	—
2015	Maple Leaf	5,102	129.95	Proof	130.	—
2015	Sea Creatures: Lobster	2,994	129.95	Proof	130.	—
2017	The Silver Maple Leaf	8,000	129.95	Proof	130.	—

Note: There were no fifty cent gold coins issued for 2016.

ONE DOLLAR GOLD COINS

| 2006
GOLD LOUIS
(1723 LOUIS D'OR MIRLITON) | 2007
GOLD LOUIS
(1726 LOUIS D'OR AUX LUNETTES) | 2008
GOLD LOUIS
(1720-1723 LOUIS D'OR AUX DEUX L) |

Actual Size   Actual Size   Actual Size

Designers:
  Obv.:   Susanna Blunt
  Rev.:   RCM Staff
Composition: 99.99% Au
Gold content: 1.55 g, 0.05 tr oz
Weight: 1.555 g
Diameter: 14.1 mm
Thickness: 0.8 mm
Case of Issue: Maroon plastic slide case, black plastic insert, encapsulated coin, COA

Engravers:
  Obv.:   Susan Taylor
  Rev.:   2006 Konrad Wachelko
               2007-2008 Marcos Hallam

Edge: Reeded
Die Axis: ↑↑
Finish: Proof

DATE	DESCRIPTION	QUANTITY SOLD	ISSUE PRICE	FINISH	PR-69	PR-70
2006	1723 Louis d'or Mirliton	5,648	102.95	Proof	100.	—
2007	1726 Louis d'or Aux Lunettes	4,023	104.95	Proof	100.	—
2008	1720 to 1723 Louis d'or aux deux L	3,793	124.95	Proof	100.	—

ONE DOLLAR, 30TH ANNIVERSARY OF THE LOONIE, 2017.

To commemorate the 30th anniversary of Canada's golden-hued circulation coin, this exquisite two-coin set revisits history by featuring the now-iconic loonie alongside its original design – Canada's $1 circulation coin that never was.

| Common
Obverse |  | Loonie
Designer:
Robert-Ralph
Carmichael |  | Voyageur
Designer:
Emanuel
Hahn |  |

Designers:
  Obv.:   Susanna Blunt
  Rev.:   See reverse illustrations
Composition: 99.99% Au
Gold content: 1.55 g, 0.05 tr oz
Weight: 31.16 g
Diameter: 30 mm
Thickness: N/A
Case of Issue: Wooden box with black beauty box, COA

Engravers:
  Obv.:   Susan Taylor
  Rev.:   See reverse illustrations

Edge: Plain
Die Axis: ↑↑
Finish: Proof

DATE	DESCRIPTION	QUANTITY SOLD	ISSUE PRICE	FINISH	PR-69	PR-70
2017	2-Coin Set, 30th Anniversary of the Loonie	350	5,499.95	Proof	5,500	–

FIVE DOLLAR GOLD COINS

FIVE DOLLARS, COMMEMORATIVE GOLD COINS, 2011-2014.

| Common Obverse | 2011
Norman Bethune
Des.: Harvey Chan
Engr.: José Osio | 2012
Diamond Jubilee
Des.: RCM Staff
Engr.: C. Paquet | 2014
Bald Eagle
Des.: Derek Wicks
Engr.: RCM Staff | 2014
Nanaboozhoo
Des.: C. Assiniboine
Engr.: RCM Staff |

| Actual
Size | 2014
Maple Leaves
Des.: Pierre Leduc
Engr.: RCM Staff | 2014
Cougar
Des.: Glen Loates
Engr.: RCM Staff |

Designers:
Obv.: Susanna Blunt
Rev.: See reverse illustrations
Composition: 99.99% Au
Gold content: 3.13 g, 0.10 tr oz
Weight: 3.13 g
Diameter: 16.0 mm
Thickness: 1.0 mm
Case of Issue:
2011, 2014: Maroon leatherette clam style case, black flocked insert, encapsulated coin, COA
2012: Wooden collector case, black flocked insert, encapsulated coin, COA, Beauty box featuring the official Diamond Jubilee Cypher

Engravers:
Obv.: Susan Taylor
Rev.: See reverse illustrations

Edge: Reeded
Die Axis: ↑↑
Finish: Proof

DATE	DESCRIPTION	QUANTITY SOLD	ISSUE PRICE	FINISH	PR-69	PR-70
2011	75th Anniversary Dr. Norman Bethune's Invention of the First Mobile Blood Transfusion Vehicle	1,457	319.95	Proof	225.	—
2012	The Queen's Diamond Jubilee	1,538	259.95	Proof	230.	—
2014	Bald Eagle	1,584	279.95	Proof	230.	—
2014	Portrait of Nanaboozhoo	1,251	279.95	Proof	230.	—
2014	Overlaid Majestic Maple Leaves	778	279.95	Proof	230.	—
2014	Cougar	1,226	279.95	Proof	230.	—

Note: The $5 gold Overlaid Majestic Maple Leaves coin was offered as part of a five coin subscription along with a $20 Silver Majestic Maple Leaves, a $20 Majestic Maple Leaves with colour, and a $20 Majestic Maple Leaves with Jade (see page 295), as well as a $5 platinum Overlaid Majestic Maple Leaves coin (see page 502).

IVE DOLLARS, CHINESE LUNAR CALENDAR GOLD COINS, 2012-2015.

| **Common Obverse** | **2012**
Year of the Dragon
Des.: Three Degrees
Creative Group Inc.
Engr.: K. Wachelko | **2013**
Year of the Snake
Des.: Aries Cheung
Engr.: Stan Witten | **2015**
Year of the Sheep
Des.: Simon Ng
Engr.: RCM Staff | **Actual Size** |

esigners:		**Engravers:**	
Obv.:	Susanna Blunt	Obv.:	Susan Taylor
Rev.:	See reverse illustrations	Rev.:	See reverse illustrations
omposition:	99.99% Au		
old content:	3.13 g, 0.10 tr oz		
eight:	3.13 g	**Edge:**	Reeded
iameter:	16.0 mm	**Die Axis:**	↑↑
hickness:	1.0 mm	**Finish:**	Specimen
ase of Issue:	Maroon leatherette clam style case, black flocked insert, encapsulated coin, COA		

DATE	DESCRIPTION	QUANTITY SOLD	ISSUE PRICE	FINISH	SP-68	SP-69
2012	Year of the Dragon	8,902	229.95	Specimen	220.	250.
2013	Year of the Snake	3,033	229.95	Specimen	220.	250.
2015	Year of the Sheep	1,399	278.88	Specimen	260.	280.

ote: The Year of the Horse, 2014, was not issued in a five dollar denomination.

IVE DOLLARS (¼ ounce), DEVIL'S BRIGADE, 2013.

Canada joined forces with the United States in World War II to create the First Special Service Force.

Actual Size

Designers and Engravers:	
Obv.:	Susanna Blunt, Susan Taylor
Rev.:	Ardell Bourgeois, RCM Staff
Composition:	99.99% Au
Gold content:	7.8 g, 0.25 tr oz
Weight:	7.8 g
Diameter:	20.0 mm
Thickness:	1.7 mm
Case of Issue:	Maroon leatherette clam style case, black flock insert, encapsulated coin(s), COA

Edge: Reeded
Die Axis: ↑↑
Finish: Proof

DATE	DESCRIPTION	QUANTITY SOLD	ISSUE PRICE	FINISH	PR-69	PR-70
2013	$5 (¼ oz), Devil's Brigade	555	649.95	Proof	550.	—

O CANADA SET 2013-2014

FIVE DOLLARS, O CANADA SET, 2013.

The O Canada Set focuses on iconic Canadian animals to celebrate Canadian pride. For other coins in the O Canada Set see pages 201-202 and 35

Common Obverse

Actual Size

Designers and Engravers:

Obv.:	Susanna Blunt, Susan Taylor
Rev.:	Pierre Leduc, See reverse illustrations

Composition: 99.99% Au
Gold content: 3.13 g, 0.10 tr oz
Weight: 3.13 g   **Edge:** Reeded
Diameter: 16.0 mm   **Die Axis:** ↑↑
Thickness: 1.0 mm   **Finish:** Proof
Case of Issue: Maroon leatherette clam style case, black flocked insert, encapsulated coin, COA

Beaver	Polar Bear	Caribou	Wolf	Orca
Engr.: S. Witten	Engr.: E. Boyer	Engr.: E. Boyer	Engr.: A. Tirabasso	Engr.: A. Tirabasso

DATE	DESCRIPTION	QUANTITY SOLD	ISSUE PRICE	FINISH	PR-69	PR-70
2013	Beaver	3,673	279.95	Proof	220.	—
2013	Polar Bear	3,634	279.95	Proof	220.	—
2013	Caribou	2,248	279.95	Proof	220.	—
2013	Wolf	2,582	279.95	Proof	220.	—
2013	Orca	1,852	279.95	Proof	220.	—
2013	Set of 5 coins	Incl. above	1,399.95	Proof	1,000.	—

FIVE DOLLARS, O CANADA SET, 2014.

Common Obverse

Actual Size

Designers and Engravers:

Obv.:	Susanna Blunt, Susan Taylor
Rev.:	RCM Staff

Composition: 99.99% Au
Gold content: 3.13 g, 0.10 tr oz
Weight: 3.13 g   **Edge:** Reeded
Diameter: 16.0 mm   **Die Axis:** ↑↑
Thickness: 1.0 mm   **Finish:** Proof
Case of Issue: Walnut display case, black flocked insert, encapsulated coin, COA

Grizzly Bear	Moose	Canada Goose	Bison

DATE	DESCRIPTION	QUANTITY SOLD	ISSUE PRICE	FINISH	PR-69	PR-70
2014	Grizzly Bear	2,896	279.95	Proof	240.	—
2014	Moose	2,471	279.95	Proof	240.	—
2014	Canada Goose	2,520	279.95	Proof	240.	—
2014	Bison	1,888	279.95	Proof	240.	—

PREHISTORIC ANIMAL SERIES

IVE DOLLARS (1/10 ounce), PREHISTORIC ANIMALS, 2014-2015.

2014 Woolly Mammoth
Des.: Michael Skrepnik

**2015 American Scrimitar
Sabre-Tooth Cat**
Des.: Julius Csotonyi

Actual Size

esigners:		Engravers:	
Obv.:	Susanna Blunt	Rev.: Susan Taylor	
Rev.:	See reverse illustrations		
omposition:	99.99% Au	Thickness:	1.0 mm
old content:	3.14 g, 0.1 tr oz	Edge:	Reeded
eight:	3.14 g	Die Axis:	↑↑
iameter:	16.0 mm	Finish:	Proof
ase of Issue:	Maroon leatherette clam style case, black flocked insert, encapsulated coin, COA, custom box		

DATE	DESCRIPTION	QUANTITY SOLD	ISSUE PRICE	FINISH	PR-69	PR-70
2014	$5 (1/10 oz), Woolly Mammoth	3,001	279.95	Proof	240.	—
2015	$5 (1/10 oz), American Scrimitar Sabre-Tooth Cat	1,455	279.95	Proof	240.	—

ote: The Woolly Mammoth was issued in a set of two coins (see page 560 for set), the second coin being the one ounce twenty-dollar silver (see page 284).

IVE DOLLARS (1/10 ounce), FIVE BLESSINGS, 2014.

Conveying the blessings of happiness, success, long life, joy and good fortune, this coin celebrates the auspicious traditions of Chinese Canadians.

Designers and Engravers:			
Obv.:	Susanna Blunt, Susan Taylor		
Rev.:	RCM Staff		
Composition:	99.99% Au		
Gold content:	3.13 g, 0.1 tr oz		
Weight:	3.13 g	Edge:	Reeded
Diameter:	16.0 mm	Die Axis:	↑↑
Thickness:	1.0 mm	Finish:	Proof
Case of Issue:	Maroon leatherette clam style case, black flock insert, encapsulated coin, COA		

Actual Size

DATE	DESCRIPTION	QUANTITY SOLD	ISSUE PRICE	FINISH	PR-69	PR-70
2014	$5 (1/10 oz), Five Blessings	1,104	279.95	Proof	260.	—

ote: The design on this coin is also utilized on the $50 (1 oz) Five Blessings maple leaf coin (see page 435).

FIVE AND TEN DOLLAR GOLD COMMEMORATIVE COINS

FIVE AND TEN DOLLAR GOLD COMMEMORATIVES 1912-2002.

Issued to mark the 90th anniversary of Canada's first five and ten dollar gold coins in 1912, these double-dated 1912-2002 coins continue commemorative series which began in 1998, with the issue recalling the first set of coins struck at the Ottawa Mint. Basing the overall design on th 1912 specimen coins from the Bank of Canada collection, the 1912-2002 gold coins differ only in the date and, of course, the obverse effigy.

$5 Obverse $5 Reverse

$10 Obverse $10 Reverse

Designers:		**Engravers:**
Obv.:	Dora de Pédery-Hunt	Obv.: Dora de Pédery-Hunt
Rev.:	W. H. J. Blakemore	Rev.: Cosme Saffioti

Denominations:	**$5**	**$10**
Composition:	90.0% Au, 10.0 Cu	90.0% Au, 10.0% Cu
Gold content:	7.52 g, 0.242 tr oz	15.05 g, 0.484 tr oz
Weight (grams):	8.36	16.72
Diameter (mm):	21.6	26.9
Thickness (mm):	N/A	N/A
Edge:	Reeded	Reeded
Die Axis:	↑↑	↑↑
Finish:	Proof	Proof
Case of Issue:	Two-coin clam style case	

DATE	DESCRIPTION	QUANTITY SOLD	ISSUE PRICE	FINISH	PR-69	PR-70
2002 (1912-)	$5	1,998	N.I.I.	Proof	450.	—
2002 (1912-)	$10	1,998	N.I.I.	Proof	850.	—
2002 (1912-)	Set of 2 coins	1,998	749.95	Proof	1,200.	*

TEN DOLLAR GOLD COINS

TEN DOLLARS (¼ ounce), THE WAR OF 1812, 1812-2012.

The reverse of this coin features a heraldic design commemorating the 250th anniversary of the war between the United States and England ov the control of Canadian territories.

Actual Size

Designers and Engravers:	
Obv.:	Susanna Blunt, Susan Taylor
Rev.:	Cathy Bursey-Sabourin, Konrad Wachelko
Composition:	99.99% Au
Gold content:	7.80 g, 0.25 tr oz
Weight:	7.80 g **Edge:** Reeded
Diameter:	20.0 mm **Die Axis:** ↑↑
Thickness:	1.7 mm **Finish:** Proof
Case of Issue:	Maroon leatherette clam style case, black flock insert, encapsulated coin(s), COA

DATE	DESCRIPTION	QUANTITY SOLD	ISSUE PRICE	FINISH	PR-69	PR-70
2012 (1812-)	$10 gold (¼ oz) The War of 1812	1,997	569.95	Proof	550.	—

EN DOLLARS (¼ ounce), POLAR BEAR, 2013.

This ten-dollar gold maple leaf was issued in a set of two coins (see page 500), the second coin being an eight-dollar silver maple (see page 587).

Actual Size

Designers and Engravers:
Obv.: Susanna Blunt, Susan Taylor
Rev.: Germaine Arnaktauyak, RCM Staff
Composition: 99.99% Au
Gold content: 7.87 g, 0.25 tr oz
Weight: 7.8 g   **Edge:** Reeded
Diameter: 20.0 mm   **Die Axis:** ↑↑
Thickness: 1.7 mm   **Finish:** Proof
Case of Issue: See page 501

EN DOLLARS (¼ ounce), THE ARCTIC FOX, 2014.

Actual Size

Designers and Engravers:
Obv.: Susanna Blunt, Susan Taylor
Rev.: Maurice Gervais, RCM Staff
Composition: 99.99% Au
Gold content: 7.8 g, 0.25 tr oz
Weight: 7.8 g   **Edge:** Reeded
Diameter: 20.0 mm   **Die Axis:** ↑↑
Thickness: 1.7 mm   **Finish:** Proof
Case of Issue: Maroon leatherette clam style case, black flock insert, encapsulated coin, COA

EN DOLLARS (¼ ounce), POLAR BEAR AND CUB, 2015.

Featuring Canada's iconic polar bear and cub, the coin is struck in proof finish.

Actual Size

Designers and Engravers:
Obv.: Susanna Blunt, Susan Taylor
Rev.: Germaine Arnaktauyok, RCM Staff
Composition: 99.99% Au
Gold content: 7.80 g, 0.25 tr oz
Weight: 7.80 g   **Edge:** Reeded
Diameter: 20.0 mm   **Die Axis:** ↑↑
Thickness: 1.7 mm   **Finish:** Proof
Case of Issue: Maroon leatherette clam style case, black flock insert, encapsulated coin, COA

DATE	DESCRIPTION	QUANTITY SOLD	ISSUE PRICE	FINISH	PR-69	PR-70
2013	$10 Gold (¼ oz) Polar Bear	4,229	N.I.I.	Proof	500.	—
2014	$10 Gold (¼ ounce) The Arctic Fox	264	649.95	Proof	650.	—
2015	$10 gold (¼ oz) Polar Bear and Cub	314	649.95	Proof	600.	—

TWENTY DOLLAR GOLD COIN

WENTY DOLLARS, CENTENNIAL OF CONFEDERATION COMMEMORATIVE, 1967.

The highlight of the coins issued in 1967 to mark the centenary of Canadian Confederation was a $20 gold coin. It was issued only as part of a $40.00 specimen et (see page 519 for the set listing), but many were later removed from the sets for separate trading. The reverse design is an adaption of the Canadian coat of ms which appears on the 50-cent piece of 1960-1966. It is the only coin in the Centennial set that bears the single date 1967 instead of 1867-1967.

Designers and Engravers:
Obv.: Arnold Machin, Myron Cook
Rev.: Thomas Shingles, Myron Cook
Composition: 90.0% Au, 10.0% Cu
Gold content: 16.443 g, 0.529 tr oz
Weight: 18.27 g   **Edge:** Reeded
Diameter: 27.1 mm   **Die Axis:** ↑↑
Thickness: 2.3 mm   **Finish:** Specimen
Case of Issue: Black leather case, black flocked insert

DATE	DESCRIPTION	QUANTITY SOLD	ISSUE PRICE	FINISH	SP-68	SP-69
1967	Centennial of Confederation	334,288	N.I.I.	Specimen	900.	—

TWENTY-FIVE DOLLAR GOLD COINS

UNTAMED CANADA SERIES

TWENTY-FIVE DOLLARS, UNTAMED CANADA SERIES, 2013-2014.

| Common Obverse | 2013 Arctic Fox | 2013 Pronghorn | 2014 Wolverine |

Designers and Engravers:

Obv.:	Susanna Blunt, Susan Taylor
Rev.:	Tividar Bote, Steven Stewart
Composition:	99.99% Au
Gold content:	7.797 g, 0.25 tr oz
Weight:	7.797 g	Edge:	Reeded
Diameter:	20.0 mm	Die Axis:	↑↑
Thickness:	N/A	Finish:	Proof
Case of Issue:	Maroon leatherette clam style case, black flocked insert, encapsulated coin, COA

DATE	DESCRIPTION	QUANTITY SOLD	ISSUE PRICE	FINISH	PR-69	PR-70
2013	The Arctic Fox	728	649.95	Proof	650.	—
2013	Pronghorn	306	649.95	Proof	650.	—
2014	Wolverine	370	649.95	Proof	650.	—

TWENTY-FIVE DOLLARS, MISS CANADA: AN ALLEGORY 2013.

Designers and Engravers:

Obv.:	Susanna Blunt, Susan Taylor
Rev.:	Laurie McGaw, RCM Staff
Composition:	99.99% Au
Gold content:	7.797 g, 0.25 tr oz
Weight:	7.797 g	Edge:	Reeded
Diameter:	20.0 mm	Die Axis:	↑↑
Thickness:	N/A	Finish:	Proof
Case of Issue:	Maroon leatherette clam style case, black flocked insert, encapsulated coin, COA

DATE	DESCRIPTION	QUANTITY SOLD	ISSUE PRICE	FINISH	PR-69	PR-70
2013	Miss Canada: An Allegory	622	649.95	Proof	650.	—

TWENTY-FIVE DOLLARS, POPE JOHN PAUL II, 2014.

Designers and Engravers:

Obv.:	Susanna Blunt, Susan Taylor
Rev.:	RCM Staff
Composition:	99.99% Au
Gold content:	7.797 g, 0.25 tr oz
Weight:	7.797 g	Edge:	Reeded
Diameter:	20.0 mm	Die Axis:	↑↑
Thickness:	N/A	Finish:	Proof
Case of Issue:	Maroon leatherette clam style case, black flocked insert, encapsulated coin, COA

DATE	DESCRIPTION	QUANTITY SOLD	ISSUE PRICE	FINISH	PR-69	PR-70
2014	Pope John Paul II	1,500	649.95	Proof	650.	—

FIFTY DOLLAR GOLD COINS

FTY DOLLARS, 60TH ANNIVERSARY OF THE END OF THE SECOND WORLD WAR, 1945-2005.

World War II was a global conflict which began September 1st, 1939 when Germany invaded Poland. By September 3rd, 1939, Britain and France clared war on Germany.

There are several ending dates: VE (Victory in Europe) Day May 8th, 1945, and VJ Day (Victory in Japan) August 14th, 1945.

Designers and Engravers:

Obv.:	Susanna Blunt, Susan Taylor
Rev.:	Peter Mossman, Christie Paquet
Composition:	58.33% Au, 41.67% Ag
Gold content:	7.00 g, 0.225 tr oz
Silver content:	5.00 g, 0.161 tr oz
Weight:	12.0 g	**Edge:**	Reeded
Diameter:	27.0 mm	**Die Axis:**	↑↑
Thickness:	2.0 mm	**Finish:**	Specimen
Case of Issue:	Maroon plastic slide case, black plastic insert, encapsulated coin, COA

DATE	DESCRIPTION	QUANTITY SOLD	ISSUE PRICE	FINISH	SP-68	SP-69
2005 (1945-)	60th Anniv. End of the Second World War	4,000	379.95	Specimen	500.	—

ote: While this $50 gold coin is listed as proof quality on the certificate of authenticity, the finish on the coins examined is specimen.

FTY DOLLARS, THE QUEEN'S DIAMOND JUBILEE, 2012.

This coin was struck for the Queen's Diamond Jubilee in 2012. It is the world's first 99.999% gold coin struck with an ultra-high relief.

Designers and Engravers:

Obv.:	Susanna Blunt, Susan Taylor
Rev.:	Laurie McGaw, Christie Paquet
Composition:	99.999% Au
Gold content:	33.17 g, 1.066 tr oz
Weight:	33.17 g	**Edge:**	Reeded
Diameter:	30.0 mm	**Die Axis:**	↑↑
Thickness:	2.5 to 4.5 mm	**Finish:**	Proof
Case of Issue:	Maroon leatherette clam style case, black flocked insert, encapsulated coin, COA

DATE	DESCRIPTION	QUANTITY SOLD	ISSUE PRICE	FINISH	PR-69	PR-70
2012	The Queen's Diamond Jubilee	499	2,999.95	Proof	2,300.	—

FTY DOLLARS, UNESCO AT HOME & ABROAD: MOUNT FUJI & THE CANADIAN ROCKIES, 2015.

The coin juxtaposes two UNESCO heritage sites, one Canadian and one non-Canadian.

Designers and Engravers:

Obv.:	Susanna Blunt, Susan Taylor
Rev.:	Trevor Tennant, RCM Staff
Composition:	99.999% Au
Gold content:	7.8 g, 0.25 oz
Weight:	7.8 g	**Edge:**	Reeded
Diameter:	20.0 mm	**Die Axis:**	↑↑
Thickness:	N/A	**Finish:**	Proof
Case of Issue:	Maroon leatherette clam style case, black flocked insert, encapsulated coin, COA, custom box

DATE	DESCRIPTION	QUANTITY SOLD	ISSUE PRICE	FINISH	PR-69	PR-70
2015	Mount Fuji & the Canadian Rockies	750	649.95	Proof	650.	—

VANCOUVER 2010 OLYMPIC WINTER GAMES

FIFTY DOLLARS (1 ounce), VANCOUVER 2010 WINTER OLYMPIC GAMES, 2008-2010

2008   MAPLE LEAF AND VANCOUVER 2010 OLYMPIC LOGO

2009   THUNDERBIRD

2010   HOCKEY PLAYER

Designers:			**Engravers:**	
Obv.:	Susanna Blunt		Rev.:	Susan Taylor
Rev.:	2008 and 2010: RCM Staff		Rev.:	2008 and 2010: Stan Witten
	2009: Xwa lac tun (Ricky Harry)			2009: Marcos Hallam
Composition:	99.99% Au		**Thickness:**	2.9 mm
Gold content:	31.1 g, 1.0 tr oz		**Edge:**	Reeded
Weight:	31.1035 g, 1 oz		**Die Axis:**	↑↑
Diameter:	30.0 mm		**Finish:**	Bullion; Bullion, Painted
Case of Issue:	Singly: Mylar pouch			
	Coloured Set: Maple wood box, black flocked insert, encapsulated coins, COA			

DATE	DESCRIPTION	QUANTITY SOLD	ISSUE PRICE	FINISH	MS-65	MS-66
2008	$50 (1oz) Maple Leaf and 2010 Logo	49,802	BV	Bullion	1,900.	—
2008	$50 (1oz) Maple Leaf and 2010 Logo, Painted	200	2,000.	Bullion	2,250.	—
2009	$50 (1oz) Thunderbird	49,802	BV	Bullion	1,900.	—
2009	$50 (1oz) Thunderbird, Painted	200	2,000.	Bullion	2,250.	—
2010	$50 (1oz) Hockey Player	49,802	BV	Bullion	1,900.	—
2010	$50 (1oz) Hockey Player, Painted	200	2,000.	Bullion	2,250.	—
—	3 coin set, 2008, 2009, 2010, Painted	200	5,999.95	Bullion	6,500.	*

Note: The RCM Annual Reports list the Olympic gold maple leafs struck as 2008 - 75,876 oz, 2009 - 74,214 oz, and 2010 - 6 oz, totalling 150,006 units struck. Using 200 reported painted sets as struck there are 149,406 coins to be divided among the three years (49,802 per year).

FTY DOLLARS (1 ounce), FIVE BLESSINGS, 2014.

This coin is offered in both a bullion and proof coloured version. This design was also used on the five dollars (1/10 ounce) gold maple leaf coin (see ge 426) and on the five dollar silver maple leaf coin (see page 601)

Obverse

Reverse
Proof with Colour

Reverse
Bullion

esigners:		
Obv.:	Susanna Blunt	
Rev.:	RCM Staff	
omposition:	99.99% Au	
old content:	31.16 g, 1.0 tr oz	
eight:	31.16 g, 1 oz	
iameter:	30.0 mm	
ase of Issue:	Proof: Maroon clam style case, black flocked insert, encapsulated coin, COA	
	Bullion: Not known	

Engravers:
Rev.: Susan Taylor
Rev.: RCM Staff
Thickness: 2.9 mm
Edge: Reeded
Die Axis: ↑↑
Finish: Proof Coloured, Bullion

DATE	DESCRIPTION	QUANTITY SOLD	ISSUE PRICE	FINISH	SP-68	SP-69	PR-69	PR-70
2014	$50 (1oz) Five Blessings, Proof, Coloured	141	2,699.95	Proof	—	—	2,400.	—
2014	$50 (1oz) Five Blessings, Bullion	N/A	BV	Bullion	1,900.	2,000	—	—

SEVENTY-FIVE DOLLAR GOLD COINS

EVENTY-FIVE DOLLARS, COMMEMORATING THE VISIT OF POPE JOHN PAUL II TO CANADA, 2005.

During a 12-day tour in April 2005, Pope John Paul II visited many cities in Canada, drawing more than two million people to the Papal events. This as his third trip to Canada.

Designers and Engravers:
Obv.: Susanna Blunt, Susan Taylor
Rev.: Susan Taylor, Susan Taylor
Composition: 41.66% Au, 58.34 Ag
Gold content: 13.1 g, 0.421 tr oz
Silver content: 18.34 g, 0.590 tr oz
Weight: 31.44 g   **Edge:** Reeded
Diameter: 36.1 mm   **Die Axis:** ↑↑
Thickness: 3.0 mm   **Finish:** Proof
Case of Issue: Maroon plastic slide case, black plastic insert, encapsulated coin, COA

DATE	DESCRIPTION	QUANTITY SOLD	ISSUE PRICE	FINISH	PR-69	PR-70
2005	Commemorating the Visit of Pope John Paul II to Canada	1,870	544.95	Proof	750.	—

ote: In 2005 a set containing both the $10 (silver) and $75 (gold) coins was issued to commemorate the visit to Canada of Pope John Paul II. This may have been a special presentation set as only nine were issued.

VANCOUVER 2010 OLYMPIC WINTER GAMES

SEVENTY-FIVE DOLLARS, COMMEMORATING THE VANCOUVER 2010 OLYMPIC WINTER GAMES, 2007-2009.

The Vancouver 2010 Olympic Winter Games $75 gold coins were sold singly, or in three-coin sets. The three different sets offered were Canadian Wildlife, Canadian Icons, and Vancouver 2010 Winter Games.

2007 COMMEMORATIVE ISSUES

| Obverse | R.C.M.P. Des.: Cecily Mok Engr.: N/A | Athletes' Pride Des.: Sheila Armstrong Engr.: Christie Paquet | Canada Geese Des.: Cecily Mok Engr.: N/A |

2008 COMMEMORATIVE ISSUES

| Obverse | Four Host First Nations Des.: Kerri Burnett Engr.: Cecily Mok | Home of the 2010 Olympic Winter Games Des.: Sheila Armstrong Engr.: Marcos Hallam | Inukshuk Des.: Sheila Armstrong Engr.: José Osio |

2009 COMMEMORATIVE ISSUES

| Obverse | Wolf Des.: Arnold Nogy Engr.: N/A | Olympic Spirit Des.: Sheila Armstrong Engr.: N/A | Moose Des.: Kerri Burnett Engr.: José Osio |

Designers:
Obv.: Susanna Blunt
Rev.: See reverse illustrations
Composition: 58.33% Au, 41.67% Ag, Colour on reverse
Gold content: 7.0 g, 0.225 tr oz
Silver content: 5.0 g, 0.161 tr oz
Weight: 12.0 g
Diameter: 27.0 mm
Case of Issue: Singly: Black display case, black flocked insert, encapsulated coin, COA, Vancouver 2010 Olympic Winter Games theme sleeve
Sets: See the $75 Vancouver Winter Olympic Game Coins Sets on pg. 390.

Engravers:
Obv.: Susan Taylor
Rev.: See reverse illustrations

Thickness: 2.0 to 2.2 mm
Edge: Reeded
Die Axis: ↑↑
Finish: Proof

OMMEMORATING THE VANCOUVER 2010 OLYMPIC WINTER GAMES, 2007-2009, PRICING TABLE.

DATE	DESCRIPTION	ISSUE DATE	QUANTITY SOLD	ISSUE PRICE	FINISH	PR-69	PR-70
2007	Royal Canadian Mounted Police	Feb. 23, 2007	6,687	389.95	Proof	425.	—
2007	Athletes' Pride	July 11, 2007	4,524	389.95	Proof	425.	—
2007	Canada Geese	Oct. 24, 2007	4,418	409.95	Proof	425.	—
2008	Four Host First Nations	Feb. 20, 2008	4,897	409.95	Proof	425.	—
2008	Home of the Winter Games	July 23, 2008	4,581	433.95	Proof	425.	—
2008	Inukshuk	Oct. 29, 2008	4,907	499.95	Proof	425.	—
2009	Wolf	Feb. 18, 2009	4,161	499.95	Proof	425.	—
2009	Olympic Spirit	June 17, 2009	4,479	499.95	Proof	425.	—
2009	Moose	Sept. 9, 2009	4,075	499.95	Proof	425.	—

SEVENTY-FIVE DOLLAR VANCOUVER WINTER OLYMPIC GAMES COIN SETS

Sets of the three $75 gold coins were offered for sale in acrylic holders. They were assembled in three themes: Canadian Wildlife, Canadian Icons, nd Vancouver 2010 Olympic Winter Games.

DATE	DESCRIPTION	QUANTITY SOLD	ISSUE PRICE	ISSUER	FINISH	MARKET VALUE
2007-2009	**Canadian Wildlife:** 2007 Canada Geese, 2009 Wolf, 2009 Moose; Acrylic holder	25	1,424.95	RCM	PR-69	1,300.
2007-2008	**Canadian Icons:** 2007 R.C.M.P., 2008 Four Host First Nations, 2008 Inukshuk; Acrylic holder	18	1,424.95	RCM	PR-69	1,300.
2007-2009	**Vancouver 2010 Winter Games:** 2007 Athletes' Pride, 2008 Home of the 2010 Olympic Winter Games, 2009 Olympic Spirit; Acrylic holder	32	1,424.95	RCM	PR-69	1,300.

FOUR SEASONS MAPLE LEAVES SET

SEVENTY-FIVE DOLLARS, FOUR SEASONS MAPLE LEAVES SET, 2010.

The four seasons, spring, summer, autumn, and winter bring an ever-changing landscape to Canada. The evolving maple leaves best mirrors th
yearly cycle.

Common Obverse

Designers:		**Engravers:**	
Obv.:	Susanna Blunt	Obv.:	Susan Taylor
Rev.:	See reverse illustrations	Rev.:	See reverse illustrations
Composition:	58.33% Au, 41.67% Ag, Painted		
Gold content:	7.0 g, 0.225 tr oz	**Thickness:**	2.0 mm
Silver content:	5.0 g, 0.161 tr oz	**Edge:** Reeded	
Weight:	12.0 g	**Die Axis:** ↑↑	
Diameter:	27.0 mm	**Finish:** Proof	

Case of Issue: Singly: Maroon leatherette clam style case, black flocked insert, encapsulated coin, COA

Sets: Maple wood display case, 4-hole black flocked insert, encapsulated coins, serialised certificate, black sleeve

Spring	Summer	Fall	Winter
Designer: A. Nogy	Designer: M. Grant	Designer: C. D'Angelo	Designer: C. Godkin
Engraver: K. Wachelko	Engraver: S. Taylor	Engraver: M. Hallam	Engraver: K. Wachelko

DATE	DESCRIPTION	QUANTITY SOLD	ISSUE PRICE	FINISH	PR-69	PR-70
2010	Spring Maple Leaves	130	589.95	Proof	500.	—
2010	Summer Maple Leaves	136	589.95	Proof	500.	—
2010	Fall Maple Leaves	162	589.95	Proof	500.	—
2010	Winter Maple Leaves	136	589.95	Proof	500.	—
2010	Set of 4 Coins	587	2,358.95	Proof	1,800.	—

SEVENTY-FIVE DOLLARS, 75TH ANNIVERSARY OF SUPERMAN™: THE EARLY YEARS, 2013.

The artwork of Joe Shuster, as seen on the cover of Superman™ Comic #1 published in 1939, is depicted on the reverse of this coi
Superman's™ native Kryptonian language encircles the rim spelling "75 Year of Superman".

Designers and Engravers:		
Obv.:	Susanna Blunt, Susan Taylor	
Rev.:	DC Comics/Warner Brothers, RCM Staff	
Composition:	58.33% Au, 41.67% Ag	
Gold content:	7.0 g, 0.225 tr oz	
Silver content:	5.0 g, 0.161 tr oz	
Weight:	12.0 g	**Edge:** Reeded
Diameter:	27.0 mm	**Die Axis:** ↑↑
Thickness:	3.0 mm	**Finish:** Proof, Painted

Case of Issue: Custom paperboard case, maroon flocked insert, encapsulated coin, COA

DATE	DESCRIPTION	QUANTITY SOLD	ISSUE PRICE	FINISH	PR-69	PR-70
2013	75th Anniversary of Superman™: The Early Years	1,995	750.00	Proof	1,500.	—

WORLD BASEBALL CLASSIC SET

EVENTY-FIVE DOLLARS, COMMEMORATING THE WORLD BASEBALL CLASSIC SET, 2013.

These coins were issued to celebrate the World Baseball Classic Tournament held March 2nd to 19th, 2013. For other coins in this set see pages '5 and 451.

Common Obverse	Ball Diamond Engr.: S. Stewart	Hardball Engr.: S. Strath

esigners:		**Engravers:**	
Obv.:	Susanna Blunt	Obv.:	Susan Taylor
Rev.:	Steve Hepburn	Rev.:	See reverse illustrations
omposition:	99.99% Au	**Thickness:**	N/A
old content:	7.8 g, 0.25 tr oz	**Edge:**	Reeded
eight:	7.8 g	**Die Axis:**	↑↑
iameter:	20.0 mm	**Finish:**	Proof
ase of Issue:	Maroon leatherette clam style case, black flocked insert, encapsulated coin, COA		

DATE	DESCRIPTION	QUANTITY SOLD	ISSUE PRICE	FINISH	PR-69	PR-70
2013	Ball Diamond	133	899.95	Proof	600.	—
2013	Hardball	121	899.95	Proof	600.	—

FIFA WOMEN'S WORLD CUP™ SET

EVENTY-FIVE DOLLARS, FIFA WOMEN'S WORLD CUP™ SET, 2015.

These coins commemorate the excitement of the FIFA Women's World Cup™ hosted by six Canadian cities in 2015. For other coins in this series ee page 214.

Common Obverse	The Soccer Ball Des.: T. Bianco	The Championship Game Des.: T. Bianco	The Trophy Des.: G. Green

esigners:		**Engravers:**	
Obv.:	Susanna Blunt	Obv.:	Susan Taylor
Rev.:	See reverse illustrations	Rev.:	RCM Staff
omposition:	99.99% Au	**Thickness:**	N/A
old content:	7.8 g, 0.25 tr oz	**Edge:**	Reeded
eight:	7.8 g	**Die Axis:**	↑↑
iameter:	20.0 mm	**Finish:**	Proof
ase of Issue:	Maroon leatherette clam style case, black flocked insert, encapsulated coin, COA, custom box		

DATE	DESCRIPTION	QUANTITY SOLD	ISSUE PRICE	FINISH	PR-69	PR-70
2015	The Soccer Ball	1,449	699.95	Proof	650.	—
2015	The Championship Game	1,523	699.95	Proof	650.	—
2015	The Trophy	1,632	699.95	Proof	650.	—

ONE HUNDRED DOLLAR GOLD COINS

ONE HUNDRED DOLLARS, MONTREAL OLYMPIC COMMEMORATIVES, 1976.

As part of the series of collectors' coins struck to commemorate and help finance the XXI Olympiad, two separate $100 gold coins were issued 1976. The reverse design for each shows an ancient Grecian athlete being crowned with laurel by the goddess Pallas Athena. The uncirculated issu is 14kt gold and has beads around the rim. The proof issue is 22k gold, slightly smaller, and lacks rim beads.

1976 Obverse
14 kt Gold

1976 Reverse
14 kt Gold

Designers and Engravers:

Obv.:	Arnold Machin, Walter Ott		
Rev.:	Dora de Pédery-Hunt, Walter Ott		
Composition:	58.33% Au, 41.67% Ag		
Gold content:	7.78 g, 0.25 tr oz		
Silver content:	5.56 g, 0.179 tr oz		
Weight:	13.338 g	**Edge:**	Reeded
Diameter:	27.0 mm	**Die Axis:**	↑↑
Thickness:	2.2 mm	**Finish:**	Circulation
Case of Issue:	Plastic flip in a cardboard sleeve		

1976 Obverse
22kt Gold

1976 Reverse
22kt Gold

Designers and Engravers:

Obv.:	Arnold Machin, Walter Ott		
Rev.:	Dora de Pédery-Hunt, Walter Ott		
Composition:	91.67% Au, 8.33% Ag		
Gold content:	15.55 g, 0.500 tr oz		
Silver content:	1.14 g, 0.045 tr oz		
Weight:	16.966 g	**Edge:**	Reeded
Diameter:	25.0 mm	**Die Axis:**	↑↑
Thickness:	2.2 mm	**Finish:**	Proof
Case of Issue:	Cowhide and wood case, black suede insert, COA		

DATE	DESCRIPTION	QUANTITY SOLD	ISSUE PRICE	FINISH	SP-68	SP-69	PR-68	PR-69
1976	Montreal Olympics, 14 kt	650,000	105.00	Circulation	450.	—	*	*
1976	Montreal Olympics, 22 kt	350,000	150.00	Proof	*	*	900.	—

NOTE FOR COLLECTORS

Beginning with the modern issues, gold coins were offered for sale by the Royal Canadian Mint at a small premium over face value giving investor a call on gold with a limited downside risk. Investors soon realised this and purchased large quantities of coins which resulted in high mintage figures Currently, modern gold coins trade close to their intrinsic value. The gold coins listed here are priced at a market value of $1,750. per ounce.

ONE HUNDRED DOLLAR ISSUES

ONE HUNDRED DOLLAR ISSUES, 1977-1986

Designers:		Engravers:	
Obv.:	Arnold Machin	Obv.:	RCM Staff
Rev.:	See reverse illustrations	Rev.:	See reverse illustrations

Composition:	91.67% Au, 8.33% Ag		
Gold content:	15.55 g, 0.5 tr oz		
Silver content:	1.413 g, 0.045 tr oz		
Weight:	16.965 g	Edge:	Reeded
Diameter:	27.0 mm	Die Axis:	↑↑
Thickness:	2.2 mm	Finish:	Proof
Case of Issue:	(A) 1977-1978:	Black leatherette case, maroon insert, plastic coin holder, COA	
	(B) 1979-1984:	Brown leatherette case, brown flocked insert, plastic coin holder, COA	
	(C) 1985-1986:	Brown leatherette book type case with maple leaf emblem, beige satin interior, encapsulated coin. All enclosed in a brown plastic box	

OBVERSE DESIGNS, 1977-1986

Obverse 1977	Obverse 1978, 1980-1981	Obverse 1979, 1983, 1986	Obverse 1982	Obverse 1984-1985

REVERSE DESIGNS, 1977-1986

1977 Silver Jubilee Des.: R. Lee Engr.: W. Ott	1978 Canadian Unity Coin Des.: R. Savage Engr.: A. Aarand	1979 Int'l Year of Child Des.: C. Tietz Engr.: V. Coté	1980 Arctic Territories Des.: A. Marchetti Engr.: S. Beveridge	1981 "O Canada" Des.: R. Savage Engr.: W. Ott

1982 Patriation of Canadian Constitution Des.: F. Peter Engr.: W. Ott	1983 Sir Humphrey Gilbert's Landing in Newfoundland Des.: J. Jaciw Engr.: W. Ott	1984 Jacques Cartier's Voyage of Discovery Des.: C. Tietz Engr.: W. Ott	1985 National Parks Centenary Des.: H. Greville Engr.: W. Ott	1986 Int'l Year of Peace Des. and Engr.: D. de Pédery-Hunt

ONE HUNDRED DOLLAR ISSUES, 1977-1986, PRICING TABLE.

DATE	DESCRIPTION	CASE	QUANTITY SOLD	ISSUE PRICE	FINISH	PR-68	PR-69
1977	Silver Jubilee Elizabeth II	A	180,396	140.00	Proof	900.	—
1978	Canadian Unity Coin	A	200,000	150.00	Proof	900.	—
1979	International Year of the Child	B	250,000	185.00	Proof	900.	—
1980	Arctic Territories	B	130,000	430.00	Proof	900.	—
1981	"O Canada"	B	100,950	300.00	Proof	900.	—
1982	Patriation of the Canadian Constitution	B	121,706	290.00	Proof	900.	—
1983	Sir Humphrey Gilbert's Landing in Newfoundland	B	83,128	310.00	Proof	900.	—
1984	Jacques Cartier's Voyage of Discovery	B	67,662	325.00	Proof	900.	—
1985	National Parks Centenary	C	58,520	325.00	Proof	900.	—
1986	International Year of Peace	C	76,255	325.00	Proof	900.	—

ONE HUNDRED DOLLAR ISSUES, 1987-2003

Designers:
Obv.: See obverse illustrations
Rev.: See reverse illustrations
Composition: 58.33% Au, 41.67% Ag
Gold content: 7.78 g, 0.25 tr oz
Silver content: 5.56 g, 0.179 tr oz
Weight: 13.338 g
Diameter: 27.0 mm
Thickness: 2.2 mm
Case of Issue:

Engravers:
Obv.: See obverse illustrations
Rev.: See reverse illustrations

Edge: Lettered
Die Axis: ↑↑
Finish: Proof

(A) 1987-1996: Brown leatherette book type case with maple leaf emblem, beige satin interior, encapsulated coin. All enclosed in a brown plastic box.
(B) 1997-1999: Black suede clam type case, black suede interior, encapsulated coin
(C) 2000-2003: Metal presentation case, wooden insert, COA

OBVERSE DESIGNS, 1987-2003

Obverse
1987
Des.: A. Machin
Engr.: RCM Staff

Obverse
1988-1989
Des.: A. Machin
Engr.: P. Brindley

Obverse
1990-1995
1997-2000
Des. and Engr.:
D. de Pédery-Hunt

Obverse
1996, 2002
Des. and Engr.:
D. de Pédery-Hunt

Obverse
2001
Des. and Engr.:
D. de Pédery-Hunt

Obverse
2003
Des. and Engr.:
D. de Pédery-Hunt

REVERSE DESIGNS, 1987-2003

1987
XV Olympic
Winter Games
Des.: F. Peter
Engr.: A. Aarand

1988
The Bowhead Whale
Des.: R. Carmichael
Engr.: A. Aarand

1989
Sainte-Marie
Des.: D. Craig
Engr.: A. Aarand

1990 International
Literacy Year
Des.: J. Mardon
Engr.: A. Aarand and
S. Taylor

1991
Empress of India
Des.: K. Smith
Engr.: S. Beveridge

1992
City of Montreal
350th Anniv.
Des.: S. Sherwood
Engr.: A. Aarand and
C. Saffioti

1993
1893 The Era of the
Horseless Carriage
Des.: J. Mardon
Engr.: A. Aarand and
W. Woodruff

1994
The Home Front
Des.: P. Clark
Engr.: S. Taylor and
A. Aarand

1995
275th Anniv. of
Founding of Louisbourg
Des.: L. Parker
Engr.: S. Beveridge

1996
100th Anniv. First
Major Gold Discovery
in the Klondike
Des.: J. Mantha
Engr.: C. Saffioti

1997
150th Anniv. Alexander
Graham Bell's Birth
Des.: D. H. Curley
Engr.: S. Beveridge

1998
75th Anniv. Nobel
Prize For Discovery
of Insulin
Des.: R. Carmichael
Engr.: S. Witten

1999
Newfoundland
Confederation
Des.: J.
Gale-Vaillancourt
Engr.: W. Woodruff

2000
150th Anniv. of the
Search for Northwest
Passage in 1850
Des.: J. Mardon
Engr. S. Witten

2001
125th Anniv. Library
of Parliament
Des.: R. R. Carmichael
Engr.: S. Taylor and
W. Woodruff

2002
Canada's Oil Industry
Des.: J. Mardon
Engr.: S. Witten

2003
100th Anniv. Discovery
Marquis Wheat
Des.: T. Nelson
Engr.: S. Witten

ONE HUNDRED DOLLAR ISSUES, 1987-2003, PRICING TABLE.

DATE	DESCRIPTION	CASE	QUANTITY SOLD	ISSUE PRICE	FINISH	PR-69	PR-70
1987	XV Olympic Winter Games, With edge lettering	A	145,175	255.00	Proof	450.	—.
1987	XV Olympic Winter Games, Without edge lettering	A	Included	255.00	Proof	2,500.	—
1988	Bowhead Whale (Balaena Mysticetus)	A	52,239	255.00	Proof	450.	—
1989	Sainte-Marie	A	63,881	245.00	Proof	450.	—
1990	International Literacy Year	A	49,940	245.00	Proof	450.	—
1991	Empress of India	A	33,966	245.00	Proof	450.	—
1992	City of Montreal, 350th Anniversary, 1642-1992	A	28,190	239.85	Proof	450.	—
1993	1893 The Era of the Horseless Carriage	A	25,971	239.85	Proof	450.	—
1994	The Home Front	A	17,603	249.95	Proof	450.	—
1995	275th Anniv. of the Founding of Louisbourg	A	16,916	249.95	Proof	450.	—
1996	100th Anniv. First Major Gold Discovery Klondike	A	17,973	259.95	Proof	450.	—
1997	150th Anniv. Alexander Graham Bell's Birth	B	14,030	254.95	Proof	450.	—
1998	75th Anniv. Nobel Prize Discovery of Insulin	B	11,220	254.95	Proof	450.	—
1999	50th Anniv. Newfoundland's Confederation 1949	B	10,242	254.95	Proof	450.	—
2000	150th Anniv. Search Northwest Passage in 1850	C	10,547	254.95	Proof	450.	—
2001	125th Anniv. Library of Parliament	C	8,080	260.95	Proof	450.	—
2002	Commemorating Canada's Oil Industry, Painted	C	9,994	260.95	Proof	450.	—
2003	100th Anniv. Discovery Marquis Wheat, Painted	C	9,993	277.95	Proof	450.	—

ONE HUNDRED DOLLAR ISSUES, 2004-2017

Designers:
  Obv.: Susanna Blunt
  Rev.: See reverse illustrations
Composition: 58.33% Au, 41.67% Ag
Gold content: 7.0 g, 0.225 tr oz
Weight: 12.0 g
Diameter: 27.0 mm
Thickness: 2.2 mm
Case of Issue:
  (A) 2004: Metal presentation case, wooden insert, COA
  (B) 2005-2006: Maroon plastic case, black plastic insert, encapsulated coin, COA
  (C) 2007-2018: Maroon leatherette clam style case, black flocked insert, encapsulated coin, COA
  (D) 2014-2016 (Superman; Batman): Custom paperboard case, black insert, encapsulated coin, COA

Engravers:
  Obv.: Susan Taylor
  Rev.: See reverse illustrations

Silver content: 5.0 g, 0.16 tr oz
Edge: Reeded
Die Axis: ↑↑
Finish: Proof

OBVERSE DESIGNS, 2004-2018

Obverse
2004, 2006

Obverse
2005

Obverse
2007-2009

Obverse
2010-2015, 2018

Obverse
2015-2017

Obverse
2017 (Raven)

Obverse
2018 (Frog)

REVERSE DESIGNS, 2004-2018

2004
50th Anniv.
St. Lawrence Seaway
Des.: J. Mardon
Engr.: J. Osio

2005
130th Anniv. Supreme
Court of Canada
Des.: S. Duranceau
Engr.: J. Osio

2006
75th Game, World's
Longest Hockey Series
Des.: T. Bianco
Engr.: K. Wachelko

2007
140th Anniv. Dominion
of Canada
Des.: B. Ross
Engr.: S. Taylor

2008
200th Anniv.
Descending
Fraser River
Des.: J. Mantha
Engr.: C. Paquet

2009
10th Anniv.
of Nunavut
Des.: A. Qappik
Engr.: S. Taylor

2010
400th Anniv. of the
Discovery of
Hudson's Bay
Des.: J. Mantha
Engr.: S. Taylor

2011
175th Anniv. Canada's
First Rail Road
Des.: J. D. Kelly
Engr.: K. Wachelko

2012
150th Anniv. Caribou
Gold Rush
Des.: T. Bianco
Engr.: RCM Staff

2013
100th Anniv. Canadian
Arctic Expedition
Des.: B. Ross
Engr.: K. Wachelko

2014
Adventures of
Superman™ #596
Des.: DC Comics/
Warner Brothers
Engr.: RCM Staff

2014
150th Anniv.
Quebec/Charlotteown
Conference
Des.: L. Normandin
Engr.: RCM Staff

2015
200th Anniv. Birth
Sir John A. Macdonald
Des.: G. Green
Engr.: RCM Staff

2015
Bugs Bunny
and Friends
Des.: Warner Bros.
Engr.: RCM Staff

2015
Superman #4 (1940)
Des.: Warner Bros.
Engr.: RCM Staff

2016
Centennial of the
Parliament Builiding Fires
Des.: Tony Bianco
Engr.: RCM Staff

ONE HUNDRED DOLLAR ISSUES, 2004-2018 (cont.).

2016	2017	2017	2018	2018
Batman V Superman: Dawn of Justice™	100th Anniversary of the Halifax Explosion	Raven Brings The Light	250th Anniversary of the Birth of Techumseh	Frog Reveals A Gift
Des.: DC Comics	Des.: Jamie Dssrochers	Des.: Andy Everson	Des.: Bonnie Ross	Des.: Andy Everson
Engr.: RCM Staff	Engr.: RCM Staff	Engr.: RCM Staff	Engr.: RCM Staff	Engr.: RCM Staff

DATE	DESCRIPTION	CASE	QUANTITY SOLD	ISSUE PRICE	FINISH	PR-69	PR-70
2004	50th Anniv. Commencement of St. Lawrence Seaway	A	7,454	277.95	Proof	450.	—
2005	130th Anniv. Supreme Court of Canada, Painted	B	5,092	289.95	Proof	450.	—
2006	75th Game, World's Longest Hockey Series, Painted	B	5,439	329.95	Proof	450.	—
2007	140th Anniv. Dominion of Canada	C	4,453	369.95	Proof	450.	—
2008	200th Anniv. Descending Fraser River	C	3,089	386.95	Proof	450.	—
2009	10th Anniv. of Nunavut	C	2,309	509.95	Proof	450.	—
2010	400th Anniv. Discovery of Hudson's Bay	C	2,133	589.95	Proof	500.	—
2011	175th Anniv. Canada's First Rail Road, Painted	C	2,283	639.95	Proof	500.	—
2012	150th Anniv. of Caribou Gold Rush, Painted	C	2,488	599.95	Proof	525.	—
2013	100th Anniv. Canadian Arctic Expedition	C	1,937	599.95	Proof	525.	—
2014	150th Anniv. Quebec / Charlottetown Conference	C	1,284	599.95	Proof	525.	—
2014	The Adventures of Superman #596, Coloured	D	2,000	750.95	Proof	750.	—
2015	200th Anniv. Birth of Sir John A. Macdonald	C	2,017	599.95	Proof	600.	—
2015	Looney Tunes: Bugs Bunny and Friends	C	1,931	799.95	Proof	650.	—
2015	Superman #4 (1940)	D	2,001	750.95	Proof	750.	—
2016	Centennial of the Parliament Buildings Fire	C	1,463	599.95	Proof	600.	—
2016	Batman V Superman: Dawn of Justice	D	3,001	749.95	Proof	750.	—
2017	100th Anniversary of the Halifax Explosion	C	1,500	699.95	Proof	700.	—
2017	Raven Brings The Light	C	2,000	709.95	Proof	710.	—
2018	250th Anniversary of the Birth of Tecumseh	C	1,500	699.95	Proof	700.	—
2018	Frog Reveals A Gift	C	1,500	709.95	Proof	710.	—

ONE HUNDRED FIFTY DOLLAR GOLD COINS

ONE HUNDRED FIFTY DOLLARS, GOLD HOLOGRAM COINS, 2000-2011.

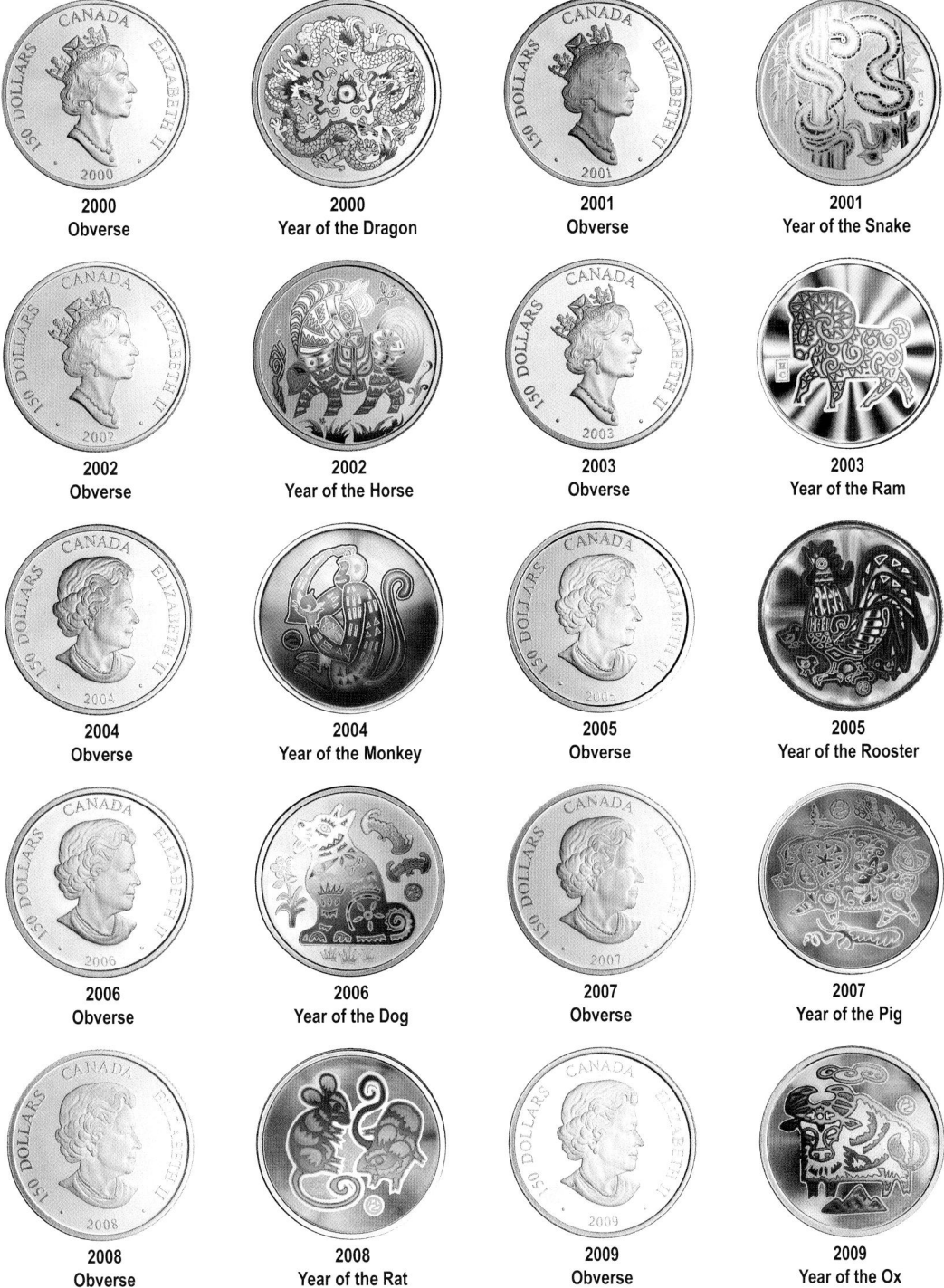

2000 Obverse	**2000** Year of the Dragon	**2001** Obverse	**2001** Year of the Snake
2002 Obverse	**2002** Year of the Horse	**2003** Obverse	**2003** Year of the Ram
2004 Obverse	**2004** Year of the Monkey	**2005** Obverse	**2005** Year of the Rooster
2006 Obverse	**2006** Year of the Dog	**2007** Obverse	**2007** Year of the Pig
2008 Obverse	**2008** Year of the Rat	**2009** Obverse	**2009** Year of the Ox

ONE HUNDRED FIFTY DOLLARS, GOLD HOLOGRAM COINS, 2000-2011 (cont.).

   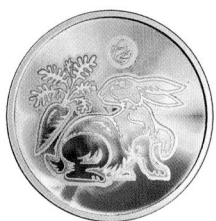

2010	2010	2011	2011
Obverse	Year of the Tiger	Obverse	Year of the Rabbit

Designers:

2000-2003	Obv.:	Dora de Pédery-Hunt
2004-2011	Obv.:	Susanna Blunt
2000-2011	Rev.:	Harvey Chan

Engravers:

	Obv.:	Dora de Pédery-Hunt
	Obv.:	Susan Taylor
	Rev.:	RCM Staff

Composition: 75.0% Au, 25.0% Ag, Hologram

Gold content:

2000-2003 10.20 g, 0.328 tr oz
2004-2011 8.88g, 0.285 tr oz

Silver Content:

2000-2003 3.40 g, 0.109 tr oz
2004-2011 2.96 g, 0.095 tr oz

Weight: 2000-2003 13.61 g
2004-2011 11.84 g

Diameter: 28.0 mm
Thickness: 1.5 to 1.8 mm
Edge: Reeded
Die Axis: ↑↑
Finish: Proof
Case of Issue: Gold satin case, taupe flocked insert, encapsulated coin, COA

DATE	DESCRIPTION	QUANTITY SOLD	ISSUE PRICE	FINISH	PR-69	PR-70
2000	Year of the Dragon, Hologram	8,874	388.88	Proof	700.	—
2001	Year of the Snake, Hologram	6,571	388.88	Proof	600.	—
2002	Year of the Horse, Hologram	6,843	388.88	Proof	600.	—
2003	Year of the Ram, Hologram	3,927	398.88	Proof	600.	—
2004	Year of the Monkey, Hologram	3,392	398.88	Proof	600.	—
2005	Year of the Rooster, Hologram	3,731	398.88	Proof	600.	—
2006	Year of the Dog, Hologram	2,609	448.88	Proof	600.	—
2007	Year of the Pig, Hologram	826	498.95	Proof	600.	—
2008	Year of the Rat, Hologram	582	508.95	Proof	600.	—
2009	Year of the Ox, Hologram	486	638.88	Proof	600.	—
2010	Year of the Tiger, Hologram	1,507	555.55	Proof	600.	—
2011	Year of the Rabbit, Hologram	4,888	638.88	Proof	600.	—

Note: The mintage figures for 2007-2009 appear to be incorrect. There were no mintage figures reported in the 2010 Annual Report.

BLESSINGS SERIES

ONE HUNDRED FIFTY DOLLARS, BLESSINGS SERIES, 2009-2016.

In China blessings of wealth abound in a multitude of ancient symbols and artistic impressions, many of which are represented on these pure gold coins.

Common Obverse	2009 Blessings of Wealth Engr.: C. Paquet	2010 Blessings of Strength Engr.: RCM Staff	2011 Blessings of Happiness Engr.: C. Mok

2012 Blessings of Good Fortune Engr.: RCM Staff	2013 Blessings of Peace Engr.: S. Strath	2014 Blessings of Longevity Engr.: C. Mok	2015 Blessings of Prosperity Engr.: RCM Staff	2016 Blessings of Good Health Engr.: RCM Staff

Designers:
Obv.: Susanna Blunt
Rev.: 2009-2011: Harvey Chan
2012: Three Degrees Creative Group Inc.
2013: Aries Cheung
2014: Charles Vinh
2015: Simon Ng
2016: Three Degrees Creative Group Inc.

Engravers:
Obv.: Susan Taylor
Rev.: See reverse illustrations

Composition: 99.999% Au
Gold content: 10.4 g, 0.334 tr oz
Weight: 10.4 g
Diameter: 22.5 mm
Thickness: 1.8 mm
Case of Issue: Maroon leatherette clam style case, black flocked insert, encapsulated coin, COA

Edge: Plain
Die Axis: ↑↑
Finish: Proof

DATE	DESCRIPTION	QUANTITY SOLD	ISSUE PRICE	FINISH	PR-69	PR-70
2009	Blessings of Wealth	1,273	799.95	Proof	1,100.	—
2010	Blessings of Strength	765	939.95	Proof	1,100.	—
2011	Blessings of Happiness	880	988.88	Proof	1,100.	—
2012	Blessings of Good Fortune	889	988.88	Proof	1,100.	—
2013	Blessings of Peace	886	988.88	Proof	1,100.	—
2014	Blessings of Longevity	887	988.88	Proof	1,100.	—
2015	Blessings of Prosperity	518	988.88	Proof	1,000.	—
2016	Blessings of Good Health	588	988.88	Proof	1,000.	—

CLASSIC CHINESE LUNAR SERIES

ONE HUNDRED FIFTY DOLLARS, CLASSIC CHINESE LUNAR SERIES. 2010-2018.

Identical designs are utilized on the Chinese Lunar Calendar Series $15 silver coins (2010-2021), see page 231.

| Common Obverse | 2010 Year of the Tiger | 2011 Year of the Rabbit | 2012 Year of the Dragon | 2013 Year of the Snake |

2014 Year of the Horse   2015 Year of the Sheep   2016 Year of the Monkey   2017 Year of the Rooster   2018 Year of the Dog

Designers:		**Engravers:**
Obv.:	Susanna Blunt	Obv.:	Susan Taylor
Rev.:	Aries Cheung	
Composition:	75.0% Au, 25.0% Ag	
Gold content:	8.78 g, 0.282 tr oz	
Silver content:	2.92 g, 0.094 tr oz	
Weight:	11.70 g	**Die Axis:**	↑↑
Diameter:	28.0 mm	**Edge:**	Reeded
Thickness:	1.6 mm	**Finish:**	Proof

Case of Issue: Singly: Gold satin-like covered case, black flocked insert, encapsulated coin, COA
Set: Hardwood exterior with high-gloss finish silk-screened paper. Interior has high-gloss finish in Chinese red with a silver design, wooden insert accommodates 12 coins.

DATE	DESCRIPTION	QUANTITY SOLD	ISSUE PRICE	FINISH	PR-69	PR-70
2010	Year of the Tiger	2,500	555.55	Proof	650.	—
2011	Year of the Rabbit	2,500	638.88	Proof	650.	—
2012	Year of the Dragon	1,430	688.88	Proof	650.	—
2013	Year of the Snake	1,452	688.88	Proof	650.	—
2014	Year of the Horse	2,128	688.88	Proof	700.	—
2015	Year of the Sheep	602	688.88	Proof	700.	—
2016	Year of the Monkey	914	688.88	Proof	700.	—
2017	Year of the Rooster	2,500	688.88	Proof	700.	—
2018	Year of the Dog	1,500	688.88	Proof	700.	—

WORLD BASEBALL CLASSIC SET

ONE HUNDRED FIFTY DOLLARS, CELEBRATE, WORLD BASEBALL CLASSIC SET, 2013.

These coins were issued to celebrate the World Baseball Classic Tournament held March 2nd to 19th, 2013. For other coins in this set see pages 275 and 439.

Designers and Engravers:

Obv.:	Susanna Blunt, Susan Taylor		
Rev.:	Steve Hepburn, RCM Staff		
Composition:	99.99% Au		
Gold content:	15.59 g, 0.5 tr oz		
Weight:	15.59 g	**Edge:**	Reeded
Diameter:	25.0 mm	**Die Axis:**	↑↑
Thickness:	2.0 mm	**Finish:**	Proof
Case of Issue:	Maroon leatherette clam style case, black flocked insert, encapsulated coin, COA, custom sleeve		

DATE	DESCRIPTION	QUANTITY SOLD	ISSUE PRICE	FINISH	PR-69	PR-70
2013	Celebrate, World Baseball Classic	129	1,549.95	Proof	1,300.	—

ONE HUNDRED SEVENTY-FIVE DOLLAR GOLD COIN

ONE HUNDRED SEVENTY-FIVE DOLLARS, 100TH ANNIVERSARY OF THE OLYMPIC MOVEMENT, 1992-1996.

Commemorating the 100th anniversary of the Olympic movement in 1996, Canada and four other countries, Australia, France, Austria and Greece, issued three-coin sets, consisting of one gold and two silver coins. One set was issued each year beginning with Canada's in 1992. See page 230 for the Royal Canadian Mint silver issues. Only the Royal Canadian Mint issued coins are listed in the Standard Catalogue.

Designers:

Obv.:	Dora de Pédery-Hunt
Rev.:	Stewart Sherwood
Composition:	91.67% Au, 8.33% Cu
Gold content:	15.556 g, 0.5 tr oz
Weight:	16.97 g
Diameter:	28.0 mm
Thickness:	2.0 mm
Case of Issue:	Blue clam style case, black insert, encapsulated coin, COA

Engravers:

Obv.:	Dora de Pédery-Hunt
Rev.:	Ago Aarand

Edge: Lettering:	Citius, altius, fortius
Die Axis:	↑↑
Finish:	Proof

DATE	DESCRIPTION	QUANTITY SOLD	ISSUE PRICE	FINISH	PR-68	PR-69
1992	100th Anniversary of the Olympic Movement	22,092	429.75	Proof	850.	—

TWO HUNDRED DOLLAR GOLD COINS

TWO HUNDRED DOLLAR ISSUES, 1990-2003 (STANDARD WEIGHT)

Designers:
 Obv.: Dora de Pédery-Hunt
 Rev.: See reverse illustrations
Composition: 91.67% Au, 8.33% Ag
Gold content: 15.703 g, 0.505 tr oz
Silver content: 1.427 g, 0.046 tr oz
Weight: 17.13 g
Diameter: 29.0 mm
Thickness: 2.0 mm
Case of Issue: (A) 1990-1996, 1999, 2002: Woven Jacquard case, black insert, encapsulated coin, COA
     (B) 1997-1998, 2000-2001, 2003: Metal trimmed case, black insert, encapsulated coin, COA

Engravers:
 Obv.: Dora de Pédery-Hunt
 Rev.: See reverse illustrations

Edge: Reeded
Die Axis: ↑↑
Finish: Proof

OBVERSE DESIGNS, 1990-2003

Common Obverse
except for date
1990-1996

Common Obverse
except for date
1997-2003

REVERSE DESIGNS, 1990-2003

1990
Canada's Flag
Silver Jubilee
Des.: S. Sherwood
Engr.: A. Aarand

1991
A National Passion
Des.: S. Sherwood
Engr.: S. Taylor

1992
Niagara Falls
Des.: J. Mardon
Engr.: S. Taylor

1993
R.C.M.P.
Des.: S. Sherwood
Engr.: S. Taylor

1994
Anne of Green Gables©
Des.: P. Gilman
Engr.: S. Taylor

1995
The Sugar Bush
Des.: J. D. Mantha
Engr.: S. Beveridge,
S. Taylor

1996
Transcontinental
Landscape
Des.: S. Duranceau
Engr.: C. Saffioti

1997
Haida "Raven Bringing
Light to the World"
Des.: R. Davidson
Engr.: C. Saffioti,
A. Aarand

1998
Legend of the
White Buffalo
Des.: A. Janvier
Engr.: C. Saffioti

1999
Mikmaq Butterfly
Des.: A. Syliboy
Engr.: C. Saffioti

TWO HUNDRED DOLLAR ISSUES, 1990-2003 (STANDARD WEIGHT) (cont.)

2000	2001	2002	2003
Mother and Child	Cornelius Krieghoff	Tom Thompson	Lionel Lemoine
Des.: G. Arnaktauyok	Des.: C. Krieghoff	Des.: T. Thompson	Fitzgerald
Engr.: S. Taylor	Engr.: S. Taylor	Engr.: S. Taylor	Des.: L. L. Fitzgerald
			Engr.: S. Taylor

DATE	DESCRIPTION	CASE	QUANTITY SOLD	ISSUE PRICE	FINISH	PR-69	PR-70
1990	Canada's Flag Silver Jubilee	A	20,980	395.00	Proof	900.	—
1991	A National Passion	A	10,215	425.00	Proof	900.	—
1992	Niagara Falls	A	9,465	389.65	Proof	900.	—
1993	Royal Canadian Mounted Police	A	10,807	389.65	Proof	900.	—
1994	Anne of Green Gables©	A	10,655	399.95	Proof	900.	—
1995	The Sugar Bush	A	9,579	399.95	Proof	900.	—
1996	Transcontinental Landscape	A	8,047	414.95	Proof	900.	—
1997	Haida "Raven Bringing Light to the World"	B	11,610	414.95	Proof	900.	—
1998	The Legend of the White Buffalo	B	7,149	414.95	Proof	900.	—
1999	Mikmaq Butterfly	A	6,510	414.95	Proof	900.	—
2000	Mother and Child	B	7,410	414.95	Proof	900.	—
2001	Cornelius Krieghoff	B	5,406	412.95	Proof	900.	—
2002	Tom Thompson	A	5,754	412.95	Proof	900.	—
2003	Lionel Lemoine Fitzgerald	B	4,118	412.95	Proof	900.	—

TWO HUNDRED DOLLAR ISSUES, 2004-2011 (REDUCED WEIGHT)

Designers:
Obv.: Susanna Blunt
Rev.: See reverse illustrations

Composition: 91.67% Au, 8.33% Ag
Gold content: 14.667 g, 0.471 tr oz
Silver content: 1.332 g, 0.043 tr oz
Weight: 16.0 g
Diameter: 29.0 mm

Engravers:
Obv.: Susan Taylor
Rev.: See reverse illustrations

Thickness: 1.8 mm
Edge: Reeded
Die Axis: ↑↑
Finish: Proof

Case of Issue:
(A) 2004: Metal trimmed case, black insert, encapsulated coin, COA
(B) 2005: Maroon plastic slide case, black plastic insert, encapsulated coin, COA
(C) 2006-2011: Maroon leatherette clam style case, black flocked insert, encapsulated coin, COA
(D) 2010: Black leatherette display case, black flocked insert, encapsulated coin, COA

OBVERSE DESIGNS, 2004-2011

Obverse	Obverse	Obverse	Obverse
2004-2006	2007	2008-2009	2010-2011
	With date and RCM Logo	Without date, With RCM Logo	

REVERSE DESIGNS, 2004-2011

2004
Alfred Pellan
Des.: A. Pellan
Engr.: C. Paquet

2005
Fur Trade
Des.: J. Mardon
Engr.: J. Osio

2006
Timber Trade
Des.: J. Mardon
Engr.: S. Witten

2007
Fishing Trade
Des.: J. Mardon
Engr.: S. Taylor

2008
Agriculture Trade
Des.: J. Mardon
Engr.: J. Osio

2009
Coal Mining Trade
Des.: J. Mardon
Engr.: C. Paquet

2010
**First Canadian Olympic
Gold Medal on Home Soil**
Des.: B. Ross
Engr.: S. Witten

2010
Petroleum and Oil Trade
Des.: J. Mardon
Engr.: RCM Staff

2011
S. S. Beaver
Des.: J. Mardon
Engr.: RCM Staff

2011
Wedding Celebration
Des.: L. McGaw
Engr.: J. Osio

2011
Wayne / Walter Gretzky
Des.: G. Green
Engr.: K. Wachelko,
J. Osio

DATE	DESCRIPTION	CASE	QUANTITY SOLD	ISSUE PRICE	FINISH	PR-69	PR-70
2004	Alfred Pellan	A	3,917	412.95	Proof	750.	—
2005	Fur Trade	B	3,669	489.95	Proof	750.	—
2006	Timber Trade	C	3,218	489.95	Proof	750.	—
2007	Fishing Trade	C	2,137	579.95	Proof	750.	—
2008	Agriculture Trade	C	1,951	619.95	Proof	750.	—
2009	Coal Mining Trade, Painted	C	2,241	849.95	Proof	750.	—
2010	First Canadian Olympic Gold Medal on Home Soil	D	2,010	989.95	Proof	800.	—
2010	Petroleum and Oil Trade, Painted	C	1,732	999.95	Proof	850.	—
2011	S. S. Beaver, Painted	C	1,392	1,099.95	Proof	850.	—
2011	Wedding Celebration, Duke and Duchess of Cambridge, Blue Swarovski element	C	760	1,199.95	Proof	1,000.	—
2011	Wayne and Walter Gretzky, Laser	C	471	1,299.99	Proof	1,000.	—

TWO HUNDRED DOLLAR ISSUES, 2012-2017 (REDUCED WEIGHT)

Designers:

Obv.:   Susanna Blunt
Rev.:   See reverse illustrations

Composition: 99.99% Au
Gold content: 15.43 g, 0.5 tr oz
Weight: 15.43 g
Diameter: 29.0 mm
Thickness: 1.6 mm
Case of Issue: Maroon leatherette clam style case, black flocked insert, encapsulated coin, COA

Engravers:

Obv.:   Susan Taylor
Rev.:   See reverse illustrations

Edge: Reeded
Die Axis: ↑↑
Finish: Proof

GREAT CANADIAN EXPLORERS, 2012-2017

Common Obverse

2012 - The Vikings
Des.: Y. Bérubé
Engr.: J. Osio

2013 - Jacques Cartier
Des.: L. McGaw
Engr.: J. Osio

2014 - Samuel de Champlain
Des.: G. Green

2015 - Henry Hudson
Des.: L. McGaw

2016 - Pierre Gaultier
De La Vérendrye
Des.: G. Green

2017 - Alexander MacKenzie
Des.: John Mantha

INTERCONNECTION SET, 2014

Common Obverse

Land - The Beaver
Des.: A. Everson

Air - The Thunderbird
Des.: A. Everson

Sea - The Orca
Des.: A. Everson

DATE	DESCRIPTION	QUANTITY SOLD	ISSUE PRICE	FINISH	PR-69	PR-70
2012	Great Canadian Explorers: The Vikings	1,749	1,199.95	Proof	1,100.	—
2013	Great Canadian Explorers: Jacques Cartier	1,474	1,199.95	Proof	1,100.	—
2014	Great Canadian Explorers: Samuel de Champlain	885	1,199.95	Proof	1,100.	—
2015	Great Canadian Explorers: Henry Hudson	815	1,199.95	Proof	1,200.	—
2016	Great Canadian Explorers: Pierre Gaultier de la Vérendrye	798	1,199.95	Proof	1,200.	—
2017	Great Canadian Expoloers: Alexander MacKenzie	1,000	1,199.95	Proof	1,200.	—
2014	Interconnection: Land - The Beaver	693	1,299.95	Proof	1,300.	—
2014	Interconnection: Air - The Thunderbird	121	1,299.95	Proof	1,300.	—
2014	Interconnection: Sea - The Orca	116	1,299.95	Proof	1,300.	—

TWO HUNDRED DOLLAR (ONE OUNCE) ISSUES, 2012-2015

Designers:
   Obv.:   Susanna Blunt
   Rev.:   See reverse illustrations
Composition: 99.99% Au
Gold content: 31.1 g, 1.0 tr oz
Weight: 31.1 g
Diameter: 30.0 mm
Thickness: N/A
Case of Issue: Maroon leatherette clam style case, black flocked insert, encapsulated coin, COA

Engravers:
   Obv.:   Susan Taylor
   Rev.:   See reverse illustrations

Edge: 2014-2015 Reeded
   2014 Royal Generations: Interrupted Serrations
Die Axis: ↑↑
Finish: Proof

OBVERSE DESIGNS, 2012-2015

Obverse
2012, 2014

Obverse
2015

REVERSE DESIGNS, 2012-2015

2012
The Challenge
Robert Bateman Series
Des.: R. Bateman
Engr.: RCM Staff

2014
Royal Generations
Des.: C. Bursey-Sabourin
Engr.: RCM Staff

2014
Zunoqua
- Celebrating Emily Carr
Des.: E. Carr
Engr.: RCM Staff

2015
Largemouth Bass
Des.: C. Atwater
Engr.: RCM Staff

DATE	DESCRIPTION	QUANTITY SOLD	ISSUE PRICE	FINISH	PR-69	PR-70
2012	*The Challenge* Robert Bateman Moose Coin Series	359	2,699.95	Proof	2,600.	—
2014	Royal Generations	340	2,799.95	Proof	2,800.	—
2014	*Zunoqua*. Celebrating Emily Carr	100	N.I.I.	Proof	2,900.	—
2015	North American Sportfish: Largemouth Bass	300	2,699.95	Proof	2,700.	—

Note: The *Zunoqua* coin is part of the Celebrating Emily Carr three coin set. For other coins see pages 293 and 504.

TWO HUNDRED DOLLAR FIVE 9's ISSUES, 2013-2015 (ULTRA HIGH RELIEF)

TWO HUNDRED DOLLARS, MOON MASK SERIES, 2013-2015.
The moon is a sacred symbol that appears in countless First Nations traditions.

| Common Obverse | 2013 Grandmother Moon Mask Des.: R. Cochrane | 2014 Matriarch Moon Mask Des.: C. Young | 2015 Singing Moon Mask Des.: A. Everson |

Designers:
Obv.: Susanna Blunt
Rev.: See reverse illustrations
Composition: 99.99% Au
Gold content: 33.33 g. 1.07 tr oz
Weight: 33.33 g
Diameter: 30.0 mm
Thickness: N/A

Engravers:
Obv.: Susan Taylor

Edge: Reeded
Die Axis: ↑↑
Finish: Proof

Case of Issue: (A) Maroon leatherette clam style case, black flocked insert, encapsulated coin, COA
(B) Wooden clam style case, black flocked insert, encapsulated coin, COA

DATE	DESCRIPTION	CASE	QUANTITY SOLD	ISSUE PRICE	FINISH	PR-69	PR-70
2013	Grandmother Moon Mask	A	498	2,999.95	Proof	2,800.	—
2014	Matriarch Moon Mask	A	419	2,999.95	Proof	2,300.	—
2015	Singing Moon Mask, Enamelled	B	296	2,999.95	Proof	2,300.	—

TWO HUNDRED DOLLAR FIVE 9'S ISSUES, 2014-2015 (ULTRA HIGH RELIEF)

| 2014-2015 Obverse | 2014 75th Anniv. First Royal Visit Des.: RCM Staff | 2014 Fierce Canadian Lynx Des.: Pierre Leduc |

Designers:
Obv.: Susanna Blunt
Rev.: See reverse illustrations
Composition: 99.999% Au
Gold content: 33.17 g, 1.07 tr oz
Weight: 33.17 g
Diameter: 30.0 mm
Thickness: N/A

Engravers:
Obv.: Susan Taylor
Rev.: See reverse illustrations

Edge: Reeded
Die Axis: ↑↑
Finish: Proof

Case of Issue: Maroon leatherette clam style case, black flocked insert, encapsulated coin, COA

DATE	DESCRIPTION	CASE	QUANTITY SOLD	ISSUE PRICE	FINISH	PR-69	PR-70
2014	75th Anniversary of the First Royal Visit	A	193	2,999.95	Proof	2,300.	—
2014	The Fierce Canadian Lynx	A	117	2,999.95	Proof	2,300.	—

TWO HUNDRED DOLLARS (1 ounce), CALL OF THE WILD SERIES, 2014-2018.

Common Obverse	2014 Howling Wolf (Pr)	2015 Growling Cougar (BU)	2016 Roaring Grizzly	2017 Elk

Designers:
    Obv.:   Susanna Blunt
    Rev.:   Pierre Leduc
Composition: 99.999% Au
Gold content: 31.16 g, 1.0 tr oz
Weight: 31.16 g, 1 oz
Diameter: 30.0 mm
Thickness: 2.8 mm
Case of Issue: Proof: Maroon leatherette clam style case, black flocked insert, encapsulated coin, COA Bullion: Card capsule

Engravers:
    Obv.:   Susan Taylor
    Rev.:   RCM Staff

Die Axis: ↑↑
Finish: See below
Edge: Interrupted serrations

DATE	DESCRIPTION	QUANTITY SOLD	ISSUE PRICE	FINISH	SP-68	SP-69	PR-69	PR-70
2014	$200 (1 oz) 99.999% gold, Howling Wolf	273	2,799.95	Proof	*	*	2,800.	—
2014	$200 (1 oz) 99.999% gold, Howling Wolf	N/A	BV	Bullion	1,800.	—	*	*
2015	$200 (1 oz) 99.999% gold, Growling Cougar	250	2,799.95	Proof	—	*	2,800.	—
2015	$200 (1 oz) 99.999% gold, Growling Cougar	N/A	BV	Bullion	1,800.	—	*	*
2016	$200 (1 oz) 99.999% gold, Roaring Gizzly Bear	246	2,799.95	Proof	*	*	2,800.	—
2016	$200 (1 oz) 99.999% gold, Roaring Grizzly Bear	N/A	BV	Bullion	1,800.	—	*	*
2017	$200 (1 oz) 99.999% gold, Elk	400	2,799.95	Proof	*	*	2,800	—
2017	$200 (1 oz) 99.999% gold, Elk	N/A	BV	Bullion	1,800.	—	*	*
2018	$200 (1 oz) 99.999% gold, Golden Eagle	N/A	BV	Bullion	1,800	—	*	*

TWO HUNDRED DOLLARS (1 ounce), CANADA'S WILDLIFE SERIES, 2014.

Common Obverse	Bald Eagle Protecting Her Nest	The Bison at Home on the Plains

Designers:
    Obv.:   Susanna Blunt
    Rev.:   Claudio D'Angelo
Composition: 99.99% Au
Gold content: 31.16 g, 1.0 tr oz
Weight: 31.16 g, 1oz
Diameter: 30.0 mm
Thickness: 2.8 mm
Case of Issue: Maroon leatherette clam style case, black flocked insert, encapsulated coin, COA

Engravers:
    Obv.:   Susan Taylor
    Rev.:   RCM Staff

Edge: Reeded
Die Axis: ↑↑
Finish: Proof

DATE	DESCRIPTION	QUANTITY SOLD	ISSUE PRICE	FINISH	PR-69	PR-70
2014	$200 (1 oz) Bald Eagle Protecting Her Nest	350	2,699.95	Proof	2,800.	—
2014	$200 (1 oz) The Bison at Home on the Plains	350	2,699.95	Proof	2,800.	—

WO HUNDRED DOLLARS (1 ounce), THE WHITE-TAILED DEER: QUIETLY EXPLORING, 2014.

Featuring multiple finishes, this coin's design has also been used on a twenty dollar silver coin (see page 296).

Designers and Engravers:

Obv.:	Susanna Blunt, Susan Taylor
Rev.:	Trevor Tennant, RCM Staff

Composition: 99.99% Au
Gold content: 31.16 g, 1.0 tr oz
Weight: 31.16 g, 1 oz   **Edge:** Reeded
Diameter: 30.0 mm   **Die Axis:** ↑↑
Thickness: 2.8 mm   **Finish:** Proof
Case of Issue: Maroon leatherette clam style case, black flock insert, encapsulated coin, COA, custom box

DATE	DESCRIPTION	QUANTITY SOLD	ISSUE PRICE	FINISH	PR-69	PR-70
2014	$200 (1 oz) White-Tailed Deer: Quietly Exploring	344	2,699.95	Proof	2,700.	—.

WO HUNDRED DOLLARS, TOM THOMSON: *PINE ISLAND, GEORGIAN BAY* (1914-1916), 2015.

Designers and Engravers:

Obv.:	Susanna Blunt, Susan Taylor
Rev.:	Tom Thomson, RCM Staff

Composition: 99.99% Au
Gold content: 31.16 g. 1.0 tr oz
Weight: 31.16g   **Edge:** Reeded
Diameter: 30.0 mm   **Die Axis:** ↑↑
Thickness: N/A   **Finish:** Proof
Case of Issue: Maroon leatherette clam style case, black flocked insert, encapsulated coin, COA

DATE	DESCRIPTION	QUANTITY SOLD	ISSUE PRICE	FINISH	PR-69	PR-70
2015	Tom Thomson: *Pine Island, Georgian Bay* (1914-1916)	198	2,699.95	Proof	2,700.	—

WO HUNDRED DOLLARS, DIWALI: FESTIVAL OF LIGHTS, 2015.

Designers and Engravers:

Obv.:	Susanna Blunt, Susan Taylor
Rev.:	Sarindar Dhaliwal

Composition: 99.99% Au
Gold content: 31.16 g. 1.0 tr oz
Weight: 31.16 g   **Edge:** Reeded
Diameter: 30.0 mm   **Die Axis:** ↑↑
Thickness: N/A   **Finish:** Proof
Case of Issue: Wooden box with gold foil design with graphic beauty box, encapsulated coin, COA

DATE	DESCRIPTION	QUANTITY SOLD	ISSUE PRICE	FINISH	PR-69	PR-70
2015	Diwali: Festival of Lights	275	2,699.95	Proof	2,700.	—

WO HUNDRED DOLLARS, GRIZZLY BEAR: THE CLAN, 2015.

Designers and Engravers:

Obv.:	Susanna Blunt, Susan Taylor
Rev.:	Lauren Crawshaw

Composition: 99.99% Au
Gold content: 31.16 g. 1.0 tr oz
Weight: 31.16 g   **Edge:** Reeded
Diameter: 30.0 mm   **Die Axis:** ↑↑
Thickness: N/A   **Finish:** Proof
Case of Issue: Maroon clamshell with custom beauty box, encapsulated coin, COA

DATE	DESCRIPTION	QUANTITY SOLD	ISSUE PRICE	FINISH	PR-69	PR-70
2015	The Clan	188	2,699.95	Proof	2,700.	—

TWO HUNDRED DOLLARS, DIWALI: FESTIVAL OF LIGHTS, 2016.

Designers and Engravers:

Obv.:	Susanna Blunt, Susan Taylor		
Rev.:	Meera Sethil		
Composition:	99.99% Au		
Gold content:	31.16 g. 1.0 tr oz		
Weight:	31.16 g	**Edge:**	Reeded
Diameter:	30.0 mm	**Die Axis:**	↑↑
Thickness:	N/A	**Finish:**	Proof
Case of Issue:	Wooden box with gold foil design with graphic beauty box, encapsulated coin, COA		

DATE	DESCRIPTION	MINTAGE	ISSUE PRICE	FINISH	PR-69	PR-70
2016	Diwali: Festival of Lights	534	2,799.95	Proof	2,800.	—

TALL SHIPS LEGACY SET

TWO HUNDRED DOLLARS, TALL SHIPS LEGACY, 2016.

Common Obverse	*Bluenose*	*Marco Polo*	*The Amazon*	HMS *Discovery*

Designers

Obv.:	Susanna Blunt
Rev.:	Neil Hamelin
Composition:	99.99% Au
Gold content:	31.16 g, 1.0 tr oz
Weight:	31.16 g
Diameter:	30.0 mm
Thickness:	N/A
Case of Issue:	Maroon clamshell with black beauty box, encapsulated coin, COA.

Engravers:

Obv.:	Susan Taylor
Rev.:	RCM Staff
Edge:	Reeded
Die Axis:	↑↑
Finish:	Proof

DATE	DESCRIPTION	QUANTITY SOLD	ISSUE PRICE	FINISH	PR-69	PR-70
2016	Tall Ships Legacy: *Bluenose*	274	2,699.95	Proof	2,700.	—
2016	Tall Ships Legacy: *Marco Polo*	275	2,699.95	Proof	2,700.	—
2016	Tall Ships Legacy: *The Amazon*	270	2,699.95	Proof	2,700.	—
2016	Tall Ships Legacy: HMS *Discovery*	244	2,699.95	Proof	2,700.	—

TWO HUNDRED DOLLARS, *STAR TREK*™: DELTA COIN, 2016.

Designers and Engravers:

Obv.:	Susanna Blunt		
Rev.:	RCM Staff		
Composition:	99.99% Au		
Gold content:	16.20 g. 0.75 tr oz		
Weight:	16.20 g	**Edge:**	Plain
Diameter:	28.68 (H) X 17.50 (W)	**Die Axis:**	↑↑
Thickness:	N/A	**Finish:**	Proof
Case of Issue:	Wood case and graphic beauty box.		

DATE	DESCRIPTION	QUANTITY SOLD	ISSUE PRICE	FINISH	PR-69	PR-70
2016	*Star Trek*™: Delta Coin	1,457	1,299.95	Proof	1,500.	—

WO HUNDRED DOLLARS, TIGER AND DRAGON YIN AND YANG, 2016.

Designers and Engravers:
Obv.:	Susanna Blunt
Rev.:	Charles Vinh

Composition: 99.99% Au
Gold content: 31.16 g. 1.0 tr oz
Weight: 31.16 g   **Edge:** Reeded
Diameter: 30.0 mm   **Die Axis:** ↑↑
Thickness: N/A   **Finish:** Proof
Case of Issue: Maroon clamshell with custom beauty box, COA

DATE	DESCRIPTION	QUANTITY SOLD	ISSUE PRICE	FINISH	PR-69	PR-70
2016	Tiger and Dragon Yin and Yang	265	2,888.88	Proof	2,900.	—

WO HUNDRED DOLLARS, MAPLE LEAF SILHOUETTE (SHAPED), 2016.

Designers and Engravers:
Obv.:	Susanna Blunt, Susan Taylor
Rev.:	RCM Staff

Composition: 99.99% Au
Gold content: 31.25 g, 1.01 tr oz
Weight: 31.25 g   **Edge:** Plain
Diameter: 39.6 x 38 mm   **Die Axis:** ↑↑
Thickness: N/A   **Finish:** Proof
Case of Issue: Maroon clamshell with black beauty box.

DATE	DESCRIPTION	QUANTITY SOLD	ISSUE PRICE	FINISH	PR-69	PR-70
2016	Maple Leaf Silhouette	776	2,799.95	Proof	2,800.	—

WO HUNDRED DOLLARS, 150 YEARS OF PASSION: THE MAPLE LEAF, 2017.

Designers and Engravers:
Obv.:	Susanna Blunt, Susan Taylor
Rev.:	RCM Staff

Composition: 99.99% Au
Gold content: 31.6 g. 1.0 tr oz
Weight: 31.6 g   **Edge:** Reeded
Diameter: 30.0 mm   **Die Axis:** ↑↑
Thickness: N/A   **Finish:** Proof
Case of Issue: Maroom clamshell with black beauty box, encapsulated coin, COA

DATE	DESCRIPTION	QUANTITY SOLD	ISSUE PRICE	FINISH	PR-69	PR-70
2017	150 Years of Passion: The Maple Leaf	247	2,699.95	Proof	2,700.	—

WO HUNDRED DOLLARS, FOOTBALL-SHAPED AND CURVED COIN, 2017.

Designers and Engravers:
Obv.:	Susanna Blunt
Rev.:	RCM Staff

Composition: 99.99% Au
Gold content: 31.32 g. 1.02 tr oz
Weight: 31.32 g   **Edge:** Plain
Diameter: 44 x 26.4 mm   **Die Axis:** ↑↑
Thickness: N/A   **Finish:** Proof
Case of Issue: Maroon clamshell with black beauty box, COA

DATE	DESCRIPTION	QUANTITY SOLD	ISSUE PRICE	FINISH	PR-69	PR-70
2017	Football-Shaped and Curved Coin	381	2,899.95	Proof	2,900.	—

TWO HUNDRED DOLLARS, WELCOME TO THE WORLD, 2017.

Designers and Engravers:

Obv.:	Susanna Blunt
Rev.:	RCM Staff
Composition:	99.99% Au
Gold content:	15.43 g. 0.5 tr oz
Weight:	15.43 g
Diameter:	29 mm
Thickness:	N/A
Case of Issue:	Premium wooden box, COA

			Edge:	Reeded
			Die Axis:	↑↑
			Finish:	Proof

DATE	DESCRIPTION	QUANTITY SOLD	ISSUE PRICE	FINISH	PR-69	PR-70
2017	Welcome to the World	35	1,199.95	Proof	1,200	—

TWO HUNDRED DOLLARS, *FENG SHUI* GOOD LUCK CHARMS, 2017.

Rooted deep in Chinese mythology, the protective figure of Pi Yao and the auspicious Wu Lou Gourd are held in high regard by the practitioners c the *Feng Shui*, individually, they represent fortune and health; together on this 99.99% pure gold holed coin, they bring an abundance of blessings an invite positive energy to ensure prosperity, longevity and continued good fortune.

Designers and Engravers:

Obv.:	Susanna Blunt, Susan Taylor
Rev.:	Charles Vinh
Composition:	99.99% Au
Gold content:	28.25 g. 0.91 tr oz
Weight:	28.25 g
Diameter:	30.0 mm
Thickness:	N/A
Case of Issue:	Maroom clamshell with black beauty box, encapsulated coin, COA

			Edge:	Reeded
			Die Axis:	↑↑
			Finish:	Proof

DATE	DESCRIPTION	MINTAGE	ISSUE PRICE	FINISH	PR-69	PR-70
2017	*Feng Shui* Good Luck Charms	388	2,788.88	Proof	2,800.	—

TWO HUNDRED DOLLARS, AUTUMN FIRE (SHAPED), 2017.

A brand new technology in introduced with this coin: GRADIENCE! There's a natural radiance to the reverse, where a translucent gradient effec re-creates the smooth transition of colour seen in nature – from the deep red tips to the natural gleam of gold at the leaf's centre.

Designers and Engravers:

Obv.:	Susanna Blunt, Susan Taylor
Rev.:	RCM Staff
Composition:	99.99% Au
Gold content:	31.25 g, 1.00 tr oz
Weight:	31.25.0 g
Diameter:	39.6 mm 38 mm
Thickness:	N/A
Edge:	Plain
Die Axis:	↑↑
Finish:	Proof
Case of Issue:	Custom wooden box, COA

DATE	DESCRIPTION	MINTAGE	ISSUE PRICE	FINISH	PR-69	PR-70
2017	Autumn Fire	600	2,999.95	Proof	3,000.	—

WO HUNDRED DOLLARS, CANADIAN COASTAL SYMBOLS: THE PACIFIC, 2018.

The coast is an irresistible place, that unique point where land meets sea, and animals from both realms interact in ways unseen just a short stance away. First issue in the three-coin Canadian Coastal Series that will also feature the Arctic (2019) and Atlantic Coasts (2020).

Designers and Engravers:

Obv.:	Susanna Blunt, Susan Taylor
Rev.:	Cathy Boursey-Sabourin

Composition:	99.999% Au	**Gold content:**	31.16 g. 1.02 tr oz
Weight:	31.16 g	**Edge:**	Interrupted reeding
Diameter:	30.0 mm	**Die Axis:**	↑↑
Thickness:	N/A	**Finish:**	Proof
Case of Issue:	Maroom clamshell with black beauty box, COA		

DATE	DESCRIPTION	MINTAGE	ISSUE PRICE	FINISH	PR-69	PR-70
2018	Canadian Coastal Symbols: The Pacific	400	2,899.95	Proof	2,900.	—

WO HUNDRED DOLLARS, EARLY CANADIAN HISTORY: FIRST NATIONS, 2018.

The Algonquian people were one of countless communities that existed in North America long before the Europeans arrived. These Indigenous eople lived in perfect harmony with nature, moving in rhythm with the seasons to access new food sources and to find refuge from the treacherous eather that would settle over the Great Lakes in winter.

Designers and Engravers:

Obv.:	Susanna Blunt, Susan Taylor
Rev.:	Alan Daniel

Composition:	99.999% Au	**Gold content:**	15.43 g. 0.50 tr oz
Weight:	15.43 g	**Edge:**	Reeded
Diameter:	29 mm	**Die Axis:**	↑↑
Thickness:	N/A	**Finish:**	Proof
Case of Issue:	Maroom clamshell with black beauty box, COA		

DATE	DESCRIPTION	MINTAGE	ISSUE PRICE	FINISH	PR-69	PR-70
2018	Early Canadian History: First Nations	1,000	1,199.95	Proof	1,200.	—

WO HUNDRED DOLLARS, BIGHORN SHEEP, 2018.

At home in the rangelands of the Canadian Rocky Mountains, the bighorn sheep is the embodiment of the rugged alpine wilderness it inhabits.

Designers and Engravers:

Obv.:	Susanna Blunt, Susan Taylor
Rev.:	Curtis Atwater

Composition:	99.999% Au	**Gold content:**	31.6g. 1.02 tr oz
Weight:	31.6 g	**Edge:**	Interrupted reeding
Diameter:	30 mm	**Die Axis:**	↑↑
Thickness:	N/A	**Finish:**	Proof
Case of Issue:	Maroom clamshell with black beauty box, COA		

DATE	DESCRIPTION	MINTAGE	ISSUE PRICE	FINISH	PR-69	PR-70
2018	Bighorn Sheep	400	2,899.95	Proof	2,900.	—

TWO HUNDRED DOLLARS, *ANCESTOR MOON* MASK, 2018.

As seen by Indigenous cultures in the Pacific Northwest—a gentle and caring ancestor who watches over the people, lighting the way whe travellers are on the water during the night, or illuminating the beach to help people dig for clams in the dark. *Ancestor Moon* is always present, alway ready to guide and protect.

Designers and Engravers:

Obv.:	Susanna Blunt, Susan Taylor		
Rev.:	Andy Everson		
Composition:	99.999% Au	**Gold content:**	31.37 g. 1.01 tr c
Weight:	31.37 g	**Edge:**	Reeded
Diameter:	30 mm	**Die Axis:**	↑↑
Thickness:	N/A	**Finish:**	Proof
Case of Issue:	Maroom clamshell with black beauty box, COA		

DATE	DESCRIPTION	MINTAGE	ISSUE PRICE	FINISH	PR-69	PR-70
2018	*Ancestor Moon* Mask	300	2,999.95	Proof	3,000.	—

TWO HUNDRED DOLLARS, ENCHANTING MAPLE LEAVES, 2-COIN SET, 2018.

Beauty. Scarcity. Pure elegance. More than a prestigious collectible, this two-coin set is a superbly crafted ode to one of Canada's most belove emblems, the maple leaf, whose natural beauty is unmistakable in the gleam of 99.999% pure gold—and on one coin, an added touch of platinum platin

Common Obverse

Designers		**Engravers:**	
Obv.:	Susanna Blunt	Obv.:	Susan Taylor
Rev.:	Nathalie Lagacé	Rev.:	RCM Staff
Composition:	99.999% Au		
Gold content:	31.16 g, 1.0 tr oz		
Weight:	31.16 g (each coin)	**Edge:**	Interrupted reeding
Diameter:	30 mm (each coin)	**Die Axis:**	↑↑
Thickness:	N/A	**Finish:**	Proof
Case of Issue:	Wood case with black beauty box, encapsulated coin, COA.		

DATE	DESCRIPTION	MINTAGE	ISSUE PRICE	FINISH	PR-69	PR-70
2018	Enchanting Maple Leaves – 2-Coin Set	175	5,899.95	Proof	5,900.	—

TWO HUNDRED DOLLARS, GOOD LUCK CHARMS – FIVE BLESSINGS, 2018.

This coin features one of the most popular good luck motifs found in old Chinese houses—five bats surrounding the Chinese symbol shou (longevity to bring five cherished blessings of health, wealth, longevity, virtue, and a peaceful natural death in old age. It's inspired by a visual pun in which th character for bat (fu) and good fortune or happiness (fu), are pronounced the same way; together they bring an abundance of blessings.

Designers and Engravers:

Obv.:	Susanna Blunt, Susan Taylor		
Rev.:	Simon Ng		
Composition:	99.99% Au		
Gold content:	28.25 g. 0.91 tr oz		
Weight:	28.25 g	**Edge:**	Reeded
Diameter:	30 mm	**Die Axis:**	↑↑
Thickness:	N/A	**Finish:**	Proof
Case of Issue:	Burgundy clamshell with black beauty box, COA		

DATE	DESCRIPTION	MINTAGE	ISSUE PRICE	FINISH	PR-69	PR-70
2018	Good Luck Charms – Five Blessings	388	2,888.88	Proof	2,900.	—

TWO HUNDRED FIFTY DOLLAR GOLD COINS

TWO HUNDRED FIFTY DOLLARS, DOG SLED TEAM, 2006.

Designers and Engravers:

Obv.:	Susanna Blunt, Susan Taylor
Rev.:	Arnold Nogy, José Osio
Composition:	58.33% Au, 41.67% Ag
Gold content:	26.25 g, 0.844 tr oz
Silver content:	18.75 g, 0.603 tr oz
Weight:	45.0 g
Diameter:	40.0 mm
Thickness:	2.9 mm
Edge:	Reeded
Die Axis:	↑↑
Finish:	Proof
Case of Issue:	Maroon leatherette clam style case, black flocked insert, encapsulated coin, COA

DATE	DESCRIPTION	QUANTITY SOLD	ISSUE PRICE	FINISH	PR-69	PR-70
2006	Dog Sled Team	953	1,089.95	Proof	1,500.	—

Note: An identical design is utilized on the $30 silver coin for 2006, see page 367.

TWO HUNDRED FIFTY DOLLARS, CANADIAN CONTEMPORARY ART, 2014.

Designed by Tim Barnard, the coin's reverse features an artistic college of over fifty images depicting distinct aspects of Canadiana from flora and fauna to First Nations art. The same design was issued in a $30 dollar silver coin (see page 371).

Designers and Engravers:

Obv.:	Susanna Blunt, Susan Taylor
Rev.:	Tim Barnard, RCM Staff
Composition:	99.99% Au
Gold content:	62.34 g, 2.0 tr oz
Weight:	62.34 g
Diameter:	42.0 mm
Thickness:	N/A
Edge:	Reeded
Die Axis:	↑↑
Finish:	Proof
Case of Issue:	Maroon leatherette clam style case, black flocked insert, encapsulated coin, COA

DATE	DESCRIPTION	QUANTITY SOLD	ISSUE PRICE	FINISH	PR-69	PR-70
2014	Canadian Contemporary Art	105	5,199.95	Proof	5,200.	—

TWO HUNDRED FIFTY DOLLARS, 75TH ANNIVERSARY OF THE DECLARATION OF THE SECOND WORLD WAR, 2014.

Designers and Engravers:

Obv.:	Susanna Blunt, Susan Taylor
Rev.:	Silvia Pecota, RCM Staff
Composition:	99.99% Au
Gold content:	62.34 g, 2.0 tr oz
Weight:	62.34g
Diameter:	42.0 mm
Thickness:	N/A
Edge:	Reeded
Die Axis:	↑↑
Finish:	Proof
Case of Issue:	Maroon leatherette clam style case, black flocked insert, encapsulated coin, COA

DATE	DESCRIPTION	QUANTITY SOLD	ISSUE PRICE	FINISH	PR-69	PR-70
2014	75th Anniv. Declaration of the Second World War	100	5,199.95	Proof	5,200.	—

Note: An identical design is utilized on the $30 silver coin for 2014, see page 371.

TWO HUNDRED FIFTY DOLLARS, 100TH ANNIVERSARY OF THE COMPLETION OF THE GRAND TRUNK PACIFIC RAILWAY, 2014.

Linking Eastern Canada to the Pacific, a feat of engineering in the early 20th century, The Grand Trunk Pacific Railway is depicted crossing the Grand Trunk Bridge in Saskatoon. The same design was issued in a $30 dollar silver coin (see page 370).

Designers and Engravers:
Obv.:	Susanna Blunt, Susan Taylor
Rev.:	Joel Kimmel, RCM Staff
Composition:	99.99% Au
Gold content:	62.34 g, 2.0 tr oz
Weight:	62.34 g
Diameter:	42.0 mm
Thickness:	N/A
Edge:	Reeded
Die Axis:	↑↑
Finish:	Proof
Case of Issue:	Maroon leatherette clam style case, black flocked insert, encapsulated coin, COA

DATE	DESCRIPTION	QUANTITY SOLD	ISSUE PRICE	FINISH	PR-69	PR-70
2014	100th Anniv. Completion of the Grand Trunk Pacific Railway	338	5,199.95	Proof	5,200.	—

FLORA AND FAUNA SET

TWO HUNDRED FIFTY DOLLARS, FLORA AND FAUNA SET, 2015.

Featuring the glass work of Giuliano Donaggio, set against the artistic backdrops designed by Maurice Gervais, the set of coins was also issued 25-cents (with the exception of the Turtle with Broadleaf Arrowhead) (see page 48) and $20 (see page 267).

Common Obverse	Tulip and Ladybug	Aster and Bumblebee

Purple Cone Flower and Eastern Tailed Blue Butterfly	Water Lily and Leopard Frog	Turtle with Broadleaf Arrowhead Flower

Designers
Obv.:	Susanna Blunt
Rev.:	Maurice Gervais, Glass: Giuliano Donaggio
Composition:	99.99% Au
Gold content:	60.08 g, 1.932 tr oz
Weight:	60.08 g
Diameter:	38.0 mm
Thickness:	N/A
Case of Issue:	Dark maple wood case, black flocked insert, encapsulated coin, COA, black outer case

Engravers:
Obv.:	Susan Taylor
Rev.:	José Osio

Edge:	Reeded
Die Axis:	↑↑
Finish:	Proof

TWO HUNDRED FIFTY DOLLARS, FLORA AND FAUNA SET, 2015, PRICING TABLE.

DATE	DESCRIPTION	QUANTITY SOLD	ISSUE PRICE	FINISH	PR-69	PR-70
2015	Tulip and Ladybug	—	N.I.I.	Proof	5,000.	—
2015	Aster and Bumblebee	—	N.I.I.	Proof	5,000.	—
2015	Purple Cone Flower and Eastern Tailed Blue Butterfly	—	N.I.I.	Proof	5,000.	—
2015	Water Lily and Leopard Frog	—	N.I.I.	Proof	5,000.	—
2015	Turtle with Broadleaf Arrowhead Flower	—	N.I.I.	Proof	5,000.	—
2015	Set of 5 coins	99	15,000.	Proof	21,000.	*

TWO HUNDRED FIFTY DOLLARS, A CELEBRATION OF HER MAJESTY'S 90TH BIRTHDAY, 2016.

Designers and Engravers:
Obv.:	S. Blunt, S. Taylor
Rev.:	RCM Staff
Composition:	99.99% Ag
Gold content:	60.08, 1.93 tr oz
Weight:	60.08 g
Diameter:	38 mm
Thickness:	N/A
Edge:	Reeded
Die Axis:	↑↑
Finish:	Proof
Case of Issue:	Maple wood case, black flocked insert, encapsulated coin, COA

TWO HUNDRED FIFTY DOLLARS, MAPLE CANOPY: KALEIDOSCOPE OF COLOUR, 2016.

Designers and Engravers:
Obv.:	S. Blunt, S. Taylor
Rev.:	Emily Damstra
Composition:	99.99% Ag
Gold content:	62.34 g, 2.00 tr oz
Weight:	62.34 g
Diameter:	42 mm
Thickness:	N/A
Edge:	Reeded
Die Axis:	↑↑
Finish:	Proof
Case of Issue:	Maroom clamshell with beauty box, encapsulated coin, COA

TWO HUNDRED FIFTY DOLLARS, MAPLE CANOPY: KALEIDOSCOPE OF COLOUR, 2017.

Designers and Engravers:
Obv.:	S. Blunt, S. Taylor
Rev.:	Emily Damstra
Composition:	99.99% Ag
Gold content:	1,000.0 g, 32.151 tr oz
Weight:	62.34 g
Diameter:	42 mm
Thickness:	N/A
Edge:	Reeded
Die Axis:	↑↑
Finish:	Proof
Case of Issue:	Maroom clamshell with beauty box, encapsulated coin, COA

DATE	DESCRIPTION	QUANTITY SOLD	ISSUE PRICE	FINISH	PR-69	PR-70
2016	A Celebration of Her Majesty's 90th Birthday	250	6,999.95	Proof	7,000.	—
2016	Maple Canopy: Kaleidoscope of Colour	150	4,899.95	Proof	4,900.	—
2017	Maple Canopy: Kaleidoscope of Colour	131	4,949.95	Proof	4,950.	—

Note: Coins illustrated are smaller than actual size.

TWO HUNDRED FIFTY DOLLARS, CELEBRATING CANADIAN BRILLIANCE, 2017.

To highlight the theme of Canadian brilliance, this coin was designed in partnership with the Canadian Intellectual Property Office, and an industrial design registered by Vancouver's Worldwide Diamond Trademarks Ltd. was selected for the diamond on this numismatic coin.

Designers and Engravers:

Obv.:	S. Blunt, S. Taylor
Rev.:	Chris Reid and Rosina Li
Composition:	99.99% Au
Gold content:	60.08 g,1.93 tr oz
Weight:	60.08 g
Diameter:	38 mm
Thickness:	N/A
Edge:	Reeded
Die Axis:	↑↑
Finish:	Proof
Case of Issue:	Wood case with custom beauty box, COA

DATE	DESCRIPTION	MINTAGE	ISSUE PRICE	FINISH	PR-69	PR-70
2017	Celebrating Canadian Brilliance	250	6,999.95	Proof	7,000.	—

TWO HUNDRED FIFTY DOLLARS, A CROWN JEWEL, 2018.

The ruby's protective powers made it a highly symbolic wedding gift from the Burmese people that have stood The Queen in good stead as she has served the Commonwealth longer than any of her predecessors. Features 17 genuine rubies and selectively plated platinum to recreate one of the Tudor roses on the Burmese tiara with breathtaking effect!

Designers and Engravers:

Obv.:	S. Blunt, S. Taylor
Rev.:	RCM Staff
Composition:	99.99% Au
Gold content:	60.08 g, 1.93 tr oz
Weight:	60.08 g
Diameter:	38 mm
Thickness:	N/A
Edge:	Reeded
Die Axis:	↑↑
Finish:	Proof
Case of Issue:	Wooden box with black beauty box, COA

DATE	DESCRIPTION	MINTAGE	ISSUE PRICE	FINISH	PR-69	PR-70
2018	A Crown Jewel	175	6,999.95	Proof	7,000.	—

TWO HUNDRED FIFTY DOLLARS, THE MAGNIFICENT MAPLE, 2018.

The beautiful diamond on the reverse adds brilliance to an already striking design,

Designers and Engravers:

Obv.:	S. Blunt, S. Taylor
Rev.:	Virginia Boulay
Composition:	99.99% Au
Gold content:	60.08 g, 1.93 tr oz
Weight:	60.08 g
Diameter:	38 mm
Thickness:	N/A
Edge:	Reeded
Die Axis:	↑↑
Finish:	Proof
Case of Issue:	Wooden case with custom beauty box, COA

DATE	DESCRIPTION	MINTAGE	ISSUE PRICE	FINISH	PR-69	PR-70
2018	The Magnificent Maple	250	6,999.95	Proof	7,000.	—

THREE HUNDRED DOLLAR GOLD COINS

HREE HUNDRED DOLLARS, TRIPLE CAMEO PORTRAITS OF QUEEN ELIZABETH II, 2002.
This 14-karat gold coin bears triple cameo portraits of Queen Elizabeth II on the obverse: a 1953-1964 portrait by Mary Gillick, a 1965-1989 portrait y Arnold Machin, and a 1990-2003 portrait by Dora de Pédery-Hunt.

esigners:			**Engravers:**	
Obv.:	Dora de Pédery-Hunt		Obv.:	Stan Witten
Rev.:	Sheldon Beveridge, Cosme Saffioti		Rev.:	Cosme Saffioti
omposition:	58.33% Au, 41.67% Ag			
old content:	35.00 g, 1.125 tr oz		**Thickness:**	2.5 mm
ilver content:	25.0 g, 0.804 tr oz		**Edge:**	Reeded
eight:	60.0 g		**Die Axis:**	↑↑
iameter:	50.0 mm		**Finish:**	Proof / Bullion
ase of Issue:	Purple laminated wooden case, cream insert, encapsulated coin, COA, black / gold outer case			

DATE	DESCRIPTION	QUANTITY SOLD	ISSUE PRICE	FINISH	PR-69	PR-70
2002 (1952-)	Triple Cameo Portraits	999	1,095.95	Proof	2,000.	—

ote: Coin illustrated smaller than actual size.

THREE HUNDRED DOLLARS, GREAT SEAL OF CANADA, 2003.

The Royal Seal, or Great Seal of Canada, is the official stamp used to bring the Queen's authority to any documents produced on her behalf.

2003 Obverse

2003 Reverse
Designer: RCM Staff
Engraver: RCM Staff

THREE HUNDRED DOLLARS, QUADRUPLE CAMEO PORTRAITS, 2004.

The four coinage portraits of Queen Elizabeth II are featured on the obverse of the $300 coin for 2004. Each is struck in 24kt gold.

2004 Obverse

2004 Reverse
Designer: Christie Paquet
Engraver: Christie Paquet

Designers:		**Engravers:**	
Obv.:	M. Gillick, A. Machin, D. de Pedery-Hunt, S. Blunt	Obv.:	Susan Taylor
Rev.:	See reverse illustrations	Rev.:	See reverse illustrations
Composition:	58.33% Au, 41.67% Ag		
Gold content:	35.00 g, 1.125 tr oz	**Thickness:**	2.5 mm
Silver content:	25.0 g, 0.804 tr oz	**Edge:**	Reeded
Weight:	60.0 g	**Die Axis:**	↑↑
Diameter:	50.0 mm	**Finish:**	Proof / Bullion
Case of Issue:	Black leatherette case, RCM plaque, black flocked insert, encapsulated coin, COA, black and gold outer case		

DATE	DESCRIPTION	QUANTITY SOLD	ISSUE PRICE	FINISH	PR-69	PR-70
2003	Great Seal of Canada	998	1,099.95	Proof	2,000.	—
2004	Quadruple Cameo Portraits	998	1,099.95	Proof	2,000.	—

VIGNETTES OF THE TWENTY-FIVE CENT
FRACTIONAL NOTES OF THE DOMINION OF CANADA SERIES

THREE HUNDRED DOLLARS, VIGNETTES OF THE TWENTY-FIVE CENT FRACTIONAL NOTES OF THE DOMINION OF CANADA, 2005-2007.
These coins commemorate the vignettes which appear on the Dominion of Canada twenty-five cent fractional note issues of 1870, 1900 and 1923.

2005-2007 Common Obverse	2005 The 1870 Shinplaster Vignette of Britannia Designer: Robert-Ralph Carmichael Engraver: José Osio	2006 The 1900 Shinplaster Vignette of Britannia Designer: Christie Paquet Engraver: Christie Paquet	2007 The 1923 Shinplaster Vignette of Britannia Designer: Robert-Ralph Carmichael Engraver: Christie Paquet

Designers:
   Obv.:   Susanna Blunt
   Rev.:   See reverse illustrations
Composition: 58.33% Au, 41.67% Ag
Gold content: 35.0 g, 1.125 tr oz
Silver content: 25.0 g, 0.804 tr oz
Weight: 60.00 g
Diameter: 50.0 mm

Engravers:
   Obv.:   Susan Taylor
   Rev.:   See reverse illustrations

Thickness: 2.5 mm
Edge: Reeded
Die Axis: ↑↑
Finish: Proof / Bullion

Case of Issue: Black leatherette case, RCM plaque, black flocked insert, encapsulated coin, COA, black and gold outer case

DATE	DESCRIPTION	QUANTITY SOLD	ISSUE PRICE	FINISH	PR-69	PR-70
2005	1870 Shinplaster Vignette of Britannia	994	N/A	Proof	2,000.	—
2006	1900 Shinplaster Vignette of Britannia	947	1,295.95	Proof	2,000.	—
2007	1923 Shinplaster Vignette of Britannia	778	1,440.95	Proof	2,000.	—

CRYSTAL SNOWFLAKE SERIES

THREE HUNDRED DOLLARS, CRYSTAL SNOWFLAKE SERIES, 2006 AND 2010

Crystal Snowflake, 2006	Crystal Snowflake, 2010

Designers:
   Obv.:   Susanna Blunt
   Rev.:   Konrad Wachelko
Composition: 58.33% Au, 41.67% Ag, Swarovski crystal elements
Gold content: 35.0 g, 1.125 tr oz
Silver content: 25.0 g, 0.804 tr oz
Weight: 60.0 g
Diameter: 50.0 mm

Engravers:
   Obv.:   Susan Taylor
   Rev.:   Konrad Wachelko

Thickness: 2.5 mm
Edge: Reeded
Die Axis: ↑↑
Finish: Proof

Case of Issue: Maroon leatherette clam style case, black flocked insert, encapsulated coin, COA

DATE	DESCRIPTION	QUANTITY SOLD	ISSUE PRICE	FINISH	PR-69	PR-70
2006	Crystal Snowflake	998	1,520.95	Proof	2,000.	—
2010	Crystal Snowflake	305	2,295.95	Proof	2,200.	—

THREE HUNDRED DOLLARS, 80TH BIRTHDAY OF QUEEN ELIZABETH II, 2006.

Designers:		Engravers:	
Obv.:	Susanna Blunt	Obv.:	Susan Taylor
Rev.:	Not known	Rev.:	Cecily Mok
Composition:	58.33% Au, 41.67% Ag, Enamelled		
Gold content:	35.0 g, 1.125 tr oz	Thickness:	2.5 mm
Silver content:	25.0 g, 0.804 tr oz	Edge:	Reeded
Weight:	60.0 g	Die Axis:	↑↑
Diameter:	50.0 mm	Finish:	Proof
Case of Issue:	Maroon leatherette clam style case, black flocked insert, encapsulated coin, COA		

DATE	DESCRIPTION	QUANTITY SOLD	ISSUE PRICE	FINISH	PR-69	PR-70
2006 (1926-)	80th Birthday Elizabeth II, Enamelled	1,000	1,520,95	Proof	2,000.	—

VANCOUVER 2010 OLYMPIC WINTER GAMES SERIES

THREE HUNDRED DOLLARS, VANCOUVER 2010 OLYMPIC WINTER GAMES SERIES, 2007-2009.

Common Obverse (except for date)	2007 - Olympic Ideals Engraver: Susan Taylor, José Osio	2008 - Competition Engraver: Susan Taylor, Christie Paquet	2009 - Friendship Engraver: Susan Taylor, José Osio

Designers:		Engravers:	
Obv.:	Susanna Blunt	Obv.:	Susan Taylor
Rev.:	Laurie McGaw, David Craig	Rev.:	See reverse illustrations
Composition:	58.33% Au, 41.67% Ag		
Gold content:	35.0 g, 1.125 tr oz	Thickness:	2.5 mm
Silver content:	25.0 g, 0.804 tr oz	Edge:	Reeded
Weight:	60.0 g	Die Axis:	↑↑
Diameter:	50.0 mm	Finish:	Proof
Case of Issue:	Black leatherette case, black flocked insert, encapsulated coin, COA	Note:	Coins illustrated smaller than actual size

DATE	DESCRIPTION	ISSUE DATE	QUANTITY SOLD	ISSUE PRICE	FINISH	PR-69	PR-70
2007	Olympic Ideals	Feb. 23, 2007	953	1,499.95	Proof	2,000.	—
2008	Competition	Feb. 20, 2008	334	1,599.95	Proof	2,000.	—
2009	Friendship	Feb. 18, 2009	880	1,999.95	Proof	2,000.	—

PROVINCIAL COATS OF ARMS SERIES

THREE HUNDRED DOLLARS, PROVINCIAL COATS OF ARMS SERIES, 2008-2014.

Designers:
  Obv.:   Susanna Blunt
  Rev.:   Reproduction of official Coat of Arms
Composition: 58.33% Au, 41.67% Ag
Gold content: 35.0 g, 1.125 tr oz
Silver content: 25.0 g, 0.804 tr oz
Weight: 60.0 g
Diameter: 50.0 mm
Case of Issue: Maroon leatherette clam style case, black flocked insert, encapsulated coin, COA

Engravers:
  Obv.:   Susan Taylor
  Rev.:   See reverse illustrations

Thickness: 2.5 mm
Edge: Reeded
Die Axis: ↑↑
Finish: Proof

Note: Coins illustrated smaller than actual size.

2008-2009
Common Obverse
With RCM Logo

2008
Newfoundland and Labrador
Engraver: Marcos Hallam

2008
Alberta
Engraver: Konrad Wachelko

2009
Yukon Territory
Engraver: Marcos Hallam

2009-2014
Common Obverse
Without RCM Logo

2009
Prince Edward Island
Engraver: Marcos Hallam

2010
British Columbia
Engraver: Konrad Wachelko

2010
New Brunswick
Engraver: Marcos Hallam

2011
Manitoba
Engraver: Cecily Mok

2011
Nova Scotia
Engraver: Konrad Wachelko

2012
Quebec
Engraver: Nick Martin

2012
Nunavut
Engraver: Christie Paquet

THREE HUNDRED DOLLARS, PROVINCIAL COATS OF ARMS SERIES, 2008-2014 (cont.).

2013	2013	2014	2014
Ontario	Northwest Territories	Saskatchewan	Canada
Engraver: Steven Stewart	Engraver: Steven Stewart	Engraver: Samantha Strath	Engraver: Eric Boyer

Designers:
  Obv.:   Susanna Blunt
  Rev.:   Reproduction of official Coat of Arms
Composition: 58.33% Au, 41.67% Ag
Gold content: 35.0 g, 1.125 tr oz
Silver content: 25.0 g, 0.804 tr oz
Weight: 60.0 g
Diameter: 50.0 mm
Case of Issue: Maroon leatherette clam style case, black flocked insert, encapsulated coin, COA

Engravers:
  Obv.:   Susan Taylor
  Rev.:   See reverse illustrations
Thickness: 2.5 mm
Edge: Reeded
Die Axis: ↑↑
Finish: Proof

DATE	DESCRIPTION	QUANTITY SOLD	ISSUE PRICE	FINISH	PR-69	PR-70
2008	Newfoundland and Labrador	472	1,541.95	Proof	2,000.	—
2008	Alberta	344	1,631.95	Proof	2,000.	—
2009	Yukon Territory	325	1,949.95	Proof	2,000.	—
2009	Prince Edward Island	236	1,949.95	Proof	2,000.	—
2010	British Columbia	421	2,249.95	Proof	2,000.	—
2010	New Brunswick	233	2,249.95	Proof	2,000.	—
2011	Manitoba	472	2,249.95	Proof	2,000.	—
2011	Nova Scotia	238	2,249.95	Proof	2,000.	—
2012	Quebec	334	2,649.95	Proof	2,000.	—
2012	Nunavut	189	2,649.95	Proof	2,000.	—
2013	Ontario	251	2,649.95	Proof	2,000.	—
2013	Northwest Territories	148	2,649.95	Proof	2,000.	—
2014	Saskatchewan	172	2,649.95	Proof	2,000.	—
2014	Canada	198	2,649.95	Proof	2,000.	—

Note: Coins illustrated smaller than actual size.

MOON MASK SERIES

THREE HUNDRED DOLLARS, MOON MASK SERIES, 2008-2009.

| Common Obverse | 2008 Four Seasons Moon Mask | 2009 Summer Moon Mask |

Designers:
  Obv.: Susanna Blunt
  Rev.: Jody Broomfield
Composition: 58.33% Au, 41.67% Ag, Enamelled
Gold content: 35.0 g, 1.125 tr oz
Silver content: 25.0 g, 0.804 tr oz
Weight: 60.0 g
Diameter: 50.0 mm
Case of Issue: Maroon leatherette clam style case, black flocked insert, encapsulated coin, COA

Engravers:
  Obv.: Susan Taylor
  Rev.: Susan Taylor

Thickness: 2.5 mm
Edge: Reeded
Die Axis: ↑↑
Finish: Proof

DATE	DESCRIPTION	QUANTITY SOLD	ISSUE PRICE	FINISH	PR-69	PR-70
2008	Four Seasons Moon Mask	544	1,559.95	Proof	2,200.	—
2009	Summer Moon Mask	N/A	1,723.95	Proof	2,200.	—

THREE HUNDRED DOLLAR GOLD COIN, REDUCED SIZE

THREE HUNDRED DOLLARS, WELCOME FIGURE (DZUNUK'WA) TOTEM POLE, 2005.

Dzunuk'wa is a giant, hairy, black-bodied, big-breasted, wide-eyed female monster. She is physically strong enough to tear down large trees, spiritually powerful enough to resurrect the dead and possesses magical treasures and great wealth.

Designers and Engravers:
  Obv.: Susanna Blunt, Susan Taylor
  Rev.: Dr. Richard Hunt, Susan Taylor
Composition: 58.33% Au, 41.67% Ag
Gold content: 26.25 g, 0.844 tr oz   **Thickness:** 3.0 mm
Silver content: 18.75 g, 0.603 tr oz   **Edge:** Reeded
Weight: 45.0 g   **Die Axis:** ↑↑
Diameter: 40.0 mm   **Finish:** Proof
Case of Issue: Maroon leatherette clam style case, black flocked insert, encapsulated coin, COA

DATE	DESCRIPTION	QUANTITY SOLD	ISSUE PRICE	FINISH	PR-69	PR-70
2005	Welcome Figure Totem Pole	948	1,199.95	Proof	1,600.	—

Note: An identical design is utilized on the $30 silver coin for 2005, see page 367

.CANADIAN ACHIEVEMENT SERIES, REDUCED SIZE 2005-2008

THREE HUNDRED DOLLARS, 120TH ANNIVERSARY OF THE INTERNATIONAL IMPLEMENTATION OF STANDARD TIME SET, 2005.

In 1885 Sir Sandford Fleming's system of standard time was implemented, dividing the world into 24 time zones. These are the first coins in the Canadian Achievements series.

Designers and Engravers:

Obv.:	Susanna Blunt, Susan Taylor
Rev.:	Bonnie Ross, Stan Witten
Composition:	58.33% Au, 41.67% Ag, Colourised
Gold content:	26.25 g, 0.844 tr oz
Silver content:	18.75 g, 0.603 tr oz
Weight:	45.0 g
Diameter:	40.0 mm
Thickness:	3.0 mm
Finish:	Proof

Edge: Reeded
Die Axis: ↑↑

Case of Issue: Anodized gold-coloured aluminum box with cherry wood stained side panels, encapsulated coin, COA

Pacific Time 4:00

Mountain Time 5:00

Central Time 6:00

Eastern Time 7:00

Atlantic Time 8:00

Newfoundland Time 8:30

DATE	DESCRIPTION	QUANTITY SOLD	ISSUE PRICE	FINISH	PR-69	PR-70
2005	Pacific Time 4:00	200	999.95	Proof	1,700.	—
2005	Mountain Time 5:00	200	999.95	Proof	1,700.	—
2005	Central Time 6:00	200	999.95	Proof	1,700.	—
2005	Eastern Time 7:00	200	999.95	Proof	1,700.	—
2005	Atlantic Time 8:00	200	999.95	Proof	1,700.	—
2005	Newfoundland Time 8:30	200	999.95	Proof	1,700.	—

Note: It is reported in the 2006 Mint Report that a total of 1,199 coins were issued, however, it did not stipulate which coin was short struck.

CANADIAN ACHIEVEMENT SERIES, REDUCED SIZE (cont.).

THREE HUNDRED DOLLARS, CANADIAN ACHIEVEMENT SERIES, 2006-2008.

2006 Obverse

2007-2008 Obverse

Designers and Engravers:

Obv.:	Susanna Blunt, Susan Taylor
Rev.:	See reverse illustrations
Composition:	58.33% Au, 41.67% Ag
Gold content:	26.25 g, 0.844 tr oz
Silver content:	18.75 g, 0.603 tr oz
Weight:	45.0 g **Edge:** Reeded
Diameter:	40.0 mm **Die Axis:** ↑↑
Thickness:	3.0 mm **Finish:** Proof, Decal
Case of Issue:	Maroon leatherette clam style case, black flocked insert, encapsulated coin. COA

2006 – Fifth Anniversary of Canadarm
Des.: Cecily Mok, Decal

2007 – Panoramic Photography in Canada,
Niagara Falls, Hologram
Des.: Chris Jordison

2008 – IMAX© Hologram
Des.: IMAX©

DATE	DESCRIPTION	QUANTITY SOLD	ISSUE PRICE	FINISH	PR-69	PR-70
2006	5th Anniversary Canadarm, Decal	581	1,089.95	Proof	1,600.	—
2007	Panoramic Photography, Niagara Falls, Hologram	551	1,111.95	Proof	1,600.	—
2008	IMAX©, Hologram	252	1,228.95	Proof	1,600.	—

THREE HUNDRED DOLLAR GOLD COIN, SMALL SIZE

THREE HUNDRED DOLLARS, THE QUEEN'S DIAMOND JUBILEE, 1952-2012.

Designers and Engravers:

Obv.:	Susanna Blunt, Susan Taylor
Rev.:	Laurie McGaw, Susan Taylor
Composition:	99.999% Au, Diamond
Gold content:	22.0 g, 0.707 tr oz
Weight:	22.0 g **Edge:** Reeded
Diameter:	25.0 mm **Die Axis:** ↑↑
Thickness:	N/A **Finish:** Proof
Case of Issue:	Wooden collector box with the official Diamond Jubilee Cypher

DATE	DESCRIPTION	QUANTITY SOLD	ISSUE PRICE	FINISH	PR-69	PR-70
2012 (1952-)	The Queen's Diamond Jubilee	684	1,999.95	Proof	1,700.	—

Note: This coin was also issued as part of a three-coin gold commemorative set. The other coins included in the set are a British £5 coin and an Australian fifty-cent piece. There were 375 sets sold to a U.S.A. distributor (APMEX).

THREE HUNDRED FIFTY DOLLAR GOLD COINS

PROVINCIAL FLORAL EMBLEM SERIES

THREE HUNDRED FIFTY DOLLARS, PROVINCIAL FLORAL EMBLEM SERIES, 1998-2011.

Begun in 1998 and issued annually, these $350 gold coins bear either a national or provincial flower.

| Common Obverse 1998-2003 (except for date) | 1998 90th Anniv. Royal Canadian Mint Designer: Pierre Leduc Engraver: Ago Aarand | 1999 Golden Slipper Prince Edward Island Designer: Henry Purdy Engraver: José Osio | 2000 Pacific Dogwood British Columbia Designer: Caren Heine Engraver: José Osio |

| 2001 Mayflower Nova Scotia Designer: Bonnie Ross Engraver: Susan Taylor | 2002 Wild Rose Alberta Designer: Dr. A. K. Hellum Engraver: William Woodruff | 2003 White Trillium Ontario Designer: Pamela Stagg Engraver: José Osio |

Designers:
 Obv.:   Dora de Pédery-Hunt
 Rev.:   See reverse illustrations
Composition: 99.999% Au
Gold content: 38.05 g, 1.222 tr oz
Weight: 38.05 g
Diameter: 34.0 mm
Thickness: 3.2 mm
Case of Issue: Anodized gold-coloured aluminum box with cherry wood stained side panels, encapsulated coin, COA

Engravers:
 Obv.:   Dora de Pédery-Hunt
 Rev.:   See reverse illustrations

Edge: Reeded
Die Axis: ↑↑
Finish: Proof

DATE	DESCRIPTION	QUANTITY SOLD	ISSUE PRICE	FINISH	PR-69	PR-70
1998	90th Anniversary of the Royal Canadian Min	1,999	999.99	Proof	2,200.	—
1999	Golden Slipper, P.E.I.	1,990	999.99	Proof	2,200.	—
2000	Pacific Dogwood, B.C.	1,971	999.99	Proof	2,200.	—
2001	Mayflower, N.S.	1,988	999.99	Proof	2,200.	—
2002	Wild Rose, Alberta	2,001	1,099.99	Proof	2,200.	—
2003	White Trillium, Ontario	1,865	1,099.99	Proof	2,200.	—

THREE HUNDRED FIFTY DOLLARS, PROVINCIAL FLORAL SERIES, 1998-2011 (cont.).

In 2004 the weight was decreased from 38.05 to 35.0 grams.

**Common Obverse
2004-2011
(except for date)**

Designers and Engravers:

Obv.:	Susanna Blunt, Susan Taylor
Rev.:	See reverse illustrations

Composition: 99.999% Au
Gold content: 35.0 g, 1.125 tr oz
Weight: 35.0 g   **Edge:** Reeded
Diameter: 34.0 mm   **Die Axis:** ↑↑
Thickness: 2.8 mm   **Finish:** Proof
Case of Issue:

2004-2006:	Maroon plastic display case, black plastic insert, encapsulated coin, COA
2007-2011:	Maroon leatherette clam style case, black flocked insert, encapsulated coin, COA

| **2004 Fireweed**
Yukon Territory
Des.: Catherine Ann Deer
Eng.: William Woodruff | **2005 Western Red Lily**
Saskatchewan
Designer: Chris Jordison
Engraver: José Osio | **2006 Iris Versicolor**
Quebec
Designer: Susan Taylor
Engraver: Susan Taylor | **2007 Purple Violet**
New Brunswick
Designer: Sue Rose
Engraver: William Woodruff |

| **2008 Purple Saxifrage**
Nunavut
Designer: Celia Godkin
Engraver: Cecily Mok | **2009 Pitcher Plant**
Newfoundland and Labrador
Designer: Celia Godkin
Engraver: José Osio | **2010 Prairie Crocus**
Manitoba
Designer: Celia Godkin
Engraver: N/A | **2011 Mountain Avens**
Northwest Territories
Designer: Caren Heine
Engraver: Susan Taylor |

DATE	DESCRIPTION	QUANTITY SOLD	ISSUE PRICE	FINISH	PR-69	PR-70
2004	Fireweed, Yukon Territory	1,836	1,099.95	Proof	2,000.	—
2005	Western Red Lily, Saskatchewan	1,634	1,295.99	Proof	2,000.	—
2006	Iris Versicolor, Quebec	1,995	1,295.95	Proof	2,000.	—
2007	Purple Violet, New Brunswick	1,392	1,520.95	Proof	2,000.	—
2008	Purple Saxifrage, Nunavut	1,313	1,675.95	Proof	2,000.	—
2009	Pitcher Plant, Newfoundland and Labrador	1,003	2,149.95	Proof	2,000.	—
2010	Prairie Crocus, Manitoba	775	2,599.95	Proof	2,000.	—
2011	Mountain Avens, Northwest Territories	1,033	2,799.95	Proof	2,000.	—

THREE HUNDRED FIFTY DOLLARS, SIR ISAAC BROCK, THE HERO OF UPPER CANADA, 2012.

Sir Isaac Brock, an English General, was killed at the first major battle of the War of 1812, at Queenston Heights.

Designers and Engravers:
Obv.:	Susanna Blunt, Susan Taylor
Rev.:	Christie Paquet

Composition:	99.999% Au		
Gold content:	35.0 g, 1.125 tr oz		
Weight:	35.0 g	**Edge:**	Reeded
Diameter:	34.0 mm	**Die Axis:**	↑↑
Thickness:	N/A	**Finish:**	Proof
Case of Issue:	Maroon leatherette clam style case, black flocked insert, encapsulated coin, COA		

THREE HUNDRED FIFTY DOLLARS, POLAR BEAR, ICONIC CANADIAN ANIMALS, 2013.

This is the first coin in a new series of Iconic Canadian Animals.

Designers and Engravers:
Obv.:	Susanna Blunt, Susan Taylor
Rev.:	Glen Loates, RCM Staff

Composition:	99.999% Au		
Gold content:	35.0 g, 1.125 tr oz		
Weight:	35.0 g	**Edge:**	Reeded
Diameter:	34.0 mm	**Die Axis:**	↑↑
Thickness:	N/A	**Finish:**	Proof
Case of Issue:	Maroon leatherette clam style case, black flocked insert, encapsulated coin, COA		

THREE HUNDRED FIFTY DOLLAR (1.125 ounce), THE MAJESTIC MOOSE, 2014.

This coin captures one of Canada's most iconic symbols of wildlife, the moose.

Designers and Engravers:
Obv.:	Susanna Blunt, Susan Taylort
Rev.:	Claudio D'Angelo, RCM Staff

Composition:	99.999% Au		
Gold content:	35.0 g, 1.125 tr oz		
Weight:	35.0 g	**Edge:**	Reeded
Diameter:	34.0 mm	**Die Axis:**	↑↑
Thickness:	N/A	**Finish:**	Proof
Case of Issue:	Maroon leatherette clam style case, black flock insert, encapsulated coin, COA		

THREE HUNDRED FIFTY DOLLARS, IMPOSING ALPHA WOLF, 2015.

Designers and Engravers:
Obv.:	Susanna Blunt, Susan Taylor
Rev.:	Maurade Baynton

Composition:	99.999% Au		
Gold content:	35.0 g, 1.125 tr oz		
Weight:	35.0 g	**Edge:**	Reeded
Diameter:	34.0 mm	**Die Axis:**	↑↑
Thickness:	N/A	**Finish:**	Proof
Case of Issue:	Maroon leatherette clam style case, black flocked insert, encapsulated coin, COA		

DATE	DESCRIPTION	QUANTITY SOLD	ISSUE PRICE	FINISH	PR-69	PR-70
2012	Sir Isaac Brock, The Hero of Upper Canada	365	2,799.95	Proof	2,600.	—
2013	Polar Bear	600	2,799.95	Proof	2,600.	—
2014	Majestic Moose	515	2,799.95	Proof	2,800.	—
2015	Imposing Alpha Wolf	400	2,799.95	Proof	2,800.	—

THREE HUNDRED FIFTY DOLLARS, THE BOLD BLACK BEAR, 2016.

Designers and Engravers:
Obv.:   Susanna Blunt, Susan Taylor
Rev.:   Pierre Leduc
Composition: 99.999% Au
Gold content: 35.0 g, 1.125 tr oz
Weight: 35.0 g   **Edge:**   Reeded
Diameter: 34.0 mm   **Die Axis:**   ↑↑
Thickness: N/A   **Finish:**   Proof
Case of Issue: Maroon leatherette clam style case, black flocked insert, encapsulated coin, COA

DATE	DESCRIPTION	QUANITTY SOLD	ISSUE PRICE	FINISH	PR-69	PR-70
2016	The Bold Black Bear	348	2,799.95	Proof	2,800.	—

THREE HUNDRED FIFTY DOLLAR, THE MAJESTIC ELK, 2017.

The wild grace of the nobel elk, or wapiti (*Cervus canadenisis*), makes it a fitting symbol of western Canada's beautifully untamed landscapes, where it is arguably one of the most photographed species in the region's national parks!

Designers and Engravers:
Obv.:   Susanna Blunt
Rev.:   Maurade Baynton
Composition: 99.999% Au
Gold content: 35.0 g, 1.125 tr oz
Weight: 35.0 g   **Edge:**   Reeded
Diameter: 34.0 mm   **Die Axis:**   ↑↑
Thickness: N/A   **Finish:**   Proof
Case of Issue: Maroon leatherette clam style case, black flock insert, encapsulated coin, COA

DATE	DESCRIPTION	MINTAGE	ISSUE PRICE	FINISH	PR-69	PR-70
2017	$350 (1.125 oz) Majestic Elk	400	2,799.95	Proof	2,800.	—

FIVE HUNDRED DOLLAR GOLD COINS

FIVE HUNDRED DOLLARS, 60TH WEDDING ANNIVERSARY OF QUEEN ELIZABETH AND PRINCE PHILIP, 1947-2007.

The coin celebrates the sixtieth wedding anniversary of HM Queen Elizabeth II and HRH Prince Philip, Duke of Edinburgh. The shields are from their respective Coats of Arms, and the mascots on the State vehicles in which they travel.

Designers: and Engravers:	
Obv.:	S. Blunt, S. Taylor
Rev.:	S. Hepburn, S. Taylor
Composition:	99.99% Au
Gold content:	155.76 g, 5.01 tr oz
Weight:	155.76 g
Diameter:	60.0 mm
Thickness:	N/A
Edge:	Reeded
Die Axis:	↑↑
Finish:	Proof
Case of Issue:	Black clam style case, black insert, encapsulated coin, COA

FIVE HUNDRED DOLLARS, 100TH ANNIVERSARY OF THE ROYAL CANADIAN MINT, 1908-2008.

This coin commemorates the 100th anniversary of the Ottawa Mint (Royal Canadian Mint) which opened January 2nd, 1908.

Designers: and Engravers:	
Obv.:	S. Blunt, Susan Taylor
Rev.:	RCM Staff
Composition:	99.99% Au
Gold content:	155.76 g, 5.01 tr oz
Weight:	155.76 g
Diameter:	60.0 mm
Thickness:	N/A
Edge:	Reeded
Die Axis:	↑↑
Finish:	Proof
Case of Issue:	Black clam style case, black insert, encapsulated coin, COA

FIVE HUNDRED DOLLARS, 150TH ANNIVERSARY OF THE START OF CONSTRUCTION OF THE PARLIAMENT BUILDINGS, 2009.

Construction of the Parliament Buildings began in December 1859, and was completed in the summer of 1866.

 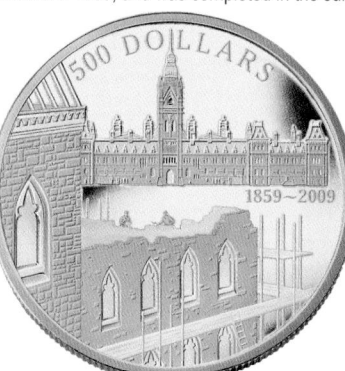

Designers and Engravers:	
Obv.:	S. Blunt, Susan Taylor
Rev.:	Cecily Mok
Composition:	99.99% Au
Gold content:	156.5 g, 5.03 tr oz
Weight:	156.05 g
Diameter:	60.0 mm
Thickness:	N/A
Edge:	Reeded
Die Axis:	↑↑
Finish:	Proof
Case of Issue:	Black clam style case, black insert, encapsulated coin, COA

DATE	DESCRIPTION	QUANTITY SOLD	ISSUE PRICE	FINISH	PR-69	PR-70
2007 (1947-)	60th Wedding Anniversary Queen / Prince Philip	198	5,999.95	Proof	9,000.	—
2008 (1908-)	100th Anniversary of the Royal Canadian Mint	248	8,159.95	Proof	9,000.	—
2009	150th Anniv. Start Construction Parliament Buildings	77	10,199.95	Proof	9,000.	—

FIVE HUNDRED DOLLARS, 75TH ANNIV. OF THE FIRST BANK NOTES ISSUED BY THE BANK OF CANADA, 1935-2010.

The reverse design on this coin is a reproduction of the central vignette that appears on the $500 bank note of 1935, a seated woman with a sickle, surrounded by the fruits of harvest, symbolising fertility.

Designers and Engravers:

Obv.:	S. Blunt, S. Taylor
Rev.:	S. Hepburn, J. Osio
Composition:	99.99% Au
Gold content:	156.5 g, 5.03 tr oz
Weight:	156.5 g
Diameter:	60.2 mm
Thickness:	N/A
Edge:	Reeded
Die Axis:	↑↑
Finish:	Proof
Case of Issue:	Maroon leatherette clam style case, black insert, encapsulated coin, COA

FIVE HUNDRED DOLLARS, 100TH ANNIVERSARY OF THE FIRST CANADIAN GOLD COINS, 1912-2012.

The first dollar denomination coins, the five and ten dollar gold coins, were struck at the Ottawa Mint in 1912.

Designers and Engravers:

Obv.:	S. Blunt, S. Taylor
Rev.:	RCM Staff, W. Woodruff
Composition:	99.99% Au
Gold content:	156.5 g, 5.03 tr oz
Weight:	156.5 g
Diameter:	60.2 mm
Thickness:	N/A
Edge:	Plain
Die Axis:	↑↑
Finish:	Proof
Case of Issue:	Maroon leatherette clam style case, black insert, encapsulated coin, COA

FIVE HUNDRED DOLLARS, 100TH ANNIVERSARY OF THE CALGARY STAMPEDE, 2012.

Designers and Engravers:

Obv.:	S. Blunt, S. Taylor
Rev.:	José Osio, L. Normandin
Composition:	99.99% Au
Gold content:	156.5 g, 5.03 tr oz
Weight:	156.5 g
Diameter:	60.2 mm
Thickness:	N/A
Edge:	Reeded
Die Axis:	↑↑
Finish:	Proof
Case of Issue:	Maroon leatherette clam style case, black insert, encapsulated coin, COA

DATE	DESCRIPTION	QUANTITY SOLD	ISSUE PRICE	FINISH	PR-69	PR-70
2010 (1935-)	75th Anniversary of the First Bank of Canada Notes	191	9,495.95	Proof	9,500.	—
2012 (1912-)	100th Anniversary of the First Canadian Gold Coins	115	12,274.95	Proof	12,275.	—
2012	100th Anniversary of the Calgary Stampede	96	11,999.95	Proof	12,000.	—

FIVE HUNDRED DOLLARS, *HMS SHANNON* AND *USS CHESAPEAKE*, 2013.

Designers and Engravers:

Obv.:	S. Blunt, S. Taylor
Rev.:	J. Horton, Cecily Mok
Composition:	99.99% Au
Gold content:	156.5 g, 5.03 tr oz
Weight:	156.5 g
Diameter:	60.2 mm
Thickness:	N/A
Edge:	Reeded
Die Axis:	↑↑
Finish:	Proof
Case of Issue:	Maroon leatherette clam style case, black insert, encapsulated coin, COA

FIVE HUNDRED DOLLARS, AN ABORIGINAL STORY, 2013.

Designers and Engravers:

Obv.:	S. Blunt, S. Taylor
Rev.:	R. Weizineau, RCM Staff
Composition:	99.99% Au
Gold content:	156.5 g, 5.03 tr oz
Weight:	156.5 g
Diameter:	60.2 mm
Thickness:	N/A
Edge:	Reeded
Die Axis:	↑↑
Finish:	Proof
Case of Issue:	Maroon leatherette clam style case, black insert, encapsulated coin, COA

FIVE HUNDRED DOLLARS, THE LEGEND OF THE SPIRIT BEAR, AN ABORIGINAL STORY, 2014.

The reverse design on this coin is an original work by Darlene Gait, a Coast Salish First Nation's artist, recounting the legend of Spirit Bear.

Designers and Engravers:

Obv.:	S. Blunt, S. Taylor
Rev.:	D. Gait, RCM Staff
Composition:	99.99% Au
Gold content:	156.5 g, 5.03 tr oz
Weight:	156.5 g
Diameter:	60.2 mm
Thickness:	N/A
Edge:	Plain
Die Axis:	↑↑
Finish:	Proof
Case of Issue:	Red lacquered wooden box, black flocked insert encapsulated coin, COA

DATE	DESCRIPTION	QUANTITY SOLD	ISSUE PRICE	FINISH	PR-69	PR-70
2013	HMS Shannon and USS Chesapeake	74	11,999.95	Proof	12,000.	—
2013	An Aboriginal Story	52	11,999.95	Proof	12,000.	—
2014	The Legend of Spirit Bear	100	12,000.00	Proof	12,000.	—

MYTHICAL REALMS OF THE HAIDA SET

FIVE HUNDRED DOLLARS, MYTHICAL REALMS OF THE HAIDA, 2016.

Common Obverse

Designers:		Engravers:	
Obv.:	Susanna Blunt	Obv.:	Susan Taylor
Rev.:	April White	Rev.:	RCM Staff
Composition:	99.999% Au		
Gold content:	156.05 g, 5.703 tr oz		
Weight:	156.05 g	Edge:	Reeded
Diameter:	60.15 mm	Die Axis:	↑↑
Thickness:	N/A	Finish:	Proof
Case of Issue:	Maplewood case with black beauty box, encapsulated coin, COA		

The Orca	The Eagle	The Bear

DATE	DESCRIPTION	QUANTITY SOLD	ISSUE PRICE	FINISH	PR-69	PR-70
2016	Mythical Realms of The Haida: The Orca	35	12,000	Proof	12,000.	—
2016	Mythical Realms of The Haida: The Eagle	50	12,000	Proof	12,000.	—
2016	Mythical Realms of The Haida: The Bear	50	12,000	Proof	12,000.	—

Note: Coins illustrated smaller than actual size.

FIVE HUNDRED DOLLARS, PEREGRINE FALCON, 2017.

Designers and Engravers:	
Obv.:	S. Blunt, S. Taylor
Rev.:	Emily S. Damstra
Composition:	99.99% Au
Gold content:	156.5 g, 5.03 tr oz
Weight:	156.05 g
Diameter:	60.15 mm
Thickness:	N/A
Edge:	Plain
Die Axis:	↑↑
Finish:	Proof
Case of Issue:	Red lacquered with custom beauty box, COA

DATE	DESCRIPTION	MINTAGE	ISSUE PRICE	FINISH	PR-69	PR-70
2017	Peregrine Falcon	99	12,629.95	Proof	12,500	—

FIVE HUNDRED DOLLARS, RED TAILED HAWK, 2017.

Designers and Engravers:

Obv.:	S. Blunt, S. Taylor
Rev.:	Emily Damstra
Composition:	99.99% Au
Gold content:	156.5 g, 5.03 tr oz
Weight:	156.05 g
Diameter:	60.15 mm
Thickness:	N/A
Edge:	Plain
Die Axis:	↑↑
Finish:	Proof
Case of Issue:	Red lacquered case with black beauty box, COA

DATE	DESCRIPTION	MINTAGE	ISSUE PRICE	FINISH	PR-69	PR-70
2017	Red Tailed Hawk	99	12,999.95	Proof	13,000.	—

FIVE HUNDRED DOLLARS, GREAT HORNED OWL, 2018.

Designers and Engravers:

Obv.:	S. Blunt, S. Taylor
Rev.:	Emily Damstra
Composition:	99.99% Au
Gold content:	156.5 g, 5.03 tr oz
Weight:	156.05 g
Diameter:	60.15 mm
Thickness:	N/A
Edge:	Plain
Die Axis:	↑↑
Finish:	Proof
Case of Issue:	Red lacquered case with black beauty box, COA

DATE	DESCRIPTION	MINTAGE	ISSUE PRICE	FINISH	PR-69	PR-70
2018	Great Horned Owl	99	12,999.95	Proof	13,000.	—

ONE THOUSAND DOLLARS

ONE THOUSAND DOLLARS, 100TH ANNIVERSARY OF THE DECLARATION OF THE FIRST WORLD WAR, 2014.

The reverse design on this coin is an original work by Yves Bérubé, to commemorate a poignant moment in history as a soldier leans against the guardrail of the *S.S. Megantic*.

Designers:		Engravers:	
Obv.:	Susanna Blunt	Obv.:	Susan Tauylor
Rev.:	Y. Bérubé	Rev.:	S. Strath

Composition: 99.99% Au
Gold content: 311.5, 10.015 tr oz
Weight: 311.5 g
Diameter: 76.1 mm
Thickness: N/A
Case of Issue: Maple wooden case, black flocked insert, encapsulated coin, COA

Edge: Reeded
Die Axis: ↑↑
Finish: Proof

DATE	DESCRIPTION	QUANTITY SOLD	ISSUE PRICE	FINISH	PR-69	PR-70
2014	100th Anniv. of the Declaration of the First World War	16	21,000	Proof	21,000.	—

ONE THOUSAND TWO HUNDRED FIFTY DOLLARS

CALL OF THE WILD SERIES, 2014-2017

| 2014 Howling Wolf | 2015 Growling Cougar | 2016 Roaring Grizzly | 2017 Elk |

Designers:

Obv.:	Susanna Blunt
Rev.:	Pierre Leduc

Composition: 99.99% Au
Gold content: 500 g, 16.08 tr oz
Weight: 500 g
Diameter: 85.36 mm
Case of Issue: Wooden case, black flocked insert, encapsulated coin, COA

Engravers:

Obv.:	Susan Taylorr
Rev.:	RCM Staff

Thickness: N/A
Edge: Reeded
Die Axis: ↑↑
Finish: Proof

Note: The same images were utilized for the 2014-2017 $200 (1 ounce) coins (see page 458).
Coins illustrated small than actual size.

DATE	DESCRIPTION	QUANTITY SOLD	ISSUE PRICE	FINISH	PR-69	PR-70
2014	Howling Wolf	25	32,000	Proof	32,000.	—
2015	Growling Cougar	25	32,000	Proof	32,000.	—
2016	Roaring Grizzly Bear	20	32,000	Proof	32,000.	—
2017	Elk	25	32,000	Proof	32,000.	—

TWO THOUSAND FIVE HUNDRED DOLLAR GOLD COINS

VANCOUVER 2010 OLYMPIC WINTER GAMES SERIES, 2007-2010

Common Obverse
(except for date)

2007 Early Canada
Designer: Stan Witten
Engraver: Stan Witten

2008 Towards Confederation
Designer: Susan Taylor
Engraver: Susan Taylor

2009 The Canada of Today
Designer: Design Team of the Vancouver
Organising Committee for the
2010 Olympic/Paralympic Games
Engraver: Konrad Wachelko

2009 Surviving the Flood
Designer: Design Team of the Vancouver
Organising Committee for the
2010 Olympic/Paralympic Games
Engraver: Christie Paquet

2010 The Eagle
Designer: Xwa lac tun (Ricky Harry)
Engraver: Stan Witten

Designers:		**Engravers:**	
Obv.:	Susanna Blunt	Obv.:	Susan Taylor
Rev.:	See reverse illustrations	Rev.:	See reverse illustrations
Composition:	99.99% Au	**Thickness:**	N/A
Gold content:	1,000.0 g, 32.15 tr oz	**Edge:**	Plain
Weight:	1,000.0 g (1 kilo)	**Die Axis:**	↑↑
Diameter:	101.6 mm	**Finish:**	Proof
Case of Issue:	Black display case, encapsulated coins, COA, 2010 Olympic Winter Games theme sleeve.		

DATE	DESCRIPTION	ISSUE DATE	QUANTITY SOLD	ISSUE PRICE	FINISH	PR-69	PR-70
2007	Early Canada	Feb. 23, 2007	20	36,000	Proof	58,000.	—.
2008	Towards Confederation	Feb. 20, 2008	20	49,000	Proof	58,000.	—.
2009	The Canada of Today	Apr. 15, 2009	50	54,000	Proof	58,000.	—.
2009	Surviving the Flood	Nov. 21, 2009	40	49,000	Proof	58,000.	—.
2010	The Eagle	Nov. 19, 2009	20	49,000	Proof	58,000.	—.

Note: Coins illustrated smaller than actual size.

TWO THOUSAND FIVE HUNDRED DOLLARS, 125TH ANNIVERSARY OF BANFF NATIONAL PARK, 2010.

Designers and Engravers:

Obv.:	S. Blunt, Susan Taylor
Rev.:	T. Bianco, S. Taylor
Composition:	99.99% Au
Gold content:	1000.0 g, 32.15 tr oz
Weight:	1,000.0 g (1 kilo)
Diameter:	101.6 mm
Thickness:	N/A
Edge:	Plain
Die Axis:	↑↑
Finish:	Proof
Case of Issue:	Black clam style case, black insert, encapsulated coin, COA

TWO THOUSAND FIVE HUNDRED DOLLARS, 375TH ANNIVERSARY OF LACROSSE, 2011.

Designers and Engravers:

Obv.:	S. Blunt, Susan Taylor
Rev.:	S. Hepburn, C. Paquet
Composition:	99.99% Au
Gold content:	1000.0 g, 32.15 tr oz
Weight:	1,000.0 g (1 kilo)
Diameter:	101.6 mm
Thickness:	N/A
Edge:	Plain
Die Axis:	↑↑
Finish:	Proof
Case of Issue:	Black clam style case, black insert, encapsulated coin, COA

TWO THOUSAND FIVE HUNDRED DOLLARS, YEAR OF THE (WATER) DRAGON, 2012.

An identical design is utilized on the $250 silver coin for 2012, see page 407 and on the $15 silver coin from the Lunar Lotus Series, see page 235.

Designers and Engravers:

Obv.:	S. Blunt, Susan Taylor
Rev.:	Three Degrees Creative Group Inc., C. Mok
Composition:	99.99% Au
Gold content:	1000.0 g, 32.15 tr oz
Weight:	1,000.0 g (1 kilo)
Diameter:	101.6 mm
Thickness:	N/A
Edge:	Plain
Die Axis:	↑↑
Finish:	Proof
Case of Issue:	Black clam style case, black insert, encapsulated coin, COA

DATE	DESCRIPTION	QUANTITY SOLD	ISSUE PRICE	FINISH	PR-69	PR-70
2010	125th Anniversary Banff National Park	20	57,000	Proof	58,000.	—
2011	375th Anniversary of Lacrosse	29	69,000	Proof	69,000.	—
2012	Year of the (Water) Dragon	37	69,000	Proof	69,000.	—

TWO THOUSAND FIVE HUNDRED DOLLARS, YEAR OF THE (CLASSIC) DRAGON, 2012.

Designers and Engravers:

Obv.:	S. Blunt, S. Taylor
Rev.:	A. Cheung, S. Witten

Composition: 99.99% Au
Gold content: 1000.0 g, 32.15 tr oz
Weight: 1,000.0 g (1 kilo)
Diameter: 101.6 mm
Thickness: N/A
Edge: Plain
Die Axis: ↑↑
Finish: Proof
Case of Issue: Black clam style case, black insert, encapsulated coin, COA

TWO THOUSAND FIVE HUNDRED DOLLARS, THE CHALLENGE, ROBERT BATEMAN MOOSE COIN, 2012.

The reverse design on this coin features the upraised head, neck and multi-pronged antlers of a moose taken from Robert Bateman's painting The Moose Family. The coin was issued to commemorate the 50th anniversary of the Canadian Wildlife Federation. For other coins in the Robert Bateman Moose series, see pages 274, 407 and 456.

Designers and Engravers:

Obv.:	S. Blunt, S. Taylor
Rev.:	R. Bateman, S. Witten

Composition: 99.99% Au
Gold content: 1000.0 g, 32.15 tr oz
Weight: 1,000.0 g (1 kilo)
Diameter: 101.6 mm
Thickness: N/A
Edge: Plain
Die Axis: ↑↑
Finish: Proof
Case of Issue: Maple wood box lacquered in walnut coloured finish, black flocked insert, encapsulated coin, COA

TWO THOUSAND FIVE HUNDRED DOLLARS, THE BATTLE OF QUEENSTON HEIGHTS, 2012.

Designers and Engravers:

Obv.:	S. Blunt, S. Taylor
Rev.:	See illustration

Composition: 99.99% Au
Gold content: 1000.0 g, 32.15 tr oz
Weight : 1000.0 g (1 kilo)
Diameter: 102.1 mm
Thickness: N/A
Edge: Reeded
Die Axis: ↑↑
Finish: Proof
Case of Issue: Maroon clam style case, black flocked insert, encapsulated coin, COA

DATE	DESCRIPTION	QUANTITY SOLD	ISSUE PRICE	FINISH	PR-69	PR-70
2012	Year of the (Classic) Dragon	37	69,000	Proof	69,000.	—.
2012 (1962-)	The Challenge, Robert Bateman	12	69,000	Proof	69,000.	—.
2012	Battle of Queenston Heights	19	69,000	Proof	69,000.	—.

TWO THOUSAND FIVE HUNDRED DOLLARS, KING GEORGE III PEACE MEDAL, THE WAR OF 1812, 2012.

Designers and Engravers:

Obv.:	S. Blunt, S. Taylor
Rev.:	John David Kelly, Marcus Hallam

Composition: 99.99% Au
Gold content: 1000.0 g, 32.15 tr oz
Weight : 1000.0 g (1 kilo)
Diameter: 101.6 mm
Thickness: N/A
Edge: Reeded
Die Axis: ↑↑
Finish: Proof
Case of Issue: Maroon clam style case, black flocked insert, encapsulated coin, COA

Reverse Des.: RCM engravers' representation of the King George III Peace Medal
Reverse Engr.: Konrad Wachelko, Matt Bowen Samantha Strath, Steven Stewart

TWO THOUSAND FIVE HUNDRED DOLLARS, YEAR OF THE SNAKE, 2013.

Designers and Engravers:

Obv.:	S. Blunt, S. Taylor
Rev.:	Three Degrees Creative Group, RCM Staff

Composition: 99.99% Au
Gold content: 1000.0 g, 32.15 tr oz
Weight: 1000.0 g (1 kilo)
Diameter: 102.1 mm
Thickness: N/A
Edge: Reeded
Die Axis: ↑↑
Finish: Proof
Case of Issue: Gold satin-like covered case, black flocked insert encapsulated coin, COA

TWO THOUSAND FIVE HUNDRED DOLLARS, 250TH ANNIVERSARY OF THE END OF THE SEVEN YEARS WAR, 2013.

Designers and Engravers:

Obv.:	S. Blunt, S. Taylor
Rev.:	L. Normandin, RCM Staff

Composition: 99.99% Au
Gold content: 1000.0 g, 32.15 tr oz
Weight: 1000.0 g (1 kilo)
Diameter: 102.1 mm
Thickness: N/A
Die Axis: ↑↑
Edge: Reeded
Finish: Proof
Case of Issue: Maple wood case, black flocked insert, encapsulated coin, COA

DATE	DESCRIPTION	QUANTITY SOLD	ISSUE PRICE	FINISH	PR-69	PR-70
2012	King George III Peace Medal	20	69,000	Proof	69,000.	—
2013	Year of the Snake	37	69,000	Proof	69,000.	—
2013	250th Anniv. of the End of the Seven Years War	12	69,000	Proof	69,000.	—

TWO THOUSAND FIVE HUNDRED DOLLARS, CANADA'S ARCTIC LANDSCAPE, 2013.

Designers and Engravers:

Obv.:	S. Blunt, S. Taylor
Rev.:	W. David Ward, S. Witten
Composition:	99.99% Au
Gold content:	1000.0 g, 32.15 tr oz
Weight:	1000.0 g (1 kilo)
Diameter:	102.1 mm
Thickness:	N/A
Die Axis:	↑↑
Edge:	Reeded
Finish:	Proof
Case of Issue:	Maple wood case, black flocked insert, encapsulated coin, COA

TWO THOUSAND FIVE HUNDRED DOLLARS, 1813 BATTLE OF CRYSLER'S FARM AND BATTLE OF CHATEAUGUAY, 2013.

Designers and Engravers:

Obv.:	S. Blunt, S. Taylor
Rev.:	A. Sherriff-Scott, H. Julie, E. Boyer
Composition:	99.99% Au
Gold content:	1000.0 g, 32.15 tr oz
Weight:	1000.0 g (1 kilo)
Diameter:	102.1 mm
Thickness:	N/A
Die Axis:	↑↑
Edge:	Reeded
Finish:	Proof
Case of Issue:	Maple wood case, black flocked insert, encapsulated coin, COA

TWO THOUSAND FIVE HUNDRED DOLLARS, THE CARIBOU, 2013.

Designers and Engravers:

Obv.:	S. Blunt, S. Taylor
Rev.:	T. Tennant, RCM Staff
Composition:	99.99% Au
Gold content:	1000.0 g, 32.15 tr oz
Weight:	1,000.0 g (1 kilo)
Diameter:	101.6 mm
Thickness:	N/A
Edge:	Reeded
Die Axis:	↑↑
Finish:	Proof
Case of Issue:	Maple wood case, black insert, encapsulated coin, COA

DATE	DESCRIPTION	QUANTITY SOLD	ISSUE PRICE	FINISH	PR-69	PR-70
2013	Canada's Arctic Landscape	13	69,000	Proof	69,000.	—
2013	1813 Battle of Crysler's Farm and Battle of Chateauguay	10	69,000	Proof	69,000.	—
2013	The Caribou	5	69,000	Proof	69,000.	—

TWO THOUSAND FIVE HUNDRED DOLLARS, YEAR OF THE HORSE, 2014

Designers and Engravers:
Obv.:	S. Blunt, S. Taylor
Rev.:	Three Degrees Creative Group, S. Witten
Composition:	99.99% Au
Gold content:	1000.0 g, 32.15 tr oz
Weight:	1,000.0 g (1 kilo)
Diameter:	101.6 mm
Thickness:	N/A
Edge:	Reeded
Die Axis:	↑↑
Finish:	Proof
Case of Issue:	Gold satin-like covered case, black flocked insert encapsulated coin, COA

TWO THOUSAND FIVE HUNDRED DOLLARS, IN THE EYES OF THE SNOWY OWL, 2014.

Designers and Engravers:
Obv.:	S. Blunt, S. Taylor
Rev.:	Anold Nogy, S. Taylor
Composition:	99.99% Au
Gold content:	1000.0 g, 32.15 tr oz
Weight:	1,000.0 g (1 kilo)
Diameter:	101.6 mm
Thickness:	N/A
Edge:	Reeded
Die Axis:	↑↑
Finish:	Proof
Case of Issue:	Maple wood case, black insert, encapsulated coin COA

TWO THOUSAND FIVE HUNDRED DOLLARS, BATTLE OF LUNDY'S LANE, 2014.

Designers and Engravers:
Obv.:	S. Blunt, S. Taylor
Rev.:	Bonnie Ross, RCM Staff
Composition:	99.99% Au
Gold content:	1000.0 g, 32.15 tr oz
Weight:	1,000.0 g (1 kilo)
Diameter:	101.6 mm
Thickness:	N/A
Edge:	Reeded
Die Axis:	↑↑
Finish:	Proof
Case of Issue:	Maple wood case, black insert, encapsulated coin, COA

DATE	DESCRIPTION	QUANTITY SOLD	ISSUE PRICE	FINISH	PR-69	PR-70
2014	Year of the Horse	5	69,000	Proof	69,000.	—
2014	In the Eyes of the Snowy Owl	10	69,000	Proof	69,000.	—
2014	Battle of Lundy's Lane	10	69,000	Proof	69,000.	—

WO THOUSAND FIVE HUNDRED DOLLARS, YEAR OF THE SHEEP, 2015.

Designers and Engravers:

Obv.:	S. Blunt, S. Taylor
Rev.:	Three Degrees Creative Group, RCM Staff
Composition:	99.99% Au
Gold content:	1000.0 g, 32.15 tr oz
Weight:	1,000 g (1 kilo)
Diameter:	101.6 mm
Thickness:	N/A
Edge:	Reeded
Die Axis:	↑↑
Finish:	Proof
Case of Issue:	Gold satin-like covered case, black insert, encapsulated coin, COA, custom red sleeve

WO THOUSAND FIVE HUNDRED DOLLARS, LOONEY TUNES™: ENSEMBLE CAST, 2015.

Designers and Engravers:

Obv.:	S. Blunt, S. Taylor
Rev.:	Warner Bros.
Composition:	99.99% Au
Gold content:	1006.1 g, 32.15 tr oz
Weight:	1,006.1 g (1 kilo)
Diameter:	101.6 mm
Thickness:	N/A
Edge:	Reeded
Die Axis:	↑↑
Finish:	Proof
Case of Issue:	Maple wood case, black insert, encapsulated coin, COA

WO THOUSAND FIVE HUNDRED DOLLARS, MAPLE LEAF FOREVER, 2015.

Designers and Engravers:

Obv.:	S. Blunt, S. Taylor
Rev.:	Celia Godkin
Composition:	99.99% Au
Gold content:	1000.0 g, 32.15 tr oz
Weight:	1,000.0 g (1 kilo)
Diameter:	101.6 mm
Thickness:	N/A
Edge:	Reeded
Die Axis:	↑↑
Finish:	Proof
Case of Issue:	Maple wood case, black insert, encapsulated coin, COA

DATE	DESCRIPTION	QUANTITY SOLD	ISSUE PRICE	FINISH	PR-69	PR-70
2015	Year of the Sheep	11	69.000	Proof	69,000.	—
2015	Looney Tunes™: Ensemble Cast	10	69,000	Proof	69,000.	—
2015	Maple Leaf Forever	10	69,000	Proof	69,000.	—

TWO THOUSAND FIVE HUNDRED DOLLARS, IN THE EYES OF THE COUGAR, 2015.

Designers and Engravers:
Obv.:	S. Blunt, S. Taylor
Rev.:	Glen Loates

Composition: 99.99% Au
Gold content: 1000.0 g, 32.15 tr oz
Weight: 1,000.0 g (1 kilo)
Diameter: 101.6 mm
Thickness: N/A
Edge: Reeded
Die Axis: ↑↑
Finish: Proof
Case of Issue: Maple wood case, black insert, encapsulated coin, COA

TWO THOUSAND FIVE HUNDRED DOLLARS, YEAR OF THE MONKEY, 2016.

Designers and Engravers:
Obv.:	S. Blunt, S. Taylor
Rev.:	Three Degrees Creative Group, RCM Staff

Composition: 99.99% Au
Gold content: 1000.0 g, 32.15 tr oz
Weight: 1,000 g (1 kilo)
Diameter: 120 mm
Thickness: N/A
Edge: Reeded
Die Axis: ↑↑
Finish: Proof with enamel
Case of Issue: Gold satin-like covered case, black insert, encapsulated coin, COA custom red sleeve

TWO THOUSAND FIVE HUNDRED DOLLARS, IN THE EYES OF THE SPIRIT BEAR, 2016.

Designers and Engravers:
Obv.:	S. Blunt, S. Taylor
Rev.:	Glen Loates

Composition: 99.99% Au
Gold content: 1000.0 g, 32.15 tr oz
Weight: 1,000.0 g (1 kilo)
Diameter: 101.6 mm
Thickness: N/A
Edge: Reeded
Die Axis: ↑↑
Finish: Proof
Case of Issue: Maple wood case, black insert, encapsulated coin, COA

DATE	DESCRIPTION	QUANTITY SOLD	ISSUE PRICE	FINISH	PR-69	PR-70
2015	In the Eyes of the Cougar	10	69,000	Proof	69,000.	—
2016	Year of the Monkey	10	69,000	Proof	69,000.	—
2016	In the Eyes of the Spirit Bear	10	69,000	Proof	69,000.	—

TWO THOUSAND FIVE HUNDRED DOLLARS, MAPLE LEAF FOREVER, 2016.

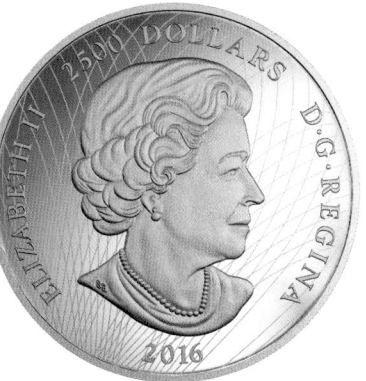 

Designers and Engravers:
Obv.: S. Blunt, S. Taylor
Rev.: Julius Csotonyi
Composition: 99.99% Au
Gold content: 1000.0 g, 32.15 tr oz
Weight: 1,000.0 g (1 kilo)
Diameter: 101.6 mm
Thickness: N/A
Edge: Reeded
Die Axis: ↑↑
Finish: Proof
Case of Issue: Maple wood case, black insert, encapsulated coin, COA

TWO THOUSAND FIVE HUNDRED DOLLARS, THE ARMS OF CANADA, 2016.

Designers and Engravers:
Obv.: Susanna Blunt
Rev.: RCM Staff
Composition: 99.99% Au
Gold content: 1000.0 g, 32.15 tr oz
Weight: 1,000.0 g (1 kilo)
Diameter: 101.6 mm
Thickness: N/A
Edge: Reeded
Die Axis: ↑↑
Finish: Proof
Case of Issue: Maple wood case, black insert, encapsulated coin, COA

TWO THOUSAND FIVE HUNDRED DOLLARS, YEAR OF THE ROOSTER, 2017.

Designers and Engravers:
Obv.: S. Blunt, S. Taylor
Rev.: Three Degrees Creative
Composition: 99.99% Au
Gold content: 1000.0 g, 32.15 tr oz
Weight: 1,000.0 g (1 kilo)
Diameter: 120 mm
Thickness: N/A
Edge: Reeded
Die Axis: ↑↑
Finish: Proof
Case of Issue: Gold satin-like covered case with custom red sleeve, COA

DATE	DESCRIPTION	QUANTITY SOLD	ISSUE PRICE	FINISH	PR-69	PR-70
2016	Maple Leaf Forever	10	69,000	Proof	69,000.	—
2016	The Arms of Canada	9	69,000	Proof	69,000	—
2017	Year of the Rooster	10	69,000	Proof	69,000	—

TWO THOUSAND FIVE HUNDRED DOLLARS, IN THE EYES OF THE TIMBER WOLF, 2017.

Designers and Engravers:
Obv.:	S. Blunt, S. Taylor
Rev.:	Pierre Leduc
Composition:	99.99% Au
Gold content:	1,000.0 g, 32.15 tr oz
Weight:	1,000.0 g (1 kilo)
Diameter:	101.6 mm
Thickness:	N/A
Edge:	Reeded
Die Axis:	↑↑
Finish:	Proof
Case of Issue:	Maple wood case, black insert, encapsulated coin, COA

TWO THOUSAND FIVE HUNDRED DOLLARS, A TRIBUTE TO THE FIRST CANADIAN GOLD COIN, 2017.

Designers and Engravers:
Obv.:	S. Blunt, S. Taylor
Rev.:	W. H. J. Blackmore
Composition:	99.99% Au
Gold content:	1000.0 g, 32.15 tr oz
Weight:	1,000.0 g (1 kilo)
Diameter:	101.6 mm
Thickness:	N/A
Edge:	Reeded
Die Axis:	↑↑
Finish:	Proof
Case of Issue:	Wood case, and black beauty box, COA

TWO THOUSAND FIVE HUNDRED DOLLARS, LUNAR LOTUS: YEAR OF THE DOG, 2018.

Designers and Engravers:
Obv.:	S. Blunt, S. Taylor
Rev.:	Three Degrees Creative
Composition:	99.99% Au
Gold content:	1000.0 g, 32.15 tr oz
Weight:	1,000.0 g (1 kilo)
Diameter:	101.6 mm
Thickness:	N/A
Edge:	Reeded
Die Axis:	↑↑
Finish:	Proof
Case of Issue:	Gold satin-like covered case with custom red sleeve, COA

DATE	DESCRIPTION	MINTAGE	ISSUE PRICE	FINISH	PR-69	PR-70
2017	In the Eyes of the Timber Wolf	10	69,000	Proof	69,000	—
2017	A Tribute to the First Canadian Gold Coin	20	75,000	Proof	75,000.	—
2018	Year of the Dog	10	75,000	Proof	75,000.	—

ONE HUNDRED THOUSAND DOLLAR GOLD COIN

ONE HUNDRED THOUSAND DOLLARS, THE SPIRIT OF HAIDA GWAII, 2011

The Spirit of Haida Gwaii is the world's first 10,000 kilogram gold coin of 99.999% purity. The design features Bill Reid's monumental sculpture which as commissioned for the courtyard of the new Canadian Embassy which was being built in Washington. The Spirit of Haida Gwaii was completed and stalled in 1992, subtitled The Black Canoe. The bronze casting was given a glossy black patina to give the appearance of argillite. The sculpture is .05 m long, 3.9 m high, 3.35 m wide and weighs 4.9 kg. A duplicate sculpture was commissioned by the Vancouver International Airport, with a green atina, in recognition of the dark green jade found in British Columbia. The Jade Canoe was completed in 1994.

Designers:
Obv.:	Susanna Blunt
Rev.:	Bill Reid

Composition: 99.999% Au
Weight: 10,000.0 g (10 kilos)
Diameter: 180.0 mm
Thickness: N/A
Case of Issue: Walnut wood case, certificate in book format

Engravers:
Obv.:	Susan Taylor
Rev.:	Cosme Saffioti

Gold content: 10,000.0 g, 321.50 tr oz
Edge: Reeded
Die Axis: ↑↑
Finish: Proof

DATE	DESCRIPTION	MINTAGE	ISSUE PRICE	FINISH	PR-69	PR-70
2011	The Spirit of Haida Gwaii, 321.50 tr oz	2	BV	Proof	Market Value	

Note:
1. An identical design is utilized on the $500 silver coin for 2012, see page 417.
2. Coin illustrated smaller than actual size.
3. Price is subject to the price of gold plus a premium on the day of purchase or sale.

GOLD AND SILVER SETS

TEN DOLLAR GOLD AND EIGHT DOLLAR SILVER POLAR BEAR SET, 2013.

 **Ten Dollars Gold**     **Eight Dollars Silver**

Designers:
Obv.:	Susanna Blunt
Rev.:	Germaine Arnaktauyok

$10 Gold
Composition:	99.99% Au
Gold content:	7.97 g, 0.25 tr oz
Weight:	7.97 g
Diameter:	20.0 mm
Thickness:	1.7 mm
Edge:	Reeded
Die Axis:	↑↑
Finish:	Proof
Case of Issue:	Maple wood box, black flock insert, encapsulated coins, COA

Engravers:
Rev.:	Susan Taylor
Rev.:	RCM Staff

$8 Silver
Composition:	99.99% Ag
Silver content:	46.65 g, 1.5 tr oz
Weight:	46.65 g
Diameter:	38.0 mm
Thickness:	4.5 mm
Edge:	Reeded
Die Axis:	↑↑
Finish:	Proof

DATE	DESCRIPTION	QUANTITY SOLD	ISSUE PRICE	FINISH	PR-69	PR-70
2013	$10 gold and $8 silver, Polar Bear Set	4,832	774.95	Proof	650.	—

FIVE DOLLAR GOLD AND TWENTY DOLLAR SILVER WOOLLY MAMMOTH, 2014.

 **Five Dollars Gold**     **Twenty Dollars Silver**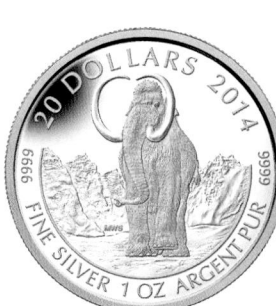

Designers:
Obv.:	Susanna Blunt
Rev.:	Michael Skrepnick

$5 Gold
Composition:	99.99% Au
Gold content:	3.14 g, 0.10 tr oz
Weight:	3.14 g
Diameter:	16.0 mm
Thickness:	N/A
Edge:	Reeded
Die Axis:	↑↑
Finish:	Proof
Case of Issue:	Maroon leatherette clam style case, black flocked insert, encapsulated coin(s), COA

Engravers:
Obv.:	Susan Taylor
Rev.:	RCM Staff

$20 Silver
Composition:	99.99% Ag
Silver content:	31.39 g, 1.01 tr oz
Weight:	31.39 g
Diameter:	38.0 mm
Thickness:	N/A
Edge:	Reeded
Die Axis:	↑↑
Finish:	Proof

DATE	DESCRIPTION	QUANTITY SOLD	ISSUE PRICE	FINISH	PR-69	PR-70
2014	$5 Gold and $20 Silver, Woolly Mammoth Set	3,000	369.95	Proof	280.	—

PALLADIUM COINS

FIFTY DOLLAR PALLADIUM COINS

IFTY DOLLARS, BIG AND LITTLE BEAR CONSTELLATIONS, 2006.

Each coin has been crafted with a special laser effect to illustrate the position of Big Bear and Little Bear constellations above a conceptual anadian forest, as they would appear when viewed from the nation's capital during each of the four seasons.

Common Obverse

Designers and Engravers:

Obv.:	Susanna Blunt, Susan Taylor
Rev.:	Colin Mayne, José Osio
Composition:	99.95% Pd, Laser effect
Palladium content:	31.144 g, 1.0 tr oz
Weight:	31.16 g
Diameter:	34.0 mm
Thickness:	3.5 mm
Edge:	Reeded
Die Axis:	↑↑
Finish:	Specimen
Case of Issue:	Maroon clam style case; black flocked insert, encapsulated coin, COA

Spring

Summer

Autumn

Winter

DATE	DESCRIPTION	QUANTITY SOLD	ISSUE PRICE	FINISH	SP-68	SP-69
2006	Spring	300	849.95	Specimen	1,700.	—
2006	Summer	300	849.95	Specimen	1,700.	—
2006	Autumn	300	849.95	Specimen	1,700.	—
2006	Winter	300	849.95	Specimen	1,700.	—

PLATINUM COINS

FIVE DOLLAR PLATINUM COINS

FIVE DOLLARS, COMMEMORATIVE PLATINUM COINS, 2014.

Actual Size

Common Obverse

Portrait Nanaboozhoo
Des.: C. Assiniboine

Bald Eagle
Des.: D. Wicks

Overlaid Majestic
Maple Leaves
Des.: P. Leduc

Cougar
Des.: G. Loates

Designers:		**Engravers:**	
Obv.:	Susanna Blunt	Obv.:	Susan Taylor
Rev.:	See reverse illustrations	Rev.:	RCM Staff
Composition:	99.95% Pt		
Gold content:	3.13 g, 0.10 tr oz		
Weight:	3.13 g	**Edge:**	Reeded
Diameter:	16.0 mm	**Die Axis:**	↑↑
Thickness:	N/A	**Finish:**	Proof
Case of Issue:	Maroon leatherette clam style case, black flocked insert, encapsulated coin, COA		

DATE	DESCRIPTION	QUANTITY SOLD	ISSUE PRICE	FINISH	PR-69	PR-70
2014	Portrait of Nanaboozhoo	2,400	299.95	Proof	260.	—
2014	Bald Eagle	1,638	299.95	Proof	260.	—
2014	Overlaid Majestic Maple Leaves	1090	299.95	Proof	260.	—
2014	Cougar	687	299.95	Proof	275.	—

Note: 1. The $5 platinum Overlaid Majestic Maple Leaves coin was offered as part of a five coin subscription along with a $20 Silver Majestic Maple Leaves, a $20 Majestic Maple Leaves with colour, and a $20 Majestic Maple Leaves with Jade (see page 295), as well as a $5 gold Overlaid Majestic Maple Leaves coin (see page 426).

2. The Bald Eagle was also offered as part of a subscription series which included three twenty dollar coins (see page 279), and a five dollar gold coin (see page 426).

THREE HUNDRED DOLLAR PLATINUM COINS

THREE HUNDRED DOLLARS, COMMEMORATIVE ISSUES, 2007-2016.

2007-2008
Obverse With RCM Logo
Des.: Susanna Blunt
Engr.: Susan Taylor

2007
Woolly Mammoth
Des.: RCM Staff
Engr.: José Osio

2008
Scimitar Cat
Des.: RCM Staff
Engr.: Christie Paquet
Obv. Without RCM Logo

2009-2015
Obv. Without RCM Logo
Des.: Susanna Blunt
Engr.: Susan Taylor

2009
Steppe Bison
Des. RCM Staff
Engr.: José Osio

2010
Ground Sloth
Des.: Jerri Burnett
Engr.: Stan Witten

2011
Cougar
Des.: William Woodruff
Engr.: RCM Staff

2012-2014
Common Obverse

2012
The Bull Moose
Des.: Robert Bateman
Engr.: Cecily Mok

2013
The Bald Eagle
Des.: Claudio D'Angelo
Engr.: Konrad Wachelko

**2013 Rocky Mountain
Bighorn Sheep**
Des.: Emily Damstra
Engr.: Steven Stewart

2013
Obverse

2013
HMS Shannon and
USS Chesapeake
Des.: Luc Normandin
Engr.: Cecily Mok

THREE HUNDRED DOLLARS, COMMEMORATIVE ISSUES, 2007-2016 (cont.).

2014 **Challenge for Power** Des.: Claudio D'Angelo Engr.: RCM Staff	**2014 Emily Carr** *A Skidegate Beaver Pole* Des.: Emily Carr Engr.: RCM Staff	**2015** **Grizzly Bear** Des.: Emily Damstra Engr.: RCM Staff

2015 **Obverse** Des.: Susanna Blunt Engr.: Susan Taylor	**2015** **Rainbow Trout** Des.: C. Atwater Engr.: RCM Staff	**2015** **White-Tailed Deer** Des.: D. McCaffrey Engr.: RCM Staff	**2016** **Grizzly Bear: The Struggle** Des.: Lauren Crawshaw Engr.: RCM Staff

Designers:
  Obv.:   Susanna Blunt
  Rev.:   See reverse illustrations
Composition: 99.95% Pt
Platinum content: 31.15 g, 1.00 tr oz
Weight: 31.15 g
Diameter: 30.0 mm
Thickness: 2.5 mm
Case of Issue: Maroon leatherette clam style case, black flocked insert, encapsulated coin, COA

Engravers:
  Obv.:   Susan Taylor
  Rev.:   See reverse illustrations

Edge: Reeded
Die Axis: ↑↑
Finish: Proof

DATE	DESCRIPTION	QUANTITY SOLD	ISSUE PRICE	FINISH	PR-69	PR-70
2007	Woolly Mammoth	287	2,999.95	Proof	2,500.	—
2008	Scimitar Cat	200	3,419.95	Proof	2,500.	—
2009	Steppe Bison	197	2,999.95	Proof	3,000.	—
2010	Ground Sloth	189	2,999.95	Proof	3,000.	—
2011	Cougar	183	2,999.95	Proof	3,000.	—
2012	The Bull Moose	250	2,999.95	Proof	3,000.	—
2013	Rocky Mountain Bighorn Sheep	188	2,999.95	Proof	3,000.	—
2013	The Bald Eagle	199	2,999.95	Proof	3,000.	—
2013	HMS Shannon and USS Chesapeake	231	2,999.95	Proof	3,000.	—
2014	A Skidegate Beaver Pole, Emily Carr	250	N.I.I.	Proof	3,000.	—
2014	Bison: Challenge for Power	24	2,999.95	Proof	3,000.	—
2014	Emily Carr: *A Skidegate Beaver Pole*	250	N.I.I.	Proof	3,000.	—
2015	Grizzly Bear	138	2,999.95	Proof	3,000.	—
2015	The White-Tailed Deer	187	2,999.95	Proof	3,000.	—
2015	Rainbow Trout: North American Sportfish	200	2,999.95	Proof	3,000.	—
2016	Grizzly Bear: The Struggle	150	2,999.95	Proof	3,000.	—

SPECIAL RCM WRAPPED ROLLS OF COINS

Specialty Rolls are generated by the Royal Canadian Mint printing a specially designed wrapper for a standard roll of a denomination.

2017 25 Cents
125th Anniversary of the Stanley Cup

DATE	DENOMINATION	DESCRIPTION	QUANTITY SOLD	PRICE
2004P	One Cent	Standard, CPS, Roll of 50	N/A	10.
2004	One Cent	Standard, CPZ, Roll of 50	N/A	12.
2005	One Cent	Standard, CPZ, Roll of 50	N/A	12.
2005P	One Cent	Standard, CPS, Roll of 50	N/A	20.
2012	One Cent	Farewell to the Penny, Roll of 50	20,000	80.
2005P	Five Cents	Standard, Roll of 40	N/A	8.
2005P	Five Cents	V-E Day, Roll of 40	N/A	12.
2005P	Ten Cents	Standard, Roll of 50	N/A	10.
2004P	Twenty-Five Cents	Poppy, Roll of 40	N/A	25.
2005P	Twenty-Five Cents	Standard, Roll of 40	N/A	18.
2005P	Twenty-Five Cents	Alberta, Roll of 40	N/A	20.
2005P	Twenty-Five Cents	Saskatchewan, Roll of 40	N/A	20.
2005P	Twenty-Five Cents	Veteran, Roll of 40	N/A	20.
2006P	Twenty-Five Cents	Breast Cancer, Roll of 40	102	25.
2006P	Twenty-Five Cents	Standard, Roll of 40	N/A	18.
2006P	Twenty-Five Cents	Bravery, Roll of 40	205	20.
2007	Twenty-Five Cents	Curling, Roll of 40	10,000	18.
2007	Twenty-Five Cents	Ice Hockey, Roll of 40	10,000	18.
2007	Twenty-Five Cents	Biathlon, Roll of 40	10,000	18.
2007	Twenty-Five Cents	Alpine Skiing, Roll of 40	10,000	18.
2007	Twenty-Five Cents	Wheelchair Curling, Roll of 40	10,000	18.
2008	Twenty-Five Cents	Snowboarding, Roll of 40	10,000	18.
2008	Twenty-Five Cents	Freestyle Skiing, Roll of 40	10,000	18.
2008	Twenty-Five Cents	Figure Skating, Roll of 40	10,000	18.
2008	Twenty-Five Cents	Bobsleigh, Roll of 40	10,000	18.
2009	Twenty-Five Cents	Speedskating, Roll of 40	10,000	18.
2009	Twenty-Five Cents	Cross Country Skiing, Roll of 40	10,000	18.
2009	Twenty-Five Cents	Ice Sledge Hockey, Roll of 40	10,000	18.
2017	Twenty-Five Cents	125th Anniversary of the Stanley Cup	50,000	20.

SPECIAL RCM WRAPPED ROLLS OF COINS (cont.)

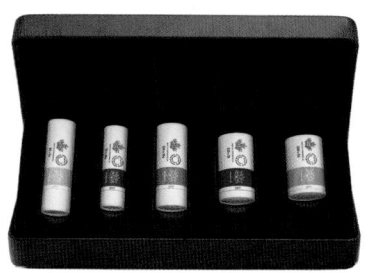

2017
Special Wrap Roll
My Canada,
My Inspiration

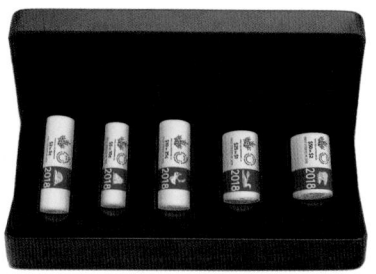

2018
Special Wrap Roll
First Strikes
in 2018

DATE	DENOMINATION	DESCRIPTION	QUANTITY SOLD	PRICE
2005P	Fifty Cents	Roll of 25	8,000	35.
2006P	Fifty Cents	Roll of 25	3,920	60.
2007	Fifty Cents	Roll of 25	4,462	40.
2008	Fifty Cents	Roll of 25	6,000	35.
2009	Fifty Cents	Roll of 25	6,000	45.
2010	Fifty Cents	Roll of 25	6,000	45.
2011	Fifty Cents	Roll of 25	6,880	45.
2012	Fifty Cents	Roll of 25	9,960	45.
2013	Fifty Cents	Roll of 25	15,000	30.
2014	Fifty Cents	Roll of 25	20,000	25.
2015	Fifty Cents	Roll of 25	25,000	25.
2016	Fifty Cents	Roll of 25	24,829	25.
2017	Fifty Cents	Coat of Arms of Canada	35,000	25.
2017	Fifty Cents	Canada 150 Official Logo	35,000	25.
2018	Fifty Cents	Roll of 25	30,000	30.
2004	One Dollar	Olympic Flame, Roll of 25	N/A	40.
2005	One Dollar	Loon, Roll of 25	N/A	40.
2005	One Dollar	Terry Fox, Roll of 25	N/A	50.
2008	One Dollar	Loon Dance, Roll of 25	10,000	40.
2009	One Dollar	Montreal Canadiens, Roll of 25	10,000	50.
2010	One Dollar	Inukshuk, Roll of 25	10,000	40.
2016	One Dollar	Lucky Loonie, Roll of 25	52,000	40.
2017	One Dollar	100th Anniversary of the Toronto Maple Leafs	50,000	55.
1996	Two Dollars	Polar Bear, Roll of 25	N/A	100.
2004	Two Dollars	Polar Bear, Roll of 25	N/A	70.
2005	Two Dollars	Polar Bear, Roll of 25	N/A	80.
2006	Two Dollars	Double Date, Roll of 25	356	100.
2006	Two Dollars	Churchill, Roll of 25	N/A	70.
2008	Two Dollars	Quebec City, Roll of 25	N/A	80.
2011	Two Dollars	Polar Bear, Roll of 25	N/A	80.
2017	Two Dollars	The Battle of Vimy Ridge	10,000	80.
2017	Special Wrap Roll Collection (5¢, 10¢, 25¢ x2, $1, $2 x2)	My Canada, My Inspiration	10,000	185.
2017	Special Wrap Roll Collection(5¢, 10¢, 25¢, $1, $2)	Classic Canadian	10,000	185.
2018	Special Wrap CollectionFirst Strikes in 2018	Classic Canadian	5,000	185.

FIRST AND LAST DAY OF ISSUE CARDS

DATE	DENOMINATION	DESCRIPTION	QUANTITY SOLD	PRICE
2005P	One Cent	Standard, CPS, First Day	1,919	10.
2006P / 2006	One Cent	Standard, CPS, Last Day / First Day	750	20.
2005P	Five Cents	Standard, First Day	1,951	10.
2006P / 2006	Five Cents	Standard, Last Day / First Day	739	10.
2006P	Five Cents	Victory, First Day	11,192	8.
2005P	Ten Cents	Standard, First Day	1,961	8.
2006P / 2006	Ten Cents	Standard, Last Day / First Day	742	10.
2004P	Twenty-Five Cents	Poppy, Coloured	N/A	12.
2005P	Twenty-Five Cents	Standard, First Day	5,000	8.
2005P	Twenty-Five Cents	Alberta, First Day	9,108	8.
2005P	Twenty-Five Cents	Saskatchewan, First Day	6,980	8.
2005P	Twenty-Five Cents	Veteran, First Day	8,361	8.
2006P / 2006	Twenty-Five Cents	Standard, Last Day / First Day	742	8.
2006P	Twenty-Five Cents	Breast Cancer, First Day	7,348	8.
2006	Twenty-Five Cents	Bravery, First Day	4,906	8.
2007	Twenty-Five Cents	Curling, First Day	10,000	5.
2007	Twenty-Five Cents	Ice Hockey, First Day	10,000	5.
2007	Twenty-Five Cents	Biathlon, First Day	10,000	5.
2007	Twenty-Five Cents	Alpine Skiing, First Day	10,000	5.
2007	Twenty-Five Cents	Wheelchair Curling, First Day	10,000	5.
2008	Twenty-Five Cents	Snowboarding, First Day	10,000	5.
2008	Twenty-Five Cents	Freestyle Skiing, First Day	10,000	5.
2008	Twenty-Five Cents	Figure Skating, First Day	10,000	5.
2008	Twenty-Five Cents	Bobsleigh, First Day	10,000	5.
2009	Twenty-Five Cents	Speed Skating, First Day	10,000	5.
2009	Twenty-Five Cents	Cross Country Skiing, First Day	10,000	5.
2009	Twenty-Five Cents	Ice Sledge Hockey, First Day	10,000	5.
2005P	Fifty Cents	Standard, First Day	2,445	12.
2006P / 2006	Fifty Cents	Standard, Last Day / First Day	1,065	15.
2004	One Dollar	Standard, First Day	34,488	5.
2005	One Dollar	Standard, First Day	2,048 1	5.
2005	One Dollar	Terry Fox, First Day	19,933	10.
2006	One Dollar	Standard, Last Day / First Day	935	15.
2006	One Dollar	Loon Settling, First Day	7,481	15.
2008	One Dollar	Loon Dance, First Day	10,000	15.
2010	One Dollar	Lucky Loonie, First Day	4,252	12.
2005	Two Dollars	Standard, First Day	2,501	12.
2006	Two Dollars	Standard, Last Day / First Day	1,971	12.
2006	Two Dollars	10th Anniversary, First Day	1,971	12.

BOOKMARKS

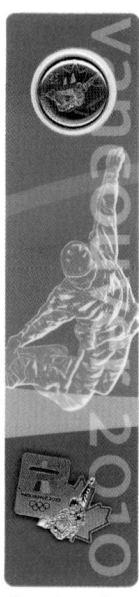

Snowboarding
Bookmark and
Lapel Pin

Ice Hockey
Bookmark and
Lapel Pin

DATE	DENOMINATION	DESCRIPTION	QUANTITY SOLD	PRICE
2004P	Twenty-Five Cents	Poppy, Coloured	29,951	30.
2005P	Twenty-Five Cents	Poppy, Coloured	N/A	25.
2006P	Twenty-Five Cents	Breast Cancer	40,911	25.
2007	Twenty-Five Cents	Curling	N/A	8.
2007	Twenty-Five Cents	Ice Hockey	N/A	8.
2007	Twenty-Five Cents	Biathlon	N/A	8.
2007	Twenty-Five Cents	Alpine Skiing	N/A	8.
2007	Twenty-Five Cents	Wheelchair Curling	N/A	8.
2008	Twenty-Five Cents	Snowboarding	N/A	8.
2008	Twenty-Five Cents	Freestyle Skiing	N/A	8.
2008	Twenty-Five Cents	Figure Skating	N/A	8.
2008	Twenty-Five Cents	Bobsleigh	N/A	8.
2008	Twenty-Five Cents	Armistice	N/A	15.
2009	Twenty-Five Cents	Speed Skating	N/A	8.
2009	Twenty-Five Cents	Cross Country Skiing	N/A	8.
2009	Twenty-Five Cents	Ice Sledge Hockey	N/A	8.

COLLECTOR CARDS FOR CIRCULATION COINAGE, 2004-2017

2004 "Lest We Forget" The Poppy Coin Collector Card

DATE	DESCRIPTION	QUANTITY SOLD	ISSUE PRICE	FINISH	MS-65
2004	**Lucky Loonie Coin Collector Card** to hold Standard 5 coins, Lucky Loonie $1	N/A	Free	Empty	5.
2004	**"Lest We Forget" Poppy Coin Collector Card** to hold Standard 5 coins, Poppy 25¢	21,738	Free	Empty	5.
2004	**400th Anniversary First French Settlement Collector Card** to hold Standard 5 coins, Île Sainte-Croix 25¢	N/A	Free	Empty	5.
2005	**Alberta Centennial Collector Card** to hold Standard 5 coins, Alberta 25¢	N/A	Free	Empty	5.
2005	**Saskatchewan Centennial Collector Card** to hold Standard 5 coins, Saskatchewan 25¢	N/A	Free	Empty	5.
2005	**"Canada Celebrates Peace" Victory Anniversary Collector Card** to hold Standard 5 coins, 1945-2005 Victory 5¢	N/A	Free	Empty	5.
2005	**Year of the Veteran Collector Card** to hold Standard 5 coins, Veteran 25¢	N/A	Free	Empty	5.
2005	**Terry Fox Coin Collector Card** to hold Standard 5 coins, Terry Fox $1	N/A	Free	Empty	5.
2005	**Creating a Future Without Breast Cancer 25-Cent Collector Card** to hold Standard 5 coins, Breast Cancer 25¢	N/A	Free	Empty	5.
2006	**Lucky Loonie Collector Card** to hold Standard 5 coins, 2006 Lucky Loonie $1	N/A	Free	Empty	5.
2006	**10th Anniversary Toonie Collector Card** to hold Standard 5 coins, Churchill $2	N/A	Free	Empty	5.
2006	**Medal of Bravery Collector Card** to hold Standard 5 coins, Medal of Bravery 25¢	N/A	Free	Empty	5.
2006	**Creating a Future without Breast Cancer Coin Collector Card** to hold Standard 5 coins, Breast Cancer 25¢	N/A	Free	Empty	5.
2007-2010	**Vancouver Landscape** display card holding 10 Olympic and 2 Paralympic 25¢ coins; $1 Loon Dance, $1 Inukshuk	48,198	29.95	Uncirculed	15.
2007-2010	**Vancouver City** display card holding 10 Olympic and 2 Paralympic 25¢ coins; $1 Loon Dance, $1 Inukshuk	47,691	29.95	Uncirculated	15.
2007-2010	**Vancouver Skier** display card holding 10 Olympic and 2 Paralympic 25¢ coins; $1 Loon Dance, $1 Lucky Loonie	46,361	29.95	Uncirculated	15.

COLLECTOR CARDS FOR CIRCULATION COINAGE, 2004-2017 (cont.).

2017 Canada 150
Collector Card

DATE	DESCRIPTION	QUANTITY SOLD	ISSUE PRICE	FINISH	MS-65
2007-2010	**Inukshuk** display card holding 10 Olympic and 2 Paralympic 25¢ coins; $1 Loon Dance, $1 Inukshuk	111,283	29.95	Uncirculated	15.
2010	**Canoe Coin Collector Card** holds Standard six coins (1¢–$2)	1,466	19.95	Uncirculated	15.
2010	**Maple Leaves Coin Collector Card** holds Standard six coins (1¢–$2)	2,734	19.95	Uncirculated	15.
2010	**Polar Bear Coin Collector Card** holds Standard six coins (1¢–$2)	2,127	19.95	Uncirculated	15.
2010	**RCMP Coin Collector Card** holds Standard six coins (1¢ – $2)	13,036	19.95	Uncirculated	15.
2010	**11-sided Red Maple Vancouver 2010 Olympic Winter Games Display Card** to hold 10 Olympic and 2 Paralympic 25¢ coins; 2008 Loon Dance $1; and 2010 Inukshuk $1	104,400	4.95	Empty	5.
2010	**11-sided Red Maple Vancouver 2010 Olympic Winter Games Display Card** holding 10 Olympic and 2 Paralympic 25¢; 2008 Loon Dance $1; 2010 Inukshuk $1	164,295	29.95	Uncirculated	20.
2010	**Vancouver 2010 Olympic Winter Games Collector Card**, to hold 10 Olympic/2 Paralympic 25¢; 2008 Loon Dance $1; 2010 Inukshuk $1	N/A	Free	Empty	5.
2010	**Remembrance Day Collector Card** contains the 2010 25¢ Remembrance Day coin, two die-cut holes to hold the 2004 and 2008 25¢ Poppy coins; Postage paid postcard	21,738	9.95	Uncirculated	10.
2011	**Our Legendary Nature Collector Card** to hold 8 coins, 2011 $2 Boreal Forest, $1 Parks Canada, 2011 25¢ coloured and plain Peregrine Falcon, Orca Whale and Wood Bison	N/A	Free	Empty	5.
2011	**CN Tower Coin Collector Card** holds Standard six coins (1¢–$2)	6,064	19.95	Uncirculated	15.
2011	**Vancouver Coin Collector Card** holds Standard six coins (1¢–$2)	3,784	19.95	Uncirculated	15.
2012	**The War of 1812 Collector Card** to hold 9 coins, 2012 $1 HMS Shannon, 2012 25¢ coloured and plain Brock, Tecumseh, de Salaberry and Secord	N/A	Free	Empty	5.
2013	**Heart of the Arctic Collector Card** to hold four 25¢ coins, two Canadian Arctic Expedition Centennial and two Arctic Symbols	N/A	Free	Empty	5.
2013	**$20 For $20 Collector Card** to hold four 2013 $20 For $20 coins	N/A	1.00.	Empty	5.
2014	**"Wait For Me, Daddy" Collector Card** to hold one $2 "Wait For Me, Daddy" coin	N/A	Free	Empty	5.
2015	**Sir John A. Macdonald Collector Card** to hold one $2 coin issued in his honour	N/A	Free	Empty	5.
2015	**Flag 50th Anniversary Collector Card** to hold one of each 25¢ coloured and non-coloured	N/A	Free	Empty	5.
2017	**My Canada, My Inspiration Collector Card** to hold 5 coins, glow-in-the-dark $2, $1, coloured 25¢, 10¢, 5¢	N/A	19.95	Uncirculated	20.
2017	**Canada 150 Circulation Collection** to hold 7 coins, glow-in-the-dark $2, $2 plain, $1, coloured 25¢, 25¢ plain, 10¢, 5¢	N/A	34.95	Uncirculated	35.
2017	**My Canada, My Inspiration Collector Card** to hold all Canada 150 coins.	N/A	Free	Empty	5

PROOF-LIKE SETS 1954-1967

SIX COIN SILVER PROOF-LIKE SETS, 1954-1960

The year 1953 saw the first use of the white cardboard six-coin holder that in 1954 became the package for public sale of sets. The holder with the coins included was wrapped in cellophane. The finish on the coins offered acquired the name Proof-like.

Prior to public sale of the 1954 Proof-like set, W. C. Ronson, the Mint Master at the time (1947-1953), ordered specially struck coins as samples, or gifts. It is during the 1947-1953 period that you find a broad sample of coins of various finishes. Please see Canadian Coins, Volume One.

1954-1959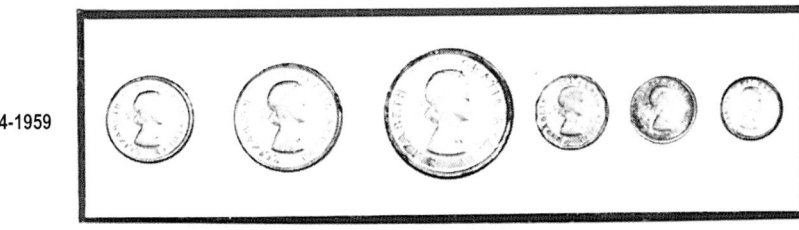

1960

In 1960 the white cardboard holders appeared with a Royal Canadian Mint domicile. Four varieties of stamps exist. A sealed wooden box containing 250 Proof-like sets was available directly from the Mint in 1960.

ROYAL CANADIAN MINT
320 SUSSEX DRIVE
OTTAWA 2, ONTARIO.

Stamp One

ROYAL CANADIAN MINT
OTTAWA   CANADA

Stamp Two

ROYAL CANADIAN MINT
OTTAWA   CANADA

Stamp Three

ROYAL CANADIAN MINT
320 SUSSEX DRIVE
OTTAWA 2, ONTARIO.

Stamp Four

DATE	QUANTITY SOLD	ISSUE PRICE	FINISH	PL-65
1954 NSF	3,000	2.50	Proof-like	2,500.
1954 SF	Included	2.50	Proof-like	800.
1955	6,300	2.50	Proof-like	500.
1955 ARN	Included	2.50	Proof-like	650.
1956	6,500	2.50	Proof-like	275.
1957	11,862	2.50	Proof-like	200.
1957 1WL	Included	2.50	Proof-like	275.
1958	18,259	2.50	Proof-like	175.
1959	31,577	3.00	Proof-like	90.
1960	64,097	3.00	Proof-like	70.

NOTES ON 1954 TO 1960 PROOF-LIKE SETS

1. The 1954 No Shoulder Fold designation applies only to the one cent coin; the balance of the coins (5) are of the Shoulder Fold variety.
2. Proof-like-65 prices are for sets in their original packaging.
3. The single denomination proof-like coins have now been incorporated into the pricing tables in the circulating coinage section of Volume One.
4. Prices are for sets that have nice full red pennies. Sets that have toned or impaired pennies should be discounted.

SIX COIN SILVER PROOF-LIKE SETS, 1961-1967

In 1961 a new system of packaging sets was introduced. The six coins were heat sealed between two layers of pliofilm which was embossed with the words ROYAL CANADIAN MINT. The set was then inserted in an envelope along with an explanatory card.

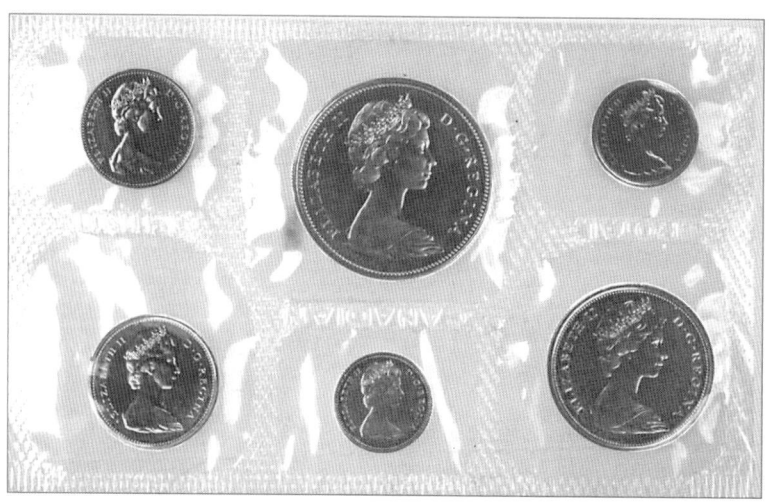

1961-1967

DATE	QUANTITY SOLD	ISSUE PRICE	FINISH	PL-65
1961	98,373	3.00	Proof-like (PL)	55.
1962	200,950	3.00	Proof-like (PL)	40.
1963	673,006	3.00	Proof-like (PL)	30.
1964	1,653,162	3.00	Proof-like (PL)	30.
1965 Type 1 $1	2,904,352	4.00	Proof-like (PL)	30.
1965 Type 2 $1	Included	4.00	Proof-like (PL)	30.
1965 Type 3 1¢	Included	4.00	Proof-like (PL)	100.
1966 LB	672,514	4.00	Proof-like (PL)	30.
1967 5¢ ↑↑	963,714	4.00	Proof-like (PL)	35.
1967 5¢ ↑↓	Included	4.00	Proof-like (PL)	500.

NOTES ON 1961 TO 1967 PROOF-LIKE SETS

1. The 1961 set, which of course was the first set packaged in the pliofilm, did not come without problems. The one cent coin was prone to discolouring, making a brilliant, red PL-65 cent a scarcity.
2. Only Types One, Small Bead, Pointed 5 and Type 2, Small Bead, Blunt 5, 1965 silver dollars were used in the assembly of proof-like sets for that year.
3. The following variety combinations will be found in the 1965 proof-like sets.
   - **A.** Type 1 dollar with Type 1 cent
   - **B.** Type 1 dollar with Type 3 cent
   - **C.** Type 2 dollar with Type 1 cent
   - **D.** Type 2 dollar with Type 3 cent
4. Since they were not officially released, no 1966 small bead dollars were issued in proof-like sets.
5. A very limited number of 1967 Proof-like sets contain a striking variety: a coinage (↑↓) five cent coin.

BRILLIANT UNCIRCULATED and UNCIRCULATED SETS, 1968-2017

SIX COIN NICKEL BRILLIANT UNCIRCULATED SETS, 1968-1987

This is a continuation of the silver proof-like sets previously offered, except that the 10 cents through one-dollar coins were now nickel in composition. Naturally, the one cent and five cents remained the same, and the pliofilm packaging continued. The outer envelope was white with blue printing. The finish on the coins in the sets is brilliant uncirculated (MS-65-NC): brilliant relief on brilliant background.

The qualities of the coins in the sets were mixed but by 1977 the quality began to improve, probably as a result of the purchase of numismatic presses in 1972 to produce Canada's first officially recognised proof coins for the Montreal Olympic sets. The finish on the coins in the sets was now advertised by the Royal Canadian Mint as brilliant relief against a brilliant background. In 1980 the Mint's marketing department began a restructuring of the selection of sets and coins offered to collectors with the result the Mint Set was officially called "The Brilliant Uncirculated Set.". This set featured one coin of each denomination issued for circulation in Canada. The quality improvement which began in 1977 continued with the 1981 introduction of a confirmed finish on the pliofilm set of "brilliant relief on brilliant background."

In 1985 the Mint experimented with a clear hard plastic package to replace the soft pliofilm package used in previous years. As it did not prove to be practical, the experimental package was not adopted. The last year the nickel voyageur dollar was used in the brilliant uncirculated sets was 1987.

1973 TWENTY-FIVE CENT VARIETIES IN SETS

1973 Large Bust
Beads near rim

1973 Small Bust
Beads far from rim

Pliofilm packaging, 1968-1987

1974 NICKEL DOLLAR VARIETIES IN SETS

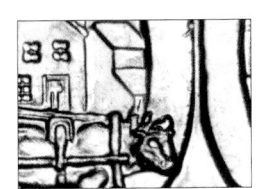

1974 Double Yoke
Doubled Die, Variety 1

1974 Double Yoke
Doubled Die, Variety 3

1968 NICKEL DOLLAR VARIETIES IN SETS

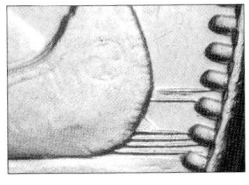

Normal Island Small Island

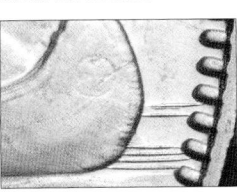

Small Island (S Is)

No Island (N Is) 1968

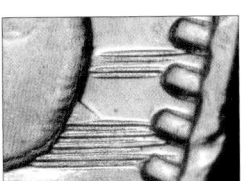

Double Waterlines
Doubled Die (DD)

DATE	QUANTITY SOLD	ISSUE PRICE	FINISH	PL-65 NC
1968	521,641	4.00	PL	5.
1968 S. Is.	Included	4.00	PL	60.
1968 No Is.	Included	4.00	PL	15.
1968 DD	Included	4.00	PL	40.
1969	326,203	4.00	PL	5.
1970	349,120	4.00	PL	7.
1971	253,311	4.00	PL	7.
1972	224,275	4.00	PL	7.
1973 L.B.	243,695	4.00	PL	350.
1973 S.B.	Included	4.00	PL	7.
1974	213,589	5.00	PL	7.
1974 Var. 1	Included	5.00	PL	1,000.
1974 Var. 3	Included	5.00	PL	1,200.

1975 NICKEL DOLLAR VARIETIES IN SETS

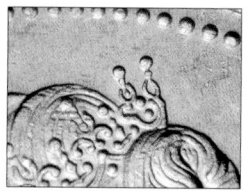
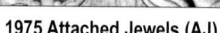

1975 Attached Jewels (AJ)

1975 Detached Jewels (DJ)

1978 FIFTY CENT VARIETIES IN SETS

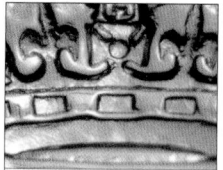

1978 Reverse
Square Jewels (SJ)

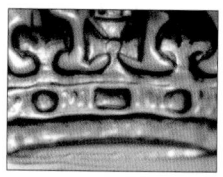

1978 Reverse
Round Jewels (RJ)

1976 NICKEL DOLLAR VARIETIES IN SETS

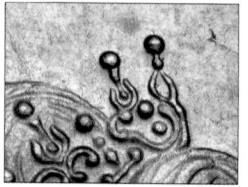

1976 Attached Jewels (AJ)

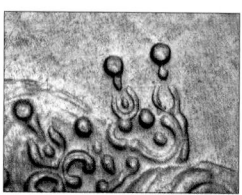

1976 Detached Jewels (DJ)

1977 NICKEL DOLLAR VARIETIES IN SETS

1977 Attached Jewels (AJ)

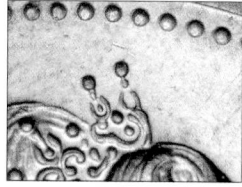

1977 Detached Jewels (DJ)

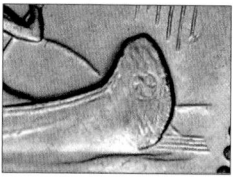

1977 Full Water Lines

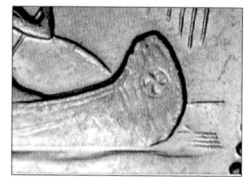

1977 Short Water Lines

DATE	QUANTITY SOLD	ISSUE PRICE	FINISH	PL-65 NC
1975 AJ, FWL	197,372	5.00	PL	10.
1975 DJ, FWL	Included	5.00	PL	10.
1976 AJ, FWL	171,737	5.15	PL	40.
1976 DJ, FWL	Included	5.15	PL	8.
1977 AJ, SWL	225,307	5.15	PL	15.
1977 DJ, FWL	Included	5.15	PL	7.
1977 DJ, SWL	Included	5.15	PL	15.
1978 SJ	260,000	5.25	PL	7.
1978 RJ	Included	5.25	PL	25.
1979	187,624	6.25	PL	8.
1980	169,390	8.00	PL	7.
1981	186,250	5.00	PL	8.
1982	203,287	5.00	PL	7.
1983	190,838	5.00	PL	9.
1984	181,415	5.00	PL	9.
1985 Pliofilm	173,924	6.95	PL	10.
1985 Experimental	Included	N/A	PL	50.
1986	167,338	6.95	PL	10.
1987	212,136	6.95	PL	10.

Note: Currently no examples of the 1977 Attached Jewel obverse and Full Water Line reverse nickel dollar have been found.

SIX COIN NICKEL BRILLIANT UNCIRCULATED SETS, 1988-1996

In 1987 the nickel Voyageur dollar was retired and in 1988 the bronze Loon dollar was introduced into the Brilliant Uncirculated Set. The finish on he coins in these sets was brilliant relief on a brilliant background.

In 1989 the pliofilm heat-sealing dies were modified. The embossed words ROYAL CANADIAN MINT were removed from the dies and replaced with the Circle M logo.

In 1996 the finish on the coins was changed to brilliant relief against a parallel lined background. This finish was first developed for the bullion maple eaf program, and used in 1981 on the Specimen sets issued by the Mint for that year.

DATE	QUANTITY SOLD	ISSUE PRICE	FINISH	MS-65 NBU
1988 RCM Logo	182,048	6.95	PL	10.
1988 Mint Logo	Included	6.95	PL	15.
1989	158,636	7.70	PL	12.
1990	170,791	7.70	PL	12.
1990 CNA	Included	7.70	PL	50.
1991	147,814	8.50	PL	28.
1992	217,597	9.50	PL	15.
1993	171,680	9.50	PL	9.
1993 CNA	Included	9.50	PL	50.
1994	141,676	9.75	PL	9.
1995	143,892	9.75	PL	9.
1996	120,217	11.95	Specimen	32.

NOTES FOR COLLECTORS

1. The 1990 and 1993 Canadan Numismatic Association sets are packaged in commemorative envelopes.
2. The 1996 Specimen set contains the 5¢ Near Six 6 variety, see Canadian Coins, Volume One, for details.

SEVEN COIN NICKEL BRILLIANT UNCIRCULATED SETS WITH SPECIMEN FINISH, 1997

In 1997 the two-dollar Polar Bear coin was added to the set. In mid-1997 the Royal Canadian Mint transferred production of the Brilliant Uncirculated Sets to the Winnipeg mint. The Ottawa and Winnipeg issues of 1997 can be distinguished by the method of packaging, and by the finish on the two dollar coins. Those produced in Ottawa have a brilliant, or shiny, polar bear, whereas on coins produced at Winnipeg, the bear has a frosted appearance. They coins are indicated by (O) for Ottawa and (W) for Winnipeg in the listings. No mint marks appear on 1997-dated coins. The finishes on both sets (1997) are technically equal, being Brilliant Relief on Parallel Lined background.

1997 Ottawa Brilliant Uncirculated Set with Specimen Finish
The $1.00 Loon is at top right
with the $2.00 (shiny) Polar Bear at top centre

1997 Winnipeg Brilliant Uncirculated Set with Specimen Finish
The $1.00 Loon is at top left
with the $2.00 (frosted) Polar Bear at top centre

DATE	DESCRIPTION	QUANTITY SOLD	ISSUE PRICE	FINISH	SP-65
1997 (O)	Loon/Polar Bear	174,692	13.95	Specimen	30.
1997 (W)	Loon/Polar Bear	Included	13.95	Proof-Like	15.

SEVEN COIN NICKEL BRILLIANT UNCIRCULATED SETS, 1998-2000

In 1998 the finish on the coins returned to a brilliant relief with a brilliant background, and this was continued until 2000. To distinguish the sets produced at the Winnipeg mint in 1998, a "W" was added to all coins from the one cent through to the two-dollar coin. This is the first time the Canadian mint placed a mint mark on Canadian coins. When the set production was moved back to Ottawa, in mid-1998, the coins were struck without a mint mark. In 2000, the mint mark appeared again as set production was moved back to the Winnipeg mint. The packaging of the sets in transparent plastic film was continued, and 2000 was the last year of issue for sets containing pure nickel coinage. The Winnipeg mint mark 'W' is found on the obverse to the lower left of the portrait.

"W" Mint Mark

DATE	DESCRIPTION	QUANTITY SOLD	ISSUE PRICE	FINISH	MS-65 NC
1998	Loon/Polar Bear	145,439	13.95	PL	30.
1998 W	Loon/Polar Bear	Included	13.95	PL	30.
1999	Loon/Polar Bear	117,318	13.95	PL	15.
1999	Loon/Nunavut	74,821	13.95	PL	18.
1999	Loon/Nun. Mule	Included	13.95	PL	300.
2000	Loon/Knowledge	186,985	15.95	PL	16.
2000 W	Loon/Polar Bear	Included	15.95	PL	16.

Note: See page 138 for the listing and explanation of the 1999 Nunavut Mule.

FIVE COIN MULTI-PLY PLATED STEEL TEST SET FOR 1999

This set is a Royal Canadian Mint test token set (TTS-3); see *Canadian Coins, Numismatic Issues, Volume One* for a complete listing.

SEVEN COIN MULTI-PLY PLATED STEEL BRILLIANT UNCIRCULATED SETS, "P" COMPOSITION MARK, 2001-2006

The first issue of the new multi-ply plated steel Brilliant Uncirculated Sets was in 2001. Five coins, one cent through fifty cents, carried the new composition mark "P". The $1.00 and $2.00 coins did not; they were struck on the standard planchets for those denominations. The finish on the multi-ply plated steel coins is brilliant relief on a brilliant background, continuing from the 2000 nickel sets.

In 2002, to commemorate the Golden Jubilee of Queen Elizabeth II, the Mint issued double dated (1952-2002) plated steel coinage for circulation. These coins were used in the collectors' sets, and are identical to those of the previous year except for the double dates. Special Edition Jubilee Sets are found on page 518.

Mid-year 2003 the tiara portrait of Elizabeth II, which had been used since 1990, was replaced with the new uncrowned portrait by Susanna Blunt. The first set with this portrait was issued in 2004.

DATE	DESCRIPTION	QUANTITY SOLD	ISSUE PRICE	FINISH	MS-65 NC
2001P	Loon/Polar Bear mintage on COA	115,897	15.95	PL	25.
2001P	Loon/Polar Bear mintage on COA	Included	15.95	PL	15.
2002P (1952-)	Loon/Polar Bear	100,467	15.95	PL	15.
2003P	Loon/Polar Bear	94,126	15.95	PL	35.
2004P	Loon/Polar Bear	96,847	15.95	PL	25.
2005P	Loon/Polar Bear	114,650	15.95	PL	18.
2005P	Loon/Polar Bear with Non-Magnetic Cent	Incl. Above	15.95	PL	1,200.
2006P (1996-)	Loon/Polar Bear	93,361	15.95	PL	20.

Note: The 2006 Brilliant Uncirculated set contains the 10th anniversary two dollar coin, double dated 1996-2006.

SEVEN COIN MULTI-PLY PLATED STEEL BRILLIANT UNCIRCULATED SETS, MAPLE LEAF LOGO, 2007-2010

Two thousand and seven saw the first coins to carrying the new Royal Canadian Mint logo (Circle M) in brilliant uncirculated sets. The composition mark "P" was now removed.

Also, in 2007 two different pairs of dies were used to strike the ten cent pieces. One pair has an obverse die carrying a small, far logo, with the reverse die having a curved 7. The other pair has an obverse die carrying a large, near logo, with the reverse die having a straight 7.

In 2009 brilliant uncirculated sets were assembled in two locations, the Mint in Ottawa, and an outside contractor. The sets assembled at the Mint have the Circle M logo embossed into the pliofilm packaging, while those assembled by the contractor do not.

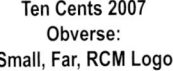

Ten Cents 2007
Obverse:
Small, Far, RCM Logo

Ten Cents 2007
Reverse:
Curved 7

Ten Cents 2007
Obverse:
Large, Near, RCM Logo

Ten Cents 2007
Reverse:
Straight 7

DATE	DESCRIPTION	QUANTITY SOLD	ISSUE PRICE	FINISH	MS-65 NC
2007	Standard 7 coins, 10 Cents Small RCM Logo / Curved	7 45,733	21.95	BU	30.
2007	Standard 7 coins, 10 Cents Large RCM Logo / Straight 7	Incl. above	21.95	BU	150.
2008	Standard 7 coins	42,833	21.95	BU	25.
2009	Standard 7 coins, with RCM logo embossed into pliofilm	37,980	22.95	BU	30.
2009	Standard 7 coins, without RCM logo embossed into pliofilm	Incl. above	22.95	BU	30.
2009	Standard 7 coins, without RCM logo; World Money Fair, Berlin, Germany	1,000	50.00	BU	75.
2010	Standard 7 coins	43,074	23.95	BU	45.

SEVEN COIN MULTI-PLY PLATED STEEL UNCIRCULATED SETS, MAPLE LEAF LOGO, 2011-2012

Beginning in 2011, the finish on the coins was lowered to circulation. The brilliant uncirculated (MS-65-NC) finish found on the coins in sets since 1968 was discontinued.

DATE	DESCRIPTION	QUANTITY SOLD	ISSUE PRICE	FINISH	MS-65 NC
2011	Standard 7 coins	37,881	23.95	Uncirculated	25.
2012	Standard 7 coins	75,083	23.95	Uncirculated	45.

SIX COIN MULTI-PLY PLATED STEEL UNCIRCULATED SETS, MAPLE LEAF LOGO, 2013-2016

With production of the penny ending May 4th, 2012, the uncirculated sets for 2013 do not contain a one cent coin. The six coins contained in the set are: 5¢, 10¢, 25¢, 50¢, $1 and $2.

DATE	DESCRIPTION	QUANTITY SOLD	ISSUE PRICE	FINISH	MS-65 NC
2013	Standard 6 coins	61,702	24.95	Uncirculated	22.
2014	Standard 6 coins	52,946	24.95	Uncirculated	22.
2015	Standard 6 coins	51,902	24.95	Uncirculated	25.
2016	Standard 6 coins	10,225	24.95	Uncirculated	25.
2017	Standard 6 coins	75,000	24.95	Uncirculated	25.
2018	Standard 6 coins	N/A	26.95	Uncirculated	27.

NOTES FOR COLLECTORS

1. In the description column of the pricing table the use of the word "standard" refers to the everyday denominations in use for daily transactions.
2. While the 2007 ten-cent coin with the Large, Near RCM Logo obverse and the Straight 7 Reverse is a relatively common coin, the rarity factor changes when it is struck with a Brilliant Uncirculated finish, and is packaged in a Brilliant Uncirculated set.
3. The 2009 Brilliant Uncirculated sets sold at the World Money Fair in Berlin, Germany, included a certificate of authenticity for the Fair. The set was issued in a limited edition of 1,000.

SPECIAL EDITION BRILLIANT UNCIRCULATED SETS, 2002-2010

QUEEN ELIZABETH II, DIADEMED PORTRAIT, GOLDEN JUBILEE, 1952-2002

The Special Edition Brilliant Uncirculated Set of 1952-2002 contains the Golden Jubilee 50-cent piece, and the 1952-2002 Canada Day 25-cent coin. The remaining coins in the set are the regular double-dated Jubilee 1952-2002P issue.

Golden Jubilee, 1952-2002

DATE	DESCRIPTION	QUANTITY SOLD	ISSUE PRICE	FINISH	MS-65 NC
2002P (1952-)	Diademed Portrait Obverse	49,869	15.95	BU	15.

QUEEN ELIZABETH II, MATURE PORTRAIT, 2003

In mid-year 2003, the "Diademed Portrait" of Queen Elizabeth, by Dora de Pédery-Hunt, was replaced by a more mature portrait by Susanna Blunt. The Special Edition Brilliant Uncirculated Set of 2003 contains the seven circulating denominations, with the new effigy of Queen Elizabeth II. This set was struck at the Winnipeg Mint, and naturally carries the mint mark W (WP). The lower denominations, one cent to fifty cents, also carry the composition mark "P."

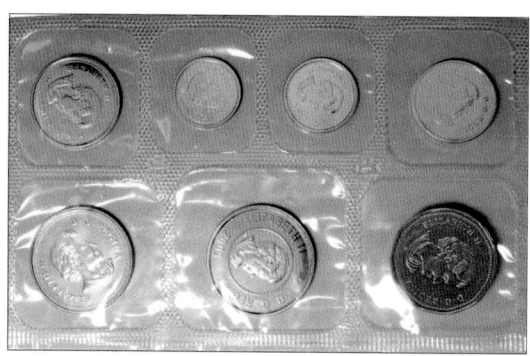

Mature Portrait Obverses

Mint and Composition Mark

DATE	DESCRIPTION	QUANTITY SOLD	ISSUE PRICE	FINISH	MS-65 NC
2003WP	Mature Portrait Obverse	71,142	15.95	BU	25.

CENTENARIES OF ALBERTA AND SASKATCHEWAN, 2005

This Special Edition Brilliant Uncirculated Set was issued to commemorate the centenaries of both Alberta and Saskatchewan. The set contains two commemorative twenty-five-cent coins, one depicting an oil derrick (Alberta), the other the Western Meadowlark (Saskatchewan). The remaining coins in the set are the regular 2005P issue.

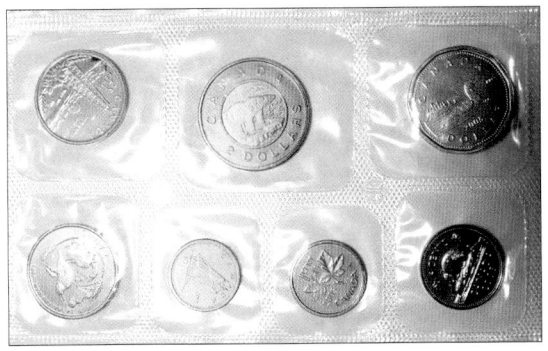

**Alberta Centenary
25¢ Coin**

**Saskatchewan
Centenary
25¢ Coin**

Alberta and Saskatchewan 100th Anniversary Set

DATE	DESCRIPTION	QUANTITY SOLD	ISSUE PRICE	FINISH	MS-65 NC
2005P	Centenaries of Alberta and Saskatchewan	N/A	15.95	BU	15.

10TH ANNIVERSARY OF THE TWO DOLLAR COIN, RCM LOGO, 2006

This 2006 Special Edition Brilliant Uncirculated Set contains the "Churchill" two dollar coin. The unique Royal Canadian Mint logo that was introduced to Canadian circulating coins in 2006 is featured on the obverse of all coins in this set.

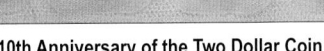

**Churchill
Two Dollar Coin**

10th Anniversary of the Two Dollar Coin

DATE	DESCRIPTION	QUANTITY SOLD	ISSUE PRICE	FINISH	MS-65 NC
2006	10th Anniversary; Churchill two dollar coin	31,636	19.95	BU	26.

VANCOUVER 2010 WINTER OLYMPIC GAMES, 2007-2008

Over the four years, 2007-2010, all Vancouver 2010 twenty-five cent coins, and the two bronze one dollar coins, were incorporated into Special Edition Brilliant Uncirculated Sets.

2007 Vancouver 2010 Olympic Winter Games

| 2007 Obverse | 2007 Reverse |
| Paralympic Logo | Wheelchair Curling |

Standard 25¢ Wheelchair Curling

| 2007 Obverse | 2007 Reverse |
| Vancouver Logo | Wheelchair Curling |

25¢ Wheelchair Curling Mule

The Vancouver Olympic obverse was paired with the Paralympic Wheelchair Curling reverse to form a mule which is found only in the 2007 Vancouver Olympic Winter Games Special Edition Set.

Note For Collectors

The 2007 Special Edition Brilliant Uncirculated Set contains the 10-cent variety: Small, Far Logo Obverse / Curved 7 Reverse

2008 Vancouver 2010 Olympic Winter Games

DATE	DESCRIPTION	QUANTITY SOLD	ISSUE PRICE	FINISH	MS-65 NC
2007	Standard 5 coins 1¢, 5¢, 10¢, 50¢ and $2; 5 x 25¢ Alpine Skiing, Biathlon, Curling, Ice Hockey, Wheelchair Curling, $1 Loon Dance; (11 coins)	28,852	23.95	BU	22.
2007	As above, but with the Mule 25¢ Vancouver Logo Obverse paired with the Wheelchair Curling Reverse	Included	23.95	BU	550.
2008	Standard 5 coins 1¢, 5¢, 10¢, 50¢ and $2; 4 x 25¢ Bobsleigh, Figure Skating, Freestyle Skiing, Snow Boarding; $1 Loon Dance; (10 coins)	16,471	23.95	BU	24.

VANCOUVER 2010 OLYMPIC WINTER GAMES, 2009-2010

The Golden Moments Set commemorates the Olympic gold medals won by the Men's and Women's Hockey Teams in 2002, and Cindy Klassen's gold medal of 2006. These quarters have the partial maple leaf painted red.

2009 Vancouver 2010 Olympic Winter Games

2010 Golden Moments Special Edition Set

DATE	DESCRIPTION	QUANTITY SOLD	ISSUE PRICE	FINISH	MS-65 NC
2009	Standard 5 coins 1¢, 5¢, 10¢, 50¢ and $2; 3 x 25¢ Cross Country Skiing, Ice Sledge Hockey, Speed Skating, $1 Loon Dance; (9 coins)	11,313	23.95	BU	24.
2010	Standard 5 coins 1¢, 5¢, 10¢, 50¢ and $2; 3 x 25¢ Painted Men's Ice Hockey 2002, Painted Women's Ice Hockey 2002, Painted Speed Skating, Cindy Klassen; $1 Inukshuk; (9 coins)	21,432	27.95	BU	40.

SPECIAL EDITION UNCIRCULATED SETS, 2010-2018

SPECIAL EDITION UNCIRCULATED SET, 2010

This set of 8 coins features the standard 1¢, 5¢, 10¢, 50¢ and $2 coins, but also includes the 2010 25¢ Remembrance Day Poppy coin, and two one-dollar coins which commemorate the 100th Anniversary of the Royal Canadian Navy, and the Saskatchewan Roughriders Centennial. The finish on all coins is circulation. The set is shrink wrapped in clear plastic.

25¢ Remembrance Day Poppies

$1 Royal Canadian Navy

$1 Saskatchewan Roughriders

DATE	DESCRIPTION	QUANTITY SOLD	ISSUE PRICE	FINISH	MS-65 NC
2010	8-coin set, $2 with 16 serrations	19,233	25.95	Circulation	30.
2010	8-coin set, $2 with 14 serrations	Incl above	25.95	Circulation	75.

SPECIAL EDITION UNCIRCULATED SET, 2011

This 8-coin set features the following coins: $2 Boreal Forest, $1 Parks Canada, 25¢ Wood Bison, coloured and uncoloured; 25¢ Orca Whale, coloured and uncoloured; 25¢ Peregrine Falcon, coloured and uncoloured. It was issued in a keepsake envelope with a serial certificate of authorization. The finish on all coins is circulation.

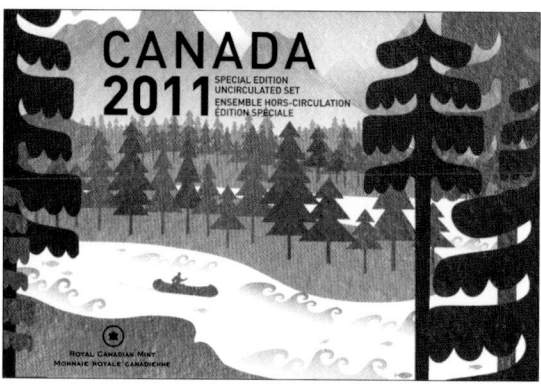

$1 Parks Canada $2 Boreal Forest

DATE	DESCRIPTION	QUANTITY SOLD	ISSUE PRICE	FINISH	MS-65 NC
2011	Special Edition Uncirculated Set (8 coins)	19,233	23.95	Circulation	32.

SPECIAL EDITION UNCIRCULATED SET, 2012

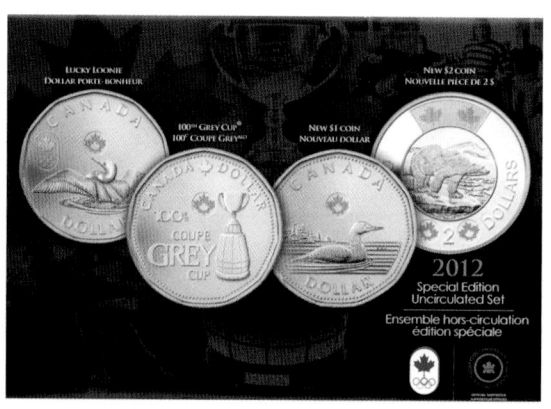

$1 Grey Cup $1 Lucky Loonie

DATE	DESCRIPTION	QUANTITY SOLD	ISSUE PRICE	FINISH	MS-65 NC
2012	Special Edition Uncirculated Set (4 coins)	14,987	19.95	Circulation	25.

SPECIAL EDITION UNCIRCULATED SET, 2013

THE WAR OF 1812

DATE	DESCRIPTION	QUANTITY SOLD	ISSUE PRICE	FINISH	MS-65 NC
2013	The War of 1812 (9 coins)	14,941	26.95	Circulation	28.

COMMEMORATIVE GIFT SET, 2013
THE WAR OF 1812

This set of 5 coins features the following coins: $2 H.M.S. Shannon, 25¢ Laura Secord, coloured and uncoloured, 25¢ Charles-Michel de Salaberry, coloured and uncoloured, all enclosed in a maroon folder.

DATE	DESCRIPTION	QUANTITY SOLD	ISSUE PRICE	FINISH	MS-65 NC
2013	The War of 1812 (5 coins)	14,831	19.95	Circulation	18.

SPECIAL EDITION UNCIRCULATED SET, 2013-2014

This set of 4 coins features the following coins: $2 Wait For Me Daddy, $1 Lucky Loonie, 25¢ Arctic Expedition - Life in the North, and 25¢ Arctic Expedition - Exploration all enclosed in a presentation folder.

DATE	DESCRIPTION	QUANTITY SOLD	ISSUE PRICE	FINISH	MS-65 NC
2013-2014	Special Edition Uncirculated Set (4 coins)	12,105	25.95	Circulation	26.

SPECIAL EDITION UNCIRCULATED SET, 2015

This set of 6 coins features the following coins: $2 200th Anniversary of the Birth of Sir John A. Macdonald, $2 100th Anniversary of *In Flanders Fields*, 25¢ 50th Anniversary of the Canadian Flag, and 25¢ Poppy, all enclosed in a presentation folder.

$2 200th Anniversary of the Birth of Sir John. A. Macdonald

$2 100th Anniversary of *In Flanders Fields*

50th Anniversary of the Canadian Flag

25¢ Colourised Flag   25¢ Plain Flag

25¢ Colourised Poppy

25¢ Plain Poppy

DATE	DESCRIPTION	QUANTITY SOLD	ISSUE PRICE	FINISH	MS-65 NC
2015	Special Edition Uncirculated Set (6 coins)	12,450	25.95	Uncirculated	30.

SPECIAL EDITION UNCIRCULATED SET, 2017

This set features the unique coins issued exclusively for 2017 that were designed by Canadians, for Canadians, and were selected through popula
vote in the *MY CANADA, MY INSPIRATION* contest as well as the 50-cent piece which illustrates the Heritage Canada — Canada 150 logo.

$2 Glow-in-the-dark   **$2 Plain**
Dance of Spirits
Des.: Timothy Hsia

$1	50 Cents	25 Cents Colourised	25 Cents Plain	10 Cents	5 Cents
Connecting A Nation		**Hope for a Green Future**		**Wings of Peace**	**Living Traditions**
Des.: Wesley Klassen	**Des.: Heritage Canada**	**Des.: Joelle Wong**		**Des.: Amy Choi**	**Des.: Gerald Gloade**

DATE	DESCRIPTION	QUANTITY SOLD	ISSUE PRICE	FINISH	MS-65 NC
2017	Special Edition Uncirculated Set (8 coins)	8,017	26.95	Uncirculated	30.

CLASSIC CANADIAN COIN SET, 2017

The *2017 Classic Canadian Coin Set* is a powerful reflection of the nation's legacy on its 150th anniversary, through the reverse designs that have become as iconic as the subjects they depict.

DATE	DESCRIPTION	QUANTITY SOLD	ISSUE PRICE	FINISH	MS-65 NC
2017	Classic Canadian Coin Set (6 coins)	15,005	24.95	Uncirculated	25.

CLASSIC CANADIAN COIN SET, 2018

The *2018 Classic Canadian Coin Set* features timeless images that come together to tell the story of a nation's past; of its varied landscape; and of the pride of its citizens, from coast ot coast to coast.

DATE	DESCRIPTION	MINTAGE	ISSUE PRICE	FINISH	MS-65 NC
2018	Classic Canadian Coin Set (6 coins)	75,000	26.95	Uncirculated	30.

BABY GIFT SETS, 1995-2018

BUNDLE OF JOY / TINY TREASURES

NICKEL BRILLIANT UNCIRCULATED SETS, 1995-2000.

First issued in 1995, the brilliant uncirculated set of coins was specially packaged for the gift market using the six coins from the brilliant uncirculate set of that year. In 1997 this set was expanded to include the two-dollar polar bear coin.

In 1998 the name changed from Bundle of Joy to Tiny Treasures Brilliant Uncirculated Sets. In that same year the packaging of the sets of Tin Treasures changed from card displays to clear plastic display units. The movement of set production to Winnipeg and back to Ottawa that occurred i 1998 also affected the Oh! Canada! and Tiny Treasures sets.

In 2000, production of the sets occurred in both the Ottawa and Winnipeg mints.

The finish on the coins in these sets (1995-2005) is brilliant relief on brilliant background, brilliant uncirculated (MS-65-NC). The finish wa downgraded in 2006 to uncirculated. See page xii for an outline on finishes.

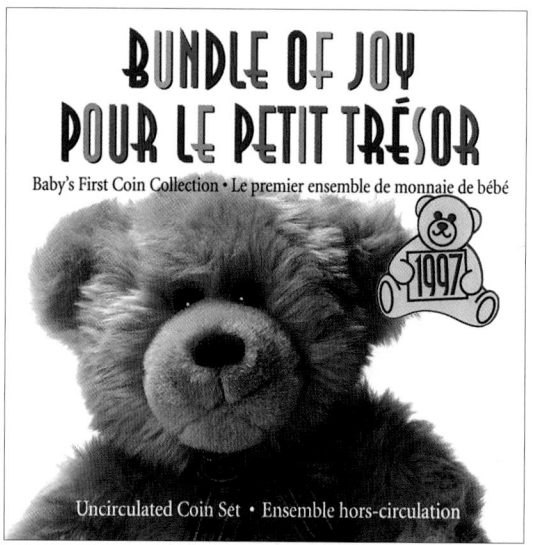

1997 Bundle of Joy Set

DATE	DESCRIPTION	QUANTITY SOLD	ISSUE PRICE	FINISH	MS-65 NC
1995	Standard 6 coins; Folder	36,443	19.95	BU	35.
1996	Standard 6 coins; Folder	56,618	19.95	BU	20.
1997	Standard 7 coins; Folder	55,199	21.95	BU	25.
1998	Standard 7 coins; Display case	46,139	21.95	BU	24.
1998W	Winnipeg Mint, 7 coins; Display case	12,625	21.95	BU	24.
1999	Standard 7 coins; Display case	67,694	21.95	BU	22.
2000	Standard 7 coins; Display case	82,964	21.95	BU	22.
2000W	Winnipeg Mint, 7 coins; Display case	Included	21.95	BU	22.

TINY TREASURES SETS, 2001-2003

MULTI-PLY PLATED STEEL BRILLIANT UNCIRCULATED SETS, 2001-2003.

As with the Brilliant Uncirculated sets of 2001, the nickel coinage of the previous year was replaced with the new patented multi-ply plated steel coins. In the 2002 set all coins bear the double dates 1952-2002 to commemorate the 50th anniversary of Her Majesty Queen Elizabeth II's accession to the throne. Two thousand and three was the last year of issue for the Tiny Treasures sets. The finish on the coins in these sets is brilliant uncirculated (MS-65-NC).

2002 Tiny Treasures Set

DATE	DESCRIPTION	QUANTITY SOLD	ISSUE PRICE	FINISH	MS-65 NC
2001P	Standard 7 coins; Display case	52,085	22.95	BU	25.
2002P (1952-)	Standard 7 coins; Display case	51,491	22.95	BU	22.
2003P	Standard 7 coins; Display case	43,197	22.95	BU	25.

BABY GIFT SETS, 2004-2018

MULTI-PLY PLATED STEEL BRILLIANT UNCIRCULATED SETS, 2004-2005.

With the revamping of the Gift Sets in 2004, a name change took place, Tiny Treasures became Baby Gift Sets. The finish on the coins remained the same as the previous sets.

DATE	DESCRIPTION	QUANTITY SOLD	ISSUE PRICE	FINISH	MS-65 NC
2004P	Standard 7 coins; Folder	53,726	19.95	BU	45.
2005P	Standard 7 coins; Folder	42,245	19.95	BU	50.

BABY GIFT SETS 2004-2018 (cont.).

MULTI-PLY PLATED STEEL UNCIRCULATED SETS, 2006-2010.

Beginning in 2006, the finish on the coins in these sets was changed to circulation. The uncirculated sets were struck and assembled at the Winnipeg Mint, however, they do not carry the "W" mint mark.

In 2007 the Caribou design on the twenty-five-cent coin was replaced with a coloured design.

DATE	DESCRIPTION	QUANTITY SOLD	ISSUE PRICE	FINISH	MS-65 NC
2006P	Standard 7 coins; Folder	33,786	19.95	Uncirculated	30.
2007	Standard 6 coins; plus coloured 25¢ Rattle; Folder	30,090	19.95	Uncirculated	150.
2008	Standard 6 coins; plus coloured 25¢ Teddy Bear; Folder	29,819	19.95	Uncirculated	125.
2009	Standard 6 coins; plus coloured 25¢ Teddy Bear and Blanket; Folder	25,182	19.95	Uncirculated	120.
2010	Standard 6 coins; plus coloured 25¢ Baby Carriage; Folder	27,048	19.95	Uncirculated	50.

MULTI-PLY PLATED STEEL UNCIRCULATED SETS, 2011-2018.

In 2011 the coloured designs used on the reverse of the twenty-five cent pieces were discontinued. The $1 coin now carries a new yearly struck design.

Born in 2017

Born in 2018

Coins contained in set:
2011	- 7 coins in set: 1¢, 5¢, 10¢, 25¢, 50¢, $1, $2
2012	- 6 coins in set: 1¢, 5¢, 10¢, 25¢, $1, $2
2013-2018	- 5 coins in set: 5¢, 10¢, 25¢, $1, $2

DATE	DESCRIPTION	QUANTITY SOLD	ISSUE PRICE	FINISH	MS-65 NC
2011	Standard 6 coins, plus 25¢ Baby's Feet, Folder	38,576	19.95	Uncirculated	110.
2012	Standard 5 coins; plus 25¢ Mobiles, Folder	43,920	19.95	Uncirculated	25.
2013	Standard 4 coins, plus 25¢ Baby's Feet, Folder	53,708	19.95	Uncirculated	35.
2014	Standard 4 coins, plus $1 Stork, Folder	54,122	19.95	Uncirculated	35.
2015	Standard 4 coins, plus $1 Teddy Bear, Folder	50,279	19.95	Uncirculated	25.
2016	Standard 4 coins, plus $1 "ABC" Building Blocks	47,733	19.95	Uncirculated	20.
2017	Standard 4 coins, plus $1 Rocking Horse, Folder	20,189	21.95	Uncirculated	25.
2018	Standard 4 coins, plus $1 Crib and Teddy Bears	W.S.L.	21.95	Uncirculated	22.

Note: For the designs of the twenty-five cent coins contained in the sets of 2007-2018 see pages 31-34.
For the design of the one dollar coin contained in the 2014-2018 set see page 131.

BIRTHDAY GIFT SETS, 2005-2018

MULTI-PLY PLATED STEEL BRILLIANT UNCIRCULATED SETS, 2005.

The Birthday Gift Set was first introduced in 2005. The finish on these seven-coin sets is brilliant uncirculated. The ten cent coins contained in the 2007 Birthday Gift Sets are the Large, Near Logo obverse / Straight 7 reverse variety.

DATE	DESCRIPTION	QUANTITY SOLD	ISSUE PRICE	FINISH	MS-65 NC
2005P	Standard 7 coins; Folder	20,227	19.95	BU	20.

MULTI-PLY PLATED STEEL UNCIRCULATED SETS, 2006-2008.

Beginning in 2006, the finish on the coins contained in the Birthday Gift Sets was uncirculated. The uncirculated sets were struck and assembled at the Winnipeg Mint, however, they do not carry the "W" mint mark.

In 2007 the Caribou design on the twenty-five-cent coin was replaced with a coloured design. The ten cent coins contained in the 2007 Birthday Gift Sets are the Large, Near Logo obverse / Straight 7 reverse variety.

For 2008 the set carried the name "Commemorative Coin Set."

The Birthday Gift Set was discontinued in 2009 and replaced by the Coins With Cards series, see page 31-34.

DATE	DESCRIPTION	QUANTITY SOLD	ISSUE PRICE	FINISH	MS-65 NC
2006P	Standard 7 coins; Folder	11,984	19.95	Uncirculated	20.
2007	Standard 6 coins; plus coloured 25¢ Balloons; Folder	13,423	19.95	Uncirculated	30.
2008	Standard 6 coins; plus coloured 25¢ Party Hat; Folder	11,376	19.95	Uncirculated	50.

MULTI-PLY PLATED STEEL UNCIRCULATED SETS, 2011-2018.

The Birthday Gift Set was reintroduced in 2011. Coins contained in the sets are:

2011 - 7 coins in set: 1¢, 5¢, 10¢, 25¢, 50¢, $1, $2   **2012** - 6 coins in set: 1¢, 5¢, 10¢, 25¢, $1, $2   **2013-2018** - 5 coins in set: 5¢, 10¢, 25¢, $1, $2

2017 Birthday Gift Set	2018 Birthday Gift Set

DATE	DESCRIPTION	QUANTITY SOLD	ISSUE PRICE	FINISH	MS-65 NC
2011	Standard 6 coins, plus 25¢ Four Balloons, Folder	21,173	19.95	Uncirculated	20.
2012	Standard 5 coins; plus 25¢ Ice Cream Cone, Folder	24,659	19.95	Uncirculated	20.
2013	Standard 4 coins, plus 25¢ Slice of Birthday Cake, Folder	22,678	19.95	Uncirculated	20.
2014	Standard 4 coins, plus $1 Gift Box and Balloons, Folder	44,539	19.95	Uncirculated	20.
2015	Standard 4 coins, plus $1 3 Balloons, Folder	24,781	19.95	Uncirculated	20.
2016	Standard 4 coins, plus $1 Cupcake, Party Hat, Present	25,648	19.95	Uncirculated	20.
2017	Standard 4 coins, plus $1 Birthday Presents, Folder	14,149	21.95	Uncirculated	22.
2018	Standard 4 coins, plus $1 Birthday Cake	W.S.L.	21.95	Uncirculated	22.

Note: For the designs of the twenty-five cent coins contained in the sets of 2007-2018 see pages 31-34.

For the design of the one dollar coin contained in the 2014-2018 set see page 131.

CONGRATULATIONS / GRADUATION GIFT SETS, 2004-2008

MULTI-PLY PLATED STEEL BRILLIANT UNCIRCULATED SETS, 2004-2005.

The gift set in 2004 was directed at the school or college graduation market. By 2006 the scope was broadened to a Congratulations Gift Set. The Graduation Sets have a brilliant uncirculated finish, while the Congratulations Gift Sets have a circulation finish.

| 2005 Graduation Gift Set | 2008 Congratulations Gift Set |

DATE	DESCRIPTION	QUANTITY SOLD	ISSUE PRICE	FINISH	MS-65 NC
2004P	Graduation Set, Standard 7 coins; Folder	22,094	19.95	BU	15.
2005P	Graduation Set, Standard 7 coins; Folder	12,411	19.95	BU	15.

MULTI-PLY PLATED STEEL UNCIRCULATED SETS, 2006-2008.

Beginning in 2006, the finish on the coins in these sets was changed to circulation. The circulation sets were struck and assembled at the Winnipeg Mint, however, they do not carry the "W" mint mark.

The ten cent coins contained in the 2007 Congratulations Gift Sets are the Large, Near Logo obverse / Straight 7 reverse variety.

These sets were discontinued in 2009 and replaced by the Coins With Cards Series, see page 34-35.

DATE	DESCRIPTION	QUANTITY SOLD	ISSUE PRICE	FINISH	MS-65 NC
2006P	Congratulations Set, Standard 7 coins; Folder	9,428	19.95	Uncirculated	15.
2007	Congratulations Set, Standard 6 coins; plus coloured 25¢ Fireworks; Folder	9,671	19.95	Uncirculated	50.
2008	Congratulations Set, Standard 6 coins; plus coloured 25¢ Trophy; Folder	6,821	19.95	Uncirculated	50.

Note: For the coloured designs of the twenty-five cent coins contained in the sets of 2007-2008, see page 31-32.

HOLIDAY GIFT SETS, 2004-2017

MULTI-PLY PLATED STEEL, BRILLIANT UNCIRCULATED SETS, 2004-2005.

In 2004 the Royal Canadian Mint introduced a new Holiday Gift Set to their product line. This set was issued in a colourful Season's Greetings folder and included a coloured twenty-five-cent coin in place of the standard Caribou design. The finish on all coins is Brilliant Uncirculated.

DATE	DESCRIPTION	QUANTITY SOLD	ISSUE PRICE	FINISH	MS-65 NC
2004P	Standard 6 coins; plus coloured 25¢ Santa Claus; Folder	62,777	19.95	BU	30.
2005P	Standard 6 coins; plus coloured 25¢ Christmas Stocking; Folder	72,831	19.95	BU	20.

MULTI-PLY PLATED STEEL, UNCIRCULATED SETS 2006-2010.

In 2006 the finish on all coins contained in these sets was downgraded to circulation.
The ten cent coin contained in the 2007 Holiday Gift Set is the Large, Near Logo obverse / Straight 7 reverse variety.

DATE	DESCRIPTION	QUANTITY SOLD	ISSUE PRICE	FINISH	MS-65 NC
2006P	Standard 6 coins; plus coloured 25¢ Santa in Sleigh Reindeer; Folder	99,258	19.95	Uncirculated	20.
2007	Standard 6 coins; plus coloured 25¢ Christmas Tree; Folder	66,267	19.95	Uncirculated	20.
2008	Standard 6 coins; plus coloured 25¢ Santa, Folder	42,344	19.95	Uncirculated	20.
2009	Standard 6 coins; plus coloured 25¢ Santa, 3 Maple Leaves; Folder	32,967	19.95	Uncirculated	25.
2010	Standard 6 coins; plus coloured 25¢ Santa, Christmas Tree; Folder	10,870	19.95	Uncirculated	25.

2016 Holiday Gift Set

2017 Holiday Gift Set

MULTI-PLY PLATED STEEL, UNCIRCULATED SETS 2011-2017.

Coins contained in set:

2011	- 7 coins in set: 1¢, 5¢, 10¢, 25¢, 50¢, $1, $2
2012	- 6 coins in set: 1¢, 5¢, 10¢, 25¢, $1, $2
2013-2017	- 5 coins in set: 5¢, 10¢, 25¢, $1, $2

DATE	DESCRIPTION	QUANTITY SOLD	ISSUE PRICE	FINISH	MS-65 NC
2011	Standard 6 coins; plus 25¢ Snowflake, Folder	41,666	19.95	Uncirculated	25.
2012	Standard 5 coins; plus 25¢ Christmas Tree Ornaments, Folder	26,404	19.95	Uncirculated	20.
2013	Standard 4 coins; plus 25¢ Wreath, Folder	26,491	19.95	Uncirculated	20.
2014	Standard 4 coins, plus $1 Reindeer	31,951	19.95	Uncirculated	20.
2015	Standard 4 coins; plus $1 Snowflake, Folder	32,994	19.95	Uncirculated	20
2016	Standard 4 coins, plus $1 Holly Leaves & Pine Cone, Folder	23,696	21.95	Uncirculated	22.
2017	Standard 4 coins, plus $1 Ornaments & Holly Leaves	W.S.L.	21.95	Uncirculated	22.

Note: For the designs of the twenty-five cent coins contained in the sets of 2004-2017 see pages 27, and 33-34, for the dollar coins, see page 131.

NHL TEAM GIFT SETS, UNCIRCULATED, 2006-2009

MULTI-PLY PLATED STEEL, UNCIRCULATED SETS, 2006-2009.

These sets were introduced for the 2005-2006 hockey season with only three Canadian NHL teams being represented: Montreal Canadiens, Ottawa Senators and the Toronto Maple Leafs. Each set contained the standard six coins, 1¢, 5¢, 10¢, 50¢, $1 and $2, with the twenty-five-cent Caribou design being replaced by a coloured NHL team logo. For the 2006-2007 Season, all six Canadian NHL teams were represented.

In the Fall of 2008 the sets issued for the 2008-2009 season had the twenty-five cent Caribou design as one of the standard six coins, but the logo design on the one dollar coin was replaced by a coloured team jersey logo.

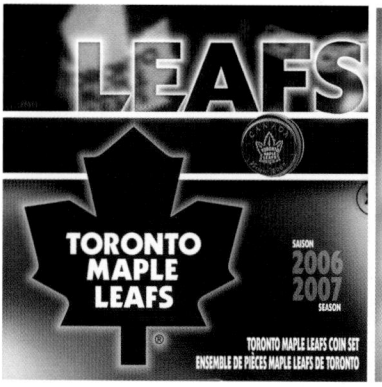  

| 2006-2007 Season | 2007-2008 Season | 2008-2009 Season |
| Toronto Maple Leafs | Edmonton Oilers | Calgary Flames |

DATE	DESCRIPTION	QUANTITY SOLD	ISSUE PRICE	FINISH	MS-65 NC
2006P	Montreal Canadiens, Standard 6 coin set; Coloured 25¢	11,765	24.95	Uncirculated	25.
2006P	Ottawa Senators; Standard 6 coin set; Coloured 25¢	Included	24.95	Uncirculated	25.
2006P	Toronto Maple Leafs; Standard 6 coin set; Coloured 25¢	Included	24.95	Uncirculated	25.
2007	Calgary Flames; Standard 6 coins; Coloured 25¢	1.082	24.95	Uncirculated	25.
2007	Edmonton Oilers; Standard 6 coins; Coloured 25¢	2,214	24.95	Uncirculated	25.
2007	Montreal Canadiens; Standard 6 coins; Coloured 25¢	4,091	24.95	Uncirculated	25.
2007	Ottawa Senators; Standard 6 coin set; Coloured 25¢	2,474	24.95	Uncirculated	25.
2007	Toronto Maple Leafs; Standard 6 coin set; Coloured 25¢	5,365	24.95	Uncirculated	25.
2007	Vancouver Canucks; Standard 6 coin set; Coloured 25¢	1,526	24.95	Uncirculated	25.
2008	Calgary Flames; Standard 6 coins; Coloured $1	N/A	24.95	Uncirculated	20.
2008	Edmonton Oilers; Standard 6 coins; Coloured $1	1,584	24.95	Uncirculated	20.
2008	Montreal Canadiens; Standard 6 coins; Coloured $1	2,659	24.95	Uncirculated	50.
2008	Ottawa Senators; Standard 6 coin set; Coloured $1	1,633	24.95	Uncirculated	20.
2008	Toronto Maple Leafs; Standard 6 coin set; Coloured $1	N/A	24.95	Uncirculated	20.
2008	Vancouver Canucks; Standard 6 coin set; Coloured $1	1,302	24.95	Uncirculated	20.
2009	Calgary Flames; Standard 6 coins; Coloured $1	382	24.95	Uncirculated	25.
2009	Edmonton Oilers; Standard 6 coins; Coloured $1	472	24.95	Uncirculated	25.
2009	Montreal Canadiens; Standard 6 coins; Coloured $1	4,857	24.95	Uncirculated	40.
2009	Ottawa Senators; Standard 6 coin set; Coloured $1	387	24.95	Uncirculated	25.
2009	Toronto Maple Leafs; Standard 6 coin set; Coloured $1	1,328	24.95	Uncirculated	30.
2009	Vancouver Canucks; Standard 6 coin set; Coloured $1	794	24.95	Uncirculated	25.

NOTES

1. For the coloured designs of the twenty-five cent coins used in the NHL Team Gift Sets see page 30-31.
2. For the coloured designs of the one dollar coins used in the NHL Team Gift Sets see pages 125-127.
3. The "Quantity Sold" numbers may or may not be reported in a single year, but may carry over to the following year. The collector must wait a year or two before the final numbers are known.
4. No "Quantity Sold" number was listed in the 2008 Royal Canadian Mint Report for the 2008 issue of NHL Team Gift Sets. There is a partial listing in 2009.
5. The 2007 NHL Team Gift Sets contain the Large, Near Logo obverse / Straight 7 reverse variety ten cent coin.

OH! CANADA! GIFT SETS, 1994-2018

BRILLIANT UNCIRCULATED SETS, 1994-2000

First issued in 1994, this set included the bronze dollar plus the other five denominations for that year. In 1997 this set was expanded to include the two-dollar polar bear coin. In 1998 the packaging of the Oh! Canada! Gift Sets changed from card displays to clear plastic display units. The coins in the Oh Canada! set are identical in finish to those of the corresponding year of the Brilliant Uncirculated Set.

1997 Oh Canada! Gift Set with Flying Loon Dollar

DATE	DESCRIPTION	QUANTITY SOLD	ISSUE PRICE	FINISH	MS-65 NC
1994	Standard 6 coins	18,794	16.95	BU	12.
1995	Standard 5 coins, Peacekeeping dollar	50,927	16.95	BU	12.
1996	Standard 6 coins	31,083	16.95	BU	22.
1997	Standard 6 coins, Flying Loon dollar	84,124	21.95	Specimen	32.
1998	Standard 7 coins	42,710	21.95	BU	25.
1998W	Winnipeg Mint, 7 coins	24,792	21.95	BU	25.
1999	Standard 7 coins	82,754	21.95	BU	15.
2000	Standard 7 coins	107,884	21.95	BU	15.
2000W	Standard 7 coins	Included	21.95	BU	15.

Note: The Oh Canada! Gift Set was struck at both the Ottawa and Winnipeg (W) branches of the Royal Canadian Mint.

MULTI-PLY PLATED STEEL BRILLIANT UNCIRCULATED SETS, 2001-2005.

In 2001, the five subsidiary coins in the Oh! Canada! Set were replaced by the five multi-ply plated steel coins.

In the 2002 set all coins bear the double dates 1952-2002 to commemorate the 50th anniversary of Her Majesty Queen Elizabeth II's accession the throne.

Beginning in 2004 the coins carried the new Susanna Blunt effigy of Queen Elizabeth II. The coins in the "Oh Canada!" set were identical in finish to coins of the Brilliant Uncirculated Set of that year.

2003 Oh! Canada! Gift Set

DATE	DESCRIPTION	QUANTITY SOLD	ISSUE PRICE	FINISH	MS-65 NC
2001P	Standard 7 coins	66,726	22.95	BU	20.
2002P (1952-)	Standard 7 coins, Double Date	61,484	22.95	BU	18.
2003P	Standard 7 coins	51,146	23.95	BU	25.
2004P	Standard 7 coins	53,111	23.95	BU	20.
2005P	Standard 7 coins	40,890	19.95	BU	15.

MULTI-PLY PLATED STEEL UNCIRCULATED SET, 2006.

In 2006 the finish on all coins contained in these sets was changed to circulation. This was also the last year the composition mark "P" would b seen on coins in the sets.

DATE	DESCRIPTION	QUANTITY SOLD	ISSUE PRICE	FINISH	MS-65 NC
2006P	Standard 7 coins	28,213	19.95	Uncirculated	20.

MULTI-PLY PLATED STEEL UNCIRCULATED SETS, 2007-2010.

Starting in 2007 several changes were made to the Oh Canada! Set. All coins now carried the Royal Canadian Mint logo on the obverse, and the Caribou design on the twenty-five-cent coin was replaced by a coloured design. For the coloured designs of the twenty-five cent coins of 2007-2010, see pages 31-32.

DATE	DESCRIPTION	QUANTITY SOLD	ISSUE PRICE	FINISH	MS-65 NC
2007	Standard 6 coins, plus coloured 25¢ Maple Leaf; Folder	24,096	19.95	Uncirculated	30.
2008	Standard 6 coins, plus coloured 25¢ Canadian Flag; Folder	30,567	19.95	Uncirculated	25.
2009	Standard 6 coins, plus coloured 25¢ Four Maple Leaves; Folder	14,451	19.95	Uncirculated	25.
2010	Standard 6 coins, plus coloured 25¢ Three Maple Leaves; Folder	19,769	19.95	Uncirculated	20.

Note: The ten-cent coins contained in the 2007 Oh! Canada! sets are the Large, Near Logo obverse / Straight 7 reverse variety.

2017 O Canada! Gift Set

2018 O Canada! Gift Set

MULTI-PLY PLATED STEEL UNCIRCULATED SETS, 2011-2018

The 2011 Oh Canada! Set saw the return of the struck twenty-five cent piece. The reverse design is a single maple leaf.

The Oh Canada! Gift Set for 2012 contains the standard coins, 1¢, 5¢, 10¢, $1, $2, and a 25¢ coin with a struck multiple maple leaf design. The fifty-cent coin is not included in the set.

Coins contained in set:

2011	- 7 coins in set:	1¢, 5¢, 10¢, 25¢, 50¢, $1, $2
2012	- 6 coins in set:	1¢, 5¢, 10¢, 25¢, $1, $2
2013-2018	- 5 coins in set:	5¢, 10¢, 25¢, $1, $2

DATE	DESCRIPTION	QUANTITY SOLD	ISSUE PRICE	FINISH	MS-65
2011	Standard 6 coins, plus 25¢ Single maple leaf design, Folder	22,475	19.95	Uncirculated	20.
2012	Standard 5 coins; plus 25¢ Multiple maple leaf design, Folder	31,464	19.95	Uncirculated	20.
2013	Standard 4 coins, plus 25¢ Maple Leaf, Folder	26,068	19.95	Uncirculated	20.
2014	Standard 4 coins; plus $1 Maple Leaf, Folder	32,289	19.95	Uncirculated	20.
2015	Standard 4 coins, plus $1 Large Maple Leaf, Folder	23,705	19.95	Uncirculated	20.
2016	Standard 4 coins, plus $1 Large Maple Leaf, Folder	40,169	19.95	Uncirculated	20.
2017	Standard 4 coins, plus $1 Large Maple Leaf, Folder	20,652	21.95	Uncirculated	22.
2018	Standard 4 coins, plus $1 Maple Leaves & Keys	W.S.L.	21.95	Uncirculated	22.

Note: For the designs of the twenty-five cent coins contained in the sets of 2007-2018 see pages 31-34, the dollar coins can be found on page 131.

WEDDING GIFT SETS, 2004-2018

MULTI-PLY PLATED STEEL UNCIRCULATED SETS, 2004-2006.

The Gift Set line was expanded in 2004 to include a Wedding set, which included the seven standard circulating denominations housed in a colourful wedding folder. The finish on these sets is circulation.

DATE	DESCRIPTION	QUANTITY SOLD	ISSUE PRICE	FINISH	MS-65 NC
2004P	Standard 7 coin set; Folder	18,660	19.95	Uncirculated	15.
2005P	Standard 7 coin set; Folder	11,597	19.95	Uncirculated	20.
2006P	Standard 7 coin set; Folder	8,012	19.95	Uncirculated	20.

MULTI-PLY PLATED STEEL UNCIRCULATED SETS, 2007-2010.

In 2007 the standard twenty-five-cent Caribou design was replaced with a coloured design which changed each year. The finish on this set is uncirculated. The ten-cent coin contained in the 2007 Wedding Gift Set is the Large, Near Logo obverse / Straight 7 reverse variety.

The Wedding Gift Set was not issued in 2009, it was replaced by the Coins With Cards series (see page 34-35), however it was reintroduced in 2010

DATE	DESCRIPTION	QUANTITY SOLD	ISSUE PRICE	FINISH	MS-65 NC
2007	Standard 6 coins; plus coloured 25¢ Bouquet; Folder	10,687	19.95	Uncirculated	25.
2008	Standard 6 coins; plus coloured 25¢ Wedding Cake; Folder	7,407	19.95	Uncirculated	50.
2010	Standard 6 coins; plus coloured 25¢ Heart and Roses; Folder	8,194	19.95	Uncirculated	20.

MULTI-PLY PLATED STEEL UNCIRCULATED SETS, 2011-2017.

Coins contained in set:

2011 - 7 coins in set: 1¢, 5¢, 10¢, 25¢, 50¢, $1, $2   **2012** - 6 coins in set: 1¢, 5¢, 10¢, 25¢, $1, $2   **2013-2018** - 5 coins in set: 5¢, 10¢, 25¢, $1, $2

2017 Wedding Gift Set

2018 Wedding Gift Set

DATE	DESCRIPTION	QUANTITY SOLD	ISSUE PRICE	FINISH	MS-65 NC
2011	Standard 6 coins, plus 25¢ Wedding Rings, Folder	20,461	19.95	Uncirculated	20.
2012	Standard 5 coins; plus 25¢ Wedding Rings/Heart Folder	24,325	19.95	Uncirculated	20.
2013	Standard 4 coins; plus 25¢ Wedding Rings, Folder	20,317	19.95	Uncirculated	20.
2014	Standard 4 coins; plus $1 Two Turtle Doves, Folder	35,742	19.95	Uncirculated	25.
2015	Standard 4 coins, plus $1 Two Swans, Folder	23,927	19.95	Uncirculated	20.
2016	Standard 4 coins; plus $1 Wedding Bells, Folder	23,788	19.95	Uncirculated	20.
2017	Standard 4 coins; plus $1 Rose, Wedding Rings, Hearts, Folder	14,145	21.95	Uncirculated	22.
2018	Standard 4 coins, plus $1 Doves & Wedding Rings	W.S.L.	21.95	Uncirculated	22.

Note: For the designs of the twenty-five cent coins contained in the sets of 2007-2018 see pages 31-34.
For the design on the one dollar coin contained in the 2014-2018 set see page 131.

MISCELLANEOUS GIFT SETS, 1983-2007

The miscellaneous gift sets issued between 1983 and 2001 have a brilliant uncirculated finish, while sets from 2006 forward have a circulation finish.

2006 Québec Winter Carnival Gift Set

DATE	DESCRIPTION	QUANTITY SOLD	ISSUE PRICE	ISSUER	FINISH	MARKET VALUE
1983	British Royal Mint, Standard 6 coins	N/A	N/A	RCM,BRM	BU	100.
1998	Canadian Imperial Bank of Commerce,"Oh! Canada!" Set; Standard 7 coins	N/A	21.95	RCM	BU	25.
2001P	Canada 2001 Set, Standard 7 coins; Medallion	N/A	N/A	RCM	BU	15.
2001P	"OH! CANADA!", Banff, Standard 7 coins	500	22.95	RCM	BU	25.
2001P	"OH! CANADA!", Calgary, Standard 7 coins	500	22.95	RCM	BU	25.
2001P	"OH! CANADA!", Halifax, Standard 7 coins	500	22.95	RCM	BU	25.
2001P	"OH! CANADA!", Montreal, Standard 7 coins	500	22.95	RCM	BU	25.
2001P	"OH! CANADA!", Niagara Falls, Standard 7 coins	500	22.95	RCM	BU	25.
2001P	"OH! CANADA!", Quebec City, Standard 7 coins	500	22.95	RCM	BU	25.
2001P	"OH! CANADA!", R.C.M., Standard 7 coins	500	22.95	RCM	BU	25.
2001P	"OH! CANADA!", St. John's, Standard 7 coins	500	22.95	RCM	BU	25.
2001P	"OH! CANADA!", Vancouver, Standard 7 coins	500	22.95	RCM	BU	25.
2001P	"OH! CANADA!", Whistler, Standard 7 coins	500	22.95	RCM	BU	25.
2006P	QUEBEC WINTER CARNIVAL; Standard 6 coins; Colourised 25¢ "Bonhomme"; Festive folder	8,200	19.95	RCM	Circulation	25.
2007	Calendar Coin Set, Standard 7 coins	5,264	29.95	RCM	Circulation	25.

Note: 1. For the coloured design of the Quebec Winter Carnival twenty-five cent coin, see page 29.
2. The 2007 Calendar Coin Set contains the Large, Near Logo obverse / Straight 7 reverse.

VANCOUVER 2010 WINTER OLYMPIC AND PARALYMPIC GAMES COIN AND STAMP SETS, 2010

These sets were issued in conjunction with Canada Post in three versions: gold, silver and bronze.

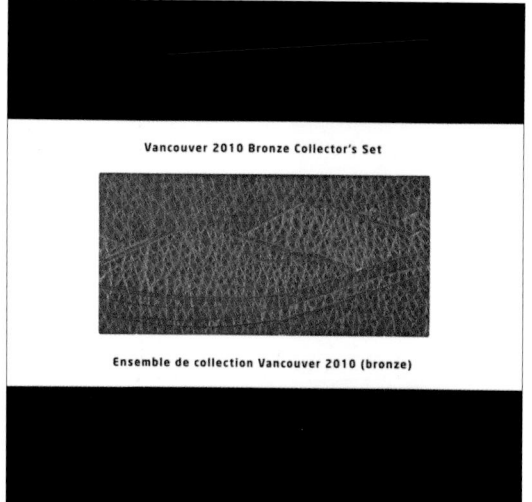

Bronze Collector Set

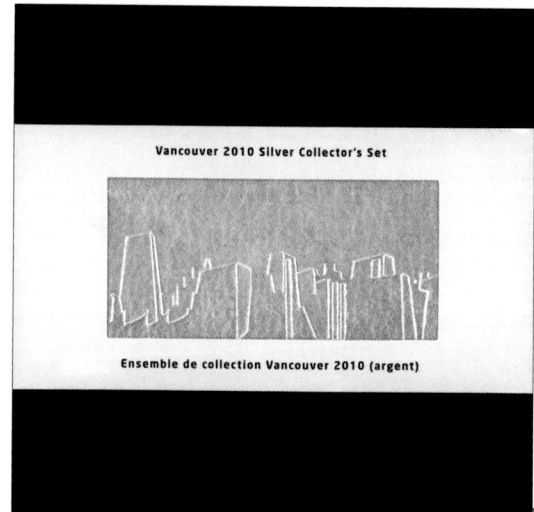

Silver Collector Set

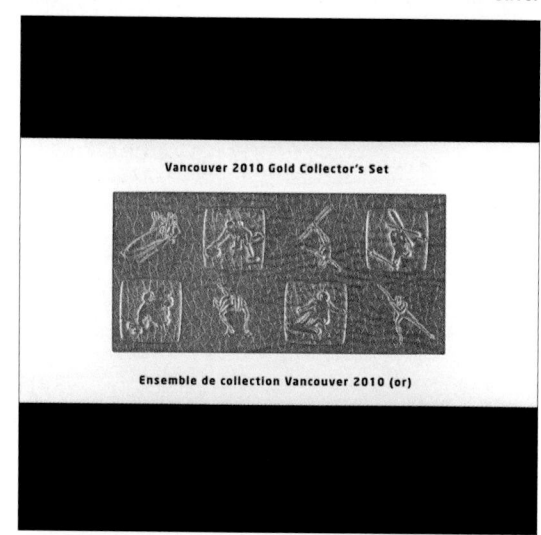

DATE	DESCRIPTION	QUANTITY SOLD	ISSUE PRICE	FINISH	MS-65 NC
2010	**Vancouver 2010 Emblems and Mascots Set, Bronze Collector Set**, Three 50¢ Mascot coins, Vancouver 2010 Souvenir Sheet of five Mascot theme stamps, 2 bronze lapel pins	16,000	49.95	Uncirculated	60.
2010	**Vancouver 2010 Winter Games Sports Set, Silver Collector Set**, Five painted 25¢ coins, Bobsleigh, Curling, Free Style Skiing, Ice Sledge Hockey, Snowboarding; Vancouver 2010 Souvenir Sheet of five Olympic theme stamps; 2 silver lapel pins	16,000	49.95	Uncirculated	60.
2010	**Vancouver 2010 Logo Set, Gold Collector Set**, Bronze Inukshuk dollar, Nickel painted Inukshuk dollar, 50¢ Inukshuk lenticular coin; Vancouver 2010 Souvenir Sheet of two stamps (Whistler and Vancouver) 2 gold plated pins.	11,991	49.95	Uncirculated	60.

COMMEMORATIVE CANADIAN COIN, TOKEN, OR MEDAL SETS, 2010-2013

COMMEMORATIVE CANADIAN COIN AND TOKEN SETS, 2010-2011.

These sets contain six coins: 1¢, 10¢, 25¢, 50¢, $1.00, $2.00, plus a copper token commemorating the Fair or Exposition where the set was introduced.

DATE	DESCRIPTION	QUANTITY SOLD	ISSUE PRICE	FINISH	MS-65 NC
2010	Beijing International Coin Exposition	500	N/A	BU	75.
2011	World's Money Fair Berlin	500	N/A	BU	75.

COMMEMORATIVE CANADIAN COIN AND MEDAL SETS, 2011.

These sets contain six coins: 1¢, 10¢, 25¢, 50¢, $1.00 $2.00, plus a copper medallion.

DATE	DESCRIPTION	QUANTITY SOLD	ISSUE PRICE	FINISH	MS-65 NC
2011	Royal Canadian Numismatic Association Convention	500	N/A	Uncirculated	75.
2011	American Numismatic Association	500	N/A	Uncirculated	75.
2011	Beijing International Coin Exposition	500	N/A	Uncirculated	75.

COMMEMORATIVE CANADIAN COIN AND TOKEN SET, 2012.

This set contains six coins: 1¢, 5¢, 10¢, 25¢, $1.00, $2.00 plus a nickel token commemorating the World Money Fair, Berlin, Germany.

DATE	DESCRIPTION	QUANTITY SOLD	ISSUE PRICE	FINISH	MS-65 NC
2012	World Money Fair, Berlin, Germany	500	N/A	Uncirculated	75.

COMMEMORATIVE CANADIAN COIN AND MEDAL SETS, 2012.

These sets contains six coins: 1¢, 5¢, 10¢, 25¢, $1.00 and $2.00 (coins with security devices), plus a nickel medallion commemorating each venue.

DATE	DESCRIPTION	QUANTITY SOLD	ISSUE PRICE	FINISH	MS-65 NC
2012	Royal Canadian Numismatic Association, Calgary	217	N/A	Circulation	80.
2012	American Numismatic Association, Philadelphia	97	N/A	Circulation	100.
2012	Beijing International Stamp and Coin Exposition, Beijing, China	500	N/A	Circulation	75.

COMMEMORATIVE COIN AND MEDAL SETS, 2013.

These set contains five coins: 5¢, 10¢, 25¢, $1.00 and $2.00 (the $1 and $2 coins have security devices) plus a nickel medallion commemorating each venue.

DATE	DESCRIPTION	QUANTITY SOLD	ISSUE PRICE	FINISH	MS-65 NC
2013	World Money Fair, Berlin, Germany	500	N/A	Circulation	75.
2013	Royal Canadian Numismatic Association, Winnipeg	667	19.95	Circulation	75.
2013	American Numismatic Association, Chicago	500	19.95	Circulation	75.
2013	Beijing International Stamp and Coin Exposition, Beijing, China	499	19.95	Circulation	75.

SEVEN COIN NICKEL CUSTOM SETS, 1971-1975

The custom set contains one coin of each denomination, with an extra cent to show the obverse. The finish of the coins is identical to the corresponding year of brilliant uncirculated, brilliant relief on a brilliant background.

Cases: 1971: Coins in black vinyl-covered case with Canada's coat of arms and the word "CANADA" stamped in gold on the top.
1972-1973: As 1971, except the outer case is red.
1974-1975: As 1971, except the outer case is maroon.

1973 Large Bust

1973 Large Bust

1973 Small Bust

1973 Small Bust

1973 Custom Set

DATE	DESCRIPTION	QUANTITY SOLD	ISSUE PRICE	FINISH	MS-65 NC
1971		33,517	6.50	BU	10.
1972		38,198	6.50	BU	10.
1973	Large Bust 25¢	49,376	6.50	BU	300.
1973	Small Bust 25¢	Included	6.50	BU	10.
1974		44,296	8.00	BU	10.
1975		36,581	8.00	BU	10.

SPECIMEN SETS, 1970-2018

SIX COIN NICKEL SPECIMEN SET, 1970

In 1968 the Royal Canadian Mint began to study the feasibility of offering for sale six-coin specimen sets to the public. The 1967 specimen set was extremely successful and opened the way for expanded offerings. Trial cases were prepared and a small number of specimen nickel and bronze coins of the years 1968 and 1969 were struck. These coins were not made available to the public.

In 1970 the Royal Canadian Mint provided special specimen sets to Prime Minister Pierre Trudeau for presentation purposes during his trip to China that year. A quantity of specimen sets in narrow cases were made up. After Trudeau's trip, some of these sets were sold to the public for $13 each. The total quantity of 1970 specimen sets issued in Canada is believed to be fewer than 1,000 and the only way 1970 specimen coins were available was in these sets. When the Mint made specimen sets available to the public starting in 1971, they were housed in larger, seven-coin cases. These sets are listed under prestige sets 1971-1980 on page 490.

In the early 1970's empty narrow specimen cases became available. The coins that could be housed in them were taken from prestige sets of the year.

Finish: Specimen, Brilliant relief on brilliant background

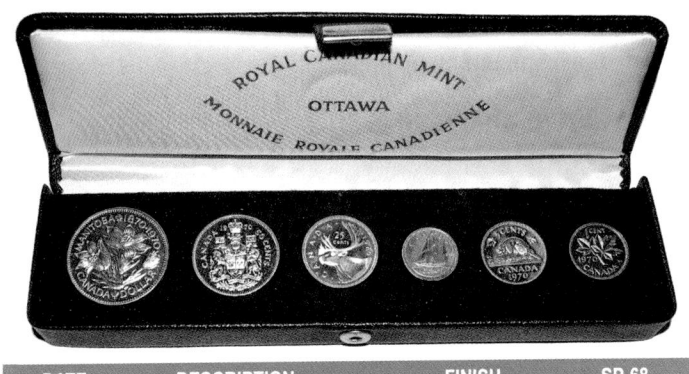

DATE	DESCRIPTION	FINISH	SP-68
1970	Specimen set in black case	Specimen	600.

SEVEN COIN NICKEL CUSTOM SPECIMEN SETS, 1976-1980

With the end of the 1976 Montreal Olympic Coin program, and with a new numismatic production facility now in place, the Mint staff turned their attention to improving the quality of their numismatic product line. The quality of the custom sets was upgraded to specimen. The packaging remained constant except for the modifications listed below.

Finish: Specimen, Brilliant relief on a parallel lined background
Cases: **1976-1978:** Coins in maroon vinyl-covered case with Canada's coat of arms and the word "CANADA" stamped in gold on the top.
     1979-1980: As 1977, except a gold maple leaf replaces the coat of arms and "CANADA"

DATE	DESCRIPTION	QUANTITY SOLD	ISSUE PRICE	FINISH	SP-68
1976 DJ	Voyageur	28,162	8.15	Specimen	12.
1977 AJ, SWL	Voyageur	44,198	8.15	Specimen	12.
1977 DJ, FWL	Voyageur	Included	8.15	Specimen	30.
1977 DJ, SWL	Voyageur	Included	8.15	Specimen	12.
1978 SJ 50¢	Voyageur	41,000	8.75	Specimen	12.
1978 RJ 50¢	Voyageur	Included	8.75	Specimen	25.
1979	Voyageur	31,174	10.75	Specimen	12.
1980	Voyageur	41,447	12.50	Specimen	12.

SIX COIN NICKEL SPECIMEN SETS, 1981-1996

1981 saw the first officially stated issue of specimen coinage. The package was redesigned, and the coins were marketed as being of specimen quality. The number of coins in the set was reduced to six. The finish on the coins from 1981 to 1995 was brilliant relief on a brilliant background, and in 1996 was changed to brilliant relief against parallel lined background.

Finish: **1981-1995:** Specimen, Brilliant relief on a brilliant background

1996: Specimen, Brilliant relief on a parallel lined background

Cases: **1981-1987:** Blue leatherette, booklet type (103 mm x 141 mm), inside a hinged blue plastic frame housing, six encapsulated coins. All enclosed in a silver box.

1988-1996: Blue leatherette, wallet type, (96 mm x 153 mm) silver stamped mint crest, inside clear plastic frame with blue plastic insert. All enclosed in a silver sleeve.

DATE	DESCRIPTION	QUANTITY SOLD	ISSUE PRICE	FINISH	SP-68
1981	Voyageur	71,300	10.00	Specimen	12.
1982	Voyageur	62,298	11.50	Specimen	12.
1983	Voyageur	60,329	12.75	Specimen	12.
1984	Voyageur	60,030	12.95	Specimen	12.
1985	Voyageur	61,533	12.95	Specimen	12.
1986	Voyageur	67,152	12.95	Specimen	12.
1987	Voyageur	74,441	14.00	Specimen	12.
1988	Loon	70,205	14.00	Specimen	14.
1989	Loon	66,855	16.95	Specimen	16.
1990	Loon	76,611	17.95	Specimen	16.
1991	Loon	68,552	17.95	Specimen	28.
1992 (1967-)	Loon	78,328	18.95	Specimen	22.
1993	Loon	77,351	18.95	Specimen	12.
1994	Loon	75,973	19.25	Specimen	12.
1995	Loon	77,326	19.25	Specimen	12.
1996	Loon	62,125	19.25	Specimen	25.

SEVEN COIN NICKEL SPECIMEN SETS, 1997-2000

In 1997 the two dollar coin was added to the set, raising the number of coins to seven. The set continued as specimen quality with the packaging being revised in 1998.

Finish: **1997-2000:** Specimen, Brilliant relief on a parallel lined background

Cases: **1997:** Blue leatherette, wallet type, (96 mm x 153 mm) silver stamped mint crest, inside clear plastic frame with blue plastic insert. All enclosed in a custom sleeve.

1998-2000: Green leatherette outer cover with RCM logo. All enclosed in a multicoloured box.

DATE	DESCRIPTION	QUANTITY SOLD	ISSUE PRICE	FINISH	SP-68
1997	Flying Loon/Bear	97,595	26.95	Specimen	32.
1998	Loon/Bear	67,697	26.95	Specimen	25.
1999	Loon/Bear	46,786	26.95	Specimen	25.
1999	Loon/Nunavut	45,104	26.95	Specimen	25.
2000	Loon/Bear	87,965	34.95	Specimen	25.
2000	Loon/Bears	Included	34.95	Specimen	25.

SIX OR SEVEN COIN MULTI-PLY PLATED STEEL SPECIMEN SETS, 2001-2017

The 2002 specimen set is a double anniversary set issued to commemorate the Golden Jubilee of Queen Elizabeth II, and the 15th anniversary of the Loon dollar coin which was introduced in 1987. This is the only set which contains the "Family of Loons" one dollar coin.

The 2004 issue carries the new uncrowned effigy of Queen Elizabeth II, by Susanna Blunt. In 2006 only the $2 coin carried the double date (1996-2006) which commemorated the tenth anniversary of the "Toonie".

From 2007 to 2009 all coins that comprise the specimen set carried the Royal Canadian Mint logo, but in 2010 the logo was discontinued.

In 2010 the finish used on specimen coinage was changed. The earlier finish, in use since 1996, was a variety of that used by the Bullion Department on their maple leaf coinage. However, this finish was surfacing on giftware coinage, so it is thought the time had arrived to again make specimen set coinage a distinct finish, brilliant relief on the obverse portrait and reverse design, with a frosted relief of the legends and date, all on a lined matte background.

The one dollar "Bird Series" that began in 1997 with the Flying Loon was continued to 2014 with the Ferruginous Hawk. For design illustrations of these coins see pages 121-122.

In 2012 production of the one cent coin was discontinued, bringing the number of coins in the specimen set to six.

Finish: **2001-2009:** Specimen, Brilliant relief on a raised lined background.
2010-2017: Specimen, Brilliant relief on obverse portrait and reverse design, frosted relief on legends and date, all on a laser lined background

Cases: Maroon leatherette display case, RCM Logo, black insert encased in clear plastic black shipping box.

DATE	DESCRIPTION	NO. OF COINS	QUANTITY SOLD	ISSUE PRICE	FINISH	SP-68
2001P	Loon	7	54,613	39.95	Specimen	25.
2002P (1952-)	Loon Family	7	67,672	39.95	Specimen	35.
2003P	Loon	7	41,640	39.95	Specimen	25.
2004P	Canada Goose	7	46,493	44.95	Specimen	45.
2005P	Tufted Puffin	7	39,818	39.95	Specimen	50.
2006P	Snowy Owl	7	39,935	44.95	Specimen	50.
2007	Trumpeter Swan	7	27,056	45.95	Specimen	60.
2008	Common Eider	7	21,227	45.95	Specimen	50.
2009	Great Blue Heron	7	21,677	47.95	Specimen	60.
2010	Northern Harrier	7	21,111	49.95	Specimen	55.
2011	Great Grey Owl	7	25,665	49.95	Specimen	55.
2012 (1987)	Loon with Chicks	7	34,975	49.95	Specimen	50.
2013	Blue-Winged Teal	6	28,884	49.95	Specimen	50.
2014	Ferruginous Hawk	6	24,381	49.95	Specimen	50.
2015	Blue Jay	6	22,739	49.95	Specimen	55.
2016	Tundra Swan	6	21,565	49.95	Specimen	55.
2017	Snow Goose	6	30,000	51.95	Specimen	52
2018	Burrowing Owl	6	30,000	51.95	Specimen	52.

Note:
1. The Loon Family design of 2002 commemorates the fifteenth anniversary of the $1.00 loon coin.
2. The ten cent coins contained in the 2007 specimen sets are the Small, Far Logo obverse / Curved 7 reverse variety.
3. The Loon Mother and Chicks design of 2012 commemorates the 25th anniversary of the $1.00 loon coin.

SPECIAL NOTE ON FINISHES

It is very important to understand the different finishes the Royal Canadian Mint uses on their various issues. These finishes are altered from time-to-time as the Mint develops new products.

For example, the brilliant relief against a parallel lined background finish first used on bullion coins was carried forward in 1996 to be used on the coins contained in the specimen set.

In 2006 this finish was used on giftware coins such as the twenty-five cent coin issued to celebrate the 80th birthday of Queen Elizabeth II.

In 2010 a new specimen finish, brilliant relief against a laser-lined background, was used for the coins contained in the specimen set. There are now two different specimen finishes being utilised on Canadian coinage.

Circulation and Brilliant Uncirculated (proof-like) finishes are another very confusing mixture of finishes, see page xii for a further explanation.

SPECIAL EDITION SPECIMEN SETS, 1967 and 2010-2015

100TH ANNIVERSARY OF CONFEDERATION, 1867-1967

In 1967 the Royal Canadian Mint produced two special cased coin sets to mark the 100th anniversary of Confederation. The silver medallion set in the red leather-covered case contained one each of the 1¢ to $1 (Proof-like finish) and a sterling silver medallion designed and modelled by Thomas Shingles. The gold presentation set contained a $20 gold coin and one each of the 1¢ to $1, all of specimen finish. This set was housed in a black leather presentation case.

DATE	DESCRIPTION	QUANTITY SOLD	ISSUE PRICE	FINISH	GRADE	PRICE
1967	Medallion	72,463	12.00	Proof-like	PL-65	70.
1967	Gold	337,687	40.00	Specimen	SP-68	950.

SPECIAL EDITION "YOUNG WILDLIFE" SPECIMEN SETS, 2010-2015

The two-dollar "YoungWildlife Series" that began in 2010 with Two Lynx Kittens was continued to 2015 with the Baby Racoons. For design illustrations of these coins see page 141.

A "finish" ten cent mule is found in the 2010 Lynx Specimen Set. The coin has an obverse with a brilliant relief on a raised lined background (2009 finish), and a reverse with a brilliant relief on the legend and date, with a lined matte finish background (2010 finish).

TEN CENT "FINISH" MULE

10¢ Obverse with
2009 Specimen Finish

10¢ Reverse with
2010 Specimen Finish

10¢ Finish Mule
Actual Size

Finish: Specimen, Brilliant relief on obverse portrait and revere design, frosted relief on legends and date, all on a laser lined background
Case of Issue: Maroon leatherette clam style case, RCM logo, 6- or 7-hole black insert in clear plastic, multicoloured box.

DATE	DESCRIPTION	NO. OF COINS	QUANTITY SOLD	ISSUE PRICE	FINISH	SP-68	SP-69
2010	$2 Two Lynx Kittens	7	14,790	49.95	Specimen	75.	—
2010	'Finish' Mule ten cent coin	7	Included	49.95	Specimen	300.	—
2011	$2 Elk Calf	7	13,899	49.95	Specimen	80.	—
2012	$2 Wolf Cubs	7	14,968	49.95	Specimen	70.	—
2013	$2 Black Bear Cubs	6	17,218	49.95	Specimen	50.	—
2014	$2 Baby Rabbits	6	11,886	49.95	Specimen	50.	—
2015	$2 Baby Racoons	6	8,504	49.95	Specimen	50.	

SPECIAL EDITION "CANADIAN ARCTIC EXPEDITION" SPECIMEN SET, 2013

This set contains a specimen silver dollar commemorating the 100th anniversary of the Canadian Arctic Expedition.

DATE	DESCRIPTION	NO. OF COINS	QUANTITY SOLD	ISSUE PRICE	FINISH	SP-68	SP-69
2013	Specimen Silver Dollar Set	7	9,787	99.95	Specimen	90.	—

PRESTIGE SETS, 1971-1980

SEVEN COIN PRESTIGE SETS, 1971-1980

When it was first introduced in 1971, the prestige set (double dollar set) contained two nickel dollars, with the second nickel dollar being used to display the obverse. This was also true for the 1972 set; however, from 1973 on the second nickel dollar was replaced with a silver dollar. The coins in the prestige sets were of specimen quality until 1980, and proof quality thereafter.

1974 Prestige Set

Finish: **1971-1980:** Specimen, Brilliant relief on a brilliant background

Cases: **1971-1973:** Crest of Canada; black leather, book type with clasp. Red satin inside red flocked 7-hole stationary display - coloured flocked jackets.

1974-1978: Crest of Canada; black leather, book type with clasp. Red satin inside, hinged black plastic 7-hole display, encapsulated coins - coloured flocked jackets.

1979-1980: Maple Leaf; black cardboard box, book type with clasp. Red satin inside, hinged black plastic 7-hole display, encapsulated coins - coloured flocked jackets.

DATE	DESCRIPTION	QUANTITY SOLD	ISSUE PRICE	FINISH	SP-68
1971	B.C./B.C.	66,860	12.00	Specimen	20.
1972	Voyageur/Voyageur	36,349	12.00	Specimen	45.
1973 LB 25¢	P.E.I./R.C.M.P.	119,891	12.00	Specimen	300.
1973 SB 25¢	P.E.I./R.C.M.P.	Included	12.00	Specimen	25.
1974	Winnipeg/Winnipeg	85,230	15.00	Specimen	25.
1974 DYT3	Winnipeg/Winnipeg	Included	15.00	Specimen	900.
1975	Voyageur/Calgary	97,263	15.00	Specimen	25.
1976	Voyageur/Parliament	87,744	16.00	Specimen	25.
1977	Voyageur/Jubilee	142,577	16.00	Specimen	25.
1977 SWL	Voyageur/Jubilee	Included	16.00	Specimen	30.
1978 SJ	Voyageur/Edmonton	147,000	16.50	Specimen	25.
1978 RJ	Voyageur/Edmonton	Included	16.50	Specimen	35.
1979	Voyageur/Griffon	155,698	18.50	Specimen	25.
1980	Voyageur/Polar Bear	162,875	36.00	Specimen	25.

Note: For images of the large bust (LB) and small bust (SB) twenty-five cent varieties of 1973, see page 540
For an image of the 1974 nickel dollar, double yoke type 3 variety, see page 513.
For an image of the 1977 nickel dollar, short water line (SWL) variety, see page 514.
For and image of the 1978 fifty cent, square jewels (SJ) and round jewels (RJ) varieties, see page 514.

PROOF SETS, 1981-2018

PROOF SETS, 1981-1995.

SEVEN STANDARD COINS

With the product reorganization in 1981, the standard coins of the Prestige Set were converted to Proof finish.

Finish: **1981-1995:** Proof, Frosted relief against a mirror background

Cases: **1981-1985:** Maple Leaf; black cardboard box, book type with clasp. Red satin inside, hinged black plastic 7-hole display, coloured flocked jackets.

1986-1995: Maple leaf; black plastic box, wallet type. Red satin inside, hinged black plastic 7-hole display, encapsulated coins

DATE	DESCRIPTION	QUANTITY SOLD	ISSUE PRICE	FINISH	PR-68
1981	Voyageur/Train	199,000	36.00	Proof	25.
1982	Voyageur/Skull	180,908	36.00	Proof	25.
1983	Voyageur/Games	166,779	36.00	Proof	25.
1984	Voyageur/Toronto	161,602	40.00	Proof	25.
1985	Voyageur/Parks	153,950	40.00	Proof	25.
1986	Voyageur/Vancouver	176,224	40.00	Proof	25.
1987	Voyageur/Davis Strait	175,686	43.00	Proof	25.
1988	Loon/Ironworks	175,259	43.00	Proof	25.
1989	Loon/MacKenzie	154,693	46.95	Proof	25.
1990	Loon/Kelsey	158,068	48.00	Proof	28.
1991	Loon/Frontenac	131,888	48.00	Proof	55.
1992	Loon/Stagecoach	147,061	49.75	Proof	35.
1993	Loon/Hockey	143,065	49.75	Proof	35.
1994	Loon/Dogsled Team	104,485	50.75	Proof	35.
1995	Loon/Hudson's Bay	101,560	50.75	Proof	35.

PROOF SET, 1996.

SEVEN COIN SET WITH FOUR STERLING SILVER COINS

Beginning in 1996, the five, ten, twenty-five and fifty cent coins were struck on sterling silver planchets (92.5% Ag and 7.5% Cu). The one cent, and both the nickel and silver dollars were of standard specifications.

Finish: Proof, Frosted relief against a mirror background
Case of Issue: Maple Leaf logo; black leatherette wallet type case. Red satin inside, hinged black plastic 7-hole display, encapsulated coins

DATE	DESCRIPTION	QUANTITY SOLD	ISSUE PRICE	FINISH	PR-68
1996	Loon/McIntosh	112,835	66.25	Proof	55.

EIGHT COIN SET WITH FIVE STERLING SILVER COINS 1997-2011

In 1997 the two dollar coin was added to the set, raising the total to eight coins. The two dollar coin, following the practice established in 1996, was made of sterling silver with a gold-plated centre. The one cent coin up to and including 2003, was not of the multi-ply plated steel, but of bronze composition.

Mid-year 2003 the tiara portrait of Elizabeth II, which had been in use since 1990, was replaced with the new uncrowned portrait by Susanna Blunt. The first Proof set with the new portrait was dated 2004.

The 2005 Proof set was the first set to feature a commemorative dollar selectively gold plated on the reverse and rim.

1997 Proof Set

Finish: **1997:** Proof, frosted relief against a mirror background
Case of Issue: 1997: Maple Leaf logo; black leather wallet type case. Red satin inside, hinged black plastic 7-hole
display, encapsulated coins

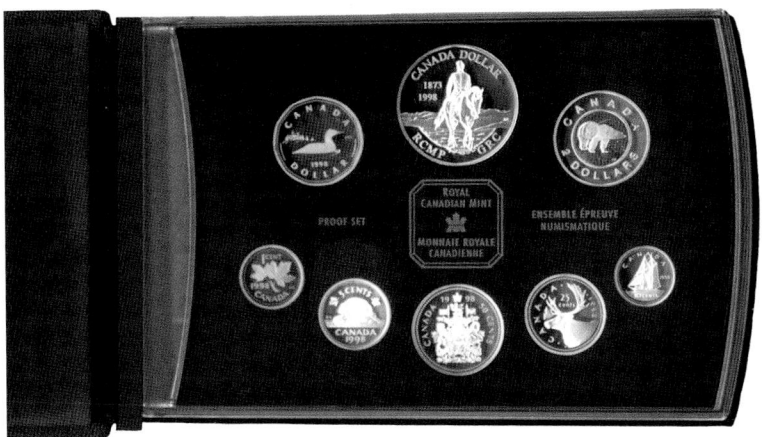

1998 Proof Set

Finish: 1998-2003: Proof, frosted relief against a mirror background
Cases: 1998-2003: Mint logo; dark green leather wallet style case, black plastic 8-hole insert, encapsulated coins,
green flocked interior; four-colour outer box

2005 Proof Set

Finish: **2004-2011:** Proof, frosted relief against a mirror background
Cases: **2004-2011:** Mint logo; maroon leather wallet style case, black plastic 8-hole insert, encapsulated coins,
                      black flocked interior; black outer box

DATE	DESCRIPTION	QUANTITY SOLD	ISSUE PRICE	FINISH	PR-69
1997	Loon/Hockey/Polar Bear	113,647	79.95	Proof	70.
1997	CNA Edition signed Cournoyer / Ferguson	N/A	N/A	Proof	90.
1997	ANA Edition, signed Gilbert / Park	N/A	N/A	Proof	90.
1998	Loon/R.C.M.P./Polar Bear	93,632	79.95	Proof	70.
1999	Loon/Juan Perez/Polar Bear	95,113	79.95	Proof	70.
2000	Loon/Discovery/Polar Bear	90,921	79.95	Proof	70.
2001	Loon/Ballet/Polar Bear	74,194	81.95	Proof	70.
2001	ANA Edition	750	69.95	Proof	90.
2001	CNA Edition	N/A	89.95	Proof	90.
2002 (1952-)	Loon/Queen Elizabeth II/Polar Bear	65,315	81.95	Proof	70.
2002 (1952-)	ANA Edition	500	69.95	Proof	90.
2003	Loon/Cobalt/Polar Bear	62,007	81.95	Proof	70.
2003	ANA Edition	500	74.95	Proof	90.
2004	Loon/French Settlement/Polar Bear	57,614	83.92	Proof	70.
2004	ANA Edition	500	74.95	Proof	90.
2004	CNA Edition	250	74.95	Proof	90.
2005	Loon/Flag (gold plated) /Polar Bear	63,562	81.95	Proof	80.
2005	CNA Edition	197	74.95	Proof	100.
2006 (1996-)	Loon/Victoria Cross (gold plated) /Polar Bear	53,822	84.95	Proof	85.
2006	CNA Edition	200	84.95	Proof	100.
2007	Loon/Thayendanegea (gold plated)/Polar Bear	37,413	89.95	Proof	90.
2008	Loon/Quebec City (gold plated)/Polar Bear	38,630	89.95	Proof	90.
2009	Loon/First Flight (gold plated)/Polar Bear	27,549	99.95	Proof	90.
2009	RCNA Edition	200	99.95	Proof	100.
2010	Loon/Corvette (gold plated)/Polar Bear	32,342	109.95	Proof	90.
2011 (1911-)	Loon/Parks (gold plated)/Canada/Bear	32,910	114.95	Proof	90.

Note: The ten cent coins contained in the 2007 proof sets are the Small, Far Logo obverse / Curved 7 reverse variety.

EIGHT STANDARD COINS, 2012

For the first time two variations of the Proof set were issued in 2012: a standard Proof set where all coins are struck in their standard circulation alloys, and a premium fine silver Proof set where all coins are struck in 99.99% pure silver.

Finish: Proof, frosted relief against a mirror background
Case of Issue: Mint logo; maroon leatherette case with black plastic 8-hole insert, encapsulated coins, black interior, black outer box

DATE	DESCRIPTION	QUANTITY SOLD	ISSUE PRICE	FINISH	PR-69
2012 (1812-)	Loon/War of 1812/Polar Bear	27,254	99.95	Proof	90.

PREMIUM PROOF SET, 2012
EIGHT COIN SET, FINE SILVER

2012 Premium Proof Set

Finish: Proof, frosted relief against a mirror background
Case of Issue: Mint logo; black genuine leather case with black plastic 8-hole insert, encapsulated coins, black flocked interior, black outer box

DATE	DESCRIPTION	QUANTITY SOLD	ISSUE PRICE	FINISH	PR-69
2012 (1812-)	Loon/War of 1812 (gold plated)/Polar Bear	19,789	224.95	Proof	150.

PREMIUM PROOF SETS, 2013-2018

SEVEN COIN SET, FINE SILVER

With the one cent coin being phased out in 2012, the number of coins contained in the premium Proof sets is now reduced to seven. Each coin contained in these sets is struck on a fine silver planchet.

2013 Premium Proof Set

Finish: Proof, frosted relief against a mirror background
Case of Issue: Mint logo; black genuine leather case with black plastic 7-hole insert, encapsulated coins, black flocked interior, black outer box

DATE	DESCRIPTION	QUANTITY SOLD	ISSUE PRICE	FINISH	PR-69
2013	100th Anniv. Canadian Arctic Expedition	20,338	229.95	Proof	200.
2013	100th Anniv. Canadian Arctic Expedition, RCNA Edition	427	229.95	Proof	250.
2014	100th Anniv. of the Start of World War I	13,416	229.95	Proof	220.
2015	50th Anniv. of the Canadian Flag	20,000	229.95	Proof	230.
2016	150th Anniv. of the Transatlantic Cable	20,000	229.95	Proof	230.
2017	150th Anniv. of Canadian Confederation	20,000	234.95	Proof	235
2017	150h Anniv. Our Home and Native Land	20,000	229.95	Proof	275.

PROOF SET, 2014-2017

SEVEN STANDARD COINS

Again, in 2014 two varieties of proof sets were issued. This set contains seven proof coins struck on the standard alloys.

Finish: Proof, frosted relief against a mirror background
Case of Issue: Mint logo; maroon leatherette case with black plastic 7-hole insert, encapsulated coins, black interior, black outer box

DATE	DESCRIPTION	QUANTITY SOLD	ISSUE PRICE	FINISH	PR-69
2014	100th Anniv. Declaration of First World War	11,251	99.95	Proof	100.
2015	50th Anniv. of the Canadian Flag	20,000	99.95	Proof	100.
2016	150th Anniv. of the Transatlantic Cable	12,500	99.95	Proof	100.
2017	150th Anniv. Our Home and Native Land	25,000	99.95	Proof	100

SPECIAL ISSUE PROOF SETS, 1994-2012 and 2018

SPECIAL LIMITED EDITION PROOF SETS, 1994-1995

First issued in 1994, these Proof sets were limited to 50,000. They contained the silver commemorative dollar, along with the bronze/nickel commemorative of the year. The other five coins are the same as contained in the Proof set of that year.

Finish: Proof, frosted relief against a mirror background
Case of Issue: Burgundy display case, wallet type, dated on spine with year of issue. Interior: White satin with brown plastic display frame
   - burgundy plastic box. Over time, the colour of the case and box fades.

DATE	DESCRIPTION	QUANTITY SOLD	ISSUE PRICE	FINISH	PR-69
1994	Remembrance/Dog Team Patrol	49,222	59.50	Proof	40.
1995	Peacekeeping/Hudson's Bay	49,802	66.95	Proof	40.

90th ANNIVERSARY OF THE ROYAL CANADIAN MINT, 1908-1998

Issued to commemorate the 90th Anniversary of the Royal Canadian Mint, this five-coin set features the same reverse designs as the original 1908 coins, except for the double date 1908-1998. The set was issued in two finishes, matte and mirror proof. The matte one cent coin does not carry the country of origin, "Canada." This error was corrected on the mirror proof cent.

1¢ Matte Issue Without CANADA

1¢ Mirror Issue With CANADA

Designers:
Obv.: Dora de Pédery-Hunt
Rev.: Ago Aarand

Engravers:
Obv.: Dora de Pédery-Hunt
Rev.: 1¢ – G. W. DeSaulles
5¢, 10¢, 25¢, 50¢ –
W. H. J. Blakemore

1¢ Mirror Issue

5¢ Mirror Issue

10¢ Mirror Issue

25¢ Mirror Issue

50¢ Mirror Issue

Finish: Proof, matte or mirror
Case of Issue: Burgundy leather clam style case, RCM Mint logo, white lining, five-hole plastic insert, COA
   Matte set with bronze logo on case. Mirror set with nickel logo on the case

COIN	COMPOSITION	WEIGHT	DIAMETER	EDGE	DIE AXIS
1¢	92.5% Ag, 7.5% Cu, copper plated	5.90	25.30	Plain	↑↑
5¢	92.5% Ag, 7.5% Cu	1.30	15.25	Reeded	↑↑
10¢	92.5% Ag, 7.5% Cu	2.50	17.90	Reeded	↑↑
25¢	92.5% Ag, 7.5% Cu	5.80	23.50	Reeded	↑↑
50¢	92.5% Ag, 7.5% Cu	11.80	29.60	Reeded	↑↑

DATE	DESCRIPTION	QUANTITY SOLD	ISSUE PRICE	FINISH	PR-69
1998 (1908-)	Without "CANADA" on 1¢	24,893	99.00	Matte proof	60.
1998 (1908-)	With "CANADA" on 1¢	18,376	99.00	Mirror proof	60.

SPECIAL LIMITED EDITION PROOF SETS, 2002-2003

The Special Edition Proof Set for 1952-2002 contains the 2002 commemorative dollar (22kt gold plated), the two-dollar coin with a 24kt gold plated inner core, and the 2002 fifty-cent commemorative coin. The remaining coins in the set are as the regular issue.

The coins in the Special Edition Proof Set for 1953-2003, carry the laureate portrait of Queen Elizabeth II which was first issued in 1953. This set commemorates Queen Elizabeth II's Coronation in 1953, and her Jubilee in 2003, with the double date 1953-2003.

Finish: Proof, frosted relief against a mirror background

DATE	DESCRIPTION	QUANTITY SOLD	ISSUE PRICE	FINISH	PR-69
2002 (1952-)	Accession, Gold Plated $1 coin	33,490	99.95	Proof	80.
2003 (1953-)	Coronation	21,537	99.95	Proof	90.

PREMIUM GIFT BABY AND WEDDING, STERLING SILVER PROOF SETS, 2006-2008

This set contains a commemorative sterling silver loon dollar and a commemorative medallion; the remaining coins are the regular Proof set issue.

2006 Premium Gift Baby Proof Set

2006 Premium Gift Baby Proof Set

Finish: Proof, frosted relief, against mirror background   **Case of Issue:**   Leatherette folder

DATE	DESCRIPTION	QUANTITY SOLD	ISSUE PRICE	FINISH	PR-69
2006	Sterling Silver Loon, Lullaby Loonie, Teddy Bear Medallion	3,863	79.95	Proof	225.
2007	Sterling Silver "Gold Plated Rattle", Baby Medallion	1,911	89.95	Proof	900.
2007	Sterling Silver Loon, Wedding Medallion	849	89.95	Proof	900.
2008	Sterling Silver Loon, Baby Medallion	1,168	99.95	Proof	250.
2008	Sterling Silver Loon, Wedding Medallion	508	99.95	Proof	800.

SPECIAL LIMITED EDITION PROOF SET, 2010

Canada's first circulating silver dollar was introduced in 1935 featuring Emanuel Hahn's classic Voyageur design. This special edition Proof set, with four other coins carrying the 1935 design commemorates the 75th anniversary of our famous dollar.

Finish: Proof
Case of Issue: Maple wood display case

DATE	DESCRIPTION	QUANTITY SOLD	ISSUE PRICE	FINISH	PR-69
2010 (1935-)	75th Anniv. of the Voyageur Dollar	4,996	159.95	Proof	230.

SPECIAL LIMITED EDITION PROOF SET, 1911-2011

This set was Issued to commemorate the 100th Anniversary of the striking of the 1911 silver dollars.

1¢ Obverse

1¢ Reverse

Designers and Engravers:
Obv.: Sir E. B. MacKennal
Rev.: 1¢, 5¢, 10¢, 25¢, 50¢ –
Original design by L. C. Wyon,
Modified by W. H. J. Blakemore

Finish: Proof
Case of Issue: Cherry wood box

| 5¢ | 10¢ | 25¢ | 50¢ | One Dollar |

DATE	DESCRIPTION	QUANTITY SOLD	ISSUE PRICE	FINISH	PR-69
2011 (1911-)	100th Anniv. of the 1911 Silver Dollar	5,952	179.95	Proof	260.

SPECIAL LIMITED EDITION PROOF SET, 2012

FAREWELL TO THE PENNY, 2012
This set was issued to commemorate the withdrawal of the one cent coin from circulation Also see page 6.

OBVERSE DESIGNS

| George W. DeSaulles 1908-1910 | Sir E. B. MacKennal 1911-1920 | Sir E. B. MacKennal 1920-1936 | Arnold Machin 1967 | Susanna Blunt 2003-2012 |

REVERSE DESIGNS

| George W. DeSaulles 1908-1910 | W. H. J. Blakemore 1911-1920 | Fred Lewis 1920-1936 | Alex Colville 1967 | G. E. Kruger-Gray 1937-2012 |

Designers:
Obv.:   See obverse illustrations
Rev.:   See reverse illustrations

Engravers:
Obv.:   Susan Taylor
Rev.:   Samantha Strath

Composition: 99.99% au
Silver content: 14.7 g, 0.473 (per set)
Weight: 2.94 g (per coin); 14.7 (set)
Diameter: 19.1
Thickness: N/A
Case of Issue: RCM branded wooden case, black flocked insert, encapsulated coins, COA, custom box

Edge: Plain
Die Axis: ↑↑
Finish: Proof

DATE	DESCRIPTION	QUANTITY SOLD	ISSUE PRICE	FINISH	PR-69
2012	Farewell to the Penny	5,001	149.95	Proof	400.

SPECIAL LIMITED EDITION PROOF SET, 2015

FIVE CENTS, LEGACY OF THE CANADIAN NICKEL, 2015.

This six coin set celebrates the history of the Canadian five-cent piece that was first minted in Canada after the Ottawa branch of the Royal Mint opened in 1908. Prior to that, Canadian coins were struck at the Royal Mint in England or the Birmingham Mint in Birmingham, England. Featuring the effigies of reigning monarchs at the time, the coins are larger than their original size. From originally containing sterling silver, to silver's removal from the coin in 1922, to an entirely-nickel composition, and a later tombac alloy due to the war's need for nickel in the 1940s, the five cent coin's current plated steel composition has changed through the years.

| Obverse:
King George V
Designer:
E.B. MacKennal
Engraver: RCM Staff | The Crossed
Maple Boughs
Designer:
W.H.J. Blakemore
Engraver: RCM Staff | The Two Maple
Leaves
Designer:
W.H.J. Blakemore
Engraver: RCM Staff | Obverse:
King George VI
Designer: T.H. Paget
Engraver:
Thomas Shingles | The Victory
Designer & Engraver:
Thomas Shingles | The Identification of
Nickel
Des.: Stephan Trenka
Engraver:
Thomas Shingles |

| Obverse: Elizabeth II
Designer:
Arnold Machin
Engraver: RCM Staff | The Centennial Five Cents
Designer:
Alex Colville
Engraver: Myron Cook | Obverse: Elizabeth II
Designer:
Susanna Blunt
Engraver: Susan Taylor | The Beaver
Designer:
G.E. Kruger-Gray
Engraver: RCM Staff |

Designers:
    Obv.:   See obverse illustrations
    Rev.:   See reverse illustrations
Composition: 99.99% Ag, Selectively gold plated
Silver Content: 31.83 g, 1.02 tr oz
Weight: 31.83 g
Diameter: 40.0 mm
Thickness: N/A

Engravers:
    Obv.:   See obverse illustrations
    Rev.:   See reverse illustrations

Edge: Reeded
Die Axis: ↑↑
Finish: Proof

Case of Issue: Singly: Maroon leatherette clam style case, black flocked insert, encapsulated coin, COA
Subscription: Six-hole wooden case, black flocked insert, encapsulated coins, COA

DATE	DESCRIPTION	QUANTITY SOLD	ISSUE PRICE	FINISH	PR-69	PR-70
2015	The Crossed Maple Boughs	6,690	109.95	Proof	100.	—
2015	The Two Maple Leaves	6,243	109.95	Proof	100.	—
2015	The Victory	6,251	109.95	Proof	100.	—
2015	The Identification of Nickel	5,595	109.95	Proof	100.	—
2015	The Centennial Five Cents	5,993	109.95	Proof	100.	—
2015	The Beaver	5,682	109.95	Proof	100.	—

SPECIAL LIMITED EDITION PROOF SET, 2017

ONE CENT, THE LEGACY OF THE PENNY, 2017.
This 5-coin set commemorates the 5th anniversary of the end of the penny's production. See also page 6

Small leaves design (1908)	Small leaves design (1911)
Designer and Engraver: George W. DeSaulles	Designer: W.H.J. Blakemore Obverse: Sir E.B. MacKennal

Two maple leaves design (1920)	Centennial design (1967)	Maple twig design (1982)
Designer: Fred Lewis	Designer: Alex Colville	Designer: G.E. Kruger-Gray
Engraver: Sir E.B. MacKennal	Engraver: Arnold Machin	Engraver: Arnold Machin

Designers:
    Obv.:   See illustrations
    Rev.:   See illustrations

Engravers:
    Obv.:   See illustrations
    Rev.:   See illustrations

Composition: 99.99% Ag, selective rose gold plating
Silver content: 157.6 g, 5.06 tr oz

	Small leaves design (1908)	Small leaves design (1911)	Two maple leaves design (1920)	Centennial design (1967)	Maple twig design (1982)
Weight:	62.67 g	62.67 g	31.39 g	31.39 g	31.39 g
Diameter:	54.0 mm	54.0 mm	38.0 mm	38.0 mm	38.0 mm
Thickness:	N/A				
Edge:	Reeded				
Die Axis:	↑↑				
Finish:	Proof				
Case of Issue:	Wooden collector's case with black beauty box. COA				

DATE	DESCRIPTION	QUANTITY SOLD	ISSUE PRICE	FINISH	PR-69
2017	Legacy of the Penny, Fine silver	1,946	709.95	Proof	650.

ROYAL CANADIAN MINT COIN LORE, 3-COIN SET, 2017

ROYAL CANADIAN MINT COIN LORE: THE FORGOTTEN 1927 DESIGNS, 2017.

In 1927, three circulation coin designs were chosen to commemorate Confederation's Diamond Jubilee; alas, they never made it onto a single coin. Ninety years later, the RCM re-visited some of Canada's coin lore, to issue this three-coin set, which artfully bridges the past and Canada 150.

Common Obverse	1 Cent Obv.: E.B. MacKennal Rev.: Gustav Hahan	5 Cents Obv.: E.B. MacKennal Rev.: J.E.H. MacDonald	25 Cents Obv.: E.B. MacKennal Rev.: J.E.H. MacDonald

Designers:
  Obv.: See illustrations
  Rev.: See reverse illustrations
Composition: 99.99% au
Silver content: 14.7 g, 0.473 (per set)
Weight: 31.39 g (per coin)
Diameter: 38 mm
Thickness: N/A
Case of Issue: Maroon clamshell with standard black beauty box. COA.

Engravers:
  Obv.: See illustrations
  Rev.: See Illustrations

Edge: Reeded
Die Axis: ↑↑
Finish: Reverse Proof

DATE	DESCRIPTION	MINTAGE	ISSUE PRICE	FINISH	PR-69
2017	The Forgotten 1927 Designs	5,500	269.95	Reverse Proof	270.

SPECIAL LIMITED EDITION PROOF SET, 2018

TEN CENTS, LEGACY OF THE DIME, 2018.

The Legacy of the Dime set is a uique retropsective look at Canada's 10-cent circulation coin through the years, as struck by the Royal Canadian Mint.

1936 Dot
Reverse: W.H.J. Blakemore Obv.: Sir E.B. MacKennal

1947 Maple Leaf
Reverse: Emanuel Hahn Obverse: T.H. Paget

1967 Centennial
Reverse: Alex Colville
Obverse: Arnold Machin

2001 Year of the Volunteer
Reverse: RCM Staff
Obverse: Dora de Pédery-Hunt

2017 Wing of Peace)
Reverse: Amy Choi
Obverse: Susanna Blunt

Designers:		Engravers:	
Obv.:	See illustrations	Obv.:	See illustrations
Rev.:	See illustrations	Rev.:	See illustrations

Composition: 99.99% Ag, selective gold plating
Silver content: 157.6 g, 5.06 tr oz

	1936 Dot	1947 Maple Leaf	1967 Centennial	2001 Year of the Volunteer	2017 Wing of Peace
Weight:	62.67 g	62.67 g	31.39 g	31.39 g	31.39 g
Diameter:	54.0 mm	54.0 mm	38.0 mm	38.0 mm	38.0 mm
Thickness:	N/A				
Edge:	Reeded				
Die Axis:	↑↑				
Finish:	Proof				
Case of Issue:	Wooden collector's case with black beauty box. COA				

DATE	DESCRIPTION	MINTAGE	ISSUE PRICE	FINISH	PR-69	PR-70
2018	Legacy of the Dime Set, Fine silver	3,000	709.95	Proof	710.	—

PROOF GOLD SET

YEAR OF THE DRAGON, 2012.

The reverse design on these coins features a mythical water dragon surrounded by lotus flowers and clouds of good fortune, the Chinese lunar symbol for the year 2012.

Obverse

Physical and chemical specifications:

	$50	$20	$10	$5
Denomination:	$50	$20	$10	$5
Weight (oz):	1.0	0.5	0.25	0.1
Diameter (mm):	30.0	25.0	20.0	16.0
Thickness (mm):	N/A	N/A	N/A	N/A
Composition:	99.99% Au			
Gold content:				
Grams	31.15	15.59	7.8	3.13
Troy ounces	1.00	0.50	0.25	0.10
Edge:	Reeded			
Die Axis:	↑↑			
Finish:	Proof			
Case of Issue:	Gold silk-covered case, black suede four-hole insert, encapsulated, COA			

$50

$20

$10

$5

Designers:
Obv.:   Susanna Blunt
Rev.:   Susan Taylor

Engravers:
Rev.:   Three Degrees Creative Group Inc.
Rev.:   Cecily Mok

DATE	DESCRIPTION	QUANTITY SOLD	ISSUE PRICE	FINISH	PR-69	PR-70
2012	Year of the Dragon	357	5,499.95	Proof	5,500.	—

PROOF PLATINUM SETS

In 1990 the Royal Canadian Mint entered the luxury market for high quality collector coins. While the proof platinum sets are scarc their value is linked to the market price of platinum. The value of these sets is based on a Canadian market price of $1,540. for platinum as of Apr 23rd, 2014.

CANADIAN WILDLIFE SERIES, 1990-1994.

1990-1994 Obverse

Physical and chemical specifications:

	$300	$150	$75	$30
Denomination:	$300	$150	$75	$30
Weight (oz):	1.0	0.5	0.25	0.1
Diameter (mm):	30.0	25.0	20.0	16.0
Thickness (mm):	2.6	2.12	1.65	1.08

Composition: 99.95% Pt

Platinum content:

Grams	31.1	15.55	7.75	3.1
Troy ounces	1.0	0.5	0.25	0.1

Edge: Reeded
Die Axis: ↑↑
Finish: Proof
Case of Issue: 1992-1994: Walnut case, black suede four hole insert, encapsulated, COA

POLAR BEARS PLATINUM SET 1990.

Canada's "Monarch of the North" has been transferred by Robert Bateman from the sparkling Arctic environment to the gleaming surfaces of pure platinum coins.

$300 $150 $75 $30

Designers:
Obv.:   Dora de Pédery-Hunt
Rev.:   Robert Bateman
Engravers:
Obv.:   Dora de Pédery-Hunt
Rev.: $300 - Terry Smith
         $150 - William Woodruff
         $ 75 - Ago Aarand
         $ 30 - Sheldon Beveridge

DATE	DESCRIPTION	QUANTITY SOLD	ISSUE PRICE	FINISH	PR-68	PR-69
1990	Polar Bears, Set of 4 coins	2,629	1,990.00	Proof	3,300.	—

SNOWY OWLS PLATINUM SET 1991.

This is the second set in the series of Proof platinum coins dedicated to Canadian wildlife.

$300 $150 $75 $30

Designers:
Obv.:   Dora de Pédery-Hunt
Rev.:   Glen Loates
Engravers:
Obv.:   Dora de Pédery-Hunt
Rev.: $300 - Sheldon Beveridge
         $150 - Ago Aarand
         $ 75 - Terry Smith
         $ 30 - William Woodruff

DATE	DESCRIPTION	QUANTITY SOLD	ISSUE PRICE	FINISH	PR-68	PR-69
1991	Snowy Owls, Set of 4 coins	1,164	1,990.00	Proof	3,300.	—

COUGARS PLATINUM SET 1992.

This is the third set in the series of Proof platinum coins dedicated to Canadian wildlife.

| $300 | $150 | $75 | $30 |

Designers:
Obv.: Dora de Pédery-Hunt
Rev.: George McLean

Engravers:
Obv.: Dora de Pédery-Hunt
Rev.: $300 - Ago Aarand,
Cosme Saffioti
$150 - Susan Taylor
$ 75 - Sheldon Beveridge
$ 30 - Ago Aarand

DATE	DESCRIPTION	QUANTITY SOLD	ISSUE PRICE	FINISH	PR-69	PR-70
1992	Cougars, Set of 4 coins	1,081	1,955.00	Proof	3,300.	—

ARCTIC FOXES PLATINUM SET 1993.

This is the fourth set in the series of Proof platinum coins dedicated to Canadian wildlife.

| $300 | $150 | $75 | $30 |

Designers:
Obv.: Dora de Pédery-Hunt
Rev.: Claudio D'Angelo

Engravers:
Obv.: Dora de Pédery-Hunt
Rev.: $300 - Susan Taylor
$150 - Sheldon Beveridge
$ 75 - Ago Aarand
$ 30 - Ago Aarand

DATE	DESCRIPTION	QUANTITY SOLD	ISSUE PRICE	FINISH	PR-69	PR-70
1993	Arctic Foxes, Set of 4 coins	1,033	1,955.00	Proof	3,300.	—

SEA OTTERS PLATINUM SET 1994.

This is the fifth and last set in the series of Proof platinum coins dedicated to Canadian wildlife.

| $300 | $150 | $75 | $30 |

Designers:
Obv.: Dora de Pédery-Hunt
Rev.: Ron S. Parker

Engravers:
Obv.: Dora de Pédery-Hunt
Rev.: $300 - Sheldon Beveridge
$150 - William Woodruff
$ 75 - Terry Smith
$ 30 - Susan Taylor

DATE	DESCRIPTION	QUANTITY SOLD	ISSUE PRICE	FINISH	PR-69	PR-70
1994	Sea Otters, Set of 4 coins	766	1,995.00	Proof	3,300.	—

ENDANGERED WILDLIFE SERIES, 1995-2004

Specifications: See page 560
Case of Issue:
1/10 oz coin: Leather display case, encapsulated coin
½ oz coin: Mahogany case, encapsulated coin
Set, 4 coins: Mahogany case, inside green satin, coins individually
                 encapsulated

CANADA LYNX PLATINUM SET, 1995.

This is the first set in the series of Proof platinum coins commemorating Canada's endangered wildlife.

Designers:
Obv.:   Dora de Pédery-Hunt
Rev.:   Michael Dumas
Engravers:
Obv.:   Dora de Pédery-Hunt
Rev.: $300 - Susan Taylor
         $150 - Cosme Saffioti
         $ 75 - Stan Witten
         $ 30 - Ago Aarand

$300 $150 $75 $30

DATE	DESCRIPTION	QUANTITY SOLD	ISSUE PRICE	FINISH	PR-68	PR-69
1995	30 Dollars	620	179.95	Proof	200.	—.
1995	150 Dollars	226	599.95	Proof	800.	—
1995	Canada Lynx, Set of 4 coins	682	1,950.00	Proof	3,300.	—

PEREGRINE FALCON PLATINUM SET, 1996.

This is the second set in the series of Proof platinum coins commemorating Canada's endangered wildlife.

Designers:
Obv.:   Dora de Pédery-Hunt
Rev.:   Dwayne Harty
Engravers:
Obv.:   Dora de Pédery-Hunt
Rev.: $300 - Sheldon Beveridge
         $150 - Stan Witten
         $ 75 - Cosme Saffioti
         $ 30 - Ago Aarand

$300 $150 $75 $30

DATE	DESCRIPTION	QUANTITY SOLD	ISSUE PRICE	FINISH	PR-68	PR-69
1996	30 Dollars	910	179.95	Proof	200.	—
1996	150 Dollars	196	599.95	Proof	800.	—
1996	Peregrine Falcon, Set of 4 coins	675	2,095.95	Proof	3,300.	—

WOOD BISON PLATINUM SET, 1997.
This is the third set in the series of Proof platinum coins commemorating Canada's endangered wildlife.

| $300 | $150 | $75 | $30 |

Designers:

Obv.:	Dora de Pédery-Hunt
Rev.:	Chris Bacon

Engravers:

Obv.:	Dora de Pédery-Hunt
Rev.:	$300 - Sheldon Beveridge
	$150 - William Woodruff
	$ 75 - Stan Witten
	$ 30 - Ago Aarand

DATE	DESCRIPTION	QUANTITY SOLD	ISSUE PRICE	FINISH	PR-68	PR-69
1997	30 Dollars	469	179.95	Proof	200.	—
1997	150 Dollars	116	599.95	Proof	800.	—
1997	Wood Bison, Set of 4 coins	413	1,950.00	Proof	3,300.	—

GREY WOLF PLATINUM SET, 1998.
This is the fourth set in the series of Proof platinum coins commemorating Canada's endangered wildlife.

| $300 | $150 | $75 | $30 |

Designers:

Obv.:	Dora de Pédery-Hunt
Rev.:	Kerri Burnett

Engravers:

Obv.:	Dora de Pédery-Hunt
Rev.:	$300 - Sheldon Beveridge
	$150 - Cosme Saffioti
	$ 75 - William Woodruff
	$ 30 - A. Aarand, J. Osio

DATE	DESCRIPTION	QUANTITY SOLD	ISSUE PRICE	FINISH	PR-68	PR-69
1998	30 Dollars	664	179.95	Proof	200.	—
1998	150 Dollars	194	599.95	Proof	800.	—
1998	Grey Wolf, Set of 4 coins	661	2,095.00	Proof	3,300	—

MUSKOX PLATINUM SET, 1999.
This is the fifth set in the series of Proof platinum coins commemorating Canada's endangered wildlife.

| $300 | $150 | $75 | $30 |

Designers:

Obv.:	Dora de Pédery-Hunt
Rev.:	Mark Hobson

Engravers:

Obv.:	Dora de Pédery-Hunt
Rev.:	$300 -William Woodruff
	$150 - Stan Witten
	$ 75 - Cosme Saffioti
	$ 30 - Sheldon Beveridge

DATE	DESCRIPTION	QUANTITY SOLD	ISSUE PRICE	FINISH	PR-68	PR-69
1999	30 Dollars	999	179.95	Proof	200.	—
1999	Muskox, Set of 4 coins	495	2,095.95	Proof	3,300.	—

PRONGHORN PLATINUM SET, 2000.

This is the sixth set in the series of Proof platinum coins commemorating Canada's endangered wildlife.

$300   **$150**   **$75**   **$30**

Designers:
Obv.:   Dora de Pédery-Hunt
Rev.:   Mark Hobson
Engravers:
Obv.:   Dora de Pédery-Hunt
Rev.: $300 - José Osio
         $150 - Susan Taylor
         $ 75 - Stan Witten
         $ 30 - William Woodruff

DATE	DESCRIPTION	QUANTITY SOLD	ISSUE PRICE	FINISH	PR-69	PR-70
2000	Pronghorn, Set of 4 coins	599	2,095.95	Proof	3,300.	—

HARLEQUIN DUCK PLATINUM SET, 2001.

This is the seventh set in the series of Proof platinum coins commemorating Canada's endangered wildlife.

$300   **$150**   **$75**   **$30**

Designers:
Obv.:   Dora de Pédery-Hunt
Rev.:   C. Saffioti, S. Taylor
         S. Witten
Engravers:
Obv.:   Dora de Pédery-Hunt
Rev.: $300 - Stan Witten
         $150 - Susan Taylor
         $ 75 - Cosme Saffioti
         $ 30 - Susan Taylor

DATE	DESCRIPTION	QUANTITY SOLD	ISSUE PRICE	FINISH	PR-69	PR-70
2001	Harlequin Duck, Set of 4 coins	448	2,395.95	Proof	3,300.	—

GREAT BLUE HERON PLATINUM SET, 2002.

This is the eighth set in the series of Proof platinum coins commemorating Canada's endangered wildlife.

$300   **$150**   **$75**   **$30**

Designers:
Obv.:   Dora de Pédery-Hunt
Rev.:   John-Luc Grondin
Engravers:
Obv.:   Dora de Pédery-Hunt
Rev.: $300 - Stan Witten
         $150 - Susan Taylor
         $ 75 - Stan Witten
         $ 30 - José Osio

DATE	DESCRIPTION	QUANTITY SOLD	ISSUE PRICE	FINISH	PR-69	PR-70
2002	Great Blue Heron, Set of 4 coins	344	2,495.95	Proof	3,300.	—

ATLANTIC WALRUS PLATINUM SET, 2003.

This is the ninth set in the series of Proof platinum coins commemorating Canada's endangered wildlife.

Designers:
Obv.: Dora de Pédery-Hunt
Rev.: Pierre Leduc
Engravers:
Obv.: Dora de Pédery-Hunt
Rev.: $300 - Susan Taylor
$150 - José Osio
$ 75 - Stan Witten
$ 30 - Stan Witten

$300	$150	$75	$30

DATE	DESCRIPTION	QUANTITY SOLD	ISSUE PRICE	FINISH	PR-69	PR-70
2003	Atlantic Walrus, Set of 4 coins	365	2,995.95	Proof	3,300.	—

GRIZZLY BEAR PLATINUM SET, 2004.

This is the tenth and final set in the Endangered Wildlife Proof platinum series, and it commemorates Canada's Great Grizzly bears.

Designers:
Obv.: Susanna Blunt
Rev.: Kerri Burnett
Engravers:
Obv.: Susan Taylor
Rev.: $300 - José Osio
$150 - José Osio
$ 75 - José Osio
$ 30 - José Osio

$300	$150	$75	$30

DATE	DESCRIPTION	QUANTITY SOLD	ISSUE PRICE	FINISH	PR-69	PR-70
2004	Grizzly Bear, Set of 4 coins	380	2,995.95	Proof	3,300.	—

MAPLE LEAF BULLION COINS
GOLD MAPLE LEAF COINS

INTRODUCTION

In 1979 the Canadian Government introduced a gold bullion coin to compete with similar coins issued by other countries (such as the Krugerrand of South Africa). From 1979 to 1981 only the 50-dollar coin (Maple Leaf) in the one troy ounce size was produced. The Maple Leaf during this period was issued with a gold fineness of .999. During November 1982 the range of the gold Maple Leaf bullion coins being offered was expanded to three sizes. Now included in the offering were the five dollar or 1/10 maple and the ten dollar or ¼ maple. With the addition of the two fractional Maple Leafs all sizes were upgraded in gold content to .9999 fine. July of 1986 saw the offering range expanded once again to include the 20 dollar or ½ maple. All four coins are produced from .9999 fine gold and are legal tender coinage of Canada. In 1988 the Royal Canadian Mint, again expanding their bullion program, introduced five new coins; four platinum (1/10, ¼, ½ and one maple) and one silver (one maple). In 1990 the reverse hub of the one ounce gold Maple Leaf was re-engraved, enhancing veins in the maple leaf design. Other changes included a more slender stem on the maple leaf and wider spacing of the letters in the legend "Fine Gold 1 oz Or Pur." In 1993 the Royal Canadian Mint added to the series of bullion coin by issuing a 1/20 of an ounce ($1.00) size in gold and platinum. Again in 1994 the $2.00 denomination was added to the bullion coin series (1/15 of an ounce) in both platinum and gold. The $2.00 - 1/15 Maple denomination was discontinued in 1995.

The original finish developed by the Mint in 1979 for the Maple Leaf Gold Program was "The Bullion Finish," a brilliant relief on a parallel lined background.

FINISHES USED ON MAPLE LEAF COINS

Bullion:	1979-2014	Brilliant relief against a parallel lined background
	2015-2018	Satin relief against a radial lined background
		Coloured
		Hologram
Specimen:		Brilliant relief on a satin background (Reverse proof)
		Coloured
		Hologram
Proof:		Frosted relief against a mirror background
		Coloured
		Hologram

PRIVY AND SECURITY MARKS ON BULLION COINS

The year 1999 marked the 20th anniversary of the Maple Leaf program. To commemorate this event a privy mark was incorporated into the reverse design of all regular issue Maple Leafs.

A special issue of maple leafs was produced for January 1st, 2000. These were given a double date, 1999-2000, and a Fireworks privy mark.

To celebrate the millennium year the privy mark added to all maple leaf denominations was "Fireworks" above the numerals 2000.

Beginning in 2013, a new security mark was added to the design of the one ounce gold maple leaf. The security mark consists of a textured maple leaf micro-engraved with a laser on a small area on the reverse of the coin. In the centre of this mark is another maple leaf containing a lasered two-digit number. The two-digit number indicates the year of issue and will change annually.

In 2015, as a security feature, a series of background radial lines was introduced.

1999
20 YEARS ANS

1999-2000
Fireworks

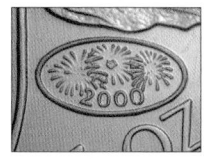

2000
Fireworks 2000

2013-2018
Security Mark

GOLD MAPLE LEAF SPECIFICATIONS

CHARACTERISTICS	.50¢ = 1/25 oz	$1 =1/20 oz	$2 = 1/15 oz	$5 = 1/10 oz	$10 = 1/4 oz	$20 = 1/2 oz	$50 = 1 oz
Fineness (1979-1982)	—	—	—	—	—	—	99.90%
Fineness (1982 to date)	99.99%	99.99%	99.99%	99.99%	99.99%	99.99%	99.99%
Weight (grams)	1.244	1.555	2.074	3.110	7.776	15.552	31.1035
Diameter (mm)	13.92	14.1	15.0	16.0	20.0	25.0	30.0
Thickness (mm)	0.63	0.92	0.98	1.22	1.70	2.23	2.93
Edge	Reeded	Reeded	Reeded	Reeded	Reeded	Reeded	Reeded
Die Axis	↑↑	↑↑	↑↑	↑↑	↑↑	↑↑	↑↑
Finish	Bullion	Bullion	Bullion	Bullion	Bullion	Bullion	Bullion

GOLD MAPLE LEAF OBVERSES 1979-2017

| Tiara Portrait 1979-1989 | Royal Diademed Portrait 1990-2003 | Uncrowned Portrait 2004-2014 | Uncrowned Portrait Radial Lines 2015-2016 | Uncrowned Portrait 150 & Maple Leaf 2015-2018 |

GOLD MAPLE LEAF REVERSES 1979-2017

.999 Fine
1979-1982

.9999 Fine
1983-1989

.9999 Fine
1990-2013
Re-engraved Leaf

.9999 Fine
Security Mark
2013-2014

.9999 Fine
Security Mark
Radial Lines
2015-2018

		Designers:	Engravers:
Obv.:	1979-1989	Arnold Machin	Walter Ott
	1990-2003	Dora de Pédery-Hunt	Dora de Pédery-Hunt
	2004-2014	Susanna Blunt	Susan Taylor
	2015	Susanna Blunt	Susan Taylor
Rev.:	1979-1982	Walter Ott	RCM Staff
	1983-1989	Walter Ott	RCM Staff
	1990-2013	Walter Ott	RCM Staff
	2013-2014	Walter Ott	RCM Staff
	2015-2018	Walter Ott	RCM Staff

GOLD MAPLE LEAF COINS

BULLION ISSUES

FINISH: 1979-2014 – Brilliant relief against a parallel lined background
2015-2017 – Satin relief against a radial lined background. The lines, which emanate from the centre and radiate outwards into the rim, are precisely machined with a specific width and pitch to create a light refracting pattern

MINTAGES: The production (quantity minted) of regular issue gold maple leaf bullion coins is on a demand basis. As coins are ordered by the distributors, they are struck and shipped by the Mint.

PRICING: Buying and selling prices are based on the interday spot price of bullion plus a small percentage premium for the striking and handling. The smaller the unit the larger the percentage premium charged on buying; however, in later selling the premium could very well disappear.

DATE	QUANTITIES SOLD					
	50¢ = 1/31.1 oz.	$1 = 1/20 oz	$5 = 1/10 oz	$10 = 1/4 oz	$20 = 1/2 oz	$50 = 1 oz
1979	–	N/I	N/I	N/I	N/I	1,000,000
1980	–	N/I	N/I	N/I	N/I	1,215,000
1981	–	N/I	N/I	N/I	N/I	863,000
1982	–	N/I	184,000	246,000	N/I	883,000
1983	–	N/I	224,000	130,000	N/I	695,000
1984	–	N/I	226,000	355,200	N/I	1,098,000
1985	–	N/I	476,000	607,200	N/I	1,747,500
1986	–	N/I	483,000	879,200	386,400	1,093,500
1987	–	N/I	459,000	376,800	332,800	978,000
1988	–	N/I	412,000	380,000	521,600	800,500
1989	–	N/I	539,000	328,800	259,200	856,000
1990	–	N/I	476,000	253,600	174,400	815,000
1991	–	N/I	322,000	166,400	96,200	290,000
1992	–	N/I	384,000	179,600	116,000	368,900
1993	–	37,080	248,630	158,452	99,492	321,413
1994	–	78,860	313,150	148,792	104,766	180,357
1995	–	85,920	294,890	127,596	103,162	208,729
1996	–	56,520	179,220	89,148	66,246	143,682
1997	–	59,720	188,540	98,104	63,354	478,211
1998	–	44,260	301,940	85,472	65,366	593,704
1999	–	62,820	709,920	98,928	64,760	627,067
1999-2000	–	Included	Included	Included	Included	Included
2000	–	31,280	52,970	31,688	24,404	86,375
2001	–	20,720	63,470	35,168	26,556	138,878
2002	–	17,140	45,020	42,940	28,706	344,883
2003	–	3,890	26,940	23,228	23,470	194,631
2004	–	9,880	33,480	18,296	13,160	253,978
2005	–	10,220	30,380	25,748	20,052	281,647
2006	–	19,340	40,960	25,964	21,138	209,937
2007	–	17,900	21,300	17,004	13,476	189,462
2008	–	15,740	38,510	34,368	28,782	710,718
2009	–	39,020	227,670	71,268	54,506	1,011,235
2010	–	9,000	111,160	41,628	34,302	1,036,832
2011	–	19,320	81,280	36,164	31,536	1,107,974
2012	–	12,400	95,700	129,156	28,594	712,193
2013	–	12,940	64,700	173,084	43,706	1,050,564
2014	–	N/A	N/A	N/A	N/A	N/A
2015	N/A	N/A	N/A	N/A	N/A	N/A
2016	N/A	N/A	N/A	N/A	N/A	N/A
2017	N/A	N/A	N/A	N/A	N/A	N/A

Note: N/I denotes Not Issued.

GOLD MAPLE LEAF SPECIAL ISSUES

SPECIAL ISSUE SINGLES

TWO DOLLAR GOLD COINS

TWO DOLLARS (1/15 OUNCE), BULLION ISSUE, 1994.

Issued 1994 as a new addition to the line of bullion coins offered by the Royal Canadian Mint, the two dollar (1/15 troy ounce) coin was not a success and was discontinued in 1995. It is a one-year type, and for this reason listed separately.

Actual Size

Designers and Engravers:

Obv.:	Dora de Pédery-Hunt
Rev.:	Walter Ott, RCM Staff

Composition: 99.99% Au
Gold content: 2.074 g, 0.067 tr oz
Weight: 2.074 g
Diameter: 13.9 mm
Thickness: 0.6 mm
Case of Issue: Mylar pouch

Edge: Reeded
Die Axis: ↑↑
Finish: Bullion

DATE	DESCRIPTION	QUANTITY SOLD	ISSUE PRICE	FINISH	MS-65	MS-66
1994	$2 (1/15 oz), Bullion Issue	3,540	BV	Bullion	400.	—

FIVE DOLLAR GOLD COINS

FIVE DOLLARS (1/10 OUNCE), MAPLE LEAF FOREVER, 2012.

The maple leaf has been a national symbol of Canada for almost 300 years. The sugar maple is an important member of the northeastern Canadian Boreal forest. Its sap produces some of the world's purest and finest maple syrup.

Actual Size

Designers and Engravers:

Obv.:	Susanna Blunt, Susan Taylor
Rev.:	Luc Normandin, Steven Stewart

Composition: 99.99% Au
Gold content: 3.13 g, 0.1 tr oz
Weight: 3.13 g
Diameter: 16.0 mm
Thickness: 1.0 mm
Case of Issue: Maroon leatherette clam style case, black flock insert, encapsulated coin(s), COA

Edge: Reeded
Die Axis: ↑↑
Finish: Proof

DATE	DESCRIPTION	QUANTITY SOLD	ISSUE PRICE	FINISH	PR-69	PR-70
2012	$5 (1/10 oz), Maple Leaf Forever	4,373	229.95	Proof	230.	—

TEN DOLLAR GOLD COINS

TEN DOLLARS, MAPLE LEAVES WITH HER MAJESTY QUEEN ELIZABETH II COINAGE EFFIGIES SERIES, 2014-2016.
Featuring Canadian maple leaves on the reverse, this series commemorates the coinage effigies of Her Majesty Queen Elizabeth II.

1953 Portrait Des.: M. Gillick	2014 Maple Leaves	1965 Portrait Des.: A. Machin	2015 Maple Leaves

Actual Size

1990 Portrait Des.: Celia Godkin	2015 Maple Leaves	2003 Portrait Des.: Susanna Blunt	2016 Maple Leaves

Designers:
| Obv.: | See reverse illustrations |
| Rev.: | Celia Godkin |

Engravers:
| Obv.: | RCM Staff |
| Rev.: | RCM Staff |

Composition: 99.99% Au
Gold content: 7.8 g, 0.25 tr oz
Weight: 7.8 g
Diameter: 20.00 mm
Thickness: N/A
Case of Issue: Maroon leatherette clam style case, black flocked insert, encapsulated coin, COA, black box

Edge: Reeded
Die Axis: ↑↑
Finish: Reverse Proof

DATE	DESCRIPTION	QUANTITY SOLD	ISSUE PRICE	FINISH	PR-69	PR-70
2014	Maple Leaves with Queen Elizabeth II Effigy (1953)	1,375	649.95	Proof	600.	—
2015	Maple Leaves with Queen Elizabeth II Effigy (1965)	958	649.95	Proof	600.	—
2015	Maple Leaves with Queen Elizabeth II Effigy (1990)	678	649.95	Proof	600.	—
2016	Maple Leaves with Queen Elizabeth II Effigy (2003)	1,000	649.95	Proof	600.	—

TEN DOLLARS (1/5 ounce), PIEDFORT MAPLE LEAF, 2010.
This ten-dollar gold maple leaf was issued in a set of two coins (see page 580), the second coin being a five-dollar silver maple (see page 600).

Actual Size

Designers and Engravers:
| Obv.: | Susanna Blunt, Susan Taylor |
| Rev.: | RCM Staff |

Composition: 99.999% Au
Gold content: 6.25 g, 0.2 tr oz
Weight: 6.25 g
Diameter: 15.9 mm
Thickness: 1.9 mm
Case of Issue: Maroon leatherette clam style case, black flock insert, encapsulated coin(s), COA

Edge: Reeded
Die Axis: ↑↑
Finish: Bullion

DATE	DESCRIPTION	QUANTITY SOLD	ISSUE PRICE	FINISH	MS-65	MS-66
2010	$10 Gold (1/5 oz) Piedfort Maple Leaf	1,264	N.I.I.	Bullion	475.	—

FIFTY DOLLAR GOLD COINS

FIFTY DOLLARS (1 ounce), 10TH ANNIVERSARY OF THE MAPLE LEAF BULLION COINS, 1989.

To commemorate the 10th anniversary of the maple leaf bullion coin program in 1989 the Royal Canadian Mint issued a series of proof quality silver, gold and platinum coins individually and in sets. The single coins and sets were packaged in solid maple wood presentation cases with brown velvet liners.

Designers and Engravers:
Obv.:	Arnold Machin, Walter Ott
Rev.:	Walter Ott, RCM Staff
Composition:	99.99% Au
Gold content:	31.10 g, 1.0 tr oz
Weight:	31.1035 g, 1oz	**Edge:**	Reeded
Diameter:	30.0 mm	**Die Axis:**	↑↑
Thickness:	2.9 mm	**Finish:**	Proof
Case of Issue:	Maple wood case, brown velvet liner, encapsulated coin, COA

DATE	DESCRIPTION	QUANTITY SOLD	ISSUE PRICE	FINISH	MS-65	MS-66
1989	$50 (1 oz) 10th Anniv. of Maple Leaf Coins	6,817	BV	Proof	2,100.	—

FIFTY DOLLARS (1 ounce), 125TH ANNIVERSARY OF THE R.C.M.P. 1997.

In 1997 the Royal Canadian Mint issued a $50.00 gold (1 oz .9999 fine) coin with a guaranteed value of U.S. $310.00 in effect until January 1st, 2000. Since that date the coin has traded at the market price of gold bullion.

Designer:	Ago Aarand
Engraver:	Stan Witten
Composition:	99.99% Au
Gold content:	31.10 g, 1.0 tr oz
Weight:	31.1035 g, 1 oz
Diameter:	30.0 mm	**Edge:**	Plain, 10-sided
Thickness:	3.3 mm	**Die Axis:**	↑↑
Finish:	Bullion
Case of Issue:	Black card folder

DATE	DESCRIPTION	QUANTITY SOLD	ISSUE PRICE	FINISH	MS-65	MS-66
1997	$50 (1 oz) 125th Anniv. R.C.M.P.	12,913	310. USF	Bullion	2,000.	—

FIFTY DOLLARS (1 ounce), 25TH ANNIVERSARY OF THE GOLD MAPLE LEAF COIN, 2004.

In 2004 a special commemorative design for the one ounce maple celebrating Canada's 25 years as a world leader in bullion coin production was issued at the A.N.A. World's Fair of Money.

Designers and Engravers:
Obv.:	Susanna Blunt, Susan Taylor
Rev.:	Cosme Saffioti, Christie Paquet
Composition:	99.99% Au
Gold content:	31.10 g, 1.0 tr oz
Weight:	31.1035 g, 1 oz
Diameter:	30.0 mm	**Edge:**	Reeded
Thickness:	2.9 mm	**Die Axis:**	↑↑
Finish:	Bullion
Case of Issue:	Mylar pouch

DATE	DESCRIPTION	QUANTITY SOLD	ISSUE PRICE	FINISH	MS-65	MS-66
2004	$50 (1 oz) 25th Anniv. Gold Maple Leaf	10,000	BV	Bullion	2,000.	—

FIFTY DOLLARS (1 ounce), TEST MAPLE LEAF, FIVE 9'S GOLD, 2005.

This was a production test for "five 9's" fineness of the one ounce maple leaf. Of the six hundred pieces which were produced, two hundred were melted, and four hundred were released sealed in Mylar pouches.

Designers and Engravers:

Obv.:	Susanna Blunt, Susan Taylor		
Rev.:	Walter Ott, RCM Staff		
Composition:	99.999% Au		
Gold content:	31.10 g, 1.0 tr oz		
Weight:	31.1035 g, 1 oz		
Diameter:	30.0 mm	**Edge:**	Reeded
Thickness:	2.9 mm	**Die Axis:**	↑↑
Finish:	Bullion		
Case of Issue:	Mylar pouch		

DATE	DESCRIPTION	QUANTITY SOLD	ISSUE PRICE	FINISH	MS-65	MS-66
2005	$50 (1 oz) .99999, Pattern	400	BV	Bullion	2,700.	—

FIFTY DOLLARS (1 ounce), MAPLE LEAF, 2012.

This coin was issued to commemorate the fifth anniversary of the striking of the one million dollar maple leaf coin in 2007.

Designers and Engravers:

Obv.:	Susanna Blunt, Susan Taylor		
Rev.:	Walter Ott, RCM Staff		
Composition:	99.999% Au		
Gold content:	31.16 g, 1.0 tr oz		
Weight:	31.16 g, 1 oz		
Diameter:	30.0 mm	**Edge:**	Reeded
Thickness:	2.9 mm	**Die Axis:**	↑↑
Finish:	Reverse Proof		
Case of Issue:	Maroon leatherette clam style case, black flock insert, encapsulated coin, COA		

DATE	DESCRIPTION	QUANTITY SOLD	ISSUE PRICE	FINISH	MS-65	MS-66
2012	$50 (1 oz) 99.999% gold	543	BV	Bullion	2,000.	—

FIFTY DOLLARS (1 OUNCE), BULLION REPLICA MAPLE LEAF, 2014.

This is a premium-struck one ounce gold maple leaf issued to celebrate the success of the gold maple leaf which was introduced in 1979.

Designers and Engravers:

Obv.:	Susanna Blunt, Susan Taylor		
Rev.:	Walter Ott, RCM Staff		
Composition:	99.99% Au		
Gold content:	31.16 g, 1.0 tr oz		
Weight:	31.16 g, 1 oz		
Diameter:	30.0 mm	**Edge:**	Reeded
Thickness:	2.9 mm	**Die Axis:**	↑↑
Finish:	Reverse Proof		
Case of Issue:	Maroon leatherette clam style case, black flock insert, encapsulated coin, COA		

DATE	DESCRIPTION	QUANTITY SOLD	ISSUE PRICE	FINISH	PR-69	PR-70
2014	$50 (1 oz) Bullion Replica Maple Leaf	268	2,699.95	Proof	2,200.	—

NOTE TO COLLECTORS

When the initials N.I.I. appear in the pricing table it indicates the coin was part of a set issued by the Royal Canadian Mint, and not issued individually. Coin designs that are found only in sets offered by the Royal Canadian Mint are listed individually by denomination, and date in Volume Two.

SP-68 / PR-69   This price is based on the item still being in the original package as sold by the Mint.

SP-69 / PR-70   This price is based on the item being graded by a reputable third-party grading company.

TWO HUNDRED DOLLAR GOLD COINS

TWO HUNDRED DOLLARS (1 ounce), MAPLE LEAF, FIVE 9'S GOLD, 2007-2012.

Testing was continued of the five 9's gold concept first started in 2005. However, the test coins were now offered to the numismatic market. The issue of 2007 was offered with and without a privy mark.

| 2007 Obverse | 2007 Reverse
Des./Engr.: Stan Witten | 2007 Obverse | 2007 Reverse, Privy Mark
Des./Engr.: Stan Witten |

| 2008 Obverse | 2008 Reverse
Des.: G. E. Kruger-Gray
Engr.: RCM Staff | 2009 Obverse | 2009 Reverse
Des.: Walter Ott
Engr.: RCM Staff |

| 2011 Obverse | 2011 Reverse
Des./Engr.: Stan Witten | 2012 Obverse | 2012 Reverse
Des./Engr.: Stan Witten |

Designers:
- Obv.: Susanna Blunt
- Rev.: See reverse illustrations

Engravers:
- Obv.: Susan Taylor
- Rev.: See reverse illustrations

Composition: 99.999% Au
Gold content: 31.1 g, 1.0 tr oz
Weight: 31.1035 g, 1 oz
Diameter: 30.0 mm
Thickness: 2.8 mm
Case of Issue: 2007-2009, 2012: Maroon clam style case, black flocked insert, encapsulated maple leaf, COA
2011: Credit card capsule

Edge: 2007: Plain
2008-2012: Interrupted serrations
Die Axis: ↑↑
Finish: Bullion

DATE	DESCRIPTION	QUANTITY SOLD	ISSUE PRICE	FINISH	MS-65	MS-66
2007	$200 (1 oz) 99.999% gold	30,848	BV	Bullion	2,000.	—
2007	$200 (1 oz) 99.999% gold, with Privy Mark	500.	1,899.95	Bullion	2,500.	—
2008	$200 (1 oz) 99.999% gold	27,476	BV	Bullion	2,000.	—
2009	$200 (1 oz) 99.999% gold	13,765	BV	Bullion	2,000.	—
2011	$200 (1 oz) 99.999% gold	N/A	BV	Bullion	2,000.	—
2012	$200 (1 oz) 99.999% gold	N/A	BV	Bullion	2,000.	—

TWO HUNDRED DOLLARS, MAPLE LEAF REFLECTION, 2015.

Designers and Engravers:

Obv.:	Susanna Blunt, Susan Taylor
Rev.:	Lilyane Coulombe
Composition:	99.99% Au
Gold content:	31.16 g. 1.0 tr oz

Weight:	31.16 g	**Edge:**	Reeded
Diameter:	30.0 mm	**Die Axis:**	↑↑
Thickness:	N/A	**Finish:**	Proof
Case of Issue:	Maroon leatherette clam style case, black flocked insert, encapsulated coin, COA		

DATE	DESCRIPTION	QUANTITY SOLD	ISSUE PRICE	FINISH	PR-69	PR-70
2015	Maple Leaf Reflection	350	2,699.95	Proof	2,700.	—

TWO HUNDRED DOLLARS, 3-COIN SET, ALLURING MAPLE LEAVES OF FALL, 2015.

Common Obverse	**Spring**	**Summer**	**Fall**

Designers

Obv.:	Susanna Blunt
Rev.:	Michelle Grant
Composition:	99.99% Au
Gold content:	31.16 g, 1.0 tr oz
Weight:	31.16 g
Diameter:	30.0 mm
Thickness:	N/A

Engravers:

Obv.:	Susan Taylor
Rev.:	RCM Staff

Edge:	Reeded
Die Axis:	↑↑
Finish:	Proof, with colour

Case of Issue: Presented in a maple wood case with a full colour custom beatuy box, COA.

DATE	DESCRIPTION	QUANTITY SOLD	ISSUE PRICE	FINISH	PR-69	PR-70
2015	3-Coin Set, Alluring Maple Leaves of Fall	108	8,000.00	Proof	8,000.	—

TWO HUNDRED DOLLARS, A HISTORIC REIGN, 2015.

Designers and Engravers:

Obv.:	Susanna Blunt, Susan Taylor
Rev.:	Cathy Bursey Sabourin
Composition:	99.99% Au
Gold content:	31.16g. 1.0 tr oz

Weight:	31.16 g	**Edge:**	Reeded
Diameter:	30.0 mm	**Die Axis:**	↑↑
Thickness:	N/A	**Finish:**	Proof
Case of Issue:	Red wooden box with black beauty box, encapsulated coin, COA		

DATE	DESCRIPTION	QUANTITY SOLD	ISSUE PRICE	FINISH	PR-69	PR-70
2015	A Historic Reign	266	2,699.95	Proof	2,700.	—

TWO HUNDRED DOLLARS, CANADA 150: ICONIC MAPLE LEAF, 2017.

Designers and Engravers:

Obv.:	Susanna Blunt, Susan Taylor
Rev.:	RCM Staff

Composition: 99.99% Au
Gold content: 31.16g. 1.0 tr oz

Weight:	31.16 g	**Edge:**	Interrupted reeding
Diameter:	30.0 mm	**Die Axis:**	↑↑
Thickness:	N/A	**Finish:**	Matte Proof

Case of Issue: Red wooden box with black beauty box, encapsulated coin, COA

DATE	DESCRIPTION	QUANTITY SOLD	ISSUE PRICE	FINISH	PR-69	PR-70
2017	Canada 150: Iconic Maple Leaf	469	2,849.95	Matte Proof	2,850.	—

TWO HUNDRED DOLLARS, GML CANADA 150, 2017.

First issued in 1979, the Gold Maple Leaf (GML) bullion coin is highly valued by collectors and investors worldwide for its outstanding combination of superior craftsmanship, purity and design.

Designers and Engravers:

Obv.:	Susanna Blunt, Susan Taylor
Rev.:	RCM Staff

Composition: 99.999% Au
Gold content: 31.16 g. 1.00 tr oz

Weight:	31.16 g	**Edge:**	Reeded
Diameter:	30.0 mm	**Die Axis:**	↑↑
Thickness:	N/A	**Finish:**	Reverse Proof

Case of Issue: Maroom clamshell with black beauty box, COA

DATE	DESCRIPTION	MINTAGE	ISSUE PRICE	FINISH	PR-69	PR-70
2017	GML Canada 150	500	2,849.95	Reverse Proof	2,850.	—

TWO HUNDRED DOLLARS, 30TH ANNIVERSARY OF THE SML, 2018.

The year 2018 marks the 30th anniversary of the iconic Silver Maple Leaf bullion coin – the standard against which other silver bullion coins are measured. This very special numismatic release includes an RCM first: incuse-struck images on both sides of this pure gold coin.

Designers and Engravers:

Obv.:	Susanna Blunt, Susan Taylor
Rev.:	RCM Staff

Composition: 99.999% Au
Gold content: 31.6 g. 1.02 tr oz

Weight:	31.6 g	**Edge:**	Interrupted reeding
Diameter:	30 mm	**Die Axis:**	↑↑
Thickness:	N/A	**Finish:**	Reverse Proof

Case of Issue: Maroom clamshell with black beauty box, COA

DATE	DESCRIPTION	MINTAGE	ISSUE PRICE	FINISH	PR-69	PR-70
2018	30th Anniversary of the SML	500	2,899.95	Reverse Proof	2,900	—

FIVE HUNDRED DOLLAR GOLD COINS

FIVE HUNDRED DOLLARS, MAPLE LEAF FOREVER, 2012, 2015-2017.

2012 Obverse

2015-2017 Obverse

2012 Designer: Luc Normandin

2015 Designer: Lisa Thomson-Kahn

2016 Designer: Celia Godkin

2017 Designer: Margaret Best

Designers		Engravers:	
Obv.:	Susanna Blunt	Obv.:	Susan Taylor
Rev.:	See illustrations		

Composition: 99.99% Au
Gold content: 156.05 g, 5.03 tr oz
Weight: 156.05 g
Diameter: 60 mm
Thickness: N/A
Case of Issue: Red lacquered wooden box, black flocked insert, encapsulated coin, COA

Edge: Plain
Die Axis: ↑↑
Finish: Proof

DATE	DESCRIPTION	QUANTITY SOLD	ISSUE PRICE	FINISH	PR-69	PR-70
2012	Maple Leaf Forever	146	11,999.95	Proof	12,500.	—
2015	Maple Leaves	97	12,000.00	Proof	12,000.	—
2016	Maple Leaves	99	12,500.00	Proof	12,500.	—
2017	Maple Leaves	99	12,999.95	Proof	13,000.	—

TWO THOUSAND FIVE HUNDRED DOLLAR GOLD COINS, 2011-2012

TWO THOUSAND FIVE HUNDRED DOLLARS, MAPLE LEAF FOREVER, 2011 and 2012.

Common Obverse (except for date)	2011 Designer: Debbie Adams Engraver: Konrad Wachelko	2012 Designer: Luc Normandin Engraver: RCM Staff

Designers:
Obv.: Susanna Blunt
Rev.: See reverse illustrations
Composition: 99.99% Au
Gold content: 1000.0 g, 32.15 tr oz
Weight: 1,000.0 g (1 kilo)
Diameter: 101.6 mm
Thickness: N/A
Case of Issue: 2011: Black clam style case, black insert, encapsulated coin, COA
2012: Maple wood case, black flocked insert, encapsulated coin, COA

Engravers:
Obv.: Susan Taylor
Rev.: See reverse illustrations

Edge: Plain
Die Axis: ↑↑
Finish: Proof

DATE	DESCRIPTION	QUANTITY SOLD	ISSUE PRICE	FINISH	PR-69	PR-70
2011	Maple Leaf Forever	35	69,000.	Proof	69,000.	—.
2012	Maple Leaf Forever	20	69,000.	Proof	69,000.	—.

Note: See also pages 489-498 for other $2,500 gold coins. Coins illustrated smaller than actual size.

ONE MILLION DOLLAR GOLD COIN

This coin was issued May 3, 2007, as a promotional item for a new line of five 9's (99.999% fine gold) maple leaf gold coins. The million-dollar gold coin, being the largest and heaviest minted, attracted buyers from all over the world. The Canadian Mint received orders for five coins. The 3,215 troy ounce coin is produced by casting, engraving and hand polishing. The reverse design of the million-dollar maple leaf coin is very similar to the five dollar (2006) coloured silver maple, see page 622.

Designers:		**Engravers:**		
Obv.:	Susanna Blunt	Obv.:	Stan Witten	
Rev.:	Stan Witten	Rev.:	Stan Witten	
Composition:	99.999% Au			
Gold content:	100 kilos, 3,215 tr oz			
Weight:	100 kilos	**Edge:**	Plain	
Diameter:	53.0 cm	**Die Axis:**	↑↑	
Thickness:	N/A	**Finish:**	Bullion	

DATE	DESCRIPTION	QUANTITY SOLD	ISSUE PRICE	FINISH	MS-65	MS-66
2007	One Million Dollar Coin, 3,215 tr oz	4	BV	Bullion	—	—

Note: 1. The last recorded sale of this coin was $4,300,250. at auction on June 25th, 2010. It was auctioned by Dorotheum of Vienna, Austria, at their headquarters.
2. Coin illustrated smaller than actual size.

GOLD MAPLE LEAF SPECIAL ISSUES

SPECIAL ISSUE SETS

10TH ANNIVERSARY OF THE GOLD MAPLE LEAF COIN, 1979-1989.
The three sets detailed below were issued for the tenth anniversary of the maple leaf bullion program.

THREE-COIN SET (1 OZ GOLD, SILVER AND PLATINUM MAPLE LEAFS)

1 oz Gold Maple Leaf

1 oz Silver Maple Leaf

1 oz Platinum Maple Leaf

THREE-COIN SET (1OZ SILVER, 1/10 OZ GOLD AND PLATINUM MAPLE LEAFS)

1 oz Silver Maple Leaf

1/10 oz Gold
Maple Leaf

1/10 oz
Platinum
Leaf

Designers:
   Obv.:   Arnold Machin
   Rev.:   Walter Ott
Specifications: Gold: See page 567
               Platinum: See page 589
               Silver: See page 595
Finish: Proof
Case of Issue: Maple wood presentation box, black flocked insert, encapsulated coin, COA

Engravers:
   Obv.:   Walter Ott
   Rev.:   RCM Staff

DATE	DESCRIPTION	QUANTITY SOLD	ISSUE PRICE	FINISH	PR-68	PR-69
1989	Set of 3 coins: 1oz gold, 1oz silver, 1oz platinum	3,966	1,795.00	Proof	3,450.	—
1989	Set of 3 coins: 1/10 oz gold, 1/10 oz platinum, 1 oz silver	10,000	195.00	Proof	450.	—

TEN DOLLAR GOLD AND FIVE DOLLAR SILVER PIEDFORT MAPLE LEAF SET, 2010.

Ten
Dollars
Gold

Five
Dollars
Silver

Designers:
    Obv.: Susanna Blunt
    Rev.: RCM Staff
$10 Gold
Composition: 99.999% Au
Gold content: 6.25 g, 0.20 tr oz
Weight: 6.25 g
Diameter: 15.9 mm
Thickness: 1.9 mm
Edge: Reeded
Die Axis: ↑↑
Finish: Bullion

Engravers:
    Rev.: Susan Taylor
    Rev.: RCM Staff
$5 Silver
Composition: 99.99% Ag
Silver content: 31.39 g, 1.01 tr oz
Weight: 31.39 g
Diameter: 34.0 mm
Thickness: 4.0 mm
Edge: Reeded
Die Axis: ↑↑
Finish: Bullion

Case of Issue: Maroon leatherette clam style case, black flock insert, encapsulated coin(s), COA

DATE	DESCRIPTION	QUANTITY SOLD	ISSUE PRICE	FINISH	MS-65	MS-66
2010	$10 Gold and $5 Silver, Piedfort Set	1,264	679.95	Bullion	600.	—

GOLD FRACTIONAL SETS

2012 5TH ANNIVERSARY OF THE ROYAL CANADIAN MINT MILLION DOLLAR COIN - 5 COIN SET.
The one ounce coin in this set features five 99999s with an edge containing interrupted serrations.

2012 Obverse

Des.: Susanna Blunt
Engr.: Susan Taylor

2012 Reverse

Des.: Stan Witten
Engr.: Stan Witten

2013 25TH ANNIVERSARY OF THE FRACTIONAL SET - 4 COIN SET (1oz - 99.99%)
The one ounce coin in this set features four 9999s with a reeded edge.

2013 Obverse

Des.: Susanna Blunt
Engr.: Susan Taylor

2013 Reverse

Des.: Claudio D'Angelo
Engr.: Konrad Wachelko

2014 INCUSED FRACTIONAL SET - 4 COIN SET (1oz - 99.99%)
The one ounce coin in this set features four 9999s with a reeded edge.

2014 Obverse

Des.: Susanna Blunt
Engr.: Susan Taylor

2014 Reverse

Des.: Pierre Leduc
Engr.: RCM Staff

SPECIFICATIONS

Specifications:	See page 510	
Gold content:	2012 Set:	1.90 tr oz
	2013-2014 Set:	1.40 tr oz
Finish:	2012:	Proof
	2013-2014:	Reverse Proof
Case of Issue:	2012-2014:	Canadian maple wood case, black flocked insert, encapsulated coins, COA, black sleeve

DATE	DESCRIPTION	QUANTITY SOLD	ISSUE PRICE	FINISH	PR-69	PR-70
2012	Set of 5 coins (1, 1/2, 1/4, 1/10, 1/20, 1/25 oz)	543	3,999.95	Proof	4,000.	—
2013	Set of 4 coins (1, 1/4, 1/10, 1/20 oz)	730	3,899.95	Rev. Proof	4,000.	—
2014	Set of 4 coins (1, 1/4, 1/10, 1/20 oz)	552	3,999.95	Rev. Proof	4,000.	—

GOLD MAPLE LEAF FRACTIONAL SET - 4 COIN SET, 2015.

Each reverse design in this set is different. The design depicts a falling maple leaf as it flutters to the ground. Each one ounce coin is edge lettered with a serialized number.

Designers:

Obv:	Susanna Blunt
Rev.:	Lilyane Coulombe

Specifications: See page 589
Gold Content: 1.40 tr oz
Finish: Reverse Proof
Case of Issue: Red lacquered box, black flocked insert, encapsulated coins, COA

Engravers:

Obv.:	Susan Taylor
Rev.:	RCM Staff

DATE	DESCRIPTION	QUANTITY SOLD	ISSUE PRICE	FINISH	PR-69	PR-70
2015	Set of 4 coins (1, 1/4, 1/10, 1/20 oz)	181	3,999.95	Proof	4,000.	—

GOLD MAPLE LEAF FRACTIONAL SET - A HISTORIC REIGN, 2016.

This magnificent set of gold coins pays tribute to Her Majesty Queen Elizabeth II, Queen of Canada, as the longest reigning Sovereign in modern Canadian history. Each reverse design in this set is different. The design depicts a falling maple leaf as it flutters to the ground. Each one ounce coin is edge lettered with a serialized number.

Designers:

Obv:	Susanna Blunt
Rev.:	Celia Godkin

Specifications: See page 589
Gold Content: 1.40 tr oz
Finish: Reverse Proof
Case of Issue: Red lacquered box, black flocked insert, encapsulated coins, COA

Engravers:

Obv.:	1 oz. Susan Taylor
	1/4 oz. Mary Gillick
	1/10 oz. Arnold Machin
	1/20 oz. Dora de Pédery-Hunt

DATE	DESCRIPTION	QUANTITY SOLD	ISSUE PRICE	FINISH	PR-69	PR-70
2016	Set of 4 coins (1, 1/4, 1/10, 1/20 oz)	599	3,999.95	Proof	4,000.	—

GOLD MAPLE LEAF FRACTIONAL SET - A CELEBRATION OF CANADA GOLD FRACTIONAL, 2017.

The British North America Act of 1867 is a key marker for Canadian history, for it represents the momentous birth of a national. Tommemorate he historic 150th anniversary odf the Confederatin, the Royal Canadian Mint celebrates the journey of a nation that is proud, strong and free, with a commemorative franctional set feating a beloved national emblem: the maple leaf..

Designers:

Obv: Susanna Blunt

Rev.: Lisa Thomson-Khan

Specifications: See page 589

Gold Content: 1.40 tr oz

Case of Issue: Custom-shaped maple wood case, COA

Engravers:

Obv.: Susan Taylor

Finish: Reverse Proof

DATE	DESCRIPTION	QUANTITY SOLD	ISSUE PRICE	FINISH	PR-69	PR-70
2017	Set of 4 coins (1, 1/4, 1/10, 1/20 oz)	577	3,999.95	Proof	4,000.	—

GOLD MAPLE LEAF FRACTIONAL SET - THE MAPLE LEAF, 2018.

Maple leaves of all sizes possess the rare ability to stir powerful feelings of pride in Canadians. This iconic emblem of Canada takes centre stage in a .99999 pure gold fractional set—the first of its kind—that stands as a superbly crafted tribute to a timeless symbol of the land and its people.

Designers:

Obv:	Susanna Blunt
Rev.:	Caren Heine

Specifications: See page 589
Gold Content: 1.40 tr oz
Case of Issue: Custom-shaped maple wood case, COA

Engravers:

Obv.:	Susan Taylor

Finish: Reverse Proof

DATE	DESCRIPTION	MINTAGE	ISSUE PRICE	FINISH	PR-69	PR-70
2018	Set of 4 coins (1, 1/4, 1/10, 1/20 oz)	600	4,219.95	Reverse Proof	4,220.	—

GOLD FRACTIONAL SETS WITH PRIVY MARKS

GOLD MAPLE LEAF PRIVY MARK SET, 2001.

Each of the five coins in this set carries the bow of a Viking ship as a privy mark. The maples in this set are: 1 oz, ½oz, ¼oz, 1/10 oz, and 1/20 oz.

**2001 Viking
Privy Mark**

Designers:

Obv.:	Dora de Pédery-Hunt
Rev.:	Walter Ott

Specifications: See page 589
Gold content: 1.90 tr oz
Case of Issue: Red mahogany wooden case, black insert, encapsulated coins, green velour with metal trim box.

Engravers:

Obv.:	Dora de Pédery-Hunt
Rev.:	RCM Staff

Finish: Specimen (reverse proof)

DATE	DESCRIPTION	PRIVY MARK	QUANTITY SOLD	ISSUE PRICE	FINISH	SP-68	SP-69
2001	Set of 5 coins (1, 1/2, 1/4, 1/10, 1/20 oz)	Viking	850	N/A	Specimen	3,500.	—

100TH ANNIVERSARY OF THE ROYAL CANADIAN MINT REFINERY, 1911-2011.

Each of the four coins in this set carries the 100 YEARS/ANS privy mark. The maples in this set are: 1 oz, ¼oz, 1/10 oz and 1/20 oz. This set includes a bronze medallion commemorating The Mint refinery.

**100 Years/ans
Privy Mark**

Designers:		Engravers:	
Obv.:	Dora de Pédery-Hunt	Obv.:	Dora de Pédery-Hunt
Rev.:	Walter Ott	Rev.:	RCM Staff

Specifications: See page 589
Gold Content: 1.40 tr oz
Finish: Specimen (reverse proof)
Case of Issue: Red mahogany wooden case, black insert, encapsulated coins, green velour with metal trim box.

DATE	DESCRIPTION	PRIVY MARK	QUANTITY SOLD	ISSUE PRICE	FINISH	SP-68	SP-69
2011	Set of 4 coins (1, 1/4, 1/10, 1/20 oz)	100 Years/ans	479	N/A	Specimen	2,700.	—

COLOURED FRACTIONAL SET WITH PRIVY MARK

20TH ANNIVERSARY OF THE MAPLE LEAF PROGRAM, 1979-1999.

This limited edition five-coin set, (1 oz, ½ oz, ¼ oz, 1/10 oz and 1/20 oz) struck by the Royal Canadian Mint and coloured in Balerna, Switzerland, was issued with a mintage of 500. They are the first coloured Canadian coins.

**1979-1999
Privy Mark**

Designers:		Engravers:	
Obv.:	Dora de Pédery-Hunt	Obv.:	Dora de Pédery-Hunt
Rev.:	Walter Ott	Rev.:	RCM Staff
Specifications:	See page 589	**Finish:**	Bullion, Coloured
Gold Content:	1.90 tr oz		

Case of Issue: Wooden maple display case, black leatherette sleeve, black flocked insert, encapsulated coins, COA, red and gold outer box.

DATE	DESCRIPTION	PRIVY MARK	QUANTITY SOLD	ISSUE PRICE	FINISH	MS-65	MS-66
1999	Set of 5 coins (1, 1/2, 1/4, 1/10, 1/20 oz)	20 Years / ans	500	N/A	Bullion	3,800.	—

Note: For the Vancouver 2010 Winter Olympic Coloured Set see page 599.

BIMETALLIC FRACTIONAL SET WITH PRIVY MARK

25TH ANNIVERSARY OF THE GOLD MAPLE LEAF, 1979-2004.
To celebrate 25 years as an international standard in bullion coins, a new bimetallic maple leaf set was issued. The six-coin set is the first to include the 1/25 oz maple leaf denomination. Each coin is double-dated 1979-2004, and the 1 ounce coin features a 25-year commemorative privy mark.

**25 YEARS / ANS
Privy Mark**

Designers and Engravers: RCM Staff
Gold Content: 1.90 tr oz
Silver Content: 0.06 tr oz
Finish: Bullion
Case of Issue: Black leather presentation case, black velour insert, encapsulated coins, COA

CHARACTERISTICS	.50¢ = 1/25 oz	$1 =1/20 oz	$5 = 1/10 oz	$10 = 1/4 oz	$20 = 1/2 oz	$50 = 1 oz
Composition						
Ring - fine silver	99.99%	99.99%	99.99%	99.99%	99.99%	99.99%
Core - fine gold	99.99%	99.99%	99.99%	99.99%	99.99%	99.99%
Weight (grams)	1.27	1.581	3.136	7.802	15.589	31.65
Diameter (mm)	16.0	18.03	20.0	25.0	30.0	36.07
Thickness (mm)	N/A	N/A	N/A	N/A	N/A	N/A
Edge	Plain	Plain	Plain	Plain	Plain	Plain
Die Axis	↑↑	↑↑	↑↑	↑↑	↑↑	↑↑

DATE	DESCRIPTION	PRIVY MARK	QUANTITY SOLD	ISSUE PRICE	FINISH	SP-68	SP-69
2004 (1979-)	Set of 6 coins	25 Years / ans	801	2,495.95	Bullion	3,800.	—

GOLD MAPLE LEAFS HOLOGRAM ISSUES

HOLOGRAM SINGLES AND SETS

TEN DOLLARS (¼ ounce), GOLD MAPLE LEAF HOLOGRAM, 2001.
A distinctive maple leaf design appears as a high resolution dot matrix hologram, which is struck directly into the coin.

Actual Size

Designers:		**Engravers:**	
Obv.:	Susanna Blunt	Obv.:	Susan Taylor
Rev.:	Walter Ott	Rev.:	RCM Staff
Composition:	99.99% Au		
Gold content:	7.775 g, 0.25 tr oz		
Weight:	7.776 g	**Edge:**	Reeded
Diameter:	20.0 mm	**Die Axis:**	↑↑
Thickness:	1.7 mm	**Finish:**	Specimen (reverse proof), Hologram
Case of Issue:	Wooden presentation case		

DATE	DESCRIPTION	QUANTITY SOLD	ISSUE PRICE	FINISH	SP-68	SP-69
2001	$10 (¼ oz)	14,614	195.00	Specimen	500.	—

GOLD MAPLE LEAF HOLOGRAM SETS 1999, 2001 AND 2009.
The Hologram gold maple leaf set of 1999 was the first official issue of hologram coins in Canada. The five coins in this set are: 1 oz, 1/2 oz, 1/4 oz, 1/10 oz and 1/20 oz. All coins carry identical designs.
The 2009 thirtieth anniversary hologram set was issued with four coins: 1 oz, ¼ oz, 1/10 oz and 1/20 oz maples.

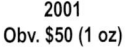

2001
Obv. $50 (1 oz)

2001
Rev. $50 (1 oz)

Designers and Engravers:	
Obv.:	Dora de Pédery-Hunt
Rev.:	Walter Ott, RCM Staff
Specifications:	See page 589
Gold Content:	1999, 2001: 1.90 tr oz
	2009: 1.40 tr oz
Finish:	Bullion, Hologram
Case of Issue:	Presentation case

DATE	DESCRIPTION	QUANTITY SOLD	ISSUE PRICE	FINISH	MS-65	MS-66
1999	20th Anniversary, Set of 5 coins (1, ½, ¼, 1/10, 1/20 oz)	500	1,995.00	Bullion	3,800.	—
2001	Set of 5 coins	600	1,995.00	Bullion	3,800.	—
2009	30th Anniversary, Set of 4 coins (1, ¼, 1/10, 1/20 oz)	739	N/A	Bullion	3,200.	—

GOLD MAPLE LEAFS WITH PRIVY MARKS

PRIVY MARK SINGLES

GOLD MAPLE LEAF PRIVY MARKS.

In 1997, the Royal Canadian Mint began adding privy marks to specific gold maple leaf denominations to commemorate special events. These privy mark maples were commissioned by different organizations and struck by the Royal Canadian Mint.

$5 — 1/10 oz Maple Leaf Privy Marks

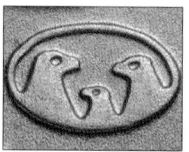

1997 $5
Family

1998 $5
Eagles

$10 — ¼ oz Maple Leaf Privy Marks

2000 $10
Expo
Hannover

2001 $10
Basle Coin Fair

2005 $10
Liberation
Royal Dutch Mint

2005-2006 $10
M7 Privy Mark

DATE	DENOMINATION	CASE OF ISSUE	QUANTITY SOLD	ISSUE PRICE	FINISH	SP-68	SP-69
1997	$5, Family (1/10 oz)	Plastic case	100,730	N/A	Specimen	250.	—
1998	$5, Eagles (1/10 oz)	Plastic case	51,440	N/A	Specimen	250.	—
2000	$10, Expo (¼ oz)	N/A	1,000	N/A	Specimen	550.	—.
2001	$10, Basle (¼ oz)	N/A	750	N/A	Specimen	700.	—
2005	$10, Liberation (¼ oz)	N/A	500	€299	Specimen	550.	—
2005	$10, M7 (¼ oz)	Wooden display case	600	N/A	Specimen	550.	—
2006	$10, M7 (¼ oz)	Mylar pouch	1,093	N/A	Specimen	550.	—

PLATINUM MAPLE LEAF COINS
BULLION ISSUES

Obverse	Obverse	Obverse	Platinum Maple
1988-1989	1990-1999	2009-2015	Leaf Reverse

Designers: See page 509
Finish: Bullion

Engravers: See page 509
Case of Issue: Mylar pouch

PLATINUM MAPLE LEAF SPECIFICATIONS

CHARACTERISTICS	$1 =1/20 oz	$2 = 1/15 oz	$5 = 1/10 oz	$10 = 1/4 oz	$20 = 1/2 oz	$50 = 1 oz
Fineness	99.95%	99.95%	99.95%	99.95%	99.95%	99.95%
Weight (grams)	1.555	2.074	3.110	7.776	15.552	31.1035
Diameter (mm)	14.1	15.0	16.0	20.0	25.0	30.0
Thickness (mm)	0.92	0.94	1.01	1.5	2.02	2.52
Edge	Reeded	Reeded	Reeded	Reeded	Reeded	Reeded
Die Axis	↑↑	↑↑	↑↑	↑↑	↑↑	↑↑

MINTAGES

The production of platinum maple leafs was on an order basis, unlike the production of coinage for circulation where the Mint will anticipate the number of coins required to fulfill the needs of the economy. Maple leafs are not struck unless ordered.

	QUANTITIES SOLD				
DATE	$1 =1/20 oz	$5 = 1/10 oz	$10 = 1/4 oz	$20 = 1/2 oz	$50 = 1 oz
1988	N/I	46,000	87,200	23,600	26,000
1989	N/I	18,000	3,200	4,800	10,000
1990	N/I	9,000	1,600	2,600	31,900
1991	N/I	13,000	7,200	5,600	31,900
1992	N/I	16,000	11,600	12,800	40,500
1993	2,120	14,020	8,048	6,022	17,666
1994	4,260	19,190	9,456	6,710	36,245
1995	460	8,940	6,524	6,308	25,829
1996	1,640	8,820	6,160	5,490	62,273
1997	1,340	7,050	4,552	3,990	25,480
1998	2,000	5,710	3,816	5,486	10,403
1999	4,000	4,080	2,092	788	3,248
2009	N/I	N/I	N/I	N/I	33,000
2011	N/I	N/I	N/I	N/I	5,000
2012	N/I	N/I	N/I	N/I	34,600
2013	N/I	N/I	N/I	N/I	19,349
2014	N/I	N/I	N/I	N/I	N/A
2015	N/I	N/I	N/I	N/I	N/A

PRICING

Buying and selling prices are based on the interday spot price of platinum plus a small percentage premium for striking and handling. The smaller the unit the larger the percentage premium charged on buying; however, in later selling the premium could very well disappear.

Note: 1. No platinum bullion coins were produced from 2000 to 2008, or in 2010.
2. N/I indicates Not Issued.

ONE AND TWO DOLLAR PLATINUM MAPLE LEAF COINS

TWO DOLLAR (1/15 ounce) BULLION ISSUE, 1994, AND ONE DOLLAR (1/20 OUNCE), 1995.

Issued 1994 as a new addition to the line of bullion coins offered by the Royal Canadian Mint, the two dollar (1/15 troy ounce) coin was not a success and was discontinued in 1995. It is a one-year type and for this reason is popular.

The 1995 one dollar (1/20 ounce) has an extremely small mintage of 460 coins. Even so, the slightest demand will affect the price without regard for the market price of platinum.

Designers and Engravers:

Designers and Engravers:	See page 567
Specifications:	See page 589
Finish:	Bullion
Case of Issue:	Mylar pouch

Actual Size

1994 Obv.
$2 (1/15 oz)

1994 Rev.
$2 (1/15 oz)

1995 Obv.
$1 (1/20 oz)

1995 Rev.
$1 (1/20 oz)

DATE	DESCRIPTION	QUANTITY SOLD	ISSUE PRICE	FINISH	MS-65	MS-66
1994	$2 (1/15 oz), Bullion Issue	600	BV	Bullion	800.	—
1995	$1 (1/20 oz), Bullion Issue	460	BV	Bullion	1,100.	—

THREE HUNDRED DOLLAR PLATINUM MAPLE LEAF COINS

THREE HUNDRED DOLLARS (1 ounce), PLATINUM MAPLE LEAF ISSUES, 2012-2018.

Designers:		**Engravers:**	
Obv.:	See obverse illustrations	Obv.:	See obverse illustrations
Rev.:	See reverse illustrations	Rev.:	See reverse illustrations
Composition:	99.95% Pt, Selectively gold plated	**Thickness:**	2.5 mm
Platinum content:	31.15 g, 1.00 tr oz	**Die Axis:**	↑↑
Weight:	31.15 g	**Edge:**	Reeded
Diameter:	30.0 mm	**Finish:**	Proof

Case of Issue: (A) 2007-2015: Maroon leatherette clam style case, black flocked insert, encapsulated coin, COA
            (B) 2014: Red wood lacquered case, black flocked insert, encapsulated coin, COA (Maple Leaf Forever)

2012 Obverse	**2012 Maple Leaf Forever**	**2013 Obverse**	**2013 25th Anniv. of the**
Des.: Susanna Blunt	Des.: Luc Normandin	Des.: Arnold Machin	**Platinum Maple Leaf**
Obv.: Susan Taylor	Engr.: José Osio	Engr.: RCM Staff	Des.: Jean-Louis Sirois
			Cecily Mok

Obverse 2014	**2014 Maple Leaf Forever**	**2015 Obverse**	**2015 Maple Leaf Forever**
Des.: Susanna Blunt	Des.: Lilyane Couloumbe	Des.: Susanna Blunt	Des.: M. Grant
Engr.: Susan Taylor	Engr.: RCM Staff	Engr.: Susan Taylor	Engr.: RCM Staff

Obverse 2016-2018	**2016 Maple Leaf Forever**	**2017 Maple Leaf Forever**	**2018 Maple Leaf Forever**
Des.: Susanna Blunt	Des.: Lilyane Coulombe	Des.: Margaret Best	Des.: Pierre Leduc
Engr.: Susan Taylor	Engr.: RCM Staff	Engr.: RCM Staff	Engr.: RCM Staff

DATE	DESCRIPTION	QUANTITY SOLD	ISSUE PRICE	FINISH	PR-69	PR-70
2012	Maple Leaf Forever	250	2,999.95	Proof	3,000.	—
2013	25th Anniv. Platinum Maple Leaf, Sel. gold plated	250	2,999.95	Proof	3,000.	—
2014	Maple Leaf Forever	250	2,999.95	Proof	3,000.	—
2015	Maple Leaf Forever, Selectively gold plated	250	2,999.95	Proof	3,000.	—
2016	Maple Leaf Forever	246	2,999.95	Proof	3,000.	—
2017	Maple Leaf Forever	250	3,099.95	Proof	3,100.	—
2018	Maple Leaf Forever, Selectively gold plated	250	3,099.95	Reverse Proof	3,100.	—

PLATINUM MAPLE LEAF SPECIAL ISSUES
FRACTIONAL SETS

10TH ANNIVERSARY OF MAPLE LEAF BULLION COINS, 1989.

This four-coin proof platinum set was issued to commemorate the 10th anniversary of the first maple leaf coins issued in 1979.

Designers and Engravers:
   Obv.:   Arnold Machin, Walter Ott
   Rev.:   Walter Ott
Case of Issue: Wooden maple presentation case, black flocked insert, encapsulated coin, COA

Specifications: See page 530
Platinum Content: 1.85 tr oz
Finish: Proof

DATE	DESCRIPTION	QUANTITY SOLD	ISSUE PRICE	FINISH	PR-68	PR-69
1989	Set of 4 coins (1 oz, ½ oz, ¼ oz, 1/10 oz)	1,999	1,995.	Proof	3,100.	—

POLAR BEAR ISSUE, 1999.

In 1999 the Royal Canadian Mint issued a special set of platinum Maple Leafs at the request of a distributor, MTB Bank. They are legal tender coins issued in five denominations with the same specifications as the bullion issues but with a polar bear reverse design. The reverse design is a modification of the two-dollar polar bear reverse by Brent Townsend.

Designers and Engravers:
   Obv.:   Dora de Pédery-Hunt
   Rev.:   Brent Townsend, Ago Aarand
Specifications: See page 530
Platinum Content: 1.90 tr oz
Finish: Bullion, Brilliant relief against a parallel
          lined background
Case of Issue: N/A

DATE	DESCRIPTION	QUANTITY SOLD	ISSUE PRICE	FINISH	MS-65	MS-66
1999	Set of 5 coins (1, ½, ¼, 1/10, 1/20 oz)	500	N/A	Bullion	3,100.	—

HOLOGRAM SET

PLATINUM MAPLE LEAF PROOF HOLOGRAM FIVE-COIN SET, 2002.

In this set the distinctive maple leaf appears as a high-resolution dot matrix hologram which has been struck directly onto regular issues of each of the five coins. The five coins are struck with the same specifications and denominations as the regular issues of 1988-1999.

Designers and Engravers:
   Obv.:   Dora de Pédery-Hunt
   Rev.:   RCM Staff

Specifications: See page 589

Finish: Specimen (reverse proof),
          Brilliant relief on a satin
          background, Hologram

Case of Issue: Red mahogany wooden case,
          black insert, encapsulated
          coins, green velour.

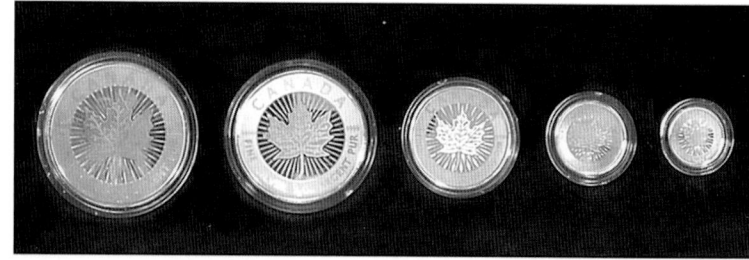

DATE	DESCRIPTION	QUANTITY SOLD	ISSUE PRICE	FINISH	SP-68	SP-69
2002	Set of 5 coins (1, ½, ¼, 1/10, 1/20 oz)	500	2,895.95	Specimen	3,100.	—

A ROYAL WEDDING ANNIVERSARY

A ROYAL WEDDING ANNIVERSARY, 2017.

On November 20, 2017 Her Majesty Queen Elizabeth II and The Duke of Edinburgh will celebrate their 70th wedding anniversary, an impressive milestone that is all the more remarkable for a royal couple that has been in the spotlight from the moment they met. Their wedding in 1947 was Britain's first major event after the war, and people everywhere embraced the occasion. Now, the world stands in awe once again at the steadfast devotion they have shown as the monarchy navigated years of unprecedented social and technological change—an extraordinary journey celebrated with this incomparable set of platinum coins!

Designers and Engravers:
Obv.: Susanna Blunt, Susan Taylor
Rev.: Marie-Élaine Cusson
Case of Issue: Wooden maple presentation case, black flocked insert, encapsulated coin, COA

Specifications: See page 589
Platinum Content: 1.85 tr oz
Finish: Reverse Proof

DATE	DESCRIPTION	MINTAGE	ISSUE PRICE	FINISH	PR-69	PR-70
2017	Set of 4 coins (1 oz, ½ oz, ¼ oz, 1/10 oz)	1,999	4,999.95	Reverse Proof	5,000.	—

PALLADIUM MAPLE LEAF COINS

BULLION ISSUES

FIFTY DOLLARS (1 ounce), PALLADIUM MAPLE LEAF, 2005-2010.

Designers and Engravers:

Obv.:	Susanna Blunt, Susan Taylor
Rev.:	Walter Ott, RCM Staff
Composition:	99.95% Pd
Platinum content:	31.1 g, 1.0 tr oz
Weight:	31.1035 g
Diameter:	30.0 mm
Thickness:	2.9 mm
Finish:	Bullion
Case of Issue:	Mylar pouch

	Edge:	Reeded
	Die Axis:	↑↑

DATE	DESCRIPTION	QUANTITY SOLD	ISSUE PRICE	FINISH	MS-65	MS-66
2005	$50 (1 oz) 99.99%	62,919	BV	Bullion	1,000.	—
2006	$50 (1 oz)	68,707	BV	Bullion	1,000.	—
2007	$50 (1 oz)	15,415	BV	Bullion	1,000.	—
2008	$50 (1 oz)	9,694	BV	Bullion	1,000.	—
2009	$50 (1 oz)	40,000	BV	Bullion	1,000.	—
2010	$50 (1 oz)	25,000	BV	Bullion	1,000.	—

Note: No palladium maple leafs were produced between 2011 and 2015.

SPECIAL ISSUES

EXPERIMENTAL FINISH TEST PALLADIUM MAPLES, 2005.

In 2005 the Royal Canadian Mint conducted tests on palladium planchets. Planchets with the Royal Canadian Mint logo A were finished outside mint facilities, and planchets with the Royal Canadian Mint logo B were finished inside the Mint. Test results showed little variation in the manufacture, resulting in the internal planchets being used in the production of palladium maple leafs.

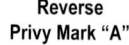

Reverse
Privy Mark "A"

Privy Mark "A"

Reverse
Privy Mark "B"

Privy Mark "B"

Designers:

Obv.:	Susanna Blunt
Rev.:	Walter Ott
Composition:	99.95% Pd
Platinum content:	31.1 g, 1.0 tr oz
Weight:	31.1035 g
Diameter:	30.0 mm
Finish:	Bullion, Brilliant relief against a parallel lined background

Engravers:

Obv.:	Susan Taylor
Rev.:	RCM Staff
Thickness:	2.9 mm
Edge:	Reeded
Die Axis:	↑↑

DATE	DESCRIPTION	QUANTITY SOLD	ISSUE PRICE	FINISH	MS-65	MS-66
2005	Royal Mint Privy Mark "A"	146	1,300.00	Bullion	2,500.	—
2005	Royal Mint Privy Mark "B"	144	1,300.00	Bullion	2,500.	—

SILVER MAPLE LEAF COINS

BULLION ISSUES

The first silver one ounce maple leaf was issued in 1988. The design is a continuation of that first conceived for the gold maples in 1979. The 1999-2000, and the 2000-dated silver maple leaf $5.00 coins carry the fireworks privy mark for 1999-2000, and the millennium privy mark for 2000.

Midway through 2013 a security mark (privy) was added to the reverse of the maple leaf. This security mark is a laser etched maple leaf, and within that leaf another smaller leaf which contains two digits representing the year of striking.

The finish used on the silver maple leaf was changed in 2014. The new finish is a series of radial lines originating at the centre and flowing out to the rim. This complex feature is part of the advanced visual security.

Numerous decals have been placed on $5 maple leafs, they were not issued by the Royal Canandian Mint.

SILVER MAPLE LEAF SPECIFICATIONS

CHARACTERISTICS	$1 =1/20 oz	$2 = 1/10 oz	$3 = 1/4 oz	$4 = 1/2 oz	$5 = 1 oz
Fineness	99.99%	99.99%	99.99%	99.99%	99.99%
Weight (grams)	1.555	3.11	7.776	15.552	31.1035
Diameter (mm)	16.0	20.0	27.0	34.0	38.0
Thickness (mm)	1.1	1.3	1.8	2.1	3.15
Edge	Reeded	Reeded	Reeded	Reeded	Reeded
Die Axis	↑↑	↑↑	↑↑	↑↑	↑↑

FIVE DOLLAR OR ONE OUNCE MAPLES

OBVERSES 1988-2018

Tiara Portrait
1988-1989

Royal Diademed Portrait
1990-2003

Uncrowned Portrait
2004-2013

Obverse
Without Radial Lines
2014

Obverse
With Radial Lines
2014-2018

REVERSES 1988-2018

Reverse
1988-2014
Reverse

With Security Device
With Radial Lines
2014-2018

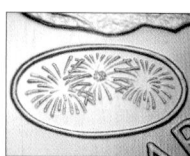

All maple leafs dated
1999-2000
"Fireworks"

All maple leafs dated
2000
"Fireworks 2000"

Security Mark
Inner leaf with 14
date of production
radial lined
background

Designers and Engravers:

1988-1989:	Obv.: Arnold Machin, Walter Ott	Rev.:	Walter Ott, R.C.M. Staff
1989-2003:	Obv.: Dora de Pédery Hunt	Rev.:	Walter Ott, R.C.M. Staff
2004-2018:	Obv.: Susanna Blunt, Susan Taylor	Rev.:	Walter Ott, R.C.M. Staff

Finish: 1988-2014:   Bullion, Brilliant relief against a parallel lined background

               2014-2018:   Brilliant relief against a radial lined background

Case of Issue: 1988-2008:   Single coin sealed in clear Mylar pouch

                   2009-2018:   Plastic tubes of 25 coin

Pricing: Please remember that silver maple leaf prices are linked to the price of silver and may be priced higher, or lower, than prices shown depending on market conditions. Unlike gold and platinum maple leafs, silver leafs do experience a collector demand which will result in price differentials between dates. The price is affected by the total mintage and the pattern of distribution during year of issue.

SILVER MAPLE LEAF SPECIFICATIONS

DATE	PRIVY MARKS	QUANTITY SOLD	ISSUE PRICE	FINISH	MS-65	MS-66	MS-67
1988		1,062,000	BV	Bullion	35.	45.	—
1989		3,332,200	BV	Bullion	35.	45.	—
1990		1,708,800	BV	Bullion	35.	45.	—
1991		644,300	BV	Bullion	35.	45.	—
1992		343,800	BV	Bullion	35.	45.	—
1993		889,946	BV	Bullion	35.	45.	—
1994		1,133,900	BV	Bullion	40.	50.	—
1995		326,244	BV	Bullion	40.	50.	—
1996		250,445	BV	Bullion	60.	70.	—
1997		100,970	BV	Bullion	60.	70.	—
1998		591,359	BV	Bullion	35.	45.	—
1999		1,229,442	BV	Bullion	35.	45.	—
1999-2000	Fireworks	Included	BV	Bullion	40.	50.	—
2000	Fireworks 2000	403,652	BV	Bullion	40.	50.	—
2001		398,563	BV	Bullion	35.	50.	—
2002		576,196	BV	Bullion	35.	50.	—
2003		684,750	BV	Bullion	35.	45.	—
2004		680,925	BV	Bullion	35.	45.	—
2005		955,694	BV	Bullion	35.	45.	—
2006		2,464,727	BV	Bullion	35.	45.	—
2007		3,526,052	BV	Bullion	32.	40.	—
2008		7,909,161	BV	Bullion	32.	40.	—
2009		9,727,592	BV	Bullion	30.	40.	—
2010		17,799,992	BV	Bullion	30.	40.	—
2011		23,129,966	BV	Bullion	30.	40	—
2012		18,132,297	BV	Bullion	28.	40	—
2013		28,222,061	BV	Bullion	26.	35.	—
2013	Security	Included	BV	Bullion	26.	35.	—
2014	Security, Without Radial Lines	N/A	BV	Bullion	26.	35.	—
2014	Security, With Radial Lines	N/A	BV	Bullion	26.	35.	—
2015	Security, With Radial Lines	N/A	BV	Bullion	26.	35.	—
2016	Security, With Radial Lines	N/A	BV	Bullion	26	35.	—
2017	Security, With Radial Lines	N/A	BV	Bullion	26.	35.	—
2018	Security, With Radial Lines	N/A	BV	Bullion	26.	35.	—

NOTES FOR COLLECTORS

1. Silver maple leafs are priced based on the world market price for silver, plus a small premium on the day the transaction takes place. Premiums will vary depending on the size of the transaction.
2. The packaging of silver maple leafs changed in 2009 from single coins in mylar pouches to twenty-five coins packaged in plastic tubes. In 2010 the silver maple leafs were available again in mylar pouches or plastic tubes of twenty-five.
3. The silver maple leafs listed in the table above are priced at a silver market value of $23.00 Cdn. an ounce. Market changes, up or down, from $23.00 will necessitate a price revision.

SILVER MAPLE LEAF SPECIAL ISSUES: SINGLES
FIVE DOLLAR SILVER COINS

FIVE DOLLARS (1 ounce), 10TH ANNIVERSARY OF MAPLE LEAF BULLION COINS, 1989.

Issued in 1989 in Proof finish to commemorate the 10th anniversary of the introduction of the maple leaf in 1979.

Designers and Engravers:

Obv.:	Arnold Machin
Rev.:	Walter Ott, RCM Staff
Composition:	99.99% Ag
Weight:	31.1035 g, 1 tr oz
Diameter:	38.0 mm
Thickness:	3.2 mm
Edge:	Reeded
Die Axis:	↑↑
Finish:	Proof
Case of Issue:	Maple wood presentation box, black flocked insert, encapsulated coins, COA, outer maple leaf printed box.

DATE	DESCRIPTION	QUANTITY SOLD	ISSUE PRICE	FINISH	PR-68	PR-69
1989	$5 (1 oz), 10th Anniv. Maple Leaf coins	29,999	39.00	Proof	75.	—

FIVE DOLLARS (1 ounce), 20TH ANNIVERSARY OF THE SILVER MAPLE LEAF, 1988-2008.

This bullion coin was issued to commemorate the 20th anniversary of the silver maple leaf which was introduced in 1988.

Designers and Engravers:

Obv.:	Arnold Machin
Rev.:	RCM Staff
Composition:	99.99% Ag, Selectively gold plated
Weight:	31.3035 g, 1 tr oz
Diameter:	38.0 mm
Thickness:	3.2 mm
Edge:	Reeded
Die Axis:	↑↑
Finish:	Bullion
Case of Issue:	Maroon leatherette clam style case, black flocked insert, encapsulated coin, COA

DATE	DESCRIPTION	QUANTITY SOLD	ISSUE PRICE	FINISH	MS-65	MS-66	MS-67
2008	$5 (1 oz), 20th Anniv. of the Silver Maple Leaf	9,998	74.95	Bullion	80.	100.	—

VANCOUVER 2010 OLYMPIC GAMES

A $50 gold version of these coins were also issued (see page 434).

FIVE DOLLARS (1 ounce), VANCOUVER 2010 WINTER OLYMPIC GAMES, 2008-2010.

2008 MAPLE LEAF AND VANCOUVER 2010 OLYMPIC LOGO

2009 THUNDERBIRD

2010 HOCKEY PLAYER

Designers:		**Engravers:**
Obv.:	Susanna Blunt	Obv.: Susan Taylor
Rev.:	2008, 2010. RCM Staff	Rev.: 2008 and 2010: Stan Witten
	2009: Xwa lac tun (Ricky Harry)	2009: Marcos Hallam
Composition:	99.99% Ag	
Weight:	31.1035 g, 1 tr oz	**Edge:** Reeded
Diameter:	38.0 mm	**Die Axis:** ↑↑
Thickness:	3.2 mm	
Finish:	1. Bullion	
	2. Bullion, Selectively gold plated	
	3. Bullion, Gilt	
Case of Issue:	Singly: Mylar pouch	
	Coloured Set: Maple wood box, black flocked insert, encapsulated coins, COA	

FIVE DOLLARS (1 ounce), VANCOUVER 2010 WINTER OLYMPIC GAMES, 2008-2010, PRICING TABLE.

DATE	DESCRIPTION	QUANTITY SOLD	ISSUE PRICE	FINISH	MS-65	MS-66	MS-67
2008	$5 (1oz) 2010 Logo	937,839	BV	Bullion	35.	40.	—
2008	$5 (1oz) 2010 Logo, Selectively gold plated	N/A	N.I.I.	Bullion	90.	110.	*
2009	$5 (1oz) Thunderbird	569,048	BV	Bullion	35.	40.	—
2009	$5 (1oz) Thunderbird, Selectively gold plated	N/A	N.I.I.	Bullion	90.	110.	*
2010	$5 (1oz) Hockey Player	79,278	BV	Bullion	35.	40.	—
2010	$5 (1oz) Hockey Player, Selectively gold plated	N/A	N.I.I.	Bullion	90.	110.	*
2010	$5 (1oz) Hockey Player, Gold plated	N/A	71.95	Bullion	70.	90.	—
—	Set of 3 coins, Selectively gold plated	4,000	199.95	Bullion	265.	*	*

Note: 1. Images illustrated smaller than actual size.
2. The mintages reported are for the total number of pieces struck that year. There is no breakdown by design reported. Total mintage for the three designs 1,586,165.

FIVE DOLLARS (1 ounce), PIEDFORT MAPLE LEAF, 2010.

This five-dollar silver Piedfort maple leaf was issued singly, or as part of the Piedfort Maple Leaf Set. The set, which consists of a ten-dollar gold and a five-dollar silver coin, is listed on page 580.

Designers and Engravers:
Obv.: Susanna Blunt, Susan Taylor
Rev.: RCM Staff
Composition: 99.99% Ag
Weight: 31.39 g, 1.01 tr oz
Diameter: 34.0 mm   **Edge:** Reeded
Thickness: 4.0 mm   **Die Axis:** ↑↑
Finish: Bullion
Case of Issue: Maroon leatherette clam style case, black flock insert, encapsulated coin, COA

DATE	DESCRIPTION	QUANTITY SOLD	ISSUE PRICE	FINISH	MS-65	MS-66
2010	$5 (1 oz), Silver Piedfort Maple Leaf	6,843	79.95	Bullion	80.	—

FIVE DOLLARS (1 ounce), 25TH ANNIVERSARY OF THE SILVER MAPLE LEAF, 2013.

This selectively gold plated silver maple leaf was issued to celebrate 25 years of the Royal Canadian Mint's silver maple leaf.

Designers and Engravers:
Obv.: Susanna Blunt, Susan Taylor
Rev.: Jean-Louis Sirois, Cecily Mok
Composition: 99.99% Ag, Selectively gold plated
Weight: 31.10 g, 1.00 tr oz
Diameter: 38.0 mm   **Edge:** Reeded
Thickness: 3.0 mm   **Die Axis:** ↑↑
Finish: Proof
Case of Issue: Maroon leatherette clam style case, black flock insert, encapsulated coin, COA

DATE	DESCRIPTION	QUANTITY SOLD	ISSUE PRICE	FINISH	PR-69	PR-70
2013	$5 (1 oz), 25th Anniv. of the Silver Maple Leaf	9,966	109.95	Proof	90.	—

FIVE DOLLARS (1 ounce), PIEDFORT, 25TH ANNIVERSARY OF THE SILVER MAPLE LEAF, 2013.

This Piedfort silver maple leaf was issued to celebrate 25 years of the Royal Canadian Mint's silver maple leaf.

Designers and Engravers:

Obv.:	Susanna Blunt, Susan Taylor
Rev.:	Jean-Louis Sirois, RCM Staff

Composition: 99.99% Ag
Weight: 31.39 g, 1.01 tr oz
Diameter: 34.0 mm   **Edge:** Reeded
Thickness: 3.8 mm   **Die Axis:** ↑↑
Finish: Proof
Case of Issue: Maroon leatherette clam style case, black flock insert, encapsulated coin, COA

DATE	DESCRIPTION	QUANTITY SOLD	ISSUE PRICE	FINISH	PR-69	PR-70
2013	$5 (1 oz), Piedfort 25th Anniv. of Silver Maple Leaf	9,978	99.95	Proof	80.	—

FIVE DOLLARS (1 ounce), 25TH ANNIVERSARY OF THE SILVER MAPLE LEAF, 2013.

This silver maple leaf was issued to celebrate 25 years of the Royal Canadian Mint's silver maple leaf program.

Designers and Engravers:

Obv.:	Susanna Blunt, Susan Taylor
Rev.:	RCM Staff

Composition: 99.99% Ag
Weight: 31.2 g, 1.0 tr oz
Diameter: 38.0 mm   **Edge:** Reeded
Thickness: 3.25 mm   **Die Axis:** ↑↑
Finish: Bullion
Case of Issue: Tubes of 25, or sealed thermotron film

DATE	DESCRIPTION	QUANTITY SOLD	ISSUE PRICE	FINISH	MS-65	MS-66
2013	$5 (1 oz), 25th Anniv. of Silver Maple Leaf	N/A	BV	Bullion	35.	—

FIVE DOLLARS (1 ounce), BULLION REPLICA SILVER MAPLE LEAF, 2014.

Designers and Engravers:

Obv.:	Susanna Blunt, Susan Taylor
Rev.:	RCM Staff

Composition: 99.99% Ag
Weight: 31.1 g, 1.0 tr oz
Diameter: 38.0 mm
Thickness: 3.3 mm
Edge: Reeded
Die Axis: ↑↑
Finish: Reverse Proof
Case of Issue: Maroon leatherette clam style case, black flock insert, encapsulated coin, COA

DATE	DESCRIPTION	QUANTITY SOLD	ISSUE PRICE	FINISH	PR-69	PR-70
2014	$5 (1 oz), Replica Silver ML	8,095	79.95	Rev. Proof	65.	—

30TH ANNIVERSARY OF THE SILVER MAPLE LEAF 2-COIN SET

FIVE DOLLARS, 2-COIN SET 30TH ANNIVERSARY OF THE SML, 2018.

Unchanged since the very first issue in 1988, the solitary maple leaf that adorns the Silver Maple Leaf (SML) coin is widely regarded as a symbol for unparalleled artistry, craftsmanship and value.

Obverse – Modified Proof

Reverse - Modified Proof

Obverse
- Modified Reverse Proof

Reverse
- Modified Reverse Proof

Designers:
  Obv.:   Susanna Blunt
  Rev.:   RCM Staff
Composition: 99.99% Ag
Silver content: 31.39, 1.0 tr oz
Weight: 31.39 g,
Diameter: 38.0 mm
Thickness: N/A
Case of Issue: Maroon clamshell with black beauty box, COA

Engravers:
  Obv.:   Susan Taylor

Edge: Reeded
Die Axis: ↑↑
Finish: Modified Proof
     & Modified Reverse Proof

DATE	DESCRIPTION	MINTAGE	ISSUE PRICE	FINISH	PR-69	PR-70
2018	2-Coin Set 30th Anniversary of the SML	5,000	189.95	Modified Proof & Modified Reverse Proof	190.	—

EIGHT DOLLAR SILVER COINS

EIGHT DOLLARS (1½ ounce), CANADIAN MAPLE LEAF: THE SUPERLEAF, 2015.
This coin features a radial line finish first used in the 2014 Maple Leaf.

Designers and Engravers:

Obv.:	Susanna Blunt, Susan Taylor
Rev.:	Stan Witten, RCM Staff
Composition:	99.99% Ag
Weight:	46.65 g, 1.5 tr oz
Diameter:	38.0 mm
Thickness:	3.2 mm
Die Axis:	↑↑
Edge:	Reeded
Finish:	Bullion, Radial lines
Case of Issue:	Plastic tubes

DATE	DESCRIPTION	QUANTITY SOLD	ISSUE PRICE	FINISH	MS-65	MS-66
2015	$8 (1½ oz), The Superleaf	N/A	BV	Bullion	60.	—
2016	$8 (1½ oz), The Superleaf	N/A	BV	Bullion	50.	—
2017	$8 (1½ oz), The Superleaf	N/A	BV	Bullion	50.	—

TEN DOLLAR SILVER COINS

TEN DOLLARS (½ ounce), MAPLE LEAF FOREVER, 2011.
The design on the reverse of this maple leaf coin commemorates the three maple leaf design that has graced Canada's one cent coin since 1937.

Designers, and Engravers:

Obv.:	Susanna Blunt, Susan Taylor
Rev.:	Debbie Adams, Konrad Wachelko
Composition:	99.99% Ag
Weight:	15.87 g, 0.5 tr oz
Diameter:	34.0 mm
Thickness:	2.0 mm
Edge:	Reeded
Die Axis:	↑↑
Finish:	Specimen
Case of Issue:	Maroon leatherette clam style case, black insert, encapsulated coin, COA

DATE	DESCRIPTION	QUANTITY SOLD	ISSUE PRICE	FINISH	SP-68	SP-69
2011	$10 (½ oz) Maple Leaf Forever	41,712	34.95	Specimen	25.	—

TEN DOLLARS (½ ounce), MAPLE LEAF FOREVER, 2012.

Designers, and Engravers:

Obv.:	Susanna Blunt, Susan Taylor
Rev.:	Luc Normandin
Composition:	99.99% Ag
Weight:	15.87 g, 0.5 tr oz
Diameter:	34.0 mm
Thickness:	2.1 mm
Edge:	Reeded
Die Axis:	↑↑
Finish:	Specimen
Case of Issue:	Black card envelope with green maple leaf design, encapsulated coin, COA, black card coin holder

DATE	DESCRIPTION	QUANTITY SOLD	ISSUE PRICE	FINISH	SP-68	SP-69
2012	$10 (½ oz) Maple Leaf Forever	29,173	34.95	Specimen	30.	—

Note: Identical designs are utilized on the $500 gold coin (page 516) and the $300 platinum maple leaf (page 591) for 2012.

THE MAPLE LEAF 2013-2018

TEN DOLLARS, MAPLE LEAF, 2013-2017.

Common Obverse

2013
Designer: Pierre Leduc
Engraver: Eric Boyer

2014
Designer: Pierre Leduc
Engraver: RCM Staff

2015
Designer: Celia Godkin
Engraver: RCM Staff

2016
Designer: Donna Kriekle
Engraver: RCM Staff

2017
Designer: Pierre Leduc
Engraver: RCM Staff

Designers:
Obv.:   Susanna Blunt
Rev.:   See reverse illustrations

Engravers:
Obv.:   Susan Taylor
Rev.:   See reverse illustrations

	2013-2014	**2015-2017**
Silver content:	99.99% Ag	99.99% Ag
Silver content:	16.1 g, 0.517 tr oz	15.85 g, 0.5 tr oz
Weight:	16.1 g	15.87 g

Diameter:	34.0 mm			
Thickness:	2.1 mm	**Edge:**	Reeded	
Finish:	Specimen	**Die Axis:**	↑↑	
Case of Issue:	Maroon leatherette clam style case, black flocked insert, encapsulated coin, COA			

DATE	DESCRIPTION	QUANTITY SOLD	ISSUE PRICE	FINISH	SP-68	SP-69
2013	Maple Leaf	5,101	39.95	Specimen	35.	—
2014	Maple Leaf	8,732	39.95	Specimen	35.	—
2015	Maple Leaf	24,577	29.95	Specimen	30.	—
2016	Maple Leaf	29,776	29.95	Specimen	30	—
2017	Maple Leaf	2,520	29.95	Specimen	35.	—

TEN DOLLARS, CANADA 150 ICONIC MAPLE LEAF, 2017.

Designers and Engravers:
Obv.:	Susanna Blunt
Rev.:	RCM Staff

Composition: 99.99% Ag,
Silver content: 15.87 g, 0.510 tr oz
Weight: 62.69 g
Diameter: 50 mm   **Edge:** Reeded
Thickness: N/A   **Die Axis:** ↑↑
Finish: Matte Proof
Case of Issue: Maroon clamshell with black beauty box.

DATE	DESCRIPTION	QUANTITY SOLD	ISSUE PRICE	FINISH	PR-69	PR-70
2017	Canada 150 Iconic Maple Leaf	5,179	169.95	Matte Proof	200	—

TEN DOLLARS, SML TRIBUTE TO 30 YEARS, 2018.

Unchanged since the very first issue in 1988, the solitary maple leaf that adorns the Silver Maple Leaf (SML) coin is widely rgarded as a symbol for unparalleled artistry, craftsmanship and vlaue.

Designers and Engravers:
Obv.:	Susanna Blunt, Susan Taylor
Rev.:	RCM Staff

Composition: 99.99% Ag, Selective gold plating
Silver content: 62.69 g, 2.02 tr oz
Weight: 62.69 g   **Edge:** Reeded
Diameter: 38.0 mm   **Die Axis:** ↑↑
Thickness: 3.2 mm   **Finish:** Modified Proof
Case of Issue: Maroon clamshell with black beauty box, COA.

DATE	DESCRIPTION	MINTAGE	ISSUE PRICE	FINISH	PR-69	PR-70
2018	SML Tribute to 30 Years	6,000	194.95	Modified Proof	200.	—

TEN DOLLARS, MAPLE LEAVES, 2018.

Designers and Engravers:
Obv.:	Susanna Blunt, Susan Taylor
Rev.:	Celia Godkin

Composition: 99.99% Ag
Silver content: 15.87 g, 0.510 tr oz
Weight: 15.87 g   **Edge:** Reeded
Diameter: 34 mm   **Die Axis:** ↑↑
Thickness: 3.2 mm   **Finish:** Specimen
Case of Issue: Folder with removable capsule.

DATE	DESCRIPTION	MINTAGE	ISSUE PRICE	FINISH	SP-68	SP-69
2018	Maple Leaves	W.S.L.	34.95	Specimen	35.	—

W.S.L. = While Supplies Last

TWENTY DOLLAR SILVER COINS

TWENTY DOLLARS (1 OUNCE), MAPLE LEAVES, GLOW-IN-THE-DARK, 2014.

Featuring autumnal colours of the sugar maple tree when viewed in light, the coin transforms to a glow-in-the-dark single maple leaf when viewed in the dark.

Designers and Engravers:

Obv.:	Susanna Blunt, Susan Taylor
Rev.:	C. Godkin, RCM Staff
Composition:	99.99% Ag, Glow-in-the-dark
Silver content:	31.39 g, 1.01 tr oz
Weight:	31.39 g
Diameter:	38.0 mm
Thickness:	N/A
Edge:	Reeded
Die Axis:	↑↑
Finish:	Proof
Case of Issue:	Maroon leatherette clam style case, black flocked insert, encapsulated coin, COA, custom box

DATE	DESCRIPTION	QUANTITY SOLD	ISSUE PRICE	FINISH	MS-65	MS-66
2014	Maple Leaves (1 oz)	7,492	104.95	Proof	105.	—

TWENTY DOLLARS, 30TH ANNIVERSARY OF THE SILVER MAPLE LEAF (INCUSE), 2018.

The year 2018 marks the 30th anniversary of our iconic Silver Maple Leaf (SML) bullion coin — the standard against which other silver bullion coins are measured. This very special numismatic release includes a RCM first: incuse-struck images on both sides of the coin, as well as edge lettering, with the number "30" flanked on both sides by a maple leaf.

Designers and Engravers:

Obv.:	Susanna Blunt
Rev.:	RCM Staff
Composition:	99.99% Ag
Silver content:	31.39 g, 1.01 tr oz
Weight:	31.39 g
Diameter:	38 mm
Thickness:	N/A
Edge:	Interruped reeding
Die Axis:	↑↑
Finish:	Proof
Case of Issue:	Maroon clamshell with black beauty box, COA

DATE	DESCRIPTION	MINTAGE	ISSUE PRICE	FINISH	PR-69	PR-70
2018	30th Anniversary of the Silver Maple Leaf (SML)	6,500	104.95	Reverse Proof	105.	—

TWENTY DOLLARS, 30TH ANNIVERSARY OF THE SILVER MAPLE LEAF (SHAPED), 2018.

The Royal Canadian Mint proudly celebrates 30 years of an icon with a maple leaf-shaped tribute to the Silver Maple Leaf (SML) bullion coin.

Designers and Engravers:

Obv.:	Susanna Blunt
Rev.:	RCM staff
Composition:	99.99% Ag,
Silver content:	31.5 g, 1.01 tr oz
Weight:	31.5 g
Diameter:	42 mm x 43 mm
Thickness:	N/A
Edge:	Plain
Die Axis:	↑↑
Finish:	Proof
Case of Issue:	Maroon clamshell with black beauty box, COA

DATE	DESCRIPTION	MINTAGE	ISSUE PRICE	FINISH	PR-69	PR-70
2018	30th Anniversary of the Silver Maple Leaf	6,000	159.95	Proof	160.	—

FIFTY DOLLAR SILVER COINS

FIFTY DOLLARS (10 ounces), 10TH ANNIVERSARY OF THE SILVER MAPLE LEAF, 1998.

In 1998 the Royal Canadian Mint issued the 10-ounce silver maple leaf in celebration of the 10th anniversary of the silver maple leaf bullion coin. The coin is accompanied by a sterling silver plaque of authenticity.

Designers:		**Engravers:**	
Obv.:	Dora de Pédery-Hunt	Obv.:	Dora de Pédery-Hunt
Rev.:	RCM Staff	Rev.:	RCM Staff
Composition:	99.99% Ag		
Silver content:	311.0 g, 10.0 tr oz	**Edge:**	Lettered, 10th Anniversary 10e Anniversaire
Weight:	311.04 g, 10.0 tr oz	**Die Axis:**	↑↑
Diameter:	65.0 mm	**Finish:**	Reverse proof
Thickness:	11.0 mm	**Nominal Value:**	$50.00
Case of Issue:	Black leather case with silver "Royal Canadian Mint" plaque, black flocked lining, encapsulated coin, Sterling silver certificate of authenticity		

DATE	DESCRIPTION	QUANTITY SOLD	ISSUE PRICE	FINISH	PR-68	PR-69
1998	$50 (10 oz), 10th Anniv. Silver Maple Leaf	13,533	200.00	Proof	600.	—

Note: Coin illustrated smaller than actual size.

FIFTY DOLLARS (5 ounces), 25TH ANNIVERSARY OF THE SILVER MAPLE LEAF, 2013.

These coins were issued to commemorate the striking of the first silver maple leaf in 1988.

Common Obverse	2013 25th Anniv. of the Silver Maple Leaf Reverse Proof Designer: Arnold Nogy Engraver: Steven Stewart	2013 25th Anniv. of the Silver Maple Leaf Matte Proof, Selectively Gold Plated Designer: Jean Louis Sirois Engraver: RCM Staff

Designers:
Obv.: Susanna Blunt
Rev.: See reverse illustrations
Composition: 99.99% Ag
Weight: 157.6 g, 5.0 tr oz
Diameter: 65.0 mm
Thickness: N/A
Case of Issue: (A) Lacquered red wooden case, black lining, encapsulated coin, COA
(B) Maroon leatherette clam style case black flocked insert, encapsulated coin, COA, custom beauty box

Engravers:
Obv.: Susan Taylor

Silver content: 157.6 g, 5.0 tr oz
Edge: Reeded
Die Axis: ↑↑
Finish: See reverse illustrations

DATE	DESCRIPTION	QUANTITY SOLD	ISSUE PRICE	FINISH	PR-69	PR-70
2013 (1988)	$50 (5 oz), 25th Anniv. Silver Maple Leaf	2,525	499.95	Rev. Proof	500.	—
2013 (1988)	$50 (5 oz) 25th Anniv. Silver Maple Leaf, Selectively gold plated	1,900	549.95	Matte Proof	500.	—

Note: Coins illustrated smaller than actual size.

FIFTY DOLLARS, 30TH ANNIVERSARY OF THE SML, 2018.

The year 2018 marks the 30th anniversary of the iconic Silver Maple Leaf bullion coin – the standard against which other silver bullion coins are measured.

Designers and Engravers:
Obv.: S. Blunt, S. Taylor
Rev.: RCM staff
Composition: 99.99% Ag,
Silver content: 94.4 g, 30.4 tr oz
Weight: 94.4 g
Diameter: 55 mm
Thickness: N/A.
Edge: Reeded
Die Axis: ↑↑
Finish: Reverse Proof
Case of Issue: Maroom clamshell with black beauty box, COA.

DATE	DESCRIPTION	MINTAGE	ISSUE PRICE	FINISH	PR-69	PR-70
2017	30th Anniversary of the SML	3,000	299.95	Reverse Proof	300.	—

TWO HUNDRED FIFTY DOLLAR SILVER COINS

TWO HUNDRED FIFTY DOLLARS (kilogram), MAPLE LEAF FOREVER, 2011-2012.
The reverse design was inspired by the spirit of the maple leaves seen on the one cent coin used since 1937.

2011 Obverse

2011 Maple Leaf Forever
Des.: Debbie Adams
Engr.: Konrad Wachelko

2012 Obverse

2012 Maple Leaf Forever
Des.: Luc Normandin
Engr.: RCM Staff

Designers:		**Engravers:**	
Obv.:	Susanna Blunt	Obv.:	Susan Taylor
Rev.:	See reverse illustrations	Rev.:	See reverse illustrations
Composition:	99.99% Ag	**Thickness:**	13.2 mm
Silver content:	1,000.0 g, 32.151 tr oz	**Edge:**	2011: Plain 2012: Reeded
Weight:	1,000.0 g (1 kilo)	**Die Axis:**	↑↑
Diameter:	101.8 mm	**Finish:**	Proof
Case of Issue:	2011: Black display case, black flocked insert, encapsulated coin, COA		
	2012: Canadian maple wood box, black flocked insert, encapsulated coin, COA, custom sleeve		

DATE	DESCRIPTION	QUANTITY SOLD	ISSUE PRICE	FINISH	PR-69	PR-70
2011	Maple Leaf Forever	997	2,195.95	Proof	2,200.	—
2012	Maple Leaf Forever	934	2,249.95	Proof	2,250.	—

Note: 1. Identical designs are utilized on the $2,500 gold (maple leaf) coins for 2011 and 2012, see page 577.
2. Coins illustrated smaller than actual size.

TWO HUNDRED FIFTY DOLLARS (kilogram), MAPLE LEAF FOREVER, 2013.

2013 Obverse

2013 Maple Leaf Forever
Des.: Emily Damstra
Engr.: RCM Staff

Designers:		**Engravers:**		
Rev.:	Emily Damstra	Obv.:	Susanna Blunt	
Composition:	99.99% Ag	**Thickness:**	12.5 mm	
Silver content:	1,000.0 g, 32.151 tr oz	**Edge:**	Reeded	
Weight:	1,000.0 g (1 kilo)	**Die Axis:**	↑↑	
Diameter:	102.1 mm	**Finish:**	2012 Proof, 2013 Proof, Selectively gold plated	
Case of Issue:	2013 Maple wood box, black flocked insert, encapsulated coin, COA			

DATE	DESCRIPTION	QUANTITY SOLD	ISSUE PRICE	FINISH	PR-69	PR-70
2013	Maple Leaf Forever, Selectively gold plated	596	2,249.95	Proof	2,250.	—

Note: Coins illustrated smaller than actual size.

SILVER MAPLE LEAFS WITH PRIVY MARKS

SINGLES

FIVE DOLLARS (1 ounce), SILVER MAPLE LEAFS WITH PRIVY MARKS, 1998-2018.
    Beginning in 1998 the Royal Canadian Mint started a special issue of the $5.00 - 1 oz silver Maple Leafs. Privy marks were added to the reverses, commemorating special events for each year. For Designers and Engravers see page 596 and for Specifications see page 595.

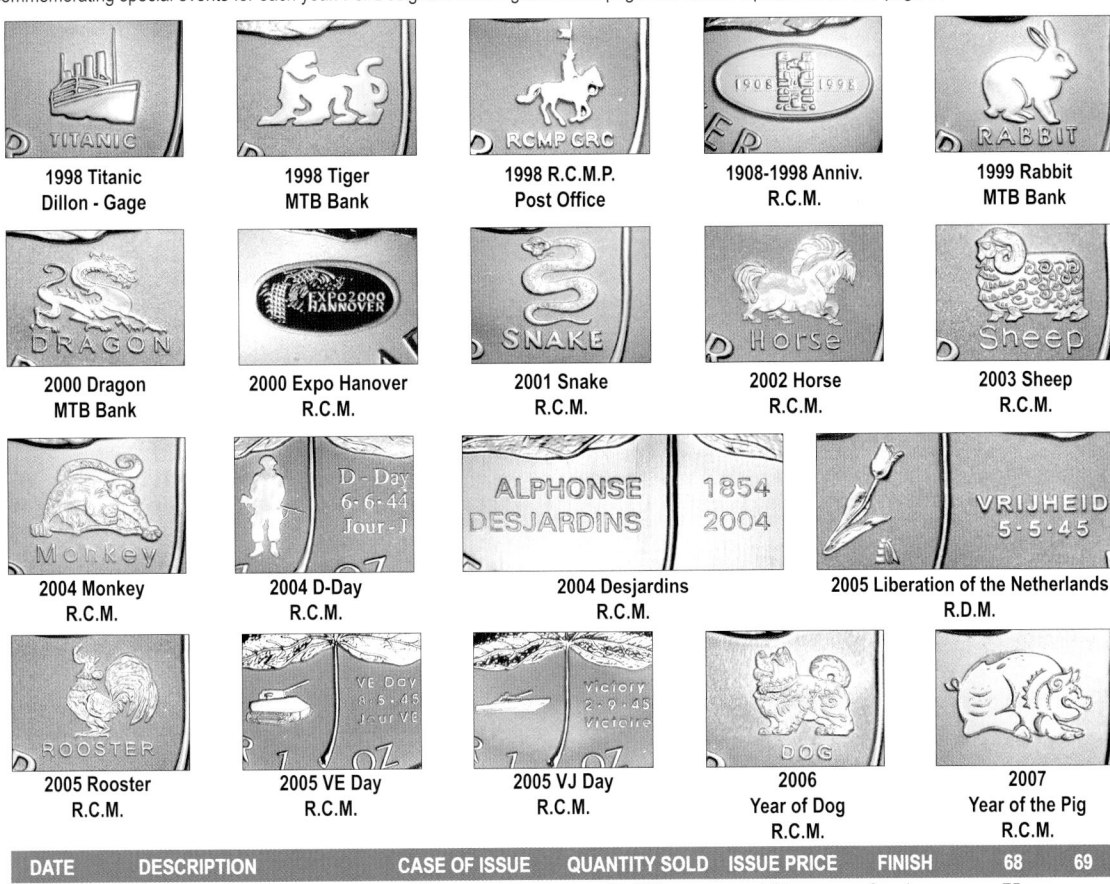

1998 Titanic Dillon - Gage	**1998 Tiger** MTB Bank	**1998 R.C.M.P.** Post Office	**1908-1998 Anniv.** R.C.M.	**1999 Rabbit** MTB Bank
2000 Dragon MTB Bank	**2000 Expo Hanover** R.C.M.	**2001 Snake** R.C.M.	**2002 Horse** R.C.M.	**2003 Sheep** R.C.M.
2004 Monkey R.C.M.	**2004 D-Day** R.C.M.	**2004 Desjardins** R.C.M.		**2005 Liberation of the Netherlands** R.D.M.
2005 Rooster R.C.M.	**2005 VE Day** R.C.M.	**2005 VJ Day** R.C.M.	**2006** Year of Dog R.C.M.	**2007** Year of the Pig R.C.M.

DATE	DESCRIPTION	CASE OF ISSUE	QUANTITY SOLD	ISSUE PRICE	FINISH	68	69
1998	Titanic	Mylar pouch	26,000	N/A	Specimen	75.	—
1998	Tiger	Mylar pouch	25,000	N/A	Specimen	60.	—
1998	R.C.M.P.	Mylar pouch	25,000	N/A	Specimen	75.	—
1998	90th Anniv.	Mylar pouch	13,025	N/A	Specimen	60.	—
1999	Rabbit	Mylar pouch	25,000	N/A	Specimen	60.	—
2000	Dragon	Mylar pouch	25,000	N/A	Specimen	60.	—
2000	Expo	Mylar pouch	15,000	N/A	Specimen	100.	—
2001	Snake	Mylar pouch	25,000	N/A	Specimen	60.	—
2002	Horse	Mylar pouch	25,000	N/A	Specimen	60.	—
2003	Sheep	Mylar pouch	25,000	N/A	Specimen	60.	—
2004	Monkey	Mylar pouch	25,000	N/A	Specimen	60.	—
2004	D-Day	Red display	11,698	39.95	Specimen	75.	—
2004	Desjardins	Red display	15,000	39.95	Bullion	75.	—
2005	Rooster	Mylar pouch	15,000	24.95	Specimen	60.	—
2005	Liberation	Mylar pouch	3,500	€45.95	Specimen	175.	—
2005	VE Day	Mylar pouch	6,998	49.95	Specimen	85.	—
2005	VJ Day	Mylar pouch	6,998	49.95	Specimen	85.	—
2006	Year of the Dog	Mylar pouch	10,000	24.95	Specimen	60.	—
2007	Year of the Pig	Mylar pouch	8,000	29.95	Specimen	60.	—

FIVE DOLLARS (1 ounce), SILVER MAPLE LEAFS WITH PRIVY MARKS, 1998-2018, (cont.).

| 2007, 2008, 2009 Fabulous 12 | 2008 Year of the Rat R.C.M. | 2008 Brandenburg Gate | 2009 Year of the Ox R.C.M. | 2009 Tower Bridge | 2012 Tower of Pisa |

| 2010-2018 Fabulous 15 | 2012 Titanic 100th Anniv. | 2012 Year of the Dragon | 2013 Year of the Snake | 2014 World Money Fair | 2014 Year of the Horse |

| 2014 A.N.A. Chicago | 2014 Dual Horse | 2015 Year of the Ram | 2015 Heart Rosland Capital Fisher House | 2015 E=mc2 | 2015 A.N.A. Chicago Tulip |

DATE	DESCRIPTION	CASE OF ISSUE	QUANTITY SOLD	ISSUE PRICE	FINISH	68	69
2007	Fabulous 12	Mylar pouch	5,000	39.95	Specimen	90.	—
2008	Fabulous 12	Mylar pouch	5,000	N/A	Specimen	140.	—
2008	Year of the Rat	Mylar pouch	8,000	24.95	Specimen	60.	—
2008	Brandenburg Gate	Mylar pouch	50,000	39.95	Bullion	60.	—
2009	Year of the Ox	Mylar pouch	8,000	23.95	Specimen	60.	—
2009	Tower Bridge	Mylar pouch	75,000	34.95	Bullion	60.	—
2009	Fabulous 12	Mylar pouch	5,000	N/A	Specimen	120.	—
2010	Fabulous 15	Plastic case	5,000	44.95	Specimen	120.	—
2011	Fabulous 15	Plastic case	5,000	44.95	Specimen	200.	—
2012	Leaning Tower of Pisa	Mylar pouch	50,000	N/A	Bullion	60.	—
2012	Fabulous 15	Mylar pouch	10,000	N/A	Bullion	80.	—
2012	Titanic 100th Anniversary	Mylar pouch	25,000	N/A	Specimen	50.	—
2012	Year of the Dragon	Mylar pouch	25,000	N/A	Specimen	50.	—
2013	Fabulous 15	Mylar pouch	10,000	55.95	Bullion	80.	—
2013	Year of the Snake	Display box	N/A	N/A	Specimen	45.	—
2014	World Money Fair, Berlin	Display box	7,429	100.00	Bullion	100.	—
2014	Year of the Horse	Mylar pouch	N/A	32.75	Specimen	40.	—
2014	American Numismatic Society	Display box	7,452	100.00	Proof	90.	—
2014	Fabulous 15	Mylar pouch	10,000	59.95	Bullion	60.	—
2014	Dual Horse, Horse & Hieroglyphic	Display box	1,000	N/A	Bullion	—	—
2015	Year of the Ram	Plastic case	N/A	25.00	Specimen	35.	—
2015	Heart	Capsule	25,000	N/A	Bullion	200.	—
2015	E=mc2	Mylar pouch	50,000	35.00	Proof	40.	—
2015	A.N.A. Chicago	Display box	5,000	79.95	Bullion	85.	—
2015	Fabulous 15	Capsule	N/A	N/A	Bullion	—	—

FIVE DOLLARS (1 ounce), SILVER MAPLE LEAFS WITH PRIVY MARKS, 1998-2018, (cont.).

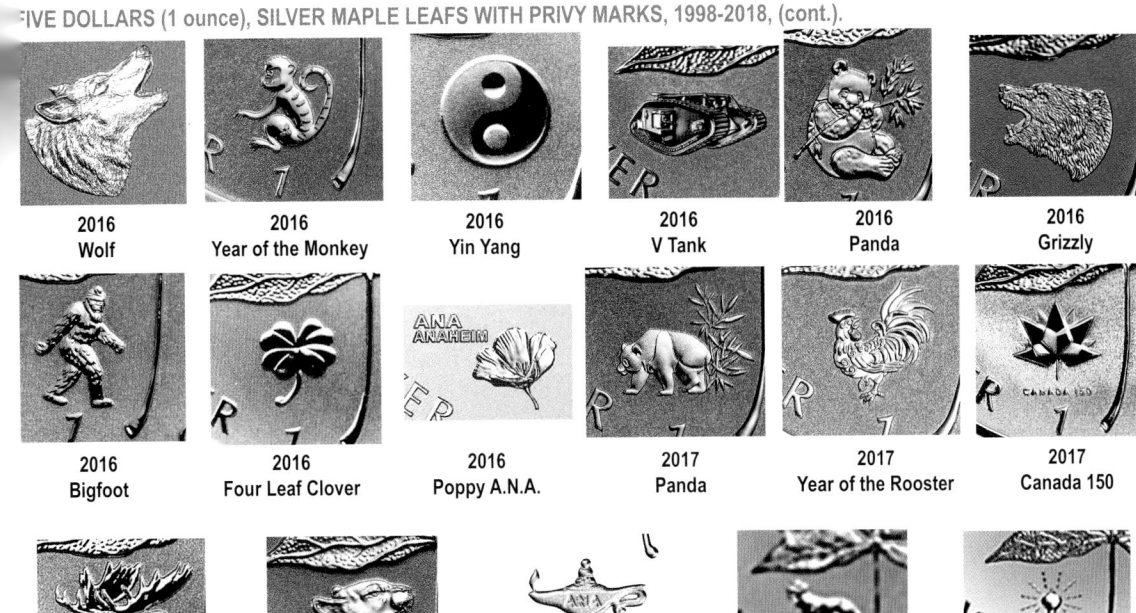

2016 Wolf	2016 Year of the Monkey	2016 Yin Yang	2016 V Tank	2016 Panda	2016 Grizzly

2016 Bigfoot	2016 Four Leaf Clover	2016 Poppy A.N.A.	2017 Panda	2017 Year of the Rooster	2017 Canada 150

2017 Wild Moose	2017 Growling Cougar	2017 A.N.A. World's Fair of Money	2018 Year of the Dog R.C.M.	2018 Edison Light Bulb

DATE	DESCRIPTION	CASE OF ISSUE	QUANTITY SOLD	ISSUE PRICE	FINISH	68	69
2016	Wolf	Capsule	50,000	N/A	Bullion	35.	—
2016	Year of the Monkey	Capsule	N/A	N/A	Bullion	35.	—
2016	Yin Yang	Capsule	50,000	N/A	Bullion	35.	—
2016	V Tank	Capsule	50,000	N/A	Bullion	35.	—
2016	Panda	Capsule	50,000	N/A	Bullion	35.	—
2016	Grizzly	Capsule	50,000	N/A	Bullion	35.	—
2016	Big Foot	Capsule	50,000	N/A	Bullion	35.	—
2016	Four Leaf Clover	Capsule	50,000	N/A	Bullion	35.	—
2016	Poppy A.N.A.	Display Box	6,000	79.95	Bullion	85.	—
2016	Fabulous 15	Capsule	N/A	N/A	Bullion	100.	—
2017	Panda	Capsule	50,000	N/A	Bullion	35.	—
2017	Year of the Rooster	Capsule	50,000	N/A	Bullion	30.	—
2017	Canada 150	Capsule	150,000	N/A	Bullion	30.	—
2017	Wild Moose	Capsule	50,000	N/A	Bullion	30.	—
2017	Growling Cougar	Capsule	50,000	N/A	Bullion	30.	—
2017	Fabulous 15	Capsule	N/A	N/A	Bullion	—	—
2017	ANA World's Fair of Money	Display box	6,000	92.95	Bullion	93.	—
2018	Fabulous 15	Capsule	N/A	N/A	Bullion	—	—
2018	Year of the Dog	Capsule	N/A	BV	Bullion	35.	—
2018	Edison Light Bulb	Capsule	N/A	BV	Bullion	35.	—

Pricing has not been established for the Fabulous 15 coins for 2015, 2017 and 2018 due to lack of information.

SPECIAL PRIVY MARK SET

FIVE DOLLARS (1 OUNCE), SILVER MAPLE LEAFS, ZODIAC PRIVY MARK SET, 2004.

This special zodiak privy mark set was issued by the Royal Canandian Mint. Of the 25,000 sets issued five thousand were boxed and sold as a packaged set with ceritficates of authenticity and sold by Universal Coins of Ottawa.

Aries

Taurus

Gemini

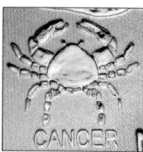
Cancer

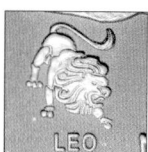
Leo

Virgo

Libra

Scorpio

Sagittarius

Capricorn

Aquarius

Pisces

Designers:
  Obv.: Susanna Blunt
  Rev.: RCM Staff
Composition: 99.99% Ag
Weight: 31.1035 g, 1 tr oz
Diameter: 38.0 mm
Finish: Specimen (reverse proof)
Case of Issue: Singly: Mylar pouch
             Set: Red 12-hole case

Engravers:
  Obv.: Susan Taylor
  Rev.: José Osio
Thickness: 3.2 mm
Edge: Reeded
Die Axis: ↑↑

DATE	DESCRIPTION	QUANTITY SOLD	ISSUE PRICE	FINISH	SP-68	SP-69
2004	Set of 12 coins	25,000	368.88	Specimen	575.	*
2004	Single coin	Included	39.95	Specimen	55.	—

NOTES

1. A specimen finish on a bullion coin is also known as a reverse proof – a brilliant relief on a matte or satin background.
2. The method of packaging may vary from the normal mylar pouch to red or black flocked clam style cases, depending on the distributor.
3. The maple leaf coins which carry either an "F12" or "F15" privy mark commemorate the winning coin design at the Berlin Money Fair for the year which they are dated.

SILVER MAPLE LEAF FRACTIONAL SETS

5TH ANNIVERSARY OF THE SILVER MAPLE (HOLOGRAM SET), 2003.

These maple leaf coins were struck to commemorate the 15th anniversary of the silver maple leaf, 1988-2003. This five-coin set contains two new denominations for Canadian coinage, a $3 and a $4 coin. All coins are struck with a maple leaf hologram.

Designers and Engravers:

Obv.:	Dora de Pédery-Hunt
Rev.:	RCM Staff
Specifications:	See page 595
Silver content:	1.90 tr oz
Finish:	Bullion, Hologram
Case of Issue:	Red wooden case, black flocked insert, encapsulated coin, COA, silver outer box

DATE	DESCRIPTION	QUANTITY SOLD	ISSUE PRICE	FINISH	MS-65	MS-66	MS-67
2003	Set of 5 coins (1, ½, ¼, 1/10, 1/20 oz)	28,947	149.95	Bullion	175.	—	—

ROYAL CANADIAN MINT LOGO SET, 2004.

Each coin in this set carries the Royal Canadian Mint logo on each coin.

Designers and Engravers:

Obv.:	Susanna Blunt, Susan Taylor
Rev.:	RCM Staff
Specifications:	See page 595
Silver content:	1.90 tr oz
Finish:	Specimen (reverse proof)
Case of Issue:	Dark blue leatherette clam style case, black insert, encapsulated coin, COA, silver sleeve

DATE	DESCRIPTION	QUANTITY SOLD	ISSUE PRICE	FINISH	SP-68	SP-69
2004	Set of 5 coins (1, ½, ¼, 1/10, 1/20 oz)	13,859	99.95	Specimen	130.	—

SILVER MAPLE LEAF FRACTIONAL SET SPECIFICATIONS

...LVER MAPLE LEAF 25TH ANNIVERSARY FRACTIONAL SET, 2013.

This set was issued to commemorate the twenty-fifth anniversary of the Silver Maple Leaf bullion coin first issued in 1988.

Designers and Engravers:

Obv.:	Susanna Blunt, Matt Bowen
Rev.:	Arnold Nogy, Steven Stewart
Specifications:	See page 595
Silver content:	1.90 tr oz
Finish:	Reverse Proof
Case of Issue:	Maroon leatherette clam style case, black flocked insert, encapsulated coins, COA

DATE	DESCRIPTION	QUANTITY SOLD	ISSUE PRICE	FINISH	PR-69	PR-70
2013 (1998-)	Set of 5 coins (1, 1/2, 1/4, 1/10, 1/20 oz)	9,993	199.95	Proof	250.	—

SILVER MAPLE LEAF FRACTIONAL SET, 2014.

Designers and Engravers:

Obv.:	Susanna Blunt, Matt Bowen
Rev.:	Arnold Nogy, RCM Staff

Specifications: See page 595
Silver content: 1.90 tr oz
Finish: Reverse Proof, Selectively gold plated
Case of Issue: Maroon leatherette clam style case, black flocked insert, encapsulated coins, COA

DATE	DESCRIPTION	QUANTITY SOLD	ISSUE PRICE	FINISH	PR-69	PR-70
2014	Set of 5 coins (1, ½, ¼, 1/10, 1/20 oz)	9,997	249.95	Proof	250.	—

.VER SUGAR MAPLE LEAF FRACTIONAL SET, 2015.
The one ounce coin features a rich translucent red enamel. All coins are struck with an incuse design.

Designers and Engravers:
    Obv.:   Susanna Blunt, Matt Bowen
    Rev.:   Lilyane Coulombe, RCM Staff
Specifications: See page 595
Silver content: 1.90 tr oz
Finish: Reverse Proof
Case of Issue: Maroon leatherette clam style case, black flocked insert, encapsulated coins, COA

DATE	DESCRIPTION	QUANTITY SOLD	ISSUE PRICE	FINISH	PR-69	PR-70
2015	Set of 5 coins (1, ½, ¼, 1/10, 1/20 oz)	834	224.95	Proof	225.	—

SILVER MAPLE LEAF FRACTIONAL SET: A HISTORIC REIGN, 2016.

The one-ounce coin in the set features the edge lettering: "LONGEST REIGNING SOVEREIGN".

Designers and Engravers:

Obv.:	Susanna Blunt, Susan Taylor
Rev.:	Donna Kriekle
Specifications:	See page 595
Silver content:	1.90 tr oz
Finish:	Reverse Proof
Case of Issue:	Maroon leatherette clam style case, black flocked insert, encapsulated coins, COA

DATE	DESCRIPTION	QUANTITY SOLD	ISSUE PRICE	FINISH	PR-69	PR-70
2016	Set of 5 coins (1, ½, ¼, 1/10, 1/20 oz)	7,297	224.95	Proof	225.	—

SILVER MAPLE LEAF FRACTIONAL SET: MAPLE LEAF TRIBUTE, 2017.

A unique design celebrating Canada's most cherished national symbol and a commemorative double-date (1867-2017) to highlight this historic year.

Designers and Engravers:

Obv.:	Susanna Blunt, Susan Taylor
Rev.:	Stan Witten

Specifications: See page 595

Silver content: 1.90 tr oz

Finish: Reverse Proof

Case of Issue: Maroon leatherette clam style case, black flocked insert, encapsulated coins, COA

DATE	DESCRIPTION	MINTAGE	ISSUE PRICE	FINISH	PR-69	PR-70
2017	Set of 4 coins (1, ½, ¼, 1/10 oz)	5,500	199.95	Reverse Proof	200.	—

SILVER MAPLE LEAFS WITH COLOUR

SINGLE COINS

FIVE DOLLARS (1 OUNCE), SILVER MAPLE LEAFS, COLOURED COIN SERIES, 2001-2007.

2001-2003 Obverse
Designer and Engraver:
Dora de Pédery-Hunt

2001 Autumn
Designer: Debbie Adams
Engraver: W. Woodruff

2002 Spring
Designer and Engraver:
William Woodruff

2003 Summer
Designer and Engraver:
Stan Witten

2004-2007 Obverse
Designer: Susanna Blunt
Engraver: Susan Taylor

2004 Winter
Designer and Engraver:
Stan Witten

2005 Bigleaf Maple
Designer and Engraver:
Stan Witten

2006 Silver Maple
Designer and Engraver:
Stan Witten

2007 Sugar Maple
Designer and Engraver:
Stan Witten

Designers and Engravers:
See obverse and reverse illustrations
Specifications: See page 595
Finish: Bullion, colourised
Case of Issue: 2001-2004:   Dark green clam case, black flocked insert, encapsulated coin, COA
    2005-2007:   Maroon plastic slide case, black plastic insert, encapsulated coin, COA

DATE	DESCRIPTION	QUANTITY SOLD	ISSUE PRICE	FINISH	MS-65	MS-66	MS-67
2001	Autumn	49,709	34.95	Bullion	55.	70.	—
2002	Spring	29,509	34.95	Bullion	55.	75.	—
2003	Summer	29,416	34.95	Bullion	55.	70.	—
2004	Winter	26,763	34.95	Bullion	55.	85.	—
2005	Bigleaf Maple	21,233	39.95	Bullion	70.	100.	—
2006	Silver Maple	14,157	45.95	Bullion	70.	100.	—
2007	Sugar Maple	11,495	49.95	Bullion	100.	130.	—

Note: Coins illustrated smaller than actual size.

SILVER MAPLE LEAFS WITH HOLOGRAMS
SINGLE COINS

/E DOLLARS (1 ounce), "MAPLE OF GOOD FORTUNE" HOLOGRAM, 2001, 2003 AND 2005.
First issued in 2001, the $5 Maple Leaf coin carries a privy mark of Chinese characters, meaning Maple of Good Fortune, or Hope, as part of the hologram.

2001 Obverse

2001 Reverse

2003 Obverse

2003 Reverse

2005 Obverse

2005 Reverse

esigners:			Engravers:	
2001, 2003:	Obv.:	Dora de Pédery-Hunt	Obv.:	Dora de Pédery-Hunt
	Rev.:	RCM Staff	Rev.:	RCM Staff
2005:	Obv.:	Susanna Blunt	Obv.:	Susan Taylor
	Rev.:	RCM Staff	Rev.:	RCM Staff

Case of Issue: Mylar pouch

pecifications: See page 595
nish: Specimen (reverse proof), hologram
ase of Issue: Red clam oval case, taupe flocked insert, encapsulated coin, COA

DATE	DESCRIPTION	QUANTITY SOLD	ISSUE PRICE	FINISH	SP-68	SP-69
2001	Good Fortune	29,817	59.99	Specimen	50.	—
2003	Good Fortune	29,731	39.99	Specimen	50.	—
2005	Good Fortune	19,888	39.95	Specimen	50.	—

SILVER MAPLE LEAFS WITH HOLOGRAMS

SINGLE COINS

FIVE DOLLARS (1 OUNCE), 15TH ANNIVERSARY OF THE ONE DOLLAR LOON, 2002.

These maple leaf coins were struck to commemorate the 15th anniversary of the one dollar loon coin issued in 1987. The reverse design on the coin depicts a male loon flapping its wings in the "Loon Dance" protecting its nest from intruders.

Designers and Engravers:

Obv.:	Dora de Pédery-Hunt
Rev.:	RCM Staff
Composition:	99.99% Ag
Weight:	31.1035 g, 1 oz
Diameter:	38.0 mm Edge: Reeded
Thickness:	3.2 mm Die Axis: ↑↑
Finish:	Specimen (reverse proof), Hologram
Case of Issue:	Black leatherette clam case, hunter green interior, encapsulated coin, COA

DATE	DESCRIPTION	QUANTITY SOLD	ISSUE PRICE	FINISH	SP-68	SP-69
2002	$5 (1 oz) 15th Anniv. of One Dollar Loon	29,970	39.95	Specimen	45.	—

SILVER MAPLE LEAF SETS

$5 SILVER MAPLE LEAF WITH PROOF SETS, 2001.

Three varieties of silver maples (colourised, hologram and regular) were combined with seven proof coins, 1¢ to $2, of the 2001 Proof Set to form the following Premium Proof sets:

DATE	DESCRIPTION	QUANTITY SOLD	ISSUE PRICE	ISSUER	FINISH	MARKET VALUE
2001	**Proof Set 2001.** Seven proof coins. Reverse proof hologram, silver maple leaf	3,000	150.00	RCM	PR-68 SP-66	110.
2001	**Proof Set 2001.** Seven proof coins. Reverse proof privy snake, silver maple leaf	Included	100.00	RCM	PR-69, MS-65	110.
2001	**Proof Set 2001.** Seven proof coins and a colourised 2001 silver maple leaf	Included	75.00	RCM	PR-69, MS-65	110.

SILVER MAPLE LEAF DERIVATIVES

DATE	DESCRIPTION	QUANTITY SOLD	ISSUE PRICE	ISSUER	FINISH	MARKET VALUE
1998	125th Anniv. of R.C.M.P., Silver maple with R.C.M.P. privy mark. Souvenir sheet. Dark blue presentation case. COA.Booklet	25,000	47.95	RCM, CP	SP-66	75.
2004	Sambro Island. Framed image and twenty dollar coin	N/A	249.00	RCM	PR-67	80.